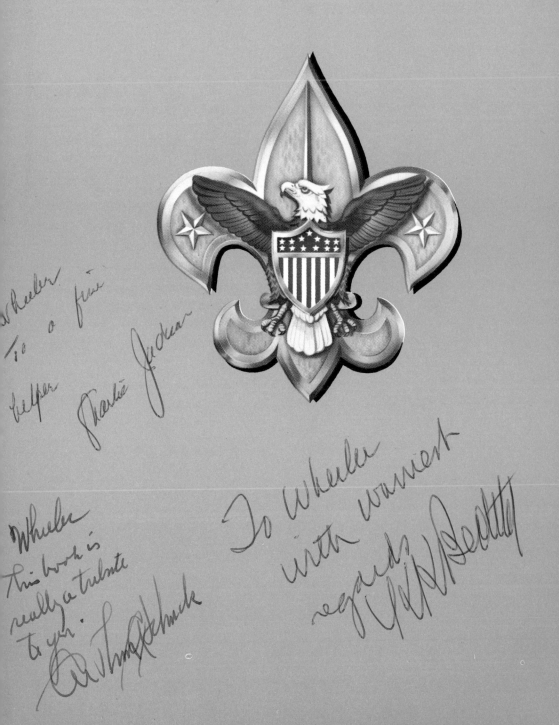

Wheeler—
To a fine
helper.
Charlie Jackson

To Wheeler
with warmest
regards
[signature]

Wheeler—
This book is
really a tribute
to you.
[signature]

BOYS' LIFE
Treasury

A Selection of the Best Stories and Articles from Boys' Life,
the Official Publication of the Boy Scouts of America

BOYS' LIFE
Treasury

Selected by the Editors of Boys' Life

Illustrations by

HAMILTON GREENE • NORMAN SAUNDERS
GERALD McCANN • DON LYNCH

SIMON AND SCHUSTER • NEW YORK

Acknowledgments

The publishers wish to thank the following people for permission to use these stories, all of which have appeared in Boys' Life *magazine, and are copyright by the* Boy Scouts of America *in the years indicated:*

Merritt P. Allen for *The Mudhen, V.S., Tied, and Sound Effects,* © copyright 1955, 1952, and 1955; E. L. Babcock for *Sea Trap,* © copyright 1955; Zachary Ball for *Man of Courage,* © copyright 1954; John Barell for *Twenty Below,* © copyright 1955; Florence D. Carter for *Patrol at Valley Forge,* © copyright 1950; Hugh B. Cave for *Flight of the Jungle Bird,* © copyright 1956; Earl Chapin for *The Great Drop Game,* © copyright 1957; Verne Chute for *Flapjack Jenny,* © copyright 1952; B. J. Chute for *Home on the Range* and *Anybody Can Ski,* © copyright 1952 and 1951; Roy Civille for *Hunting With Bow and Arrow,* © copyright 1957; Irving Crump for *Thundermakers* and *Og's Dogs,* © copyright 1955 and 1956; Christine H. De Vries for *Roadblock* and *The Hunch,* © copyright 1952 and 1953; Dee Dunsing for *The Vireo's Song,* © copyright 1949; James W. English for *The Straw Vote Machine, The Tailbone Patrol,* and *The Rainmakers,* © copyright 1956, 1952, and 1954; Arnold Fenton for *Fancy Footwork,* © copyright 1955; George Fichter for *Start Fishing,* © copyright 1956; Frederick Gonner for *Blood of the Kashids,* © copyright 1955; Josephine Gorsuch for *Boy on a Uranium Hunt,* © copyright 1957; Hank Greenberg for *Who Makes the Majors?,* © copyright 1956; D. S. Halacy, Jr., for *Latch On!,* © copyright 1956; Anne Hall for *Private Eye, Yi! Yi!,* © copyright 1953; William F. Hallstead III for *Space Lane Cadet* and *El Berty Rapido,* © copyright 1952 and 1955; William Hillcourt for *Camping on Brownsea Island,* © copyright 1957; S. Kurtz Hingley for *A Shamrock for O'Toole,* © copyright 1954; Alan Hynd for *Man With the Camera Eyes* and *Amateur Sleuth,* © copyright 1953 and 1951; C. Paul Jackson for *Scared Scatback,* © copyright 1953; Raymond P. Kaighn for *The First Basketball Game,* © copyright 1955; Robert J. H. Kiphuth for *Swimming for Speed,* © copyright 1951; Jim Kjelgaard for

Blood on the Ice and *Four-Footed G-Men,* © copyright 1947 and 1950; David Lavender for *Man for Bait* and *Oliver's Ox,* © copyright 1950 and 1954, Burr W. Leyson for *Sea Scout Style* and *What It Takes,* © copyright 1941 and 1953; J. Paul Loomis for *Cap Shott,* © copyright 1954; Joe Louis for *The Manly Art,* © copyright 1947; Roland A. Martone for *The Boy Who Saved the World,* © copyright 1956; Bob Mathias for *Talking Track,* © copyright 1955; William B. McMorris for *Kit's Big Decision* and *Abner's Gold Mine,* © copyright 1955 and 1957; David B. Parker for *Only Fighters Are Wanted,* © copyright 1955; Stanley Pashko for *Secret and Urgent, Inside Baseball, What Did You Catch?,* and *Easier Ways to Better Grades,* © copyright 1955, 1957, 1949, and 1956; Frank R. Pierce for *The Return of Private Kerry,* © copyright 1954; Carl Henry Rathjen for *Conserving Charlie, Sacrifice Spurs,* and *Spiked Switches,* © copyright 1954, 1955, and 1952; Paul Richards for *Smart Baseball,* © copyright 1952; William Saroyan for *The Lonesome Sardine,* © copyright 1956; Gordon D. Shirreffs for *Wolf Warrior of the Pawnees, Yellow Dust Madness,* and *The Sinker,* © copyright 1952, 1954, and 1951; Hugh R. Smith for *Welly's Orphan Animals,* © copyright 1953; Joseph S. Stocker for *It's The Ham in Them,* © copyright 1955; Paschal N. Strong for *Terror of Buccaneer Bay* and *The Airtight Case,* © copyright 1952 and 1953; Douglas Tate for *Ghost Men of Coronado,* © copyright 1953; Millard Ward for *Left-Handed Monkey Wrench,* © copyright 1952; Manly Wade Wellman for *Tall Bram of Little Pigeon,* © copyright 1956; Wallace West for *Scoops Gets the Birdie* and *Siren Song,* © copyright 1955 and 1953; Walter J. Wilwerding for *The Big Boss of Africa's Night Life,* © copyright 1955; E. A. Wood for *The Chastisement of Horsey,* © copyright 1956; Jay Worthington for *Sabor's Shoes,* © copyright 1954.

Foreword

JUST as a treasury is a place where precious things are stored, BOYS' LIFE TREASURY contains a collection of some of the best-loved stories and most stimulating articles that have appeared in Boys' Life magazine during the past years.

There is great variety here—tales of mystery, the Wild West, the sea, high adventure, and Scouting stories. Each one has been judged by Boys' Life readers to be among their favorites. You will find, also, sports articles written by some of America's outstanding athletes and coaches, telling you how to train and practice to become good in whatever sport you most enjoy.

But, for the most part, this is a book designed for reading fun—a book you will want to pick up again and again to read the particular story suited to your mood of the moment. You will want to keep it for a long time. It may even become part of your permanent library—just as I still have in my library many of the books I read as a boy.

I hope this book will open up for you new horizons in reading, Scouting, hobbies, and, perhaps, even vocations. I hope also that it will lead you to explore further your favorite kinds of books, and that you will make good books your lasting friends.

Good reading!

DR. ARTHUR A. SCHUCK
Chief Scout Executive

Contents

CONTENTS

7

CONTENTS

CONTENTS

9

The Man with the Camera Eyes

By ALAN HYND

A true story of a New York detective with a photographic mind

Not long ago, the New York Police Department boasted one of the most unique detectives in the whole history of law-enforcement—a man known to the police and the underworld of two continents as Camera Eyes. His real name was Henry Oswald; he was a big athletic man with a pleasant, though knowing, face and mild blue eyes behind gold-rimmed glasses. His eyes were literally cameras; Detective Oswald never forgot a face. Sometimes, walking along a crowded street or sitting in the grandstand at Yankee Stadium, he would spot fugitives from justice whom he hadn't seen in years. The sleuth was never able to explain, even to himself, his phenomenal memory for faces.

Some time back, Detective Oswald was down in Montevideo, Uruguay, on an extradition matter when, taking a walk late one night before retiring, he was accosted by a sailor who asked him for a light for his cigarette. As Detective Oswald obliged, striking a match and holding it up to the sailor's cigarette, he studied the fellow's face from force of habit. The sailor was light-complexioned, blue-eyed, round of face, and altogether quite pleasant looking. He thanked the detective and went on his way. Both, naturally, thought no more of the incident.

Two years later, far from Montevideo—

in Brooklyn, as a matter of fact—there was an armed holdup. A light-complexioned, good-looking young man of about twenty-five, sharply dressed in a tight-fitting black overcoat with a velvet collar and wearing a derby at a jaunty angle, walked into a little stationery store on Bleecker Street with a revolver in his right hand. He held up the proprietor, an aged man named Samuel Walters; during the crime, Mr. Walters' wife, drawn to the store from living quarters in the rear, got a good look at the fellow. So did several residents of the neighborhood, as the criminal, still waving his gun, darted along Bleecker Street, ducked into an alley, and disappeared from view.

Next day, acting on a description of the criminal, furnished by the victim, his wife, and several others who had seen the fellow, Brooklyn detectives went to the home of a youth of twenty-five by the name of Jimmy Campbell, and arrested him. Campbell was taken to the precinct station and placed in a lineup with a group of assorted felons. Then the holdup witnesses were brought in to see if they could pick out the culprit. The victim and his wife and five residents of the neighborhood unhesitatingly picked Campbell.

Campbell, a mild-mannered chap who was something of a neighborhood celebrity as a sandlot baseball player, had an alibi. At the

13

hour of the crime he claimed to have been across the East River in Manhattan, standing in a line in front of an employment agency. Campbell had not obtained work, however, nor had he known anybody in the employment line; thus he couldn't prove his alibi.

Camera Eyes Oswald was assigned to talk to Jimmy Campbell and try to get a confession from him. Oswald was startled when he walked into the prisoner's cell. "We've met before," were his opening words to Campbell. "Where?" asked Campbell.

"Down in Montevideo," said Camera Eyes. "You stopped me on the street there two years ago and asked me for a match. You were in the Navy."

"I was in the Navy, all right, but I was never in Montevideo."

"Come now," said Oswald, "we're not going to get anywhere if you're going to lie. Why don't you admit what you've done?"

"But I tell you I didn't commit that crime. I was trying to find a job that afternoon."

Detective Oswald was walking to his car parked outside the jail when a young fellow of about sixteen stopped him and asked, "You're the detective who's going to send Jimmy Campbell to prison, aren't you?"

Oswald, curious, stopped. "Are you a friend of Jimmy?" he asked.

"Yes, sir. Jimmy didn't hold up that man."

"How do you know, young fellow?"

"He just *couldn't* have done it, sir. That's all I know; he just *couldn't* have done it."

"You'd have to have more proof than just a *belief* in Jimmy Campbell's innocence, you know."

Oswald got into his car. Before he put the car into motion, he glanced at the chap, standing on the sidewalk looking in his direction. His camera eyes took a photograph of Jimmy Campbell's young friend. That night, Camera Eyes saw the photograph of the trusting boy who, for some reason or other, had supreme faith in the fellow charged with such a serious crime. What, wondered Detective Oswald, had inspired such faith? Obviously, Campbell was guilty; the victim himself and six other reputable

citizens had positively identified him. And Campbell was lying through his teeth when he said that he had never been in Montevideo. Or *was* he?

The Navy records, usually complete and very detailed, were incomplete and not at all detailed concerning Jimmy Campbell's exact whereabouts on the date when Detective Oswald had lit the cigarette for the sailor in Montevideo. Campbell had been on a ship in South American waters at the time in question, but exactly what ship wasn't clear. He had been transferred from one ship to another during the period in question and his record had been misfiled. All the indications were, however, that he could very well have been on shore leave in Montevideo the night Camera Eyes had studied the sailor's face while lighting his cigarette.

Detective Oswald spent a little time with Jimmy Campbell in the Brooklyn jail each day. A grand jury had indicted Campbell for the holdup of Samuel Walters; if ever a man was headed straight for prison, Campbell was. He continued to protest his innocence, however; continued to insist not only that he had not been in Brooklyn when the crime was committed, but that he had never set foot in the city of Montevideo.

One day, when Detective Oswald called to conduct another questioning session, he learned that Campbell had just been taken to a hospital. He had slashed his wrists in his

cell in an attempt at suicide—a classic indication, under the circumstances, of guilt.

When Camera Eyes walked out of the jail that day, the young man who had previously exhibited such faith in Campbell was waiting for him. "I know what you're thinking, sir," he said. "You're thinking Jimmy Campbell tried to commit suicide because he was guilty."

"What else can I think, young fellow?" asked Oswald. The detective grew suddenly thoughtful. "Say," he suggested, "what do you say you and I go around the corner and have a banana split?" That was fine with the boy, who identified himself as Bill Hoffman.

"How long," asked Detective Oswald of Bill Hoffman, as the two tackled their banana splits, "have you known Jimmy Campbell?"

"For about three years, sir."

"And just why do you think he's such a wonderful fellow?"

"Well, sir, I broke a window last year by hitting a home run through it. I didn't have the money to pay for the window, and the man who owned the house was goin' to come around and tell my father when Jimmy Campbell heard about it. He gave me the money to pay the man so my father wouldn't know about it."

As Bill Hoffman ate his banana split, he detailed other acts of kindness of the fellow ticketed for prison—how he had bought baseball bats and other equipment for the guys in the neighborhood when, it was fairly obvious, he didn't have mucn money to spare; how, very late one night, he had once heard that a mother of one of the young baseball players needed some rare medicine, obtainable at that hour only across the river in Manhattan, and had gone to get it himself. Things like that.

"Well," said Oswald when the splits were finished and he got into his car for the drive back to his Squad headquarters, "we'll see what turns up."

In his time, Camera Eyes had known many people who had vested blind faith in criminals. Somehow, though, the faith of Bill Hoffman in Jimmy Campbell was different. Here was a fellow who, despite his comparative youth, struck the detective as an instinctive judge of character. He would be unlikely to be fooled by the surface behavior of a man who was evil at heart. Then, too, the acts of kindness on Jimmy Campbell's part that Bill Hoffman had related hardly seemed compatible with the makeup of a man who would be capable of premeditated crime.

Weeks passed. Jimmy Campbell recovered from his attempt at suicide and was returned to jail. His trial was to come up in about a month. Then there came some routine intelligence from the Chicago Police to the New York Police. A man of twenty-five named Jesse Reklaw had been picked up in Chicago while trying to pawn some valuable jewelry stolen during a robbery in the town of Mattoon, Illinois—some two hundred miles from the Windy City. When arrested, Reklaw had been found to possess a diary— a diary in which he had recorded, just for his own information, a long record of robberies in several cities, including New York. Chicago thought New York might like to take a look at the diary. The Reklaw record was not divided up into days, but into weeks. During one week, a couple of months previously, Reklaw had made the laconic notation:

Well, I guess I got away with that
job in Brooklyn.

The diary was turned over to Camera Eyes for examination. What job did the entry in the diary refer to?

Detective Oswald closed the diary. Then the picture of the trusting, earnest face of Bill Hoffman flashed into his mind's eye. So far as Bill Hoffman was concerned, *somebody* had gotten away with a job in Brooklyn—the crime for which his friend Jimmy Campbell was charged. Oswald opened the diary again. He noticed that the got-away-with-it Brooklyn entry had been made during the week of the holdup of Samuel Walters.

Detective Oswald found himself racked by conflict. Here he had a case in Brooklyn all wrapped up—until this young man named Bill Hoffman had come along to put doubt in his mind. Should he go out to Illinois to question this fellow Jesse Reklaw, go on what could very well be a wild goose chase —just because Bill Hoffman, in spite of the evidence given by the victim and six other reputable witnesses against Jimmy Campbell, said Campbell couldn't possibly be guilty? Camera Eyes looked again and again at that trusting, intelligent face of Bill Hoffman in his mind's eye and pondered anew the good deeds ascribed to Jimmy Campbell by young Hoffman. Within an hour, he was on a plane for Illinois.

If Oswald had been startled when walking into the Brooklyn jail and seeing Jimmy Campbell for the first time, he was doubly startled when, walking into the jail in the town of Mattoon, he looked through the bars of a cell and laid eyes on Jesse Reklaw for the first time. *Detective Oswald might as well have been looking at the twin of Jimmy Campbell.* The prisoner in Brooklyn and the prisoner in Mattoon were the same age, the same height, the same approximate weight, and had the same blond complexions, blue eyes and round, pleasant countenances. Reklaw even had a Chesterfield coat, as Campbell had, and a derby. Oswald saw at once that because of the almost unbelievable similarity in appearance between the two men, plus the strange coincidence that they had dressed alike, the victim and the other wit-

nesses could easily have mistaken Jimmy Campbell for Jesse Reklaw.

Camera Eyes did not speak to Reklaw for a little while. He just stood outside of the bars of the prisoner's cell looking at him. Now he realized for the first time a basic difference between Campbell and Reklaw, despite their many similarities. Reklaw had mean eyes; Campbell didn't. Campbell could look a man straight in the face; Reklaw couldn't.

Oswald asked to be let into the cell. He thought of Bill Hoffman, the trusting young man who had hit a home run through a window, and told himself that had it not been for that, and other incidents seemingly unrelated to crime, a hideous miscarriage of justice might have taken place in Brooklyn. For Camera Eyes Oswald was certain, as certain as he had ever been of anything, that he was entering the cell of the fellow who had stuck up Samuel Walters.

"Well, Walker," Oswald began to the prisoner, "you're sure in a fine jam."

"What do you mean calling me Walker? That's not my name."

"Reklaw is Walker spelled backwards. That's old stuff, Walker, trying to hide your real identity by changing your name. But that's beside the point; tell me, when did you get out of the Navy?"

Jesse Walker stiffened.

"The Navy? How did you know I was in the Navy?"

The detective ignored the question. He was measuring the prisoner. Oswald's two statements out of the blue—the prisoner's real name and the fact that he had been in the Navy—had knocked Walker off balance. A good detective senses the propitious moment to rush in for a quick knockout.

"Two years ago," Camera Eyes continued, "when you were in the Navy, you were on shore leave in Montevideo one night and you stopped a man on the street and asked him for a match. Think hard, Walker, and you'll remember that. It wasn't so long ago —only two years."

Jesse Walker's eyes widened as he stared at Oswald. "How do you know all this stuff about me? What are you, a magician?"

The detective was calm in contrast to Walker's rising turmoil. "It's my business to know everything about you, Walker," he went on. "I know, for instance, that you stuck up an old man named Samuel Walters on Bleecker Street in Brooklyn nine weeks and three days ago."

"You *what!*"

"You're not very smart, Walker, you've just been lucky up to now. Another fellow who looks like you might have gone to prison for your crime, but he won't now—thanks to a young man who had faith in him."

"What do you mean by that?"

"It's something you wouldn't understand, Walker. But as I was saying, you're not very smart. You had to write everything down in a diary."

Jesse Walker confessed to the Brooklyn crime. He went to prison for it.

Jimmy Campbell was, of course, released —the victim of a stranger-than-fiction set of coincidences, yet the recipient of a priceless faith on the part of a young friend. Detective Oswald got Jimmy Campbell a good job. One of the first things Campbell did was to seek out Bill Hoffman.

"Listen, Bill," he said with a grin, "if you ever hit any more home runs through windows, let me know. I'll be glad to pay for them."

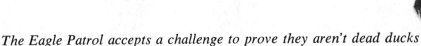

The Tailbone Patrol

By JAMES W. ENGLISH

The Eagle Patrol accepts a challenge to prove they aren't dead ducks

It is difficult to explain how a single event can completely change a Patrol *overnight,* but that is what the Camelback Mountain hike did for the old Eagle Patrol of Troop Ten, Phoenix.

Believe me, we needed changing, and I should know. My name is Mike Peterson. I'm Patrol Leader. Toby Tyler, the blimp-shaped human cavity, was Assistant PL. The rest of the Eagles were Tenderfoot Scouts, in which status they appeared completely happy. All of which accounted for our being a Patrol in name only.

However, Doc, our Scoutmaster, wasn't content to have such an outfit in Ten, so he shoved the needle in us right before the entire Troop.

I still remember what he said. "We have a bunch of buzzards here who call themselves Eagles. They have been living off the Troop's good reputation, earned by the other three Patrols. This must stop! So I am challenging these buzzards to get off their tailbones and for one week act like a Patrol; take a hike, hold a Patrol Meeting, and then if they still don't want to act like Troop Ten-ers, I'll wash my hands of them. But I challenge them to do this much for the Troop they have let down."

I am certain this was a desperate final attempt on Doc's part to ignite a spark of life in us, and in one sense it did work. We were ashamed not to take up his challenge, but those of us in the Patrol knew whatever we did was merely the swan song for the Eagles. We weren't a Patrol, and we knew it.

Well, that was the situation when the Eagles took the Camelback Mountain hike. By now I've forgotten how we decided on that particular destination, for Camelback is a 2000 foot high mountain of red sandstone that stands up abruptly out of the desert northeast of Phoenix. It is not an easy climb.

However, on Saturday morning we took the Arcadia bus to a point near the start of the trail. The trail itself leads to the hump, but it starts beneath the towering cliffs and talus slopes that form the head. You see, the mountain derives its name from its shape, which is remarkably like that of a kneeling camel, from pointed nose and head to high hump. We, of course, were going to follow the trail, which is steep but not dangerous like the sheer cliffs of the head, which deter most mountain climbers.

We were two hours late getting started, and if it hadn't been for the grumbling I might have called the hike off. Yet, this was one chore we had to do, although no one looked forward to it. However, once we left the bus, good-natured Toby tried to make the best of a bad situation.

"Boy!" he exclaimed, as he surveyed the mountain ahead, "I don't see why this Patrol couldn't have died a natural death. This climb will kill me."

Little Billy Spears laughed. "It's darn near worth the climb just to see you lose a few pounds, Toby."

Our corpulent assistant grinned. "Skinny one," he replied, "I don't see how you could spare an ounce, but if you attempt to lug all that gear up Camelback you're going to lose a few pounds yourself."

For the first time I noticed Billy's stack of gear, which was enough to overload a pack burro.

"This is just a one day hike," I pointed out, directing my remarks to our swaybacked Tenderfoot. "A stiff climb at that. You'll not need half that gear."

"Well, how did I know what to bring, Mike?" he asked. "I've never been on a hike before."

I had forgotten that Billy, our newest member, hadn't been along on our other sad attempts at a Patrol hike. I should have remembered; there was plenty I should have remembered, but hadn't.

"Let me give you a hand," I said. "We'll sort through the stuff and cache what you won't need. We can pick the rest up on our way back."

Billy shook his head. "My folks just bought most of this stuff. They'd skin me alive if I lost all of it on my first hike."

I nodded. "There's room in my pack for some of it. Maybe the other fellows will help with the rest of your gear."

It was another half hour before we got our packs readjusted, and took off. Tommy Thompson fell in step beside me. "Look, Mike," he said, "you and Toby are First Class Scouts, have been in other Patrols. You know how a Patrol works. What's wrong with us?"

"I guess Toby and I haven't been very good leaders," I replied, thinking about Billy and his oversized pack.

"Nuts!" Tommy retorted. "It's like Doc said, we've sat on our tailbones entirely too long. But we really aren't a snafu outfit. Yet we aren't a Patrol, either."

"I suppose it's too late to do much now," put in Beans Roberts, who had joined us. "But I wish we'd tried."

"That's why we're all on this hike," Toby said. "We'd like to show Doc and the Troop we aren't as bad as we've led them to believe. But you know, I think the hardest guys to convince will be ourselves."

"Well, one thing I do know," I said. "As far as Troop Ten is concerned, the Eagle Patrol is a dead duck."

Everyone agreed, and for a moment that stopped the conversation. We were almost at the end of the dusty desert road, when we came in sight of a big limousine, with Eastern license plates, parked near the head of the trail. A woman and her chauffeur got out to await our arrival.

"Wonder what they are doing up here?" Tommy asked.

"How can anyone tell what an Eastern tourist will do," retorted Beans.

However, we didn't have long to wait for an answer. The woman was quite excited, and it developed she had ample reason. That morning her eleven-year-old son had started to climb Camelback. However, when he was but a short distance up the trail, the chauffeur saw him turn off and disappear over the talus slopes of the head. When the boy hadn't reappeared by noon, the chauffeur summoned the boy's mother.

After getting the story straight, I glanced at the fellows. There was no doubt they wanted to search for the lost boy.

"We don't have mountain climbing equipment," I pointed out, addressing the woman, "and we aren't mountaineers. However, we'll try to track him as far as we can safely go. But that might not be very far. I think the best thing for you to do is return to your hotel and call the sheriff's office. They'll organize a search party with trained climbers."

She nodded.

"But first," I added to the chauffeur, "you'd better point out where the boy took off on his own."

We had covered not more than a quarter mile of the trail, when the chauffeur stopped. "I think he cut off about here," he said.

Little Billy Spears, who was slowed down by his still bulky pack and was bringing up the rear, let out a yell. "Hey! I think I've found the trail."

He pointed to a squawbush plant that had been trampled, and there were several overturned rocks nearby. The sun hadn't as yet dried out the earth which clung to the underside of the rocks, and the leaves on the broken branches of the squawbush weren't wilted.

The Patrol let out a yell and gathered around Billy.

"Wait a minute!" I shouted. "We'll never find the trail if you guys tramp all over the area. Billy, lead off. I'll follow. The rest will get a chance, but keep in line now."

Bill promptly sounded off again, like a hound dog on a hot scent. This time he had discovered a bit of blue wool on a mesquite bush, and the chauffeur informed us the boy, whose name was Reginald Pearson Newell III, had been wearing a blue sweater.

Confidently we set off, following a fairly distinct trail, while the chauffeur returned to drive Mrs. Newell back to her hotel.

"Wouldn't it be something," Tommy Thompson said, grinning like a cat eating canaries, "if the Eagle Patrol found this lost boy, just when we were supposed to roll over and play dead?"

The fellows let out a yell.

"We'll show 'em!" shouted Beans Roberts.

"I'm all for it," put in Two-Bits Karsten, our scribe and treasurer who has a slide rule mind, "but the odds are against it. This isn't a climb for amateurs."

We had been following a sandy wash, which was becoming hemmed in by a rim of low cliffs and long talus slopes. It seemed like a good spot and occasion to halt for lunch.

"Go easy on the water," I said, "and I'd advise saving half of your chow. We may need both before we get out of here. We all want to find young Newell, but we want to get back safely too. If we pull a boner and have to be rescued, we'll never live it down."

This quieted the fellows momentarily as they slowly commenced to realize the seriousness of what we were undertaking.

"He must have scaled this cliff somewhere nearby," observed Tommy Thompson, surveying the terrain ahead.

I nodded, pointing to some tracks I'd observed cutting across the talus slopes. "He probably wriggled up that vertical crack over there. I just hope we can make it."

"If that kid could make it, we can," replied Beans.

Toby cut in. "Look, fellows, that's not the point. We don't want anyone coming in here to rescue us. If Mike decides it's too much of a risk to go on, that's it. We don't go on. That kid probably took some foolhardy chances, and we'd be crazy to take such risks ourselves."

"If we had a rope, I bet we'd make it," stated Tommy a little wistfully.

"I've got a rope in my pack," replied Billy Spears, who promptly dug out a hundred-foot-long piece of one-quarter inch nylon.

I'll admit I felt better myself.

It wasn't difficult for me to worm my way up the crack in the cliff face, which wasn't over twenty feet high. Using Billy's rope I hauled up the packs, and then with Toby to see that each man tied himself in with a bowline, I played anchor man on the rope as they climbed the cliff.

Each man came over the cliff's face wearing a big grin.

"Never knew those Tenderfoot knots would come in so handy," stated Tommy as he helped untie Toby, the last man up.

"And that stuff I learned in tracking is okay too," piped up Billy Spears.

Toby and I grinned. We'd been telling them this for six months, but somehow hadn't gotten our point across.

When we reassembled I had Tommy take the lead. We were on a rocky plateau that extended to the rimming cliff that formed the neck of the camel. The trail wasn't so easy to follow now, for there was no soft earth and very few plants.

Finally I directed four fellows to leave their packs with us and scatter, looking for signs.

In about ten minutes Beans Roberts let out a yell. He had found a definite footprint in a windswept pocket of sand between two flat rocks.

"Looks like he's headed for the neck of the camel's head," observed Toby. "He must have found a ledge or chimney in order to get over that cliff."

"Maybe he brought along a self-service elevator," suggested Two-Bits, but all this crack earned was threatening looks.

I sent Toby and Tommy off to the base of the cliff to scout for signs, while the rest of us tried to follow the track across the barren rocks.

The boys had hardly reached the base of the cliff before they signaled for us to join them. There, in the soft debris beneath the cliff's face were the footprints we were looking for. They were definitely young Newell's, for we had established the fact he was wearing sneakers with the tread worn off the left heel.

Toby pointed to an oblique ledge, which followed a tilt in the strata of sandstone. The tracks led up that ledge.

"He's crazy, that kid," muttered Toby.

"Let's raise a big cry and see if we get an answer," I suggested, for I didn't want any part of that ledge.

The Apache yell that followed should have been heard in Phoenix, but we got no response.

"The cliff's like a sounding board," Toby pointed out. "It throws our yell back over the area we have covered."

I turned to our scribe. "Two-Bits, take over the Patrol and keep them here, while Toby and I scout out the trail. No need for all of us to get stuck on that ledge."

Toby had already tied himself in on Billy's rope. I put a good bowline around my middle, and we started up the ledge.

For the first hundred yards the ledge was wide enough. It was just a matter of picking our way through the loose stones. But then it narrowed down so that it was frequently necessary for Toby to brace himself in some niche in the wall while I climbed on carefully to a place where I could play anchor while Toby climbed.

As we climbed higher up the face of the cliff, there were some windcaves where the soft sandstone had been hollowed out, and they provided safe places in which to take a blow. I began to think we might make it all the way to the top, but about twenty feet from the crest, the ledge petered out in a steep slope. Obviously young Newell had scaled that open cliff face, using toe and hand holes in the soft rock. I wasn't about to try that climb, let alone allow the Patrol to try it.

Toby shook his head. "He's crazy all right, but I think we can make it at that."

I didn't understand, so he led me back to the last windcave. Instead of being a hollowed-out pocket, like the other niches, this cave had cut right through to the top of the cliff. There was about fifteen feet of flooring and then a forty-foot climb over a well-ridged slope.

"Think we can make it?" Toby asked.

I nodded. However, I had glanced at my watch, and it was then after three o'clock. If the entire Patrol came up it would be nearly dark before we reached the top of the cliff, and no telling where Newell was.

Toby must have read my thoughts. "Let's try another yell," he suggested. "We might be high enough now for the sound to carry over the cliff."

We cut loose with all the lung power at our command.

In a matter of seconds we had a reply, faint but unmistakably a cry for help.

"That does it," I said, "but I only wish we had some way of notifying our folks we're going to be out all night."

Toby grinned. "I asked Mrs. Newell to tell the sheriff that a Patrol from Troop Ten was starting out on the boy's trail. He'll undoubtedly notify Scout Headquarters and they'll notify Doc."

Good old Toby. That's the sort of assistant to have.

When we rejoined the Patrol we explained what had happened and then held a vote. Naturally, everyone was for going on. I'll have to admit, at this point I felt mighty proud of the fellows, something that hadn't happened before in the Eagle Patrol.

The sun was setting when we reached the top of the cliff, which was little more than a flat shelf between the cliff we had scaled and a tremendous drop on the other face of the mountain.

Finding young Newell wasn't difficult. He had slipped, jumping from rock to rock, and lay crumpled in a heap. He had been crying but was trying not to let it show. But he made no pretense about being frightened, and it was obvious he was in considerable pain.

"How are we going to get down?" was his first question.

"We're going to sit right here on our tail-bones until help comes," I replied.

He looked startled. "But who are you?"

"We're Scouts of Troop Ten," I replied.

"You might call us the Tailbone Patrol," retorted Toby, who had dug the Patrol's first aid kit out of his pack, and was kneeling down beside young Newell.

I'm not too clear myself as to what happened in the next few minutes. Tommy Thompson said something about our having a new name, the Tailbone Patrol.

"But what'll we use for an emblem?" demanded Billy Spears.

"We could use the south end of a—" started Two-Bits.

Our obstreperous scribe was promptly sat upon.

"How about sewing a cut-out of a bone in white felt on top of a red felt patch, and attaching a piece of black yarn to represent the tail?" I suggested.

We took time out for another war dance.

"We're Tailboners of old Troop Ten," we yelled.

You'd have thought we were cheering at a high school football game, instead of being stranded at nightfall on the neck of Camelback Mountain. However, a scream from young Newell brought us back to reality, but quick.

Toby stood up. "He fractured his left leg just above the ankle," he said, pointing to Newell. "The bone just snapped back in place. We'll have to splint it."

"Golly! What'll we use for splints?" de-

manded Billy Spears. "Nothing here but rocks."

"We'll use whatever we can. There's a screwdriver in your Scout knife," I replied, "and some braces on your Trapper Nelson pack frame that would make wonderful splints. Get busy."

I dropped down by young Newell to give Toby a hand cutting off his trouser leg and shoe. The leg was already swollen.

While Toby and I administered first aid, the rest of the Patrol found a sheltered spot between some boulders, where we were protected from the wind. They came back and gave us a hand carrying young Newell.

We made him as comfortable as possible, and then held a consultation a short distance away.

"How is he, Toby?" Tommy Thompson asked.

"I think he'll be all right, unless shock sets in," said our Assistant Patrol Leader. "Wish we had some blankets or some way to keep him warm."

"Would a plastic poncho help?" asked Billy Spears. "Might keep the wind out."

He didn't have to be told to dig it out of his pack.

"Suppose we'd better eat," I said.

"Boy, a cup of hot chocolate would sure go good right now," sighed Toby. "Don't have any in your pack, do you, Bill?"

Billy shook his head. "Have some bouillon cubes and heat tabs though."

We set up such a yell Newell must have thought he was being held for ransom.

However, when Billy brought out his supplies, there obviously wasn't enough to go around, and I was already doubting the advisability of using all of our water for bouillon, which is rather salty.

"Why don't we save that for Newell?" I suggested. "He needs warm stuff more than we do."

There wasn't a single gripe. Tommy Thompson handed me his canteen. "I drink water like a camel," he said. "And I put away a lot back at the bus stop. Use my canteen."

"I'll make the bouillon," Billy offered.

Toby grinned. "Billy, your over-sized pack is a life-saver. I'm going to nominate you for Patrol Quartermaster of the Tailbones."

Billy was elected by acclamation, and young Newell, who seemed to sense the elation of the fellows, joined in.

Two-Bits Karsten, who is something of a lone wolf, tapped me on the shoulder. "From the top of that rock," he said, pointing to a nearby house-sized boulder, "you can see the desert road. It's lined with cars. The sheriff's radio must have carried the story of Newell getting lost and all the thrill seekers are down there."

"Too bad we haven't any way to signal them," I said. "Our folks would feel a lot easier if they knew we were okay, not to mention Newell's mother."

"What we need is a flashlight," muttered Toby, who suddenly turned to Billy, only to find him already digging into his voluminous pack.

"Got a flashlight, Quartermaster?"

Billy nodded.

"That's my boy," stated Toby. "Never lets us down."

Two-Bits is the best signaler in the Patrol, and we started him flashing an SOS signal in Morse code. It wasn't long before the headlights of a car could be seen bucking the flow of traffic on the road below us. The car pulled off, in full view of us, and a powerful spotlight, such as you'll find on a police car, swung across our line of vision. In rapid fashion someone sent out the message, "Identify yourself."

Two-bits started chuckling. "Is somebody going to get a surprise."

He replied. "We are the Tailbone Patrol of Troop Ten. We have young Newell with us."

"How is he?" was the next question.

"Broken leg. Okay otherwise. No sign of shock yet."

"How are you?"

"Okay."

"Can you hold out until morning?"

"You bet."

There was a pause before the next message was sent. "The sheriff's posse will start up first thing in the morning. Stay right where you are. Stretcher, ropes, food, water, and first aid equipment will be brought up. Stay where you are."

There was another pause down below before the spotlight blinked again. "This is Doc," the message read. "I'll notify your folks you are okay. Congrats on a swell job. But who did you say you were?"

I'm sure Doc didn't have to read the message of our tiny flashlight, but must have heard us shouting at the top of our lungs. "We're the Tailbone Patrol!" And from that time on no one in Troop Ten has ever mentioned the old Eagle Patrol.

The Boy Who Saved the World

By ROLAND A. MARTONE

A Roastie-toastie space-ace man meets Captain Mex-On from Mars

The Williamsons were coming to visit the Goulds. On such a seemingly simple event, the future of human life was balanced this fateful day.

Jimmy Gould lingered in the kitchen eating a banana. He didn't want to go outdoors this Saturday afternoon because dad was busy with the refreshments and mom was putting fudge frosting on a cake. Besides, the Goulds had just moved into a new neighborhood and he had no friends here.

But the Williamsons were coming soon, and he knew what to expect.

"Jimmy," mom said, "please, please try not to say anything embarrassing, will you, dear?"

"They're only coming to look at our new house," dad said. "They'll be gone before six. Maybe it would be best if you went out to play, Jim."

"O.K.—O.K.," Jimmy agreed. He was nearly ten now, and he tried to sound sporting about it. "But save me some of the good stuff."

He went out aimlessly into the gray afternoon, hesitated a bit in the yard, and walked right up by the spot where he had tossed his Captain Space-Ace Special Atomic Pistol the day before. Then, suddenly aware that he was going forth unarmed, he turned and scooped up his trusty plastic weapon. A crisis was passed as he strapped the holster securely to his thin waist and tugged it into place.

Across the plowed-up building sites, Jimmy wandered. He squinted his eyes and tried to imagine the streets already in; the houses already there with lots of kids to play with. He looked at the sign that read: "Woodland Heights Homes—More Building Soon." He threw clods of dirt at each capital letter.

Finally, he started wandering off toward the paved section of street, hesitated, then turned toward the wooded area where the trees would soon be uprooted to create space for more houses. His choice was a fateful one, his hesitation awesome in its potential. Had Jimmy gone in another direction, he would have been missed by the Martian spaceship that at that very moment was shrieking through the skies after a long and hazardous journey.

The interplanetary trip had started a week earlier, as Earth-time is measured. The spaceship had been launched by the Planet-Seeking Emergency Council on Mars, and it was on a definite and calculated mission.

In announcing what he called the "ultimate decision" in the Inner Chamber, Doctor Bar-Don, wisest of the Martian Master

Scientists, had kept his voice strong even after the long years of strain.

"We must now follow our most desperate course," he had told the council. "With our supply of oxygen nearing an end, we have no other choice but to move our people to another planet, and we are here today to take the first step in such a project."

The murmur from his audience was one of understanding and approval. The plan had been in preparation for an eon or two, and putting it into effect now seemed to be as normal and as natural as living—even more so.

"We know of six possible targets that can be converted into New Mars," he continued, "and the one that calls itself Earth is the closest to us. It will be scouted first."

Captain Mex-On, bravest of the Martians, brought his four-foot frame into the position of attention. This charge was his, and his antenna quivered with pride as he listened to Doctor Bar-Don.

"Through our radio waves for the past two centuries, we have been learning the chief languages of the planets to be explored," the master scientist went on. "In addition, we have learned much concerning the scientific and materialistic achievements of the various target-globes, especially the one called Earth."

The assembled wise ones nodded in weary agreement; the research library had a few thousand cubic feet of literature on Earth.

Doctor Bar-Don took a whiff of synthetic luxygen from his tube and went on, his voice sadder, a little weaker.

"Unfortunately, we have not been able to learn too much of the intangible qualities—if any—that may be possessed by the inhabitants of the target-globes. We are rather certain that they must have some of these qualities—even if in crude form—and the success of our invasion may depend on just such elements as the unknown essences to which I refer."

Doctor Bar-Don turned to address Captain Mex-On directly.

"Your mission is to test the various global inhabitants for those qualities we believe may be universal. When you find the planet that will offer the least resistance—where the natives are inferior in the essential qualities —send us the signal to attack, and the invasion forces will be launched at once."

"I have been given my instructions," Captain Mex-On declared. "Nu-Mon, Mi-Not and Or-Von are ready with me. Our mission has now begun."

"Scout in safety and success," said Doctor Bar-Don.

"Agreed—agreed," chanted the gathered leaders of Mars, and they adjourned to the launching platform.

Soon after entering Earth's atmosphere, the twirling platter spun into a cloud, slid down into a layer of fog, and then went skimming over tree tops, skirting the edge of a new community. Or-Von was a master at the controls, and he responded quickly to Mi-Not's directions from the navigational line-plate.

The cabin hummed evenly as the craft moved and hung, moved and hung—and then Captain Mex-On called excitedly: "There's one now! There's one now!"

Through the floor-viewer, they looked down upon Jimmy Gould, who was busy decimating hordes of the enemy, hidden among the trees.

"Kack-kack-kack! Take that! Take that . . . and that!" Jimmy shouted as he aimed his Space-Ace Special at a log, a rock, and a stump.

"The language is English—or something close to it," Nu-Mon observed as Jimmy's voice came into the cabin over the exterior pick-up.

"He must be an adult male," Mi-Not said. "Who else would be armed and alone in the woods?"

"An adult male is exactly the specimen we want. Take the ship down a short distance from him," Captain Mex-On ordered. "We might as well get right to work."

"Remember to speak in English," Or-Von warned, as he turned to push the "down" button.

Jimmy was just drawing a bead on a hornet's nest when he saw the motion in the brush out of the corner of his eye and whirled to face the quartet.

Wow! What sharp space suits the kids have around here. Wonder where they got 'em," he muttered, working up to the group.

Then he called, "Hi, who are you guys?"

"We're scouts," Mi-Not told him truthfully as the four drew nearer.

"I'm gonna be a Scout next year," Jimmy said.

"Hmmmmm. Didn't think they were sending out patrols from Earth," Captain Mex-On whispered to Or-Von.

"What sort of weapon is that?" Mi-Not asked bluntly. He had been anxious to find out ever since he noticed the Earthman was armed.

"It's an atomic pistol," Jimmy answered proudly. "A real atom-cracking disintegrator."

The four Martians froze visibly. The shock of the answer chilled them for a moment.

"An atomic pistol!" Mi-Not thought softly on their own wavelength. "We knew they

had exploded a few large and clumsy atom bombs—but our scientists were sure that Earthmen had no such hand-weapons as yet!"

"Nothing even close to atomic hand-weapons," Or-Von thought back to him.

"Maybe he's stretching the truth a bit," Captain Mex-On suggested hopefully. "Aim the T-Verax unit at him."

Nu-Mon got out the scope with the glass-plate on it and aimed the mouth at Jimmy.

"Is that truly an atomic disintegrator?" Nu-Mon asked.

Of course, it is, Jimmy thought, a bit indignantly.

"Of course it is," he said.

Three Martian faces turned toward Nu-Mon as he studied the plate on the T-Verax unit.

"Only one line shows up," Nu-Mon reported with obvious concern. "His mental waves for the thought and his mental waves for controlling his speech are exactly the same. He's telling the truth!"

"Incredible!" Captain Mex-On vibrated. "Our scientists should have known of this advanced stage in Earth's weapons."

Nu-Mon fidgeted with the T-Verax unit and aimed it at Jimmy again.

"What can your atom disintegrator do?" he asked.

Jimmy was puzzled. Surely, he thought, these guys know what it does.

"You guys know what it does," he said, a bit peevishly.

"Of course, we do," Captain Mex-On admitted, feeling it might be useless to deny it. "But tell us anyway."

"Why," said Jimmy, "it makes all the atoms scatter, that's what it does. If I aim it at something and pull the trigger— WHAM! There go all the atoms, and the thing disappears."

He had the principle down pat.

"Amazing! Amazing!" said Captain Mex-On, and he began to get a cheese-like taste in his throat that surprised him. Then, quickly, he asked: "And do *all* of you have atom guns?"

"Of course, we all have 'em," Jimmy

shouted. He was becoming angry at their stupidity. "And some of us have two." He had reference to Billy and Eddie Webster, who possessed no fewer than four Space-Acers between them.

"He's still telling the truth," Nu-Mon reported weakly.

"Imagine! Two billion Earthmen—and each one armed with a disintegrating hand-weapon." Captain Mex-On was in obvious awe.

"And some of them have two," Mi-Not reminded him.

Instinctively, the Martian group huddled more closely; Earth was taking on a dangerous hue now.

"Perhaps the T-Verax unit is broken," Or-Von suggested with more hope than conviction.

Nu-Mon swung the unit around and aimed it directly at Or-Von.

"Do you fear these Earthmen?" he asked.

"Why—why, no. I don't fear them in the least," Or-Von answered. He tried to make it sound good.

Sadly, Nu-Mon shook his head. "The T-Verax unit is not broken," he announced.

"Well, their weapons may be better than we expected," Captain Mex-On admitted reluctantly, "but perhaps there's something lacking in them basically. Or in their leadership."

"Who is your leader?" Nu-Mon inquired of Jimmy. "Who would lead you in combat?"

Jimmy came to attention and raised his arm in salute.

"Captain Space-Ace," he shouted. "I'm one of the captain's men!" His voice was spirited.

"Such joy he takes in his leader," Or-Von noted. "Such love and respect he shows."

Then Jimmy remembered. The visit from the Williamsons had disrupted this Saturday afternoon, or he'd be home this very minute looking at the Space-Ace program.

"He's on right now!" he fairly screamed. "Maybe with a message, too! Follow me."

Cutting through the brush to the fence and over it into his yard went Jimmy with the Martians right after him. Near the garage, he spotted the Williamson's car—a low MG —and he stopped for a moment.

"We better go in the back door," he said. "That way we won't bother my family."

"Such thoughtfulness these Earthmen have," Mi-Not observed.

Up the rear stairway and into his own room, Jimmy led them. Quickly he turned on his television set—and there was Captain Space-Ace himself, just about ready to conclude his program.

"All Space-Ace scouts—Attention!" Space-Ace shouted. "Stand by for a special code message—and for a delicious serving of the best cereal ever made—ROASTEE-TOASTEES!"

"Aim the T-Verax unit at him," Captain Mex-On ordered.

Nu-Mon took out the truth-verifier once more and pointed its mouth directly at Space-Ace himself while that intrepid leader went into ecstasy over the goodness of ROASTEE-TOASTEES. The effect was startling.

"I get dozens of lines on the plate," Nu-Mon reported. "He's nothing but a mass of lies!"

"So! They're not so pure after all," Captain Mex-On scoffed. "I ought to signal for the invasion to begin at once."

"Wait a minute! Wait!" Mi-Not interrupted. "Remember, this Earthman on the view-box announced he was speaking in code!"

Captain Mex-On's spirits sagged again. He nodded his head.

"You're right," he said. "I suppose I was just trying to manufacture a little hope for us, but I should know better. Even among us, code-speech always confuses the T-Verax unit."

Meanwhile, Jimmy had opened his Space-Ace Code Book and was ready for the real message.

"Here it comes," he said.

"Twenty-eight, ninety-nine, four hundred," Captain Space-Ace intoned the awful sylla-bles. "Three thousand, eighty-eight, and sixteen. This is all."

Then the man came on who said you were listening to K-A-L-K, T-V, and this, of course, was the absolute truth.

"Aw, that's the same old message he gave us last week," Jimmy said in disgust as he completed the decoding. He clicked off the television set; the weather report came next, and it was usually wrong.

"What message was that?" asked Captain Mex-On.

"Aw, the same old story," Jimmy told him as he tossed the code book into a corner. "Giving us the warning about an invasion from Mars. Let 'em come. Who cares?"

Or-Von nearly fainted into Nu-Mon's arms; Mi-Not gasped out a small explosion of air—and even Captain Mex-On's senses reeled.

"The best kept secret in all Martian history," he gasped out loud. *"And they knew it here on Earth a week ago!"*

"Why, that was just about the time Doctor Bar-Don was announcing the committee's decision!" Nu-Mon responded weakly.

"Did you get that 'Who cares?' business?" Or-Von asked nobody in particular.

"Incredible!" Mi-Not repeated the word many times.

"It's not just that they know about a possible invasion," answered Captain Mex-On. "What gets me is that they treat it so casually!"

"Why not?" asked Or-Von. "After all, they are two billion Earthmen, and each one has an atomic disintegrator as a mere hand-weapon!"

"And some of them have two," Nu-Mon reminded them. He shook his head sadly, hopelessly.

"Let's get out of here," Captain Mex-On ordered not too firmly, and they went—with Jimmy following.

Some jokers, these guys, Jimmy thought. Making fun of Captain Space-Ace like that. But inwardly he admitted the captain was slipping and deserved a little ribbing.

It was while they were going along the path leading into the woods, that Nu-Mon

reminded Captain Mex-On of a rather important item in the series of events.

"So far," said the scouts' scientist, "the Earthman has been armed all through our investigations. How do we know how he might act if he were unarmed?"

"A good point," admitted Captain Mex-On. "At least, we should explore in that direction before we leave. His qualities without that atom gun may be somewhat different from those he shows us with it."

They tramped on toward the spot where they had first seen Jimmy, and Captain Mex-On worked his way toward Mi-Not.

"As soon as you get a chance, disarm the Earthman," he whispered quickly.

Mi-Not nodded and dropped back to be walking near Jimmy.

Just as they entered the clearing again, the Martian struck. His hand swung upward and out, hitting Jimmy's wrist from beneath and sending the Space-Ace Special whirling through the air to fall on the ground near Captain Mex-On, who pounced on it eagerly.

Nu-Mon aimed the T-Verax unit at once while the other Martians whipped out their own atom guns and faced Jimmy—but there was no stopping his natural impulse, no checking his spontaneous reaction. And on Mars the scientists had not prepared their

scouts for the eventuality of taking a favorite toy from an energetic nine-year-old Earth being.

Lowering his head, Jimmy charged with a sudden viciousness that was powered more by emotion than by thought. Straight at the stomach of Captain Mex-On he rushed, letting out a stream of rage as he hit his target.

Captain Mex-On, expecting anything but this, caught the force of the butt in what passed for his solar plexus and toppled over in pain, sprawling on the ground with Jimmy. The atomic disintegrators, both the Space-On Special and the genuine Martian article, fell into the grass.

Quickly getting to his feet, Jimmy snatched up his own weapon and sprinted off a short distance. Then he paused and turned. Having escaped unhurt, he decided that he had enjoyed the bit of rough-and-tumble. It was kind of exciting, and he didn't mind playing around a little bit rough. Especially since he was in a new neighborhood and had to impress the kids.

Keeping at a respectful distance so he would have a head start for a fast sprint home, Jimmy jumped up and down, tossing his gun into the air and catching it in rhythm with his body's motion.

"Yah-Yah! Yah-Yah!" he taunted them. "You can't take my gun away from me! Yah-Yah! I doubledare you!"

Nu-Mon looked up from the T-Verax unit in complete, unabashed astonishment.

"I can't understand it! It's beyond my comprehension," he said. "The Earth being didn't even think 'attack'! He simply attacked! On pure impulse! And now he actually wants to continue the fray!"

"Look, Captain Mex-On!" Mi-Not pointed into the grass. "He took only his own weapon—leaving yours untouched!"

Slowly, Captain Mex-On got to his feet and straightened the equipment laced into his uniform. Very deliberately, he walked over to where the gun lay and picked it up.

"We were four armed fighters—and he was alone and unarmed," Captain Mex-On said reverently. "Never have I seen such bravery—such chivalry." He turned toward Jimmy and bowed three times from his hinge-bones, and the other Martians joined him.

"I did not dream," continued Captain Mex-On, "that I would ever encounter, in the entire universe, a race of beings completely lacking in the elements we know of as falsehood, deceit, doubt, and cowardice—a race whose very essence consists only of truthfulness, bravery, and native resoluteness."

"More than two billion of them—completely united in a brotherhood of thought and strength," added Nu-Mon.

"And entirely devoted to their wise, all-knowing leaders," continued Captain Mex-On, feeling a touch of envy at the wonderful position enjoyed by Captain Space-Ace.

Once more, the four bowed, and then they turned and walked into the woods toward their hidden ship.

Jimmy took a few perplexed steps after them, then paused. He wasn't sure now whether he liked these kids in this new neighborhood. They talked kind of goofy-talk.

He let them disappear into the brush, not feeling inclined to follow them at all. And then he heard a brief whirr of sound—just a quick motion through the air—or thought he did. He saw nothing, so swift are the Martian ships.

Aboard the space craft, Captain Mex-On turned toward the message-dispatcher and clicked it on.

"Stay clear of the planet that calls itself Earth," he reported to headquarters on Mars, "for there be brave men there—courageous and righteous beyond all our men. Their weapons are about equal to ours, but their qualities as living beings, I regret to say, are so far superior to what we Martians have that the conquest of this planet would be impossible. Such is the unity and strength and perfection of these Earthmen!"

He bowed his head a moment, then straightened it once more to face the message-dispatcher again.

"And now," he said in a crisp, military tone, "we proceed to the planet that calls itself Xor, in the eighth Quadrain."

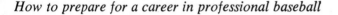

Who Makes the Majors?

By HANK GREENBERG as told to BOB HOOD

How to prepare for a career in professional baseball

Recently elected to baseball's Hall of Fame, Henry B. "Hank" Greenberg is general manager of the Cleveland Indians. He started with Hartford of the Eastern League and spent three years in the minors before becoming Detroit's first baseman in 1933. In 1938, he hit 58 homers, two less than Babe Ruth's record for one season. In the majors, Greenberg hit 331 home runs with a lifetime batting average of .313.

Every year, more people play baseball in America than the year before. On the sandlots, in high schools and colleges, in the semipro ranks and in the armed forces, Americans keep proving that baseball is our national game. It is estimated that over a million youngsters alone participate annually in the youth leagues.

These statistics add up to a lot of fun. They mean that every boy who wants to play this clean sport now has the chance. It's the kind of exciting experience that a boy takes with him into manhood, making him a fan for life. For baseball is everybody's game. About forty million Americans watch professional baseball every year. Fifteen to twenty million watch amateur and semipro games.

Circulating among the twenty million spectators at amateur and semipro games is a crack corps of major league scouts. These hawk-eyed experts go into every corner of the nation, continually on the lookout for a future Bob Lemon, Mickey Mantle, or Willie Mays. And these "professional spectators" know what qualities to look for in a young player. They have reduced spectatorship to a science. For it's their job to pick the green amateur that a big league team can convert into a seasoned professional.

Major league clubs, like our Indians, compete with each other to sign the best young talent possible. You can't win pennants with mediocre players. Exceptional "prospects"— young players—have received as high as $100,000 for signing a contract. But this is rare. The average prospect must go through the farm system—the minor leagues—and attend special schools where he'll master all the fundamentals.

What qualities must you have to catch the eye of a scout? What can you do to prepare for a career in baseball? What will life be like down on the baseball farm? I'll try to answer these questions from the standpoint of the Cleveland organization, although the answers could apply to most major league clubs.

The next time you see a major league game, look the players over carefully. Physically, what do they all have in common, with very few exceptions? The answer is *size,* one of the first requirements for playing in the majors. We rate a player under 5'10" as small, unless he happens to have the powerful build of a Yogi Berra.

Why do we insist on big fellows? We play along with the law of averages. For example, generally a big horse can do more work than a smaller one. That applies to a big ballplayer and a smaller one. The big guy has more power and stamina, and baseball calls for plenty of both. Modern baseball is a slugging game. Look over the home run leaders in the American League for the past five or six years.

One season Mickey Mantle hit thirty-seven homers to lead the league. He stands 5'11" and weighs 175 pounds. Larry Doby, a former Cleveland Indian, led the league in 1954 and 1952. Doby is 6'1" and 182 pounds. Our Al Rosen won the homer crown in 1953 and 1950. He's 5'10½" and 185 pounds. In 1951, Gus Zernial, a 6'3", 210-pound outfielder of the Athletics, copped the crown.

Or look at the top sluggers in the National League one year. Willie Mays, 5'11" and 170 pounds; Eddie Mathews, 6'1½" and 195; Ernie Banks, 6'1" and 180; Duke Snider, 6' and 190; Ted Kluszewski, 6'2" and 236 pounds. If you run down the rosters of all major league teams, you won't find many small players—even among the infielders, the quick, agile fellows.

Size means stamina, too. Major league baseball is tough. Every grueling game of the 154-game schedule is played under pressure, and the boiling summer sun melts off pounds in a hurry. A player may lose ten to fifteen pounds in a season. Some pitchers drop five pounds in a game.

A small player can't afford to lose so much weight, for it weakens him. Of course, a small fellow comes along occasionally with both power and stamina, a Phil Rizzuto, for example. There's no formula here that says small fellows can't make the majors. They can—but the odds are against them.

Another thing we look for is speed. Slow runners clog up the base paths, kill rallies. A slow outfielder may lose as many games with poor fielding as he wins with his batting. Some organizations value speed more highly

than others. When Branch Rickey headed up the Brooklyn Dodgers, he held tryout camps and graded the young players on their speed by staging a mass race. He tested their throwing arms, too, for a fine throwing arm is another requirement, whether you happen to be an outfielder, infielder, catcher or pitcher.

Physically, the ideal young prospect would look something like this: He'd be around six feet tall and weigh between 170 and 200 pounds. He'd be between eighteen and twenty-two years old and would have finished high school, possibly even college. He'd have powerful arms and legs, fine running speed, good stamina, and excellent coordination. This description pretty well fits our Al Smith, an all-around player.

Remember this is the ideal prospect. Lots of players get to the majors and don't measure up to all these requirements. But if they're weak in one department, they overcome this handicap with superior ability in another.

For example, an outfielder with a mediocre throwing arm will make the grade if he's a powerful hitter. If he's also a slow runner, he still *may* make good IF he works hard and hits for a very high average. A speedy infielder with "sure" hands and a good arm often makes the majors in spite of a low batting average. A crack catcher, one who can handle pitchers, throw well, and spark a team, will go to the top even if he's a mediocre hitter.

Of course, a pitcher doesn't have to hit well, although we expect him to learn how to bunt. Speed afoot isn't important either, but strong arms and legs and good stamina are musts. When scouts study a young pitcher, the first thing they look for is a fast ball. If he doesn't have that, he'll need an exceptionally good curve, control, and poise. You can't teach a pitcher a fast ball but you can teach a curve, poise, and, usually, control.

Sometimes a youngster will be gifted with a blazing fast ball but can't learn to control it no matter how hard he works. Rex Barney, former Brooklyn Dodger pitcher, was an example of this. But he was an exception. Generally, you can learn control.

The next time you go to a professional game, watch the pitchers during practice. They'll be running constantly, shagging fly balls, jogging up and down, or sprinting. A pitcher's legs must be in top shape, or he will tire after a few innings. That's why a prospect must have strong legs to start with. And he should be a big, husky fellow, for he'll work harder than any other player on the team. A little guy like Bobby Shantz is a rarity in the pitching profession. His determination and fighting spirit make up for his small size.

You Have to Hustle

You must have the right mental attitude to make good in baseball. You must be eager to work hard to improve. We want "hustlers" on the Cleveland club, fellows who will go all out on every play. Major leaguers play before one of the toughest audiences in the world. The average baseball fan knows the game and won't stand for fakers or loafers. A lazy player doesn't last very long in baseball.

Temperament is important. Nervous players worry themselves right out of the game. You must be able to relax, to leave the game at the park and not take it home to bed with you and convert it into insomnia. And if you're easily discouraged, baseball isn't for you.

Given the right physical equipment and temperament, would you make the majors? Not necessarily. There is another requirement that no scout can test and only you can determine. You must want to play baseball more than any other job in the world!

Professional baseball is a career, and the players take their jobs seriously. Of course, they have fun, too. But the pressure is there just the same. In the long days from April through September, American and National League teams set a torrid pace in the race for the pennants and the chance to play in the World Series. The fact that they can look relaxed on the field is a tribute to their talent.

If you have the talent, physical and mental, there are some things you can do to prepare for a baseball career. Learn the proper fundamentals early—batting, base running, throwing, sliding, fielding. Join a team that has a capable coach, a man who can correct your faults. Bad baseball habits formed early in life are tough to break later on.

Learn to "take" coaching. Don't gripe at the coach when he wants you to bunt and you feel like socking one out of the park. Practice hard to overcome your faults. Develop good, clean living habits—exercise regularly and follow a well-balanced diet. Learn the baseball book—the rulebook. Memorize the rules. Be a smart player as well as a skillful one. Some day you may want to coach or manage a team.

But the most important thing is to play baseball as often as you can. You'll have fun even if you decide it's not your life work.

Suppose you *do* decide to make baseball your career and you've signed a contract with Cleveland. What happens next?

In the spring you'll go to our minor league training base at Daytona Beach, Florida, a former naval base with six well-groomed baseball diamonds and fine living quarters. You'll be watched and coached by a staff of experts including Mike McNally, Steve O'Neill, Red Ruffing, Tris Speaker, and all our scouts and minor league managers.

These men meet every night during the spring session to evaluate each of the three hundred young players in camp. They are familiar with the quality of play in the various classifications of professional baseball—from class D, C, B, A, AA, AAA, and "Open" to the majors.

They'll watch you for a month so they can place you in the class league closest to your ability and experience. Their judgment is generally accurate. They seldom place a player in a class A league when he belongs in class C, or in class D when he should be in B.

All managers send in reports on their players later in the summer. On the basis of these reports, farm club director Mike

McNally reassigns the players for next season's play. If you're with Fayetteville in the class B Carolina League and have a fine season, you'll be promoted to a higher classification. Players move up on their performances, and no one man's opinion will judge your ability. Scouts, managers, coaches will watch you every spring at Daytona Beach.

The organization will keep a master chart on you, tracing your progress, season by season, grading you on hitting, throwing, running, sliding. Each manager you play for will make out a report on you after each game. This gives us here in Cleveland a running report on each of our minor leaguers throughout the season so that we can watch for improvements—or spot failures.

The chart will show your weakness and your manager will work with you to correct it. For example, if you have trouble hitting a curve ball, batting practice pitchers will throw you a lot of curves.

How Long in the Minors?

The goal of every dedicated player is the majors. How long will it take you to get there? That depends on your ability and rate of improvement. The average big leaguer first spends four or five years in the minors.

Al Rosen, our third baseman, is an example of a man who fought his way up through the minors. He signed a Cleveland contract in 1942, spent three years in the Navy, and returned in 1946. Rosen originally had been scouted by the Boston Red Sox and told to forget it because he didn't have the ability.

In 1946, Cleveland officials also got discouraged with him and released him. But a Cleveland scout, Laddie Placek, persuaded Al to try again at Pittsfield, Mass. Al played with five minor league clubs before he became an Indian regular in 1950. In the minors he was always a good hitter while a poor fielder. But he overcame his weakness to become one of the best third basemen in the business, a fine example of how a determined and talented player can improve.

Once you make the majors, you'll have to work hard to stay there. Don't forget: There are over four thousand ballplayers in the minors, all scrambling for four hundred big league jobs.

The Rewards

What will be your reward if you win a job on a major league club? Financially, the minimum salary is $6,000 per year. The average salary on the Cleveland team is $20,000 a season. A star earns $25,000 and up. When your active playing days are over, you may become a manager, scout, or a coach.

But there are other rewards. You'll be a celebrity, respected for your ability. Hundreds of youngsters will imitate your batting or pitching style. Thousands of fans will pay to see you play, wishing they were in your shoes. Maybe they'll call you lucky— and you are! You've reached the top of the greatest game in the world. You're one in a million.

Wolf Warrior of the Pawnees

By GORDON D. SHIRREFFS

A fight to the death between a young Pawnee and a rival chieftain

Young Wolf opened his eyes. He was lashed to a tree in a cottonwood grove. Beyond the grove were many tepees. His head ached. He had been unconscious a long time. He saw that Young Hawk was lashed to a tree close by. Then Young Wolf remembered. They had been scouting the Ponca village. Young Wolf had been careless. He had been stunned from ambush. There was not time to warn Young Hawk.

"What will become of us, Young Hawk?"

"We will die. It is bad medicine for me to die with a foolish youth who was so careless."

Young Wolf looked away. He had never liked Young Hawk.

Warriors came from the village. One of them, with the feathers of a chief, stopped and stood before Young Wolf.

"I am Crooked Hand," the Ponca said in poor Pawnee. "Do you understand me?"

"Yes."

"Are you afraid to die, young one?"

"I am Young Wolf, grandson of Knife Chief, chief of the Wolf People!"

The Ponca nodded gravely. "I know him well. I have fought against him. It is too bad you must die. If you had been honorably wounded in battle, I would have killed you. But you were struck down without a fight. Therefore the women's society has claimed you." There was a gleam of pity in his eyes.

"I have no son, Pawnee. It is in my power to save you if you will become my son."

"The Poncas are dogs! I would rather die!"

Crooked Hand shrugged and walked slowly away. Soon a strange procession of women entered the grove. They wore war bonnets of corn husks and carried shields of hoops covered with husks. They blew dust through sunflower stems. A bulky pock-marked squaw led them. They built a fire between the captives and pranced in ludicrous imitation of the war dance. The leader touched Young Wolf with a smoldering brand. He winced but made no sound.

Young Hawk sang his death song. A brand smashed against his mouth silencing him. The fat hag heated a lump of buffalo fat. She waddled behind Young Wolf. He screamed involuntarily as the searing fat touched his skin.

"You are no Pawnee," sneered Young Hawk.

Lightning forked across the darkening sky. Fat drops of rain slapped the dusty earth. The women scuttled away and a young Ponca brave came to guard the captives.

Young Wolf hung in his bonds. The rain soothed his blistered flesh. Lightning lanced across the sky and thunder split the night. The rain came down in blinding sheets. The young Ponca fled in superstitious awe. Young

37

Hawk tugged at his bonds. He tore one hand loose and then untied his other wrist and his ankles.

"Young Hawk!" called Young Wolf. "Untie me also!"

"You screamed before these dogs of Poncas. You are a coward. We do not want you back at Turikaku." Young Hawk disappeared into the dripping underbrush.

Throughout the stormy night Young Wolf suffered in shame. He prayed to the thunder and the lightning, the voices of the Great Spirit. By late morning the next day the rain had stopped but the women did not appear until the afternoon was almost gone.

"Where is the other dog?" screamed the fat hag. The squaws spread-eagled him on the ground. They brought dry wood and kindled little fires close to his body. The flames were searing his flesh when Crooked Hand came and kicked away the fires. The women jabbered furiously.

Crooked Hand silenced them. "You have had your pleasure. Now begone! You have spent too much time from your work."

Crooked Hand cut Young Wolf loose. Young Wolf looked at him curiously.

"Young Wolf, there has been war between Pawnees and Poncas far too long. It is very foolish. I have decided to take you into my lodge for a time. Perhaps you will change your mind and become my son."

"Why do you do this?" asked the Pawnee.

"I did not want to see you die. During the storm a bolt of lightning killed my best horse. The Great Spirit was angry with me. It was a sign that I was doing wrong." The chief's voice was calm.

Young Wolf looked up through the trees. A brilliant star had appeared in the west. It was a good omen, for he was of Turikaku, the center village of the thirteen confederated Pawnee villages, where the sacred mother bundle of the Evening Star was kept under his grandfather's custodianship. Crooked Hand was lost in his thoughts. Young Wolf's hand closed on a chunk of firewood. He swung it hard and Crooked Hand fell silently. Young Wolf took the Ponca's knife and faded into the underbrush.

Young Wolf was gaunt and weak when at last he saw the domed sod lodges of Turikaku beside a fork of the Platte. The late afternoon sun shone on sacred whitened shields hanging beside tall scalp poles. Young braves played at the wheel game. They hurled cross-barred hooked sticks at the wheel trying to hook it. Young Wolf smiled. He usually stopped the wheel with the hook rather than the red bead cross bar or the black bead cross bar. Few of the young men could thrust as many scoring sticks into the earth as he could when he played. He waded across the stream. A young brave snatched up a lance.

"Brothers! It is I, Young Wolf."

The brave drew back the lance ready to hurl it. "Young Wolf is dead!"

"Do you not remember me, Little Pipe?"

Little Pipe dropped the lance. "Young Hawk said the Poncas had tortured you to death." There was a strange tone to his voice.

A bulky youth eyed Young Wolf coldly. "He said you screamed before their women; that you had walked foolishly into a trap."

Young Wolf did not answer. Young Hawk had done his work well. A crowd of villagers approached, led by Knife Chief, gaunt with his many years but still as erect as a sacred lance.

"It *is* my grandson. My medicine said you would return."

Young Hawk sauntered up. "He screamed like a wounded horse under the torture. Is he welcome here? If so, let him do women's work, for he is no man."

Knife Chief threw back his blanket and touched his scars. "Do you see these? They are the record of many battles. This is my grandson. *I* make him welcome here. Do you wish to challenge me for the right?"

Young Hawk looked away. "I have no quarrel with you."

The older warriors muttered amongst themselves.

Knife Chief tore his sacred war shield from its pole. He looped it over Young Wolf's shoulder. "This is his answer. He raids the Poncas when his wounds are healed. If he does not return with honor, I will give up my chieftainship and my custodianship of the sacred Evening Star bundle! I have spoken."

The people covered their mouths. It was a great thing he had done. If Young Wolf did not fulfill his task, Knife Chief would also be a man without honor.

Young Wolf's grandmother held him close when he entered his grandfather's lodge. "It is my grandson who has come back from the spirit land. Aiiie!"

His grandmother helped him into his bunk. The smell of hot meat filled the lodge. He lay back on the buffalo robes. He had never expected to see the lodge again. He had lived there all his life, for his father and elder brother had died in battle against the Poncas and his mother had died when he was very young.

Knife Chief came into the lodge. "You will rest here until you can walk as a man. I do not like Young Hawk's story. You must prove that you *are* a warrior. We need horses for our forthcoming buffalo hunt. You will raid the Ponca herd. If you fail, you must do squaw's work!"

In the days that followed Young Wolf grew strong under the skillful hands of his grandmother. Knife Chief spent much time consulting the medicine men of Turikaku.

Little Pipe organized the war party. At last he came to Little Wolf. "The young men have voted for you as leader. Twenty young men will go."

"They will go with one who has been accused of cowardice before the Poncas?"

Little Pipe nodded.

"But why?"

"The wolf is your guardian spirit. Is that not right?"

"It appeared to my mother in a dream before I was born."

"That is good medicine. We have been asked to go as part of the Society of the White Wolf. It is a great honor."

Young Wolf smiled. The Society of the White Wolf taught that to be successful a warrior must follow the ways of the wolf, for the wolf was held in high esteem.

When Young Wolf was well, Knife Chief opened the Evening Star bundle and gave Young Wolf the regalia for the war party. There was a sacred pipe with no opening between stem and bowl, an otterskin collar, a lariat, a hawkskin, an ear of corn representing Mother Corn, red paint, eagle down and a leader's feather.

For three days the villagers carried out the ceremonies preparatory to the war dance. On the fourth night the war party was ready. Each man carried three extra pairs of moccasins filled with parched corn. They had small bags of pemmican and carried a coiled lariat, tomahawk, war club, scalping knife and a bow.

Young Wolf divided the party into two sections, one to be led by himself and the other by Little Pipe. Each section had two scouts disguised in wolf skins, two soldiers to keep order and several young untried men to act as servants. The warriors daubed their faces and robes with white clay. The scouts wore two eagle feathers set in wolf skin caps to look like wolf ears.

The musicians filed into the center of the village with their tom-toms, dried gourd rattles and sticks with antelope toes fastened to the ends.

Knife Chief wore his white buffalo robe pictured with his deeds and on his feet were sacred black moccasins signifying that he had consecrated the buffalo four times. He raised his arms toward the Evening Star. "Young Wolf will lead this war party, O Evening Star. He is not a member of the Society of the White Wolf, nor of the Two Lances, the Red Lances, the Crow Lances, the Brave Ravens nor even of the Crazy Dogs. Yet I ask you to give him success so that he may wash out the stain of his shame." He took roots from his medicine bag and chewed on them. He spat the juice on Young Wolf's chest. "This will make you brave and virtuous. If you fail, do not come back. It will be better for you to die."

The tom-toms struck up. The gourds rattled. The antelope toes clashed. The war party formed a circle and danced. When it was almost midnight, Knife Chief handed

Young Wolf a sacred lance from the Society of the White Wolf. He pointed to the northeast. Young Wolf howled and dashed from the village followed by the war party. There could be no turning back.

For five days they traveled by night and slept by day until they reached Ponca land. The scouts sped off into the windy darkness. It was close to dawn when the faint howling of a wolf far out on the prairie warned Young Wolf that the scouts had found the village.

It was light when the scouts trotted into the grove where the war party was hidden. "They are preparing to hunt. Tonight they will dance the Buffalo Dance. They will be sleepy tomorrow morning."

Young Wolf grunted in satisfaction. A quick raid on the horses, a few scalps, and the war party would be satisfied. The Pawnees never took chances. Many a war party leader had never had the chance to lead again because he had lost but one man.

Young Wolf folded his arms. "We will perform the ceremony to see our fortune."

Little Pipe cut the sod from a circular patch of ground. Young Wolf placed the articles from the Evening Star bundle on the altar. A buffalo skull was placed with them. Young Wolf kindled a tiny fire. The war party lined up on each side of the altar. A youth cut drumsticks and placed them on top of his rolled robe. He howled like a wolf.

Young Wolf lit the sacred pipe. He drew on it. The kinnickinic continued to burn although there was no opening between stem and bowl. If it had gone out, they would have gone back to Turikaku without shame.

Each warrior tied a personal trinket to a small stick, dedicated it to earth and sky and placed it on the altar. Little Pipe beat softly on the robe while the warriors chanted and danced.

When the dance was over a scout drew a map on the earth with a sharpened stick. "The village is half a day's journey away. The tepees are beside a stream. Behind the village is a curved butte. Horses are herded within the arc with the stream across its foot like a bow string."

Young Wolf nodded. "It has not changed. We rest until darkness. When we reach the village, I will lead my section through the grove on this side of the stream. Little Pipe will circle behind the butte and come down behind the herd. My party will cross the stream and silence the guards. Then Little Pipe's men will drive the herd toward us. Perhaps we will get away. If we do not, each man must fight like three for there are at least sixty Ponca warriors in that village."

Young Wolf led his men through the grove before dawn. Mist swirled through the trees and across the flats. The faint cry of a wolf came from the butte top. The warriors stripped off their robes and tied them around their waists. They would go into battle bare-chested to prevent wound infection. Young Wolf trotted forward. The clay-daubed faces looked like ghosts in the swirling mists.

They waded through the water. The mist came up to their shoulders. They circled the herd. A guard dozed on his horse. An arrow drove into his heart. Another guard died with a knife in his back. Little Pipe snatched up the guard's musket, powderhorn and bullet pouch. The other guards were on the far side of the stream. Lariats looped through the mist. The herd began drifting toward the stream. Little Pipe's men were driving them. Young Wolf whooped and waved his robe. The Pawnees drove the herd through the stream.

Guards shouted. A musket crashed. Poncas ran to horses picketed near their tepees. The Pawnees drove the herd up the far bank and raced out on the wet prairie grass.

Many hours later Young Wolf and Little Pipe looked back from a ridge. The Poncas were closing in.

"We can outride them if we turn the extra horses loose, Young Wolf."

"No! Our people need all of them. If they catch up with us, we fight."

The afternoon was waning when the Pawnees reached the Platte. The wide shallow river looped through sandy bottoms. The ground was flat and broken only by a deep brushy draw. The Poncas were riding down the low bluffs to the north.

Little Pipe rode close to Young Wolf. "It would be well to do as I suggested. They will catch us crossing the river."

Young Wolf looked at the Poncas. The prestige of a leader depended on bringing back all of his men unharmed rather than on the number of enemies slain.

"I will stay here, Little Pipe."

"You will die!"

Young Wolf shook his sacred lance. "I will challenge their leader. If he is a warrior, he will fight me for the herd. If I win, I will return to Turikaku, a man amongst men. If I die, you must yield the herd and go in peace."

Little Pipe silently gave Young Wolf the captured musket. He gripped Young Wolf's shoulders and galloped to the river. Young Wolf planted the sacred lance, rode about it three times and then stripped off his robe.

A Ponca galloped up. It was Crooked Hand. "Who is this who defies the Poncas?"

"Young Wolf of the Pawnees!"

"Do you dare to fight for the herd?"

"I have planted my sacred lance."

"I am a chief. I lead the Wa-zha-zhe, the first clan of the Poncas. It is not for me to fight one of lesser rank because of a challenge."

"I am the grandson of Knife Chief. I have stolen your horses. I defeated you while I was unarmed. I have your knife in my belt. Are you afraid to fight me while I *am* armed, Ponca?"

Crooked Hand rode forward in circles until he planted his lance beside that of Young Wolf. Neither of them could leave that place until one of them was dead. It was the no-flight obligation.

Crooked Hand charged and fired his breech-loading carbine. Young Wolf returned the fire. They dashed apart to reload. Crooked Hand's next shot tore through the Pawnee's shield. Young Wolf sent a ball into the Ponca's horse. They circled through a cloud of dust and powder smoke. A lucky shot tore through Young Wolf's powder horn. The powder flowed out. He held the shattered horn up high. Crooked Hand cast aside his carbine and charged with waving war club.

Young Wolf slapped his chest and whooped as he met the charge. The horses crashed together. The clubs beat a savage tattoo on the shields. Young Wolf crashed his club on the Ponca's naked thigh. Crooked Hand involuntarily lowered his shield. Young Wolf aimed a blow at the Ponca's head but the war club thong parted from his wrist and the club fell beneath the horses.

Crooked Hand threw down his club and strung his bow. Young Wolf sent a shaft into the Ponca's horse. Whizzing shafts crossed each other in their flight. The shields bristled with them. An arrow cut a furrow across Young Wolf's shoulder. The Ponca's horse reared and went down with an arrow in its heart. Crooked Hand sprang to the ground.

Young Wolf slid from his horse and slapped its rump. An arrow flashed past his face. He backed toward the draw to get out of the dust. A shaft grazed his skull. He staggered and blood trickled down his face. Crooked Hand whooped and closed in. He stripped his empty quiver off and drew his tomahawk. He looped its thong about his wrist and whirled it over his head. Young Wolf dropped his bow and felt for his tomahawk. It was gone. He whipped out the knife he had taken from Crooked Hand.

Crooked Hand advanced. "Come and die, Pawnee!"

They circled warily. Crooked Hand forced the fight. Chips flew from Young Wolf's shield as he parried the tomahawk blows. He raked his knife across the Ponca's ribs. The tomahawk slashed halfway through the glue-hardened buffalo hide of Young Wolf's shield.

Young Wolf slammed his shield against the Ponca's face. Crooked Hand kicked Young Wolf's feet from under him. Young Wolf went down. He wrapped his arms about the Ponca's legs and threw him to the ground. Their bodies were slick with sweat and blood. They rolled over the brink of the draw and crashed down through brush and over rocks. Now one held the advantage, now the other. Crooked Hand's fingers closed on Young Wolf's throat but his head smashed against a rock. His fingers loosened. Young Wolf threw the Ponca back and fell exhausted.

His body trembled violently as he got to his feet. He must finish off Crooked Hand. The Ponca was helpless. It would add greatly to his prestige to bring back Crooked Hand's scalp. He raised the knife and stood for a long time staring down at the Ponca. At last he lowered the blade. He had won the herd.

Crooked Hand opened his eyes. He gripped his tomahawk but Young Wolf stepped on the haft.

"Why did you not kill me, Pawnee?"

Young Wolf threw down the knife. "I owed you my life. I have paid my debt. Go in peace."

Crooked Hand got to his feet. He wiped the blood from his face. "These are strange words to hear from a warrior who fights like a mad wolf."

"Perhaps there is great medicine in our meeting. Surely your medicine did not have you spare me so that I might kill you. Perhaps the Great Spirit is angry because Ponca and Pawnee have fought too long without cause."

Crooked Hand nodded. "You speak wise words for one so young. Take my lance to your people. Tell Knife Chief that Crooked Hand desires peace. Perhaps we can meet and talk peace when the summer buffalo hunt is over."

"And the horses?"

Crooked Hand smiled. "Take them. They are the price for my life. Good hunting, Young Wolf."

Young Wolf stood with the lances in his hands and watched the Poncas ride to the north. Crooked Hand was as brave as any Pawnee. Young Wolf could think of no greater honor.

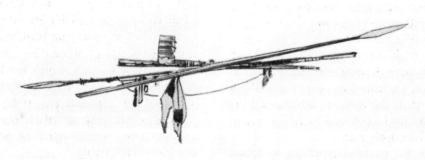

Four-Footed G-Men

By JIM KJELGAARD

When it comes to following a cold trail, no man or beast can beat the bloodhound

The keenest nose in the world belongs to the bloodhound, a creature literally created by man.

A Chicago breeder of one of the finest strains of American bloodhounds sells puppies on the guarantee that, if properly trained, they can follow a twenty-four-hour-old trail over Chicago's Michigan Boulevard. Art Hoag, an Arizonan who runs a bloodhound with his pack of lion hounds, has, in dry and hot Arizona, where scenting conditions are far from ideal, seen the dog start a two-day-old lion trail and lead his companions to the lion.

The late Martin Hogan, probably one of the world's foremost authorities on dogs, was running a bloodhound over a twenty-hour trail on England's Salisbury Plain. Army maneuvers were in progress, and three batteries of field artillery and a regiment of cavalry crossed the trail. But the bloodhound followed the elusive thread of scent through the maze.

These are not isolated or outstanding examples, but are fairly representative. Even when scenting conditions are poor, a good bloodhound can follow through on a ten-hour scent. When conditions were good, they have many times come successfully to the end of seventy-two-hour trails. Nick Carter, one of the greatest bloodhounds of all time, pursued a hundred-and-twenty-hour trail and found his man.

Due to this miraculous ability to follow old and elusive trails where even a wolf—providing it was possible to train one—would be baffled, bloodhounds have been employed in criminal apprehension by nearly every law-enforcement agency. They were used on the trail of the infamous Pretty Boy Floyd. And not long ago, near Cartersville, Georgia, bloodhounds led officers, including FBI men, to three desperate fugitives who had escaped from a United States marshal.

In addition, bloodhounds have countless times found lost persons, and in so doing have saved many lives. They probably have contributed more to the general welfare of humanity than any other dog—and they still remain as the most misunderstood and feared of beasts.

The Name Is Not What It Seems

The very name, bloodhound, conjures up a mental image of a ravening, slaver-jawed monster that thinks only of tearing some unlucky fugitive to pieces. But Uncle Tom's Eliza, crossing the ice with her baby, needn't have hurried at all if true bloodhounds had been on her trail; when they caught her they would have tried to lick her hand and probably they would have wanted to play with the baby. The savage dogs that pursued fugitive slaves, though they were called bloodhounds, were mongrel hound-mastiffs bred for their ferocity.

43

Bloodhound, an unfortunate title attached to the beast when English gentlemen were evolving him from the old St. Hubert's breed, means literally blooded or thoroughbred, hound. And no dog is more gentle.

A convict in a southern penitentiary could see no percentage in remaining there and went over the wall. A single bloodhound was put on his trail. Ordinarily, when trailing, they're kept on a leash. But this one, set free, outdistanced the officers and came upon his man. Following the customary bloodhound behavior—they're always overjoyed when they do a job well—the dog wagged his tail and licked the convict's hands.

Not one to miss a trick, the convict kept running and took the dog with him. He ran right into another state, and sold the fine bloodhound for seventy-five dollars to a sheriff there.

Another hound, loosed on the trail of a lost five-year-old child, was discovered by the men who followed, sprawled before the baby. The dog was wagging its tail.

This propensity to gentleness is almost an unvarying bloodhound trait. Children are often used in training them, and no child has ever yet been nipped by what supposedly is the most savage of dogs.

The Training Is a Science

Though most law enforcement agencies use bloodhounds, not many maintain their own. And because they are supposedly vicious—the universally known Uncle Tom's Cabin is largely responsible for this erroneous idea—they aren't a popular dog and few are available. But there are men who have interested themselves in bloodhounds as a hobby, and it is upon these men that officers call when the use of a hound is indicated. Outstanding among them are George Brooks, a restaurant man who has worked his hounds on the incredible total of twelve thousand cases and solved most of them, and Walter Lesniak, a butcher. But good hounds are so few, and the need in an emergency so pressing, that the men who own one have on various occasions been called upon to take them thousands of miles by plane.

Training a bloodhound to follow men—and probably there are not more than ten thoroughly trained, wholly dependable, man-hunting hounds in the United States—is an exact science that calls for special skills. Not all bloodhounds have the inborn ability to trail men. Many of those that do possess such ability are ruined by inept trainers. A good trainer must understand his pupil from the tip of his black nose to the end of his slim tail. Literally he must be able to look inside the dog's brain and interpret the mental processes that transpire there. He must know exactly when to administer punishment—many an otherwise fine dog has been completely spoiled by a slap or even a harsh word at the wrong moment—and when to heap on praise.

Usually hounds start their education when they are between a year and eighteen months old. A runner lays a short trail and the hound is urged to find him. Succeeding, he is lavishly rewarded with bits of liver or whatever delicacy he likes best. Other runners—to give the hound experience in trailing different people usually a different runner is employed each time—lay longer and longer trails and more time is permitted to elapse before the hound is allowed to start. Finally the dog is following trails twenty-four or more hours old.

When the dog has mastered that much, he is initiated into the more complicated arts of his trade. He is permitted to smell a handkerchief, hat, or shoe, and taught to find the owner. He learns the "missing member" method. Any number of people might be in the same room, and all of them take turns sitting on the same chair or chairs. One will depart and the bloodhound is brought in. He sniffs the various objects to find out who has been present. Then he carefully goes to each person in the room to discover who is present. By some method that only the bloodhound knows he has retained in his brain the scent of the absent person and that's the one he'll follow.

This is all highly useful. If, for instance, a store is robbed, the robber may and may not drop something that will establish his scent. But, if nothing has been left behind, the store manager and his clerks may be assembled. The hound is induced to sniff at the cash register, safe, or whatever has been robbed, and catalogue the scents there. Then he takes olfactory census of the people in the room and follows the absent member. However, there are various ways to put the dog on the correct scent.

Thieves entering by a window will leave their scent on the sill. Or, breaking in by any other way, they may erase their fingerprints but never their scent. In at least one instance, where the thief broke through the cupola of a building and stole some valuable furs, the bloodhound was permitted to smell an eight-inch piece sawed from the cupola. Unerringly he led officers straight to the home of the culprit, and a conviction resulted when the man confessed. In another case the trail led to a bus stop, and ended. But the schedules of the various buses were checked, police were telephoned to be on the alert at all future stops, and the thief was apprehended.

Both in training, and in following trails, bloodhounds are usually kept on leash. Those who break the law know that they can lay a getaway trail to baffle the keenest eye, but they can't baffle a bloodhound's nose. And desperate men are highly averse to being followed. Typical of what happens when unleashed hounds are set upon a criminal's trail is the incident of the murderer who escaped from a southern penitentiary. Unknown to the pursuing officers he had somehow secured a gun, and he shot three hounds when they came in sight. This has happened time and again. Even when they aren't following anyone, bloodhounds are frequently poisoned by lawless men who know that they cannot run away from hounds when future crimes are committed.

Cars Make Things Tough

Of course no dog can follow an automobile, and the advent of the motor car has supposedly made bloodhounds useless. But not long ago, in a western state, the mutilated body of a sixteen-year-old girl was dis-covered in the willows near a small stream. A bloodhound traced the murderer's scent to the road, and lost it. But, a few days before, the girl had been seen with a man who lived more than thirty miles away. The bloodhound was taken there, paraded up and down the streets of the small town, and when he passed in front of it went straight into the house where the man lived. Told that the hound had followed him clear from the scene of his crime, he confessed.

In more than one instance bloodhounds have saved officers' lives. A sheriff and his deputy were on the trail of a man known to be desperate. Their hound had its nose to the trail. Suddenly he raised his head and set off at right angles to the course. The officers, experienced bloodhound men, knew that the dog had body scent and they were prepared to deal with him when they came upon the criminal. Later, when tracing the trail out, it was discovered that the man they followed had gone more than a mile from where the hound had left his scent and made a great U turn to come back and lay an ambush. But the hound had detected his body scent when he was more than a thousand feet away.

The very presence of a bloodhound may have a salutary effect in suppressing potential criminals. There were a great many chickens stolen in one rural community until a sheriff two counties away brought in a bloodhound and caught a chicken thief with it. The story was given free play in all the local papers, and after that no more chickens were missing.

Exactly wherein lies the bloodhound's miraculous power of scent has never been satisfactorily explained. A competent veterinarian has stated that the hound's keen scent can be attributed to the heavy folds of skin that cover his head and face, and the vast number of nerves they contain. Walter Lesniak thinks that the secret of the bloodhound's olfactory superiority lies in his heavy lips. When the dog's head is close to the ground, these lips hang open and moisten the scent it is following.

But nobody even attempts to explain the

bloodhound's steadfast singleness of purpose. Once he has started it, he simply cannot be dissuaded from a trail. A bloodhound, following a man, was attacked by a herd of young horses. The horses were driven off but, though the hound had received several broken ribs and a broken leg, he still wished to follow the trail. This trait of following to the end whatever trail he starts makes the bloodhound invaluable to hunters.

But even if it were absolutely useless for hunting, and there were never any criminals to trail, a trained bloodhound would be a wonderful asset to any community and the cost of acquiring and training one would not be excessive.

An eighteen-year-old son of a wealthy farmer went to feed the cattle. He did not return, and the father's search disclosed only the boy's jacket. Further search revealed nothing, and a posse of five hundred men looked in every conceivable place where the boy might be. Forty hours after the boy had disappeared, George Brooks was asked to bring his bloodhounds.

They sniffed the boy's cap, found his trail in the barn, and traced it to the ladder leading to the haymow. Brooks was told that his dogs were on the wrong track; every bit of hay had been thrown out of the mow and the boy was not there. The bloodhounds were taken to the boy's room, and again ended up at the haymow ladder. Despite assurances that the boy couldn't possibly be there, Brooks climbed into the haymow and discovered him, unconscious and wedged in a grain chute. The boy lived, but the attending physician asserted that he could not have survived six hours more.

It is not at all inconceivable that, if a trained bloodhound had been available and promptly used, both the Lindbergh baby and his kidnaper would have been found in a very short time. But of course, though they come very near to so doing, bloodhounds cannot do the impossible. A certain chief of police, six weeks after a shocking murder-robbery, let a bloodhound sniff a strip of cloth that supposedly came from the killer's coat and expected him to find the criminal.

But numberless times they have averted tragedy. In Kentucky's mountains a bloodhound was put on the trail of a missing four-year-old girl. The trail led over a high mountain, and excited many charges of faking on the bloodhound's part because so small a girl could not climb so high a peak. But the dog led directly to her—halfway down the other side.

In Minnesota a small boy strayed from his home, and after a big search party failed to find him, bloodhounds were put on the trail. It led to the Mississippi River, and ended. When the river was dragged, the boy was found. In this case, of course, the only thing saved was further efforts on the part of the search party.

But countless times trained bloodhounds have led straight to lost people, an eighty-nine-year-old man, two small children, a thirty-year-old woman, a lost fisherman, and others.

Sometimes They're Safe

Not all such "lost" people were in danger. One time Walter Lesniak was frantically summoned from work. His two-year-old son was missing, and a hundred men were organizing a search party. Lesniak bade them wait, and turned a bloodhound loose. The dog went directly to the empty house next door, climbed the steps, and the boy was discovered contentedly playing on the floor. At other times, when one of his household failed to show up at meal time, Lesniak let a bloodhound smell some small article of clothing and sent him to bring the absent member home.

Of course it cannot be expected that, because a dog is called a bloodhound, it can unerringly ferret out a missing person. The dog must be competently trained, and under the direction of a trainer who knows what he's about.

But if you or any member of your family are ever lost, the best thing you can do is forget everything you've ever heard about savage bloodhounds tearing people to bits, and pray that such a man and such a hound are available.

Blood of the Kashids

By FREDERICK GONNER

An Arab boy earns a new name in a waterless waste of sand dunes and vultures

The boy Mifleh, the son of Sheikh Ahmed el Kashid, the son of Yusuf el Arar el Kashid, slipped from the shadow of the palm trees fringing the pool which gave Arar life, and which gave life to the caravans that halted at the oasis.

Mifleh was tall, after the fashion of his people, and his body was lean and hard. Barely fourteen, his brows were already bushy beneath the white kuffiy.

He stared out over the arid, yellow face of the desert, darkly aware that the pool was drying up. For a month the water had dwindled, shrinking to a mere trickle, taking with it the life of Arar. Tomorrow it would vanish completely, leaving only a crack in the earth, to the village a fatal wound, for fever had already overtaken the village.

His eyes swept the ribbed caravan trail, which bore the impress of the feet of many camels, but his survey encompassed the hills and troughs between, without hope. The young men would not return to Arar for twelve days, much too late to save the women and children.

Only once before had he known the fear which now knotted his breath in his throat. Then he had been out with his father, Ahmed the Brave, as he was called, and two camels. The pack animal, led by his father, had been large and slow, while his own, under whose feet he had often seen the sand become liquid

gold as it raced over the caravan trails, had been fleet as a high desert wind.

Mifleh had been fatigued when the fear laid its prickly hand on him, and he had been unable to loosen its hold. The Berbers, six of them, had ridden up out of the desert, and his father had advanced to meet them. Mifleh had tarried only long enough to see his father strike down two of the Berbers before they overwhelmed the man. Then, in the grip of panic, Mifleh had fled across the desert on his swift-moving mehari.

That was two years ago, but his youth and inexperience had not saved him from the scorn of his people. Mifleh the Coward, they jeered, the unworthy son of Ahmed the Brave, and they spat their contempt into the ground. Old Yusuf, his grandfather, himself once a sheikh of the Kashid, had mourned half a year for his son, and he silently despised Mifleh. Yet, because the boy was the son of his son, Yusuf had grown to love Mifleh again.

"One day you will prove to them that you have the blood of the great Kashid," he said.

Mifleh watched the sun smolder away to a deep glow on the horizon, the night hurriedly drawing its dark, bestarred cloak over the desert. In the village behind him the women and children and old men prayed to Allah that the young men might return in time; and then those not tormented by fever escaped from thirst and fear in the cool darkness of sleep.

It was a full hour before dawn when old Yusuf wakened Mifleh.

"Eat well," said the old man, "for we must travel to Shida, the great white city, two days' journey to the east. The women and children cry for water, and the young men are away. As they have taken the camels with them, we must travel on foot, Mifleh."

Mifleh, knowing well the heat of the desert and the cruel way it had with those who were without water and who lost their way, could not hide his fear. Yusuf laid an encouraging hand on the boy's shoulder.

"You are a son of the great Kashid," he said. "A Kashid does not show fear."

Mifleh gritted his teeth and clenched his hands, mustering his resolution. Yet he could not help wishing that the young Britisher, Wilson, were here with one of the planes which so swiftly spanned the desert.

Wilson had crept in from the desert one day, his plane clawed out of the sky by a sandstorm. He had been mad with thirst and an injured leg made every yard of his progress agony. For two months he had stayed at the oasis while his leg healed, and in that time he had taught Mifleh many things. He had explained how airplanes took to the air, how they received and sent messages while in flight, and he had tried to make simple the mystery of communication by signaling across the desert to him with a mirror held against the rays of the sun. Mifleh had been twelve then, and he had marveled that a piece of glass could be made to flash letters over many leagues of sand.

Most important of all, Wilson had taught him that it was not wrong to feel fear, but that you should try to understand it and not give way to it. That had made Mifleh feel brave, but now, as he prepared for his journey and fear made it hard for him to swallow his food, he wished fervently that he did not have to go to Shida.

Yusuf took two bags of camel-skin, filled one with meat, dates and grain, and handed it to the boy. Into the second he poured a small quantity of water, the little they could

take from the village, and this he secured about his own shoulder. Mifleh knew that, at midsummer, it was possible to live in the desert only a day and a night without water.

Perhaps because it helped to shore up a confidence all too ready to crumble, the boy took the long, curved dagger with its silver tracings, once the property of his father, and thrust it into his kumr.

Yusuf, his kerchief high about his face against a heat that would soon possess them as if their blood had changed to fire, carried a long white stick, thin and wizened as himself, but, also like himself, unbending.

Their feet upon the packed sand of the caravan trail, they found the ground easy, walking in silence and making good progress. By midday, with the sun high in the sky and the heat wrapping them in its parching crucible, their faces glistened and their mouths were salt dry. Soon they could no longer turn their faces toward the sun. The heat seemed to bruise their bodies with speared flame; it seemed as if their limbs were encased in metal, and their fatigue grew unbearable.

The sand tangled about their feet, and

Mifleh marveled at the endurance of the old man. As they halted to eat a little food and drink some of the water, the boy asked, "Is there *no* shade in the desert?"

Yusuf merely shook his head, and they resumed their journey, pursuing the clearly defined caravan track. Both felt the heat in their throats like a burning cinder. For what seemed like hours Mifleh set his teeth against the fatigue and the terrifying thirst. At last, determination failed him, and he cried out for water.

Yusuf gave him a little from the skin, taking not even a drop for himself. Yet his long Arab strides were slowing and shortening, and several times he stumbled, only the stick saving him from falling.

Mifleh, too, walked more slowly, not to suit his pace to Yusuf's, but because he could move no faster. Toward midafternoon, the old man fell, and the boy, terrified of being alone, pulled him in a panic to his feet. A little later, when the sun had reached a new harshness in its scourging heat, they were staggering, their legs no longer capable of measured movement.

Mifleh's thoughts became confused. He was no longer praying to go back. Indeed, he no longer cared about anything; his limbs moved by an impulse that seemed alien to himself. Once or twice the track vanished in the shifting sands, and they sought it as desperately as the hands of a drowning man grope for a lifeline. Now, their way was marked by bones, white and bleached, the results of the combined attention of heat, vultures, and kites.

At last the sun began to swing toward the horizon and they came to a halt. It was a little cooler, and for an hour they rested, drinking the niggardly remnants of the water. The boy tried to eat, but he could not persuade the food to pass his parched throat. He cast the bag of meat and dates away, sitting, like Yusuf, hunched forward, his eyes closed.

It was thus that the sandstorm caught them, a thing of black fury, whose whirling folds pirouetted the choking sand, hot needles that sought to lacerate every exposed inch of their bodies. Mifleh's kerchief was torn from him by the first savage tug of the wind, and the sand whipped into his face. Groping and struggling blindly to escape the wrath of the storm, he stumbled

49

into Yusuf and they went down together into the yielding sand. They held on to one another, fearful that they might be separated in the blackness.

The storm passed quickly, a black shadow upon the desert, and the sun resumed its interrupted sway. But its passage had created new drifts and hollows and had completely obliterated the caravan trail.

They shook the sand from their clothes and made partially successful efforts to clear it from their nostrils, mouths and ears. And then, fatigued and despairing, they pressed on, Yusuf taking his directions from the low sun and hoping to strike the trail again.

For some time they moved on, so automatically that it would have been an effort to halt, knowing only that the man who rests in the desert sheds some of his strength and that there comes a time when he is unable to rise.

Night slipped over them, bringing out the stars, and the old man urged Mifleh onward, anxious to take advantage of the brief cool hours before they must once again endure the naked flame of the sun.

All night they went forward, their steps slower and more uncertain as thirst and fatigue became more urgent. Once, when Mifleh had an overwhelming desire to rest and his body sagged sharply, Yusuf, with great understanding, rested his hand on the boy's shoulder. And Mifleh, believing that the old man was depending on him, remained upright and staggered on. The lips of Yusuf, cracked and parched, moved slightly as he prayed. He knew he could not go much farther, and he was appealing to Allah for the life of the boy.

At last, as the sun marched remorselessly over the horizon and the heat licked hungrily towards them, the old man fell for the last time, the boy falling with him. For a long time they lay, but the desire to live was strong in Mifleh, and fear of isolation in the desert reached him even through his thirst.

In panic he shook the old man. "Get up, get up!" he shouted. "You must not leave me!" But his words lacked moisture and barely passed the gag of his swollen lips.

Fear took hold of him, and only want of strength prevented him from running blindly across the sand. Lacking Yusuf's encouragement, he had only his own resources, and courage and resolution failed him.

His weeping was brief and rending, with

few tears, but it was a storm that left a measure of calm in its wake.

He felt vaguely the need for action, and he responded to it by rising slowly to his feet. It was then that his foot touched the waterbag lying at Yusuf's side, and, incredibly, he felt water move inside it. He pulled open the skin and had raised it to his lips when understanding invaded his dulled mind. Yusuf had reserved these drops of water, not for himself, but for Mifleh.

He had kept his secret, denying his own immeasurable need, resisting the searing desire to relieve his burning, flaming thirst so that Mifleh, in his extremity, might have water.

Understanding of the old man's sacrifice caused Mifleh to tremble. Impelled by a strange emotion, he tried to bring the water to Yusuf's mouth, but his hands were unsteady, and the precious drops were lost in the sand.

He almost gave way to despair. Perhaps it was the vultures which roused him into action. There were two of them at first, large black birds circling overhead. They dropped clumsily onto a rock only a few yards away, as if they understood that he was helpless against them. For a moment he watched their scrawny necks outstretched menacingly. They would wait patiently, guided by their uncanny instinct of anticipating the imminence of death.

Hardly conscious of any intention, he placed the old man's kerchief about his own face to protect it from the sun. And, with considerable effort, he picked up Yusuf's stick. Then he stumbled away, forcing himself through the cruel intensity of the heat flaming about him anew as the sun climbed the sky. Soon he was talking, stupidly and irrationally, in the first stages of delirium.

He was unaware of the treacherously yielding sand, of his irregular fumbling prog-

ress, of his body, swaying and lurching. But he was vividly alive to strange and alluring things. He saw the oasis at Arar so clearly that he could make out the fronded palm trees and his father's tent at the well that was brimming with water. Mifleh staggered toward the water. He pushed forward one weighted leg and then the other, until, although he did not know it, he was standing on the top of a high dune.

Immediately the oasis of Arar expanded into a white and gleaming city. He could see palm trees and pools of water, graceful buildings and slender minarets. Some lingering shade of reason warned him of its unreality, and the warning was sharpened by a shadow passing between himself and the sun. It was a vulture.

It took him many moments to turn in the soft sand and look back to where Yusuf was lying. A vulture crouched near him, its clumsy wings stirring as it inched its way ever nearer to the old man. Mifleh dared not turn his head again, knowing that another glimpse of the entrancing city would draw him toward it, and he had the prompting to go back to protect his grandfather.

Yusuf had done something wonderful for him. He could not remember what it was, but the impression of it remained strong within him. Resolution clamped his arid lips, and gripping the stick he went down the dune. Falling, he crept forward on hands and knees, as the needling sand bit hotly into his palms.

He pushed to his feet when only a few feet from the vulture, and his forward run was a clumsy, stumbling thing. He raised the stick and, as he brought it down, he lost his balance. Nevertheless, the thin, unyielding staff caught the bird on the neck, killing it outright.

The success filled Mifleh with a curious pride—sufficient at least to urge him to his feet again. The desert was still, but he swayed as though buffeted by a furious wind. He swayed still more, as recalling the beautiful city, he began to climb the dune once more.

He was unaware that he had lost his stick,

and that once more he was on his hands and knees. He was barely conscious that he was moving. But he saw the city, bright and shining, wrapped in a slight iridescent haze. He could make no further move towards it. He could merely lie in the sand, regarding it with immense longing. It was then that his hand brushed against the hilt of his dagger. He drew it out of his girdle, staring at the broad, glittering blade as though seeing it for the first time. This had been his father's dagger, entirely forgotten in the torment of his thirst and exhaustion. It flashed and flickered in the sun, evoking shadowy memories.

Long, long ago someone had told him something about the use that could be made of a bright and glittering thing in the desert. For several minutes he lay, his head on his arm, striving to remember. There were letters, if only he could recall them, which had a very special meaning. He cast about in his fevered mind, striving to find the knowledge that he needed.

Slowly he discovered some of the connections. Other symbols came back to him. He was uttering dry little moans as he forced himself to a sitting position. With both hands he held out the knife, turning it so that the sun flashed fire upon it in long and short periods. He no longer wondered about the reality of the city. His whole attention was fixed agonizingly on the task of supporting and twisting the knife as the sun stabbed blindly upon it the painfully remembered code. "S.O.S. A-R-A-R. W-A-T-E-R. S.O.S."

He repeated the message, pain sweeping agonizingly up his arm. Once more he began to flash his call for help, but the knife fell from his fingers. At full stretch in the sand, he looked for some answering signal, but he could detect none. The desert maintained its sinister immobility and silence. For a long time he lay there incapable of movement, the sun holding him in its flaming embrace. Then he heard the airplane. For several moments the increasing throb of the engines meant nothing to him. Then he saw it, over the city, climbing into the sky, silver in the sun. Now it was almost above him, and he traced its swift shadow over the desert. He tried to take off his kerchief to wave, but he lacked the strength to do so, and the plane continued on its course, still climbing. The effort robbed him of his last reserve of energy, and he fell prone in the sand, darkness blotting out the brilliance and heat of the sun.

And the vultures, now five in number, wheeled overhead, uttering their desolate cries.

Mifleh became aware of pain in his mouth and in his body. But his mouth was moist and he could move his tongue. For a long time he lay still, more and more aware of the light beating upon his eyelids. He opened his eyes. About him was the desert and above him was the sky, but it was not empty. Filling it was a man's head. Then he remembered everything.

"Water—Arar," he said.

"We received your signal, Mifleh el Kashid," the man said. "Already a plane has taken water to Arar."

"Yusuf? Where is Yusef el Kashid?"

"He is alive. Like you he is a Kashid, and the Kashids do not die without fighting."

Mifleh closed his eyes, well content. He had fought like a Kashid, and he had won.

On a litter which protected him from the sun, Yusuf lay some yards away. His eyes were open, fixed on the camels being made ready to take him and Mifleh into Shida. He felt weak, but he was happy. Born of the desert and reared on its indifferent face, he took life and death as they came, without resentment and without fear. He was trying to think back over the last part of their journey. He remembered falling and being unable to rise. Then he recalled the menacing vultures.

They lifted him onto one of the camels, and somewhere nearby he could hear one of the men talking.

"Mifleh is the name of the boy," he was saying. "He is very brave."

The old man smiled, repeating to himself, "Mifleh—Mifleh the Brave."

The boy had not deserted him after all. Yusuf glanced over to the sleeping boy. A few yards beyond him he saw something that no one else had noticed, a dead vulture. Yusuf was well content. His smile now was wise and altogether happy. "Mifleh the Brave," he repeated. "Yes, the boy has the blood of the Kashids. All will be well with him."

The Manly Art

By JOE LOUIS

Learn about the basic techniques of boxing offense and defense from a ring expert

The sport of boxing is a physical contact activity which teaches a boy many important skills. It develops coordination, agility, body balance, and self-control. Although it has a definite place in self-defense, and has even come to be accepted as the "manly art of self-defense," it is definitely not a brutalizing influence as some people seem to fear. One need only point to Gene Tunney and Colonel Edward Eagan as classic examples of top-notch boxers who retained all the attributes of gentlemanliness throughout their entire careers.

An indication that boxing is a genuine sport is to be inferred from the small role it played in modern commando fighting and jungle fighting, where the emphasis was placed more on a combination of tactics which involved Apache woods fighting, jiu-jutsu, wrestling, street fighting, and garroting in the manner of the India thuggee. However, boxing is a characteristically American self-defense skill, and in the course of learning something about it, you will develop ease and poise of manner, besides strengthening your body.

Your Stance Is Important

The very first thing to learn in boxing is a good stance. The correct position must become a habit if you hope to make any progress as a boxer. There are several schools of thought on the subject, but most authorities agree that the following is a sound boxing stance.

Keep your left foot flat on the floor with the toes pointing off at a slight angle. The right foot is kept back with the heel off the ground and the knees bent. The arms are carried free at the sides, with the elbows protecting your lower ribs. The left hand is held high, and about a foot in front of the body, while the right hand is palm up toward your opponent in a position to catch any blows which he might launch. Keep your chin in, but not awkwardly cramped into your shoulder—just try not to stick it out too prominently.

A boxer moves in a series of sliding shuffles like a waltzer, except that he never changes the relative position of his feet if he can possibly keep from doing so. He moves forward or backward in a series of short, sliding steps without lifting the feet at all. Each foot moves only a few inches at a time. For a quick advance in pursuing a retreating opponent, however, you may take a long step forward with your left foot; then bring your right foot up to it quickly so that the basic boxing stance is immediately resumed.

Tips on Punching Technique

Really good hitters among the ring masters punch in a straight line. If you watch a champion do it in the newsreels, it will appear very easy; yet, you will find that it is a difficult accomplishment to acquire. You see, it is not the natural way for humans to swing, and therefore requires much practice. Study the art carefully if you really want to learn, or you will continue to swing like a grizzly bear, and the other fellow will beat you to the punch with a snappy, straight blow.

Remember, a straight line is the shortest distance between two points; if one of the points is your nose, you will wish that you were not on the receiving end. Now, let's learn a few blows.

The Left Jab

The left jab is most commonly used because most of your "leads" will be made with your left hand. If you can acquire a rapier-like flick with your left hand, that stings hard, you can keep an opponent off balance and out of effective range.

The power of a left jab comes from the turn of your left shoulder to the right, and the sudden shooting out of your left arm. When your blow strikes its mark, the knuckles of your clenched fist should be pointing up.

Now, for a rule that applies to all of your punches. Whenever you punch, try to punch right through your target—not just at it. In a good jab, the hand shoots back to your guard position as though it had an elastic tied to it. The right stays open and ready to block or parry a counter blow.

Throwing a Hook

A hook is a blow that travels in an arc. It is more powerful than a jab because more body weight can be put behind it. In making a left hook, shift your weight to your right foot and whip your left hand around in an arc that would land on your right shoulder if it missed your opponent.

Don't lower the hand or pull it back to make the punch. Any such motion will "telegraph" the blow to your opponent who will duck or parry it easily. In the hook, your knuckles should point out and away from your body when the blow lands. Try to drive your fist through your target.

In making a right hook, shift your weight to your left foot, raise the right elbow, and, with a half-bent arm, swing your right fist in an arc toward the opposite shoulder. Don't let your wrist turn or the force of your blow may sprain it.

The Uppercut

An uppercut is swung like a hook, except that the angle of the blow is different. Instead of being parallel to the ground, an uppercut is swung with either hand in an arc toward your opponent's solar plexus and jaw. If you miss the first, your fist goes on up to meet the jaw. This is done from a crouch so that the sudden straightening of your body gives your blow the additional benefit of your leg drive and body weight.

THE LEFT JAB

LEFT HOOK TO HEAD

RIGHT HOOK TO BODY

THE CATCH

PARRYING BLOW TO HEAD

How to Learn Punching

Practice these punches on a heavy bag as much as you can. You can make such a heavy bag by stuffing a strong flour sack with sand. This may then be hung from a beam in your garage or cellar, or from a tree limb in your yard. Be sure to wear some sort of heavy training gloves to protect your hands. Work at the blows conscientiously and practice hitting at a specific target each time. Don't just hit the bag, hit a spot on it. The same rule goes for boxing an opponent. Aim at his jaw, nose, solar plexus, or some other spot—not just at his head or body.

Defensive Boxing

There is a classic boxing anecdote which shows that punching isn't the only skill in a fighter's repertoire. A college boxer was getting a terrific licking from his ring opponent. In the first round, he was knocked down three times. He came back to his corner, and his student manager encouragingly told him: "You're doing great. He can't even hit you."

The second round found him flat on his back no fewer than five times, yet, when he staggered back to his corner the manager cheerfully yelled: "Great! Great! He can't touch you! That's the way to box him."

In the third round he was buffeted and belabored so heavily that the manager and trainer had to go out to guide him back to his corner. But, again, the manager shouted

into his ear: "You're doing swell. He hasn't laid a glove on you. He can't hit you at all."

"In that case," replied the weary and discouraged gladiator, "you'd better keep an eye on the referee because somebody's giving me an awful beating in there."

As this little tale shows, knowing how to punch isn't everything. You've got to avoid the other fellow's blows, too. Now that you have learned how to make your punches, you must also learn the methods by which punches are avoided or blocked, or you'll wind up like the boxer in the story.

Protect Yourself

A good boxer knows many ways of rendering a punch harmless. He may avoid it by a quick deflecting motion of his head, so that the blow goes off to the side of his body. When parrying a blow, wait until it is well on its way before you deflect it; otherwise you may be hit by the other hand, should the opponent suddenly change his mind.

Blows may also be stopped with the open hand and ducked by bending or dipping the body under them. Sometimes, when they can't be avoided, the expert boxer will block them with his elbows or take them upon his body, rolling backwards at the same time so that the blow's force is diminished.

How to Stop Punches

The best defenses against a left jab are the catch, in which the blow is caught in the open right hand, or the parry, in which the blow is brushed aside by the right hand.

An uppercut is best avoided by suddenly taking a step backward, or by bringing your open glove down against the opponent's forearm to deflect the blow.

Whenever you think you are in trouble, clinch with your opponent by getting his left hand under your right armpit and tying up his right arm with your left hand. Keep close in the clinch until the referee breaks you.

The fighter who bobs and weaves his body presents a hard target for his opponent to hit. Don't distort your boxing stance into a caricature, however, but try to get a good weaving motion that will keep your opponent confused.

Remember the following hints in forming your boxing strategy:

1. The solar plexus and jaw are vital points.

2. Use your head—plan your attack.

3. Keep your eyes on your opponent's eyes; whenever he gets set to hit, upset his plans by moving out of range.

4. Never show that you are hurt or tired.

5. The left is your safest lead; in fact, there is an old boxing adage which says, "Never lead with your right."

6. If you stand still, you will get hit. This does not mean, however, that you should jump about like a jack rabbit. Keep moving, but preserve a good stance.

7. Whenever your opponent gets within range, punch him; otherwise he will punch you.

8. Try to punch through your target.

9. You can't hit hard if you are back-pedaling. Step in when you hit.

10. The safest place is right close to your opponent with your hands high and your head low.

The Art of Feinting

A most important skill for both offensive and defensive boxing is feinting. A feint is a deception which makes your opponent think you are going to attack and thereby draws his guard up or down to ward off the impending blow. This momentary, sometimes instinctive, reaction on his part will expose him to attack from another point. I have seen a boxing instructor warn an opponent that he would hit him on the jaw and no other place. Then, by a series of feints he would draw the novice's guard down time after time, despite the fact that the beginner had been warned it would happen.

You should learn to feint with movements of your shoulders, hands, eyes, and trunk. If you can trick your opponent into covering up his face, that will naturally leave his body open for a blow, and vice versa. The time spent in learning to feint will pay good dividends. Boxing with an imaginary opponent (called shadow boxing) is one good way to practice this skill.

PARRYING BLOW TO BODY

BLOCKING BLOW WITH ARM

Ghost Men of Coronado

By DOUGLAS TATE

A young Indian brave risks his life among mysterious ghost men and their elk-dogs

Mahtocheega edged forward through the mesquite, his dark eyes watching every move of the lone Comanche at the water hole below him.

The warrior's low chant grew in volume as he mixed warpaint and made great dripping splashes across his body. Mahtocheega counted them, one by one, knowing that each mark was a badge of honor and covered a wound received in combat.

From his medicine pouch the warrior drew burnt sage and bat's wing and scattered them to the spirit gods of the east and to the lesser spirits of the north and west. When he faced the south, however, the chant ended suddenly and his lance, smeared red with blood paint, was driven deep into the sand.

To Mahtocheega it was a sign, a strong sign, and it was the second in as many days. Casting aside his caution, the boy rose to his feet and, holding his bow high above his head in a gesture of friendship, stepped into the open.

At the sound the Comanche swung with the agility of a panther. The war axe left his hand in a single smooth motion. Mahtocheega leaped aside and the tomahawk was a dull blur as it whipped past his head and clattered into the mesquite.

"I am Mahtocheega!" the boy cried, "I come in peace."

"You are Mandan." The warrior dropped his arm. "The Comanche have no war with the Mandans."

"I am name-traveling," Mahtocheega said. "I have come of age and must find a man's name for myself."

"There is no stronger name than Mahtocheega, the Little Bear."

"But it was not of my own choosing," Mahtocheega said. "It was given to me when I was very young. We were berrying far from the village when a grizzly scattered the women and I lay still and pretended death while the bear pawed over me."

The Comanche squatted in the hot sand and grinned appreciatively.

"You did well," he said. "It is known that a man lying still is medicine to a grizzly bear."

Mahtocheega knelt by the water hole and drank long and deep, quenching the thirst that burned in him.

"Three days I fasted, waiting for a sign," he said. "Then on the third day it came. A war eagle circled low overhead, then flew south very fast."

"A strong sign." The Comanche nodded in agreement while the lines of his face grew hard. "But there is great danger in the south. Even among the Comanche, who know the country, the south is forbidden."

"Yet you make war on the south."

The warrior went into the mesquite after his war axe and was long in answering.

"Among the Comanche I am known as Burning Foot. I have won many coups but the wolf of misfortune has stalked my house

for many days. I go now to rescue my son Shonka who is held captive by the ghost men."

"I have heard of the ghost men," Mahtocheega said slowly. "The tales are many in our village but no Mandan has ever seen them."

"They are pale, bloodless creatures with hard shells that glitter in the sun." Burning Foot raised his bow. "The strongest shaft shatters against them. They do not travel afoot as do our people, but ride upon the backs of great elk-dogs that race with the wind."

Mahtocheega turned to face the great plains that fell away to the south and the lines about his mouth were grim as he spoke.

"The war eagle flew south. Were I to turn aside it would be the act of a cowardly dog." Slipping his tomahawk from his belt the boy threw it with great force into the sand beside the Comanche lance. "Mahtocheega will travel with you against the ghost men."

Far to the south Francisco Vasquez Coronado sought relief from the burning heat of the prairie and sat fanning himself in his tent and reckoning the days with the aid of the white man's calendar. It was the year 1541. The expedition had been two years on the way.

From New Spain they had trekked northward through the wild lands of North America in search of the fabulous wealth which had been reported. They had located the seven golden cities of Cibola and the fabled city of Quivira but had found them to be only stone and adobe houses inhabited by the strange red men. Aside from a few trinkets there was no wealth among them.

Could Francisco Coronado have known that a lone Comanche warrior and a Mandan youth not yet bearing a man's name were at that moment declaring war on his expedition, he would have laughed. Indeed, he had grown to laugh at all the red men in their futile efforts to delay him when he entered their cities. He had but to ride among them on his great white horse and they fled in terror. They were an agricultural people, they traveled afoot with their pack dogs, and horses were unknown to them.

The corn season had been long and dry. No rains fell. The prairies were bone dry and crackled with heat under the torrid sun. Mahtocheega and Burning Foot forged southward, traveling much at night, subsisting on pemmican and berries, and pausing only for short periods of rest.

On the fourth day they came upon a broad dusty trail that led eastward. It might have

been a buffalo trail but for the strange elongated crescents that marked each sharp print. Kneeling, Mahtocheega examined them carefully, measuring, touching them until every depression was stamped indelibly upon his mind.

"The elk-dogs." Burning Foot traced the fresh hoofprint with the tip of his finger. "The ghost men will camp tonight in the bottom beyond the river."

The trail led them to an old buffalo crossing and they stopped many times to examine it. Each time the worry deepened in the face of the Comanche warrior.

"It is not good," he said at last. "The ghost men have divided. We follow a small party that travels east into the sun."

"There are no moccasin prints." Mahtocheega searched the trail. "Does Shonka ride with the ghost men?"

"Prisoners do not ride," the Comanche said bitterly. "They are led like savage dogs on a leash. The feet of the elk-dogs are heavy and they have erased all other sign."

Retaining only their war axes they cached their bows and together swam the river below the buffalo crossing. Creeping forward through the sagebrush they located the tented camp in the gathering dusk. Cooking fires had been lighted and they threw weird shadows over the armored figures moving slowly among them.

Mahtocheega crept nearer, searching the camp, and his heart beat fast when at last he located the picketed horses. He lay there, his eyes devouring the sight, and thought of his people, and of the tales he would have to tell when he returned to his village.

"They are hopeneche!" he whispered, using the Mandan word for mystery and great medicine. No greater compliment did he know. "To ride upon the backs of these elk-dogs would be a great coup indeed!"

He turned to Burning Foot beside him but found that he was alone. The Comanche warrior had slipped away into the sage and Mahtocheega knew that he was stalking the ghost men, intent on searching the camp for the captive Shonka.

Mahtocheega sniffed the strange odors from the cooking fire and the glands of his mouth hungered at the smell of cooking meat. There were other smells from the great black pots but they, like the endless chatter of the ghost men, were strange and uninviting.

Impatient at being left alone, Mahtocheega waited until he saw the dark figure of Burning Foot crouching at the rear of the largest of the tents, then quit his own concealing sagebrush and crept flat on his stomach toward the shadowy horses.

He was among them when a strange woman-like cry, high-pitched and foreign, broke the night silence. The clatter about the fires stopped suddenly, then the dark figures were running for their arms. Above the angry cries, Mahtocheega heard the Comanche war cry and he recognized it as a warning.

There was a sharp, explosive sound and a flash of fire near the main tent. By the firelight he saw Burning Foot fling his war axe, then turn at a run for the river. With the Mandan battle cry ringing in his throat Mahtocheega plunged into the sage in pursuit.

He caught up with the Comanche at the spot where they had cached their bows and they ran together until the camp was lost in darkness.

"The tents of the ghost men were empty," Burning Foot panted. "I searched well but Shonka was not among them."

"But we will find him," Mahtocheega urged. "It will be a great coup. Already you have gone among the ghost men without harm."

"They are but men," the Comanche agreed. "I, Burning Foot, crept among them close enough to touch. I heard their talk, and saw them eat buffalo meat. I know also that their glittering shells are but war shields worn close over their chests. One I saw lay his shield aside and walk without it."

"And I, Mahtocheega, went among the elk-dogs. I touched them and they are gentle animals. They are strong and their fur is smooth and one ate grass from my hand."

The main camp of the Spaniards was a day's march over their back trail. The way of the Indians led through the shadows of two great yellow buttes that stood as lonely outposts in the desert. Beyond lay a village of prairie dogs. The tiny mounds covered the plain as far as the eye could reach. As the two men crossed through the town, the curious little animals followed their every move, chattering and barking, popping underground when they approached and scurrying out again when they had passed on.

The Spanish camp was sprawled on a bare flat plain. The grasses underfoot were parched and dry and the only concealment lay in a clump of big willows that clustered about the water hole. The men and horses had pushed deep among them to escape the burning heat of the sun.

Approaching as close as they dared, Mahtocheega and Burning Foot lay for long hours in a dry arroyo watching the slow life about the camp. Their tongues were thick with thirst but neither spoke of it as they waited through the long evening.

The shadows were lengthening when the Comanche raised his head above the level of the plain and watched intently.

"They take food to the smaller lodge," he hissed. "And a warrior is sent to stand before it with a firestick. When the dark comes I shall enter their camp and set free my son."

"I, Mahtocheega, will go with you into the camp of the ghost men."

Burning Foot shook his head.

"No. It is better that I go alone," he said. "The passage of one warrior will be like soft wind in the willows. More would clatter like buffalo at a water crossing."

Although he saw the wisdom in the Comanche's decision, the thoughts of the Mandan youth were bitter as he plucked idly at the dry prairie grass. He broke off a clump and it rustled in his fingers. He let it sift slowly to the parched ground, watching, thinking.

"This, then, will I do." Mahtocheega turned suddenly upon the Comanche. "Your war-name was earned when the raiding Sioux fired the dry prairie grasses about your village. You raced through the flames when all were asleep and warned your people in time. Tonight, when you have entered the camp, I, Mahtocheega, will fire the grasses and draw the ghost men away."

"It is good," Burning Foot nodded. "The cry of the nighthawk will be our signal. When it is twice repeated, fire the grasses."

When the camp had quieted, the Comanche slipped away and Mahtocheega watched him disappear into the night.

Dropping back into the arroyo, he gathered an armful of the grasses and, working rapidly, fashioned several dry brittle torches. Crouching below the embankment, he drew tinder from his medicine pouch and kindled a flame.

Sheltering the faint glow with his body he added grass wisps slowly to keep it alive as he listened for the signal. Feverish plans were running through his mind; plans of which the Comanche knew nothing. Had he known, even Burning Foot hardly would have approved.

The Spaniards, supreme in their arrogance, had turned the horses into a spindly corral of sticks and rope and had posted a single guard who drowsed near the fire. The thought of the horses drew Mahtocheega like a lodestone. To return to his village on the back of a beautiful elk-dog would be a coup such as no Mandan had ever accomplished. It was the kind of coup that all young men dreamed of when it came their time to go name-traveling. Mahtocheega fed the tiny fire and waited impatiently.

It came suddenly, sharp across the plain, the cry of a nighthawk twice repeated.

Thrusting the tips of the torches into the flames, he turned them until they burned steadily, then ran lightly down the shallow arroyo and tossed them one by one into the dry grasses at the top of the embankment.

He heard the warning cry of the sentry even before he left the dry watercourse. There was a moment of stark silence; then the entire camp erupted in a confusion of sound.

Running at a half crouch he crossed the level plain toward the rear of the corral. To his right the flames from his scattered torches were eating into the dry grass, steadily making headway, and already throwing a red glow against the sky. The light made the shadows appear even darker.

He saw men running, aimlessly it seemed and in wild disorder. For the briefest instant he caught a glimpse of the dark figure of the Comanche merging into the deeper shadows of the camp, then the startled horses, surging in the corral, moved between them and there was only the confused noise and

the red glow growing against the night sky. He found himself sawing madly at the corral ropes.

There was a sharp shouting of orders and through the milling horses Mahtocheega caught the strange pale face of the leader directing his men. Francisco Coronado stood there so squarely, his strange white face bloodless in the fire-light, that Mahtocheega felt a wave of fear. He fought against it, repeating the words of Burning Foot and forcing himself to remember that he was dealing with men and not creatures of the ghost world.

The line of the fire was crackling nearer, advancing rapidly across the plain toward the camp. Under Coronado's orders the Spaniards had run forward to meet it, beating at the flames with blankets, tarpaulins, and even the capes from their backs. Showers of sparks shot into the air and the acrid smoke billowed overhead.

The horses had caught the hated smell and were churning about in the narrow enclosure on the verge of panic. When the last stubborn rope parted, Mahtocheega plunged into their midst and using his bow as a flail drove them toward the opening.

There was a cry of rage from the sentry and Mahtocheega knew that he had been seen. Men were coming at a run toward the corral. The stocky sentry dropped to one knee and Mahtocheega saw that he held one of the dreaded firesticks.

Jamming a war arrow into his bow, Mahtocheega drew it to the head and was in the act of freeing the sinew string when a shocking blast rocked him back upon his heels and shattered the bow just above his fingers.

The sentry was on his feet and charging again before Mahtocheega recovered. Throwing the useless bow aside, the Mandan caught the flowing mane of a great white horse as it swept by and ran beside it with long leaping strides out onto the prairie.

There was another shot from behind, then others in quick succession. Terrified by the gunfire and the long line of flame that threatened, the big white horse shied away and fought to free itself from the thing that clung so desperately to its mane. Mahtocheega hung on, fighting and dodging the flying hoofs, and when the horse turned at a gallop after the rest of the herd, Mahtocheega ran beside it, half carried, half dragged by the galloping horse.

When the horse hit its stride Mahtocheega saw his chance. Drawing himself in close and throwing his weight on the animal's shoulders, he flung one leg over the broad back and clung there, bouncing and fighting to keep his place.

Over his shoulder he saw that three of the Spaniards had caught the last of the horses and were streaming out of the corral in pursuit.

The herd was circling far across the plain. The sound of their hoofs was drumming thunder in his ears but they were approaching a low range of rolling hills before he caught a glimpse of their flying manes and tails.

Something else he saw. Outlined against the sky were the great yellow buttes that had marked their trail on the way south. The herd swept past them and was soon lost in the shadows.

Behind him the Spaniards were pressing close. The moonlight was bright on their armor and they were driving their horses hard upon his heels. They were experienced horsemen and Mahtocheega held no illusions about winning the race by speed alone.

Leaning forward, he laid his hand on the smooth neck and pressed the head of the big horse toward the left and at last turned him into the darkened prairie-dog town.

Then leaping from the horse's back, Mahtocheega held on to the mane and ran with him, weaving and guiding the horse through the tiny mounds and deep burrows that dotted the plain.

Again the Mandan war cry rang out over the plains and he was rewarded by an answering shout as the Spaniards turned after him hot upon his trail.

Then, when it seemed they might unbelievably keep coming, the first of the horses struck the treacherous earth and went down with a piercing scream. Close upon his heels, the other two were down a moment later. Running for the clear ground beyond the prairie-dog town, Mahtocheega saw the tangle of men and horses struggling to free themselves. The first horse had regained its feet but neither men nor horses were in condition to continue.

Mounted again and swinging easily now with each motion of the big white horse, the young Mandan turned toward the low rolling hills and was swallowed up by the deep shadows.

On the second night Mahtocheega camped by the water hole far to the north. The big horse was close by in the mesquite, tethered by a leather rope looped about his neck. A nighthawk cried in the distance and Mahtocheega looked up, snatching his weapon. When it was repeated, he gradually gave the answering call.

He heard them coming long before Burning Foot stepped into the clearing. He trailed a lead rope and two dark satin-smooth horses followed into the light. Mahtocheega searched the back trail but the Comanche was alone.

"Shonka?" the Mandan asked, frowning. "Where is Shonka?"

"My son is free," Burning Foot smiled. "Not only is Shonka free but others who were held captive by the ghost men. They go now with many elk-dogs to my people."

Burning Foot turned to the two dark horses at his elbow.

"It is fitting that these, the strongest and swiftest of the many we captured, should go to Mahto Hopeneche. I have brought them."

Mahtocheega ran his hand through the silken manes of the dark Arabians and looked up frowning.

"Mahto Hopeneche?" he asked.

"The Little Bear is no more." Burning Foot placed the lead rope in Mahtocheega's hand. "You have earned your warrior's name. In the councils of the Comanche you will be known by the most honored name of all. That name is Mahto Hopeneche, The Medicine Bear."

Scoops Gets the Birdie

By WALLACE WEST

Golf takes a beating when Scoops invents a ball with a built-in gyroscope

"Tom," said Mrs. Traylor with a frown, "you are getting much too fat."

"I know." Her husband pushed back from the dinner table and looked sadly at the slight bulges above and below his belt.

"You should take more exercise," said Mrs. Traylor. "You spend all day at Northern Electric just sitting around."

"Just sitting around! I work like a dog out at the laboratory."

"And after dinner you and Scoops dash out to the garage and sit around again tinkering until all hours."

"May I have another piece of pie, please, mother?" Scoops asked.

"That's your third piece," his father groaned. "Why don't *you* get fat? You must be hollow."

"Don't change the subject," said Mrs. Traylor. "Why don't you take up golf again?"

"Oh, no," Scoops cried between bites. "Dad's awful! The last time I caddied for him he did break 100—but he only played nine holes. How about dieting instead? I just read an article. It said that if you eat nothing but boiled turnip tops and steak you can lose ten pounds a week."

"Young man," said Martha Magruder, the Traylors' cook, as she brought coffee from the kitchen, "are *you* willing to eat boiled turnip tops? I've got too much to do to run a restaurant around here. What one eats, you all eat."

"I'm a growing boy," Scoops hedged.

"All right. All *right*," groaned his father as he rose from the table. "I don't even like turnip *bottoms*. Where are my clubs and that soft ball? I've got to get in training before I dare show my face on the golf course again."

For the next two hours Thomas Traylor "addressed" the practice ball while Scoops coached him from a workbench top out of the range of hooks and slices. Finally the scientist threw his clubs into a corner of the garage.

"I don't understand it," he panted as he mopped his face. "At the lab I can make billions of electrons jump through holes so small that you can't even see 'em. Golf balls obey the same laws of motion that electrons do. But when I hit one, it refuses to go into a hole as big as my fist. Instead, it curves around and tries to bite me on the leg!"

"Oh, you're not as bad as that, dad," said Scoops. "I've caddied for a lot of fellows who are worse than you. You go along fine for two or three holes. Then you happen to slice or hook. That makes you nervous and your game goes to pieces."

"I know," his father sighed. "People behind yelling 'Fore' and wanting to play through while you and I wander around in the rough hunting for a lost ball—that's what gets me."

"Maybe I can fix that," said Scoops as he climbed down from his perch. "I'm getting

65

an idea. You go on to bed, and let me tinker out here awhile."

Bright and early the following Saturday, the two Traylors drove out to the Laurel Creek Country Club for a practice round. The course was deserted when they arrived, but another car drove up as Traylor, senior, was preparing to tee off from the first hole. Two men and two women climbed out of it.

"Let's let them go first," Tom suggested nervously.

"No," said Scoops. "Other players will be arriving any minute. You go right ahead." He handed his father a ball. "And remember: Keep your head down."

His father swung grimly. The ball sailed straight and true down the fairway for almost two hundred yards.

"Nothing wrong with that," said Scoops.

Par for the hole was five. Traylor made it in a very creditable six. He got a passable seven on the second hole. As he was teeing off on the third, the dread cry of 'Fore' drifted across the dew-covered links from one of the following foursome. Traylor sliced. The ball bounded into the rough.

"There goes the game," he muttered. "We'll never find it."

"Sure we will," Scoops said with a confident grin. "Just follow me."

As he approached the lost ball's general position, the boy cocked his curly head and listened intently. A faint chirping came from the long grass. He followed the sound. A moment later he picked up the ball.

"What kind of magic is that?" his father asked.

"It's Traylor's Byrdflyte Ball." Scoops shook the thing until it stopped chirping, then presented it with a low bow. "I made it with my own little hatchet."

"You've really got something there, son. How does it work?"

"Sort of like a self-winding watch. There's a midget gyroscope inside, hooked up to a generator and a vibrator. When you hit the ball true, nothing happens. But when you slice or hook, the ball starts spinning. That sets the gyroscope going. That turns the gen-

erator. And *that* makes the vibrator chirp."

"You've got all that stuff inside the cover of one golf ball?"

"It *is* a little crowded," the boy chuckled.

"Hello there!" a faint call drifted from behind them. "May we play through?"

Scoops looked at his father expectantly.

"We've found the ball," Traylor shouted back. "We'll go ahead."

He finished the nine holes with a score of 59. When he described the round to Mrs. Traylor at the breakfast table, though, it sounded as if he were just one jump from the United States Open Championship. After that, of course, he could hardly wait for the next weekend to show off his improved game to fellow scientists from the N.E. lab.

"What kind of handicap shall we give this poor dub, fellows?" asked burly President Theodore Jenkins of Northern Electric when the foursome met at the first tee on that fatal Saturday morning.

"I'd say twenty strokes would be about right, boss," answered Hal Stevens, red-haired chief of N.E.'s Chemistry Department.

"Better make it twenty-five," said Wayne Adamson, the lab's chief accountant. "And let Tom drop a new ball without penalty whenever he goes into the rough. Otherwise we'll be here all day even though he does have Scoops to hunt lost balls for him." Adamson shook his bald head and sighed loudly.

"Now look here," Traylor grinned at them. "I'm not going to let you gang up and rattle me the way you used to. Give me a ten handicap and I'll make you all say 'uncle.' If you don't believe I can do it, ask Scoops. He's been coaching me."

"He has, eh?" Jenkins knew that the boy had been runner-up in the club's last junior tournament. "I'll tell you what, then. We'll spot you twelves in two matches, this one and another next Saturday. If you win _either_ game, I'll caddy for you for two weeks while Scoops takes my place in this foursome. If you lose *both* matches, Scoops still will play, but you'll have to be my caddy. Could anything be fairer than that?" He dropped a broad wink at the other men.

"Don't do it, dad," cried the boy. "They don't intend to play fair. Look how they're all grinning. They'll get your goat. Then you'll lose and everybody will laugh at you."

"It never hurt anybody to be laughed at," said his father. "All right, fiends, I'll take you up on that deal. Let's get going."

"You go first," said Jenkins. "We want to study your improved form."

Traylor marched up to the tee. He swung smartly—and sent a long, long drive whistling down the fairway. Even Jenkins let out a whistle of surprise. Scoops' heart swelled with pride.

With such a good start, Traylor made a par five on the 450-yard hole. Jenkins took six. The others made sevens.

The scientist continued to play way above his head and held his lead until the sixth hole. Then the strain began to tell. He dried his sweating hands repeatedly. He studied the lay of the course until the others jeered. Finally he raised his head at the wrong moment and sliced badly.

"Shall we have lunch sent out from the clubhouse?" Adamson asked as Scoops dashed for the rough.

"Better order crow if you do," Traylor answered. "See. He has found it already."

"Is your son a boy or a bird dog?" Stevens marveled.

Traylor played grimly and carefully after that. Nevertheless, he got into trouble with increasing frequency. As the morning wore on, he trailed Jenkins, the best golfer of the group, by four, five, seven, and nine. When he failed to sink an easy putt on the seventeenth hole, he was ten down to his employer, six to Stevens, and seven to Adamson.

"Take it easy, dad," Scoops coached him anxiously. "This is a short hole. You can win easily with your 12-stroke handicap."

His father took a deep breath and swung gamely. The ball drifted slowly to the right while the others whooped discouragement. It landed just short of the rough.

"That's a good lie," said the boy. "I'd say use your #4 iron to get over that little hill."

"Nuh uh," cried Jenkins. "That's a brassie shot if I ever saw one."

"Better use a spoon, baby," chuckled Adamson. "That's about your speed."

Traylor used the #4 but swung much too high and too hard. The ball bounced wildly along the right side of the fairway and finally buried itself deep in the rough.

Scoops ran forward to locate it. His steps slowed after a time. He looked around in dismay. This time no chirp sounded from the long grass. He cast back and forth desperately. Nothing could be heard but the twitter of real birds and the mocking laughter of the N.E. needlers as they, too, joined the search.

Finally a spot of white caught his eye. He started to call his father's attention to it but changed his mind after a closer look. The edge of the iron had cut a deep gash through the side of the ball. Its tiny gears were a shambles. Traylor's Byrdflyte #1 was grounded for good!

"Better drop another ball, dad," he called. "Here comes somebody behind us."

Traylor obeyed. But the loss of his magic ball had taken the heart out of him. He took a ten for the hole and limped in with a 110 against Jenkins' 88, Stevens' 92, and Adamson's 96 for the 72-par course.

As they were walking back to the clubhouse, Jenkins noticed genuine misery on the loser's face and dropped his banter.

"Don't take it so hard, Tom," he said as he slipped a mighty arm around the scientist's shoulders. "I guess we shouldn't have ribbed you, but we always have acted like morons when we are playing together and it's pretty hard to stop. You've really improved a lot since the last time we went around together. Why don't you take a lesson or two from the club pro this week? All you need now is confidence."

Later, as he was driving his father home, Scoops apologized abjectly.

"That confounded ball!" he groaned. "I'll build you another one and make the case stronger this time."

"Don't bother," said Traylor. "I've given up golf again."

"You can't quit now!"

"Just watch me. I know when I'm licked."

"You'll have to caddy for sure then. Try once more, anyway. Please, dad. Be a good sport."

"Oh, all right." Traylor tried to smile. "Who is that pro?"

That night Scoops held a council of war with Junkie Smithers. Smithers was a tall, lean high school classmate who got his nickname because his father operated a scrap metal yard on the outskirts of Laurel Creek.

"We can't let dad lose that game next Saturday," Scoops told his always-hungry friend as they sat on a workbench in the Traylor garage munching an after-dinner snack. "If he doesn't win, he may develop an inferiority complex or something."

"I wouldn't worry too much about it. The fellows out at the lab tease each other all day long. I once heard President Jenkins say that he encourages such high jinks. He thinks it helps his staff to relax when they get all tied in knots working on a hard project. Your father ought to be used to it by now."

"Oh, he doesn't mind it at all on the job. But this is different. Dad has his heart set on winning. We just have to help him."

"You've already helped him by making that Byrdflyte."

"Yes. But we need something more than that. Look. I think that I may have another Idea."

"Oh no!" Junkie pretended to be terrified. "I can't bear it!"

"Quiet!! This is a humdinger. You know how a proximity fuse works, don't you?"

"Sure." Junkie didn't sound at all sure. "The teacher explained it in physics class once. Let's see—in the old days an artillery shell had to make a direct hit before it would explode. But now a lot of shells carry tiny radar sets in their noses. The sets send out radio impulses and pick up the reflections, or echoes, that bounce back from nearby metal objects. Say a shell is fired at an enemy airplane but just misses it. With an old-type fuse it would just go on by without exploding, or maybe a time fuse might explode it some-where near by. But a proximity fuse automatically touches off the explosion at the exact split second when the shell is nearest the target. Down goes the plane!"

"You're way behind the times, Junkie. The radar in the very latest proximity fuse works a gyroscope that actually makes the shell turn enough to hunt its target and hit it head-on. Here. Let me show you one."

Scoops rummaged in a cardboard box and brought out a gadget so small that it rested comfortably in the palm of his hand.

"Gollies!" Junkie marveled. "What will they think of next?"

"N.E. is developing the thing. Dad brought this one home because it is defective, but it ought to be good enough for us to use."

"For us to use?" Junkie wailed. "Leave me out of this."

"Nuh uh. You have to be the target . . . for Traylor's Starflyte."

"What!" Junkie jumped as if he had been stung.

"Oh, you won't get hit or anything," Scoops assured him. "We'll tune this fuse to respond to a good strong electromagnet. Then we'll seal it in a golf ball. Then you'll sneak out ahead of the foursome and stay between dad and the next cup. If he makes a good shot, you do nothing. If he hooks or slices, you switch on the magnet till the ball straightens out and heads for the cup. Then you switch off again. Nothing to it. He will win in a walk."

Junkie picked up the golf ball, slid off the workbench, and bowed low.

"Scoops Traylor, the mad professor of the comic books!" he cried.

"Stop clowning," Scoops said. "We have to protect the honor of the Traylor name."

Scoops and his father both put in long, hard hours of overtime work that week, the former in the garage and the latter on the golf course. They didn't get much sleep. They skipped so many meals that Mrs. Traylor and even Cook Magruder began to worry that they would lose too much weight. Thomas Traylor boasted of steady progress under the pro's instruction, but Scoops found himself in deep trouble.

The one proximity fuse he had to work with showed little taste for being beaten over the head with a golf club. When he and Junkie tested the Starflyte in the backyard, it behaved as Scoops had hoped for a few strokes. Then the delicate mechanism turned cranky or refused to work at all. After readjusting it for the tenth time, they worked out a compromise. They built a tougher model of the original Byrdflyte chirping ball and decided to hold the homing Starflyte in reserve for use in a really dire emergency.

"I've got this thing licked," Traylor crowed as he drove out to the country club with his wife and son on Saturday. (Junkie had gone on ahead with the magnetic "target" in order to keep the new ball a secret from everyone.) "My stance was wrong. That was the whole trouble. Feet too far apart. Didn't bend my knee enough. Too much weight on the left foot. I've corrected every one of those faults. Jenk is in for a spell of caddying or I've missed my calling."

"Don't get over-confident, Tom," Mrs. Traylor pleaded. "After all—"

"Don't you worry, honey." He patted her hand. Then he showed his inner nervousness by turning to Scoops and asking: "By the way, you did make another of those chirpers for me, didn't you?"

"Yeah, dad," said Scoops. "This one ought to hold up unless you hit it with a sledge hammer. But don't depend too much on it." Already he was wishing wholeheartedly that the game were over.

The Traylors gulped in amazement when they reached the club. News of the "match of the century" had gotten around town, it seemed. A sizeable gallery, made up mostly of workers at the laboratory, had gathered to watch the foursome tee off.

"Wolves!" said Mr. Traylor with a shaky laugh. "Well, I'll show 'em."

The game started without the usual banter, although Jenkins, Stevens, and Adamson exchanged occasional winks. They solemnly congratulated Traylor when he made a six on the first hole. They told him "not to take it too hard" when he muffed a putt and took another six on the par-four second hole.

"You don't have to go easy on me, fellows," Traylor said at last. "I can take anything you can dish out now."

"We wouldn't think of hurting your tender feelings," cooed Jenkins. "Fair play. That's our motto. Isn't it, fellows?"

"Yes, indeedy," said Stevens with a smirk.

"Live and let live," boomed Adamson, as he clapped his opponent on the back.

This new thoughtfulness for his thin skin bothered Traylor almost as much as the teasing had done. For a hole or two his game threatened to go to pieces. Then, under Scoops' quiet coaching, he pulled himself together. He got his share of hooks and slices after that, but Scoops found the softly chirping ball before he had a chance to become nervous. He sank a nice putt on the ninth green for a total score of 50. Jenkins had a 45, Adamson a 46, and Stevens a 48. The crowd gave Traylor a real ovation then. Scoops and Mrs. Traylor glowed with pleasure.

The tenth, eleventh, and twelfth holes were about evenly divided. Then, on the thirteenth, Traylor blew up in the way that all golfers have done at one time or another. His approach was weak. He became entangled in a sand trap and wasted three strokes. One lie was behind a tree. Finally he had to use that unlucky #4 iron to get over a rise in the ground. Worst of all, just as he

started his swing, someone in the gallery sneezed! It was too much to bear.

Scoops realized what was going to happen. He closed his eyes so he wouldn't see it. Then he opened them and listened in pure horror. His father had chopped again. The ball was bounding wildly in search of the rough. And, as it went, it was squawking as loudly as a frightened chicken!

For a moment the gallery stood silent and goggle-eyed. Then somebody snickered. A roar of delight went up. People were pounding one another's backs and weeping with laughter before the Byrdflyte had a chance to hide its shame.

"Hey, Tom," Laurel Creek's Mayor Horton yelled from the crowd, "they told me your golf was terrible, but I didn't imagine it was so bad that you even scared the poor balls."

Traylor's ears were as red as beets. He looked daggers after his son as the boy ran to choke off that awful squalling.

Scoops found the badly dented ball without the slightest trouble. He stamped on it until it grew silent. He wigwagged frantically to Junkie, who was lurking in a sand trap near the green. He dashed back to his father, told him to take the two-stroke penalty for a lost ball and handed him a new one.

"Is this another of those confounded Byrdflytes?" Traylor asked sourly.

"No, sir," Scoops answered truthfully.

There was nothing left for him to do after that but pray!

Traylor fought to control himself as the noise from the gallery slowly died down. He took several long breaths. He took a careful stance. He swung.

It was a hook!

The ball soared over the hill all right but slanted to the left as it went. Then it seemed to change its mind. It straightened out and headed directly for the green. It rolled to a stop only three feet from the cup. Traylor sank it in one. Sadly he chalked up a ten for the ill-fated hole and a 79 total. Even counting his handicap, he was one down to Jenkins' 66. Barring a miracle, he had no chance of winning the match.

"Say, Tom," his boss marveled as the foursome moved to the next tee, "when you get that self-locating ball perfected, it should be a sensation."

"If it can *be* perfected," Traylor sighed. "I suspect it's just another one of Scoops' brainstorms."

"And what kind of a spin did you put on that last drive?" his boss continued. "I never saw anything like it."

"I don't know," Traylor confessed. "It surprised me as much as it did you."

"Dad's a lot better than you think," Scoops spoke up quickly.

"He'll be better still after he gets through caddying for me," Jenkins chuckled. Then

70

he apologized. "I'm sorry, Tom. There I go ribbing you again when I know that golf is your sore spot. I needled you into these matches because I thought they would teach you a lesson, but the thing has got out of hand. Why don't you concede defeat and end the massacre right now? This nine is a lot tougher than the first one. You haven't a chance in the world."

"I'll play it out." Traylor stuck out his square jaw. "Let 'em laugh."

Jenkins made a par five on the fourteenth hole. Stevens and Adamson took sevens, conceded, and joined the grinning gallery.

Traylor waved grimly to his wife, teed off on the difficult dogleg approach and watched the ball bound a hundred yards and stop at the edge of the rough.

Something had gone wrong. Scoops looked for Junkie and saw him tinkering madly with the package in which his target was concealed. The tall boy got the trouble fixed too late to get into position behind the cup for the second stroke. It also went wild. He did manage to attract the ball to the edge of

the green after two more tries. But he couldn't help the putting without attracting attention to his activities. Traylor took three more strokes for a total of seven.

"Good try, Tom," Jenkins sympathized. "Want to quit now?"

"Tee up, Jenk," Traylor gritted.

"You asked for it!" His boss sent the ball whistling down the fairway straight and true. The gallery cheered when he took the hole with a neat one-above-par five. It cheered even louder, though, when Traylor trailed him by only one stroke. Junkie was getting the hang of managing the Starflyte, Scoops realized with a thrill.

Jenkins scored another one-above-par on the sixteenth.

With three long drives that started badly but ended by lining up almost exactly with the cup, plus an excellent putt, Traylor brought the house down with a four. It was the first birdie of his golfing career.

"Just beginner's luck," Jenkins said as he stepped back so that Traylor could go first. "A flash in the pan. Tom's washed up now."

A long, looping drive took the lucky beginner halfway to the seventeenth. Jenkins tried too hard and fell short. Another wavering sizzler carried Traylor's ball almost to the center of the green. Jenkins took two strokes to reach it. Traylor's shaky putt half-circled the cup but dropped at last. He had scored an eagle! Two under par!

The crowd went wild and Scoops saw Junkie turning cart-wheels of pure joy behind a tree up ahead.

"Never saw anything like it," Jenkins muttered as he marked a five for the hole on his card. "I begin to suspect monkey business, but go ahead, Tom. Unless I miss my guess, you're due for a hole-in-one on the eighteenth."

"I don't know what you're talking about," said his friendly enemy. "We really ought to toss a coin to see who goes first this time. Our total scores are tied at 87 if you subtract my twelve-stroke handicap."

They tossed and Jenkins won. He made his best drive of the day, a good two hundred and fifty yards straight toward the flag. Traylor was straight, too, but only went one hundred and seventy yards. Their second shots evened the distance and left the two balls lying about ten yards apart at the edge of a tiny lake. Jenkins lofted across easily. Traylor swung true, but the results were spectacular. The Starflyte flew straight for a few yards. Then its path took on a corkscrew look. It acted as if it were boring through a thick plank. One of its wild spins dipped it into the lake. But, as the astonished gallery yelled, it leaped out of the water in a shower of spray and landed on the farther bank.

"Scoops!" thundered his father. "What happened to that confounded ball?"

"Y-you j-just must have hit it funny."

"Not *that* funny. You've been gadgeteering again. . . . All right, Jenk," he added between clenched teeth. "That ball must be a ringer. I concede."

"Oh, no, you don't!" Jenkins' eyes flashed. "I gave you your chance. It's too late to quit now. *Play that ball!*" The crack of his club, as he chipped to the edge of the nearby green, put punch in his command.

Traylor snatched his #4 from the bag and whaled away at the Starflyte as though it were a vicious snake. Behind his back, Scoops wigwagged desperately to Junkie to demagnetize the target. But Junkie couldn't see him. Too many members of the gallery were crowding the green to watch the end of this mad match.

The Starflyte rode again before Traylor's tremendous blow. This time its mechanism went completely insane. Halfway to the flag it slanted off to the left. A moment later it was circling—"hunting" its target blindly. The ball picked up speed as the diameter of its circle decreased. Soon it was whizzing round and round like a bullet.

The gallery scattered in all directions. Junkie dropped the target and ran. Only Jenkins still stood in the line of fire.

Scoops scampered for the green, yelling at Jenkins to duck. When the big man seemed not to hear him, Scoops swung the golf bag like a club. Twice he missed the whistling ball. The third time he connected solidly. The Starflyte fell. Just to be sure, he threw the bag on top of it.

"So that's it," Jenkins said softly. "Clever.

Very clever indeed." As calmly as though his life had not been in danger a few seconds before, he tapped his ball sharply with his putter. It rolled to within a foot of the cup.

"All right, Tom," he said coldly. "Play up."

"Play up?" Traylor almost screamed at him. "With what?"

"With that proximity fuse . . . Get up, Scoops . . . and Tom, if you deliberately muff this shot the way you tried to muff the last one, you'll play alone in the future."

Scoops felt like a whipped pup. He picked up the bag, crept to the target lying in the sand trap and cut off its current.

The Starflyte lay, white and innocent-looking, about three feet from the cup. Traylor approached it gingerly. He wiped his hands on the seat of his trousers. He made a couple of practice swings. He putted.

The ball just missed the hole and rolled on for eighteen inches.

"You really did try," Jenkins admitted as he sank his own ball.

A moment later, the Starflyte dropped in, too.

"All even at 93, subtracting your handicap," said the older man. "Nobody will have to caddy for anybody. Right?"

"Certainly I'll caddy for you," Traylor protested. "The game was fixed."

"Don't talk nonsense, Tom. We were determined to make you lose. Scoops was determined that we wouldn't. That squares everything. Fact is, this was the most exciting and instructive golf I ever played." Jenkins could keep his face stern no longer. He chuckled. Then he roared. The gallery joined him.

"I'll take Scoops to the woodshed when we get home, though," Traylor promised.

"Don't blame *him*," said Jenkins. "I'd have done the same thing if someone had put my dad on the spot."

"All right." Traylor surrendered. "There is one thing though that I insist on. Scoops, you must throw that Starflyte in the ash can and forget it. Golf's a noble old game. It teaches many lessons in self-control and good sportsmanship. We wouldn't want to ruin it, would we?"

"No, dad," said Scoops from the bottom of his heart. "We sure wouldn't!"

Space Lane Cadet

By WILLIAM F. HALLSTEAD III

Formation flying in the stratosphere is a test of nerves for patrol pilots

Patrol trainee Stan Hunter's gloved hands tightened on the control column as his Unit Commander's voice snapped in his earphones.

"Hunter! You're straggling. Close in."

This was the order Stan had been dreading since take-off on the training mission into the stratosphere. Close in. Keep the formation tight.

He couldn't do it. He'd known he wouldn't be able to fly formation since he'd seen two of his fellow students smash their ships together not forty-eight hours ago. They had plunged through fifty miles of space into the North Atlantic, and B Flight had only five men left.

"Hunter," the ship-to-ship radio blurted, "did you receive?"

Stan looked through the inch-thick plastic canopy. The six-rocket formation stretched away in echelon to the right. His was tail ship on the high end of the line of interceptors. The ships gleamed dully in the black sunlight of the upper stratosphere. They were sleek bullets of manganese-alloy, their smooth lines broken only by the stubby tips of the semi-retractable wings and tail assembly.

The six SF-7s, United States Strato Force, were built for patrol of U. S. Control Lane 4. The SF-7s were part of the patrol wing based at Niagara Falls. Each year, the Strato Force selected a small group of prospective patrol

pilots. These trainees were sent to Niagara Falls where they were trained, tested, and finally assigned to the growing Space Lane Patrol.

At eighteen, tall dark Stan Hunter was the youngest student thus far accepted at the training center. Stan had studied rocketry since he'd learned to read. He soloed his first jet at sixteen, and joined the Strato Force when he was old enough. Stan's progress through Niagara's training had been rapid. But two days ago, two of his fellow trainees had rammed each other in practice formation. The shock of this accident had done something to Stan. He could fly, but when it came to thinking about formation: no good.

Now the moment Stan feared had come. "Hunter! I'm giving you a direct order to close in. Acknowledge this order."

Stan tripped the mike button on the control stick. "Hunter. Wilco."

Desperately, he nudged the SF-7 to the right. The adjacent ship loomed larger as the space between them diminished to hundreds of feet. Stupid, Stan thought. Millions of miles of space around them, and the Strato Force stuck to its regulation requiring formation on all flights above the tropopause. Traineers lacked astrogational experience.

He was almost in close formation before the fear got him. His muscles jerked the controls. He veered two miles out before he could get a grip on himself and deflect to a straight course. Shaken and angry, Stan watched the five sister SF-7s cruise in smooth formation on his right, hanging against black outer space.

"What's the matter with you, Hunter?" Commander Wheaton's voice blasted. "Close in here. Now."

"I . . . I can't, sir," Stan blurted, and he felt shame in his cheeks.

"You're disobeying a direct order, Hunter. I'm going to recommend disciplinary action."

Stan tried to swallow the tightness in his throat. This had happened so fast, he hadn't realized the consequences until now. Wheaton was strict—he'd washed out other Trainers for less than Stan had done.

The curve of the earth's horizon flattened as the six rockets hurtled into the lower atmosphere and slowed their drive. At thirty-five thousand, six sets of retracted wings slid from their fuselage grooves and locked in place. The rockets took on the appearance of ordinary 1980 jet planes.

The crackle of atmospheric static filled Stan's earphones. Stretching his legs after this eight hour flight would be fine, but it meant an ordeal. He shuddered at the bitterness in Commander Wheaton's voice, but he still couldn't forget the two shattered patrol rockets. Their image haunted him.

The stratosphere ships plunged toward North America in a long diving arc. Ten thousand feet off the coast of New Jersey, the flight levelled out and the pilots shut off their cockpit pressurization and oxygen systems. They decelerated to Mach 2, twice the speed of sound. In minutes, the familiar white horseshoe of Niagara Falls drifted below the purple haze layer.

Stan banked into the two-mile final approach. The other planes of B Flight were lining up on the broad ramp as he came in nose-high under partial power.

He flipped a lever, and the ship slowed as big flaps slid into the slipstream. The tricycle landing gear squealed on cement, and the pilot punched a snake-eye switch with two fingers. He lurched against his shoulder harness as the landing chute bellied from its tail compartment and cracked open. The

plane slowed under the parachute's braking action.

Stan released the chute at the marked point on the runway where it would be picked up by a waiting truck. He ruddered the plane toward the flight line.

As he slid back the heavy canopy and climbed from the cockpit, Commander Wheaton strode toward him. The Commander was a big, beefy man, and his face was red with anger.

Stan snapped to attention.

"Sir, I—I'm sorry. I—"

"Just how do you explain disobeying my orders? Do you realize the trouble you're in? We've lost men because they flew poor formation. Are you trying to make the casualty list longer?"

"No, sir. I'm sorry, but I couldn't make myself close in. Not after what happened Monday."

It was out now.

Wheaton hesitated before answering.

"I'll give this more thought, Hunter, but you'll have to report to the screening board. If you can't carry out flight orders, you're a hazard to your squadron. I'll make the appointment for you. You'll be considered for elimination from the training program."

"Yes, sir," Stan murmured as the Commander hurried to the debriefing room. This was the end of his dream. Next week he'd be looking for a job, any job, around a space port.

Crushed with his own failure, Stan turned in his altitude gear for the last time. Slowly, he walked to the mess hall. He took sandwiches and coffee and plunked down near the end of the table where his flight mates were already eating a late lunch.

"Tell you what I was doing up there," Bill Almond was saying. "Well, I throttled back at seventy thousand and . . ."

His high-pitched voice went on, and the others seemed to be listening intently. Bill was a great spinner of space tales, mostly about himself, and usually nobody paid much attention. But now the other three space trainees hung on every bragging word.

Stan knew why. If they listened to Bill,

they wouldn't have to speak to him. Leaving his food untouched, he shoved back his chair and walked out.

As he opened the barrack door, the base communications loudspeaker over his head rattled. A tense voice began reading orders in sharp, crisp tones.

"B Flight, attention. All pilots report to Operations. B Flight pilots report to the Operations Officer."

Stan's flight. He sat on his tightly made bunk; pictured his buddies scrambling from the mess hall, dashing to the Operations Building. But B Flight had been scheduled for a twenty-four hour rest. Something was up. And here he was under orders to report for wash-out.

Stan hunched on the cot, staring at the varnished floor. The base was quiet under the early summer sunlight, but he sensed excitement in the silence.

Thirty minutes later, the afternoon was shattered by the bark of jet engines firing one after another. Stan jumped to his feet. Certainly there was no training flight assigned. B Flight must have been assigned an actual mission!

He tried to relax and forget it. But that was no good. In ten minutes, he was pushing through the aluminum door of Operations.

Just inside, a shiny-helmeted Strato Force guard stopped him, glanced at his Trainee pass and nodded. Stan entered a second door.

The Assignment Room was deserted, but he saw where the clerks had gone. A small crowd clustered in the doorway of the room marked Radar Tracking. Stan joined the hushed group and studied the large rectangular radar screen built into the wall at the far end of the radio-packed room.

On the left portion of the darkened screen, Stan spotted a group of greenish pin points of light. Slowly, they drifted toward the right, across the radar field.

"What is it?" he asked the clerk at his elbow.

The little assignment clerk answered without taking his eyes off the screen. "Meteor field. Drifting right into the inbound space lane. B Flight's gone after them."

"What about A and C Flights?"

"Out since noon, but we can't get in touch with them. They're below the earth's curve, so radar can't make contact. We tried bouncing a sky wave to them, but they must be above the ionosphere."

Stan studied the tense faces around him. "What's all the worry for? We've had meteors in the space lanes before."

"The ore freighter on the moon run is flying an interception course with the meteor field."

"Oh-oh." Stan knew the freighter would be out of radio contact until the crew needed landing instructions. The freighters were tramp ships with no long range liaison radio sets.

"B Flight will swerve the meteors," he said. "A few good shots and they'll scatter."

"Hope so," said the other. "But the meteors are out of flight range, I think."

"There's B Flight!" a voice cried.

A hush settled over the gathering. In the lower right corner of the radar field, a compact group of five light specks appeared. With painful slowness, Commander Wheaton and his trainees climbed toward outer space.

They couldn't make it. The radar men saw that from the beginning. The meteors sizzled through the space lane, sucked in by gravity. The dots that were B Flight moved one third up the screen and no further. The SF-7s had reached their range limit, and the meteors drifted on.

"Increase your field," an officer snapped.

The pips on the radar screen seemed to grow smaller, but Stan realized the radar tracker had adjusted his range to take in a larger portion of space.

"There's the Alioth, high at center," the operator said. There was a flurry of whispers, then a hush fell over the room. The freighter sped unswerving into the meteor field.

The pin point of light was lost for a second, then reappeared flying a slightly different course.

"She's through!"

"But she's been hit. That course changed too fast."

The radar tracker killed the hub-bub of voices. "The Alioth's off course, sir. Her new course will take her somewhere near Chicago. She's scheduled for Boston."

"Her steering tubes," a quiet voice said. "She must be damaged; out of control. Gravity's pulling her in like a bomb. I'm afraid we'll have to stop her."

"No pilots," someone said. "They're all out on missions."

"Not all of them," Stan heard himself say. He shoved through the group, emerged in the murky radar room. Then he stiffened and saluted. The speaker with the quiet voice was the base commander, Richard Mason! His short-cropped gray hair was rumpled with worry.

"Your name, Airman?"

"Hunter, sir. Trainee Stanley Hunter."

"Trainee, eh? Well, Hunter, there's no time to lose. I'll have an SF-7 prepared im-mediately. You're to intercept that freighter, and find if it is disabled. If it is, order the crew to abandon ship at fifteen thousand feet, then shoot the freighter out of the air. We can't afford to take the chance of its hit-ting some town and blowing up."

"Sir," a thin, worried officer protested, "that freighter is carrying ore samples for the Cambridge Research Institute. Losing that shipment will set back our propulsion pro-gram six months."

"Can't help it," Mason replied. "The Alioth is a menace to the people of the Mid-west."

Stan fought his conscience. The mission was everything he wanted in the Strato Force. But he'd been grounded. Did the base commander know that? And suppose Mason didn't know—would it matter? If he knocked down the Alioth as ordered, the whole inci-dent of this morning's failure might be for-gotten. Yet, it just wasn't right.

No. If Stan had proved a poor pilot this

morning, he wasn't going to be a poor air-man now. He spoke clearly.

"Sir, I think you should know. I've been grounded by Commander Wheaton for dis-obeying orders this morning."

A silence hit the room. Then the Com-mander spoke. "Unofficially, I'm aware of that, Hunter. But it takes several hours for training notices to reach my office. I haven't seen any report on you yet, so officially I know nothing about that incident. My orders are to take off immediately."

Stan tried to hold back his grin, but it broke through.

"You're an honest pilot, anyway," the officer said. He held out his hand. "Good luck."

Half an hour later, at full throttle with the afterburner on, Stan's SF-7 roared through the thin air of the stratosphere. On his gyro compass, he held the heading given him by the radar astrogator which would in-tercept him with the Alioth four thousand miles out in space.

He turned off his jet drive and switched to full rocket propulsion. He retracted the wings until only their outer third was visible.

The earth's curve became sharper. It wouldn't be long before he sighted the Alioth. Stan looked over his shoulder through the canopy and saw that night had fallen over the eastern United States, and darkness was extending west toward the long California coastline. Niagara was well into the eve-ning.

"Hunter," the high intensity radio blared, "change your course to azimuth 047, eleva-tion 087. Expect intercept in twenty-two minutes."

The astrogator back at Niagara was right. Just over twenty minutes later, Stan squinted against the brilliantly reflected sun from his silver cowling and stared ahead. A tiny alu-minum tube suspended in space grew into the moon freighter, Alioth.

As she fell toward him, Stan saw the ship was disabled, all right. A deep meteor gash extended from amidships aft to the direc-tional rocker drive. With these tubes out, the Alioth was a derelict.

Stan tuned his ultra high frequency set to the commercial space frequency. "Freighter Alioth, this is Space Patrol. Over."

Scratchily, the Alioth answered. "This is Alioth. Go ahead."

"You are disabled by meteor collision. Is that roger?"

"That is roger, Space Patrol. We're drift-ing. Glad to have you along, but there's nothing you can do."

"What do you mean?" Stan asked. "My orders are to tell you to abandon ship at fif-teen thousand."

"And you destroy the ship?" the Alioth radioman asked.

"Those are my orders."

The freighter loomed ahead like an old-fashioned dirigible. Hurtling toward earth, it seemed to drift lazily by, three miles to the left, as Stan cut his forward drive and fired a blast from his turning tubes. He swung into a parallel course behind the derelict and waited for an answer.

The reply came slowly. "This is the Alioth's Captain. We won't abandon ship. Five men hurt when the meteor hit. Shoot us down, but we won't bail out."

The man was in a shocked state, Stan real-ized. That made it tough. He could never shoot down a ship full of men, orders or no orders. But if they wouldn't bail out. . . .

An amber instrument panel light flashed. He switched to the air-to-earth radio.

"Hunter, did you contact the Alioth?"

"Roger," Stan said. "They are derelict, but won't abandon ship—they have wounded aboard."

"Stand by."

There was a fifteen second silence. "Hun-ter. This is the base commander. What is your position?"

"Trailing the Alioth three miles behind."

"You'll have to destroy that freighter."

"Sir, I—"

"Orders, Hunter." Twenty men could not be spared to endanger hundreds. But Stan could not yet make himself accept the job. There must be another way. If he could only orbit a while; think it over—

Stan's brain hummed, hardly daring to accept his sudden idea. Orbit! That might be it. The Alioth might be able to orbit, circle the earth on centrifugal force like a miniature moon. A repair ship could get to her easily then.

But how could it be done? The freighter was helpless with no direction power.

Then Stan's stomach tightened. He knew how to do it. *His* ship had directional power.

"Hunter," the radio demanded, "you'll be through the tropopause in ten minutes."

"Roger, sir. Will you stand by ten minutes?"

"Keep that ship from blowing up Chicago, and I will."

Stan drew a long breath. "Roger, sir."

With fear he couldn't fight down, Stan opened his rocket valves and closed the distance between the ships. The Alioth was huge, a metal wall ahead. Stan's hand trembled on the control stick; he was sweating, but he wouldn't turn back now.

Side by side, the two craft hurtled toward earth. Slowly, Stan opened the climb valve. His patrol ship eased toward the Alioth. He could see the meteor pocks on the Alioth's hull. If he tangled in that gash. . . .

Carefully, he inched on full power. The SF-7 neared the freighter until mere yards separated them. It was hard to believe they were traveling at thousands of miles per hour. The optical illusion made them appear to hang in space. He drew in oxygen, held it. The SF-7 bumped the Alioth. Stan rammed the throttle open the rest of its travel, glued the patrol ship against the freighter with acceleration and stuck there.

In a long arc, the two craft swerved off their downward course and angled across the earth's surface. Then they paralleled. It had worked!

"Space Patrol to Alioth!" Stan shouted. "You're orbiting. I'll have a repair ship sent. Good luck."

The captain's voice was choked. "We don't know how to thank you."

"Roger, Alioth," Stan grinned. He shifted to ground frequency.

"Heard it all," Mason rapped. "You're in that close." There was a pause. "When you land, there's a short course in understanding orders you ought to take."

"Yes, sir," Stan said.

"By the way, Hunter, Wheaton sends his congratulations. Looks like you can fly formation all right when you have to. Another thing, after Wheaton landed, we looked for that wash-out report on you. Seems like I lost it. No need to make another."

Stan leaned back. He was tired and happy. Now he wouldn't even mind listening to Bill Almond's wild tales.

Talking Track

By BOB MATHIAS

An Olympic champ points the way to success in a fast-stepping article

Lt. Robert Bruce Mathias, USMC, has achieved a phenomenal track and field record. He has held the world decathlon championship; he is the only man to win two Olympic decathlon championships; and he is the only man to win the U.S. decathlon title four times.

What does it take to make a winning trackman? Well, there are many pointers that can help you but, of course, just discussing the subject won't make you a winner. That takes time and hard work—plus natural ability. I know. I've trained and practiced track and field events most all my life. That's the best reason why I was able to win my first Olympic Decathlon in London in 1948. I was just seventeen then, right out of high school, and the years of training, practicing and following my coaches' advice paid off.

The points I'm going to talk about are far from the whole story on how to train for a successful track career. They can't put speed in your legs, wind in your lungs, or courage in your heart. But they can do some things.

They can correct faulty habits and suggest techniques that can help you improve your natural ability. They can also strengthen your body as well as your confidence.

One thing I'd like to say about confidence: Don't be afraid of the other guy getting ahead of you. Sure, you'll be beaten in the beginning. Everybody is. But the sooner you start training and practicing, the quicker you'll develop a winning stride. It may take a long time. It may not. But if you keep at it, sooner or later you're bound to win, if you have any natural ability at all.

In the attic bedroom I used to share with my brother Jim, I had a sign on the wall which read: A Winner Never Quits and a Quitter Never Wins.

Some fellows may think that sounds corny. Maybe it is. But I know it made me never give up hope of winning, even when I was bone-tired and nearly ready to drop.

When I won my first Olympic Decathlon title in 1948, I was completely exhausted—just knocked out. I swore I'd never go through that grind again. But when the next Olympics came around in 1952, I was right back there ready to defend my title. It was the same physical punishment all over again. Luckily, I won. I did it by pacing myself properly and driving myself when the chips were down.

Maybe I'd better explain a little bit about the Decathlon. It's practically a track meet in itself. There is a total of ten events. Each contestant must perform all ten: five events one day and five the next. The one who piles up the highest score wins. There are four running events and six field events. Running events include the 100-meter, 400-meter, and 1500-meter flat races, and the 110-meter high hurdles. The six field events are: pole vault, broad jump, high jump, discus, javelin, and shot-put. Believe me, it's a tough two-day workout.

In starting your track career, one of the first things to do is to study form. Unfortunately, not many high school trackmen do this. Watch a champion in action or study the form of the fellow who beats you out on the high school track.

During the 1952 Olympics in London, I worked out with pole-vault champ Bob Richards just to see how he did it. The things I learned from him helped me get a good mark in the Decathlon pole vault. So watch the winners and learn from them.

All trackmen are runners. But before you start running, you should learn to walk properly. By constant walking you'll build up your leg muscles and develop wind, as well as the drive needed for a sprint finish.

You don't have to walk fast, but you should take long, full strides, stepping off with your feet straight, your toes straight ahead. When you learn to walk correctly, you can run correctly.

Sometime during your track career, you'll probably try out for the 100-yard dash. This sprint can be discussed in four parts: starting positions, starting action, sprinting action, and finishing action.

The start is made from foot holes dug in the track—or from starting blocks if you have them—about sixteen inches apart. The most popular method of taking the "on your mark" position puts almost all your weight on the knee touching the track. This rests the fingers but requires an upward and forward motion to the "set" position. This motion is tricky, because you may roll too far forward on your fingers and stumble during your first few strides.

The other method of getting "on your mark" puts your weight more on your fingertips so that your shoulders are advanced about an inch beyond the starting line. From this position, getting "set" merely involves raising your hips with no forward motion.

In either method, spread your arms just a bit wider than vertical from your shoulders.

Don't Put Weight on Back Foot

At the command "get set," raise your hips upward—and forward if your position requires it—to a point where your back leg is in its most powerful pushing position. Don't put any body weight on the back foot, but dig your toes in against the starting holes, with your weight on your forward foot and your fingertips.

Lift your head only slightly and keep your eyes focused on a point five to twenty feet down the track.

At the word "set," take a deep breath and hold it. This permits rigid concentration and muscle control so that you are ready to release explosive power at the gun.

At "go," the drive is straight ahead, not up and out. The eyes are the key to this forward motion. If they are focused on a spot five to twenty feet down the track, the body angle will usually be correct.

Leg action at the start should be as rapid as possible, with a natural stride. Come out digging, but don't chop your stride or try to increase its length during the first fifteen yards. Drive your rear leg forward from the starting hole with all the speed and power you have.

During the start, arm action is of tremendous importance. If you start with your right leg back, throw your left arm straight ahead, with only a slight bend at the elbow. Throw your right arm straight back. But don't move your arms with too much force or you'll twist out of balance.

During the dash, swing your arms vigorously. Your forward hand should not rise above the level of your shoulder, and your rear hand should not drive more than eight inches back of your hip.

Lean Forward as You Run

Try to breathe normally and maintain a forward body lean. Take long, rapid strides with high knee action. Bring your rear foot forward as close to the ground as possible, and get a bounce in your leg action but not in your whole body. When your toe touches the track, your ankle should be relaxed.

There are three styles of finish: A simple

ON YOUR MARK . . . GET SET . . . GO!

run through the tape; a "lunge" at the tape, with the upper body thrown forward and the arms down and back; and a "shrug," with the upper trunk twisted to one side. The lunge or the shrug should be made at the last possible moment on the last stride.

Those are the essentials of the 100-yard dash, which is an all-out drive from start to finish. The 220- and 440-yard dashes are about the same, except that you ease up some during the 440 and then drive for a sprint finish.

In distance running, there are variations of form, but pace is the important thing. You've got to know when to ease up on your speed and when to pour it on. Your coach can teach you this.

Some trackmen are good in several events, but most of them find one particular event they are best suited for. That's what you should do. Pick the event you are best in. Then concentrate on it and perfect it.

Choosing the event best for you depends mainly on how you are built. Have you the legs of a sprinter? Are you husky enough for

the shot-put? Have you the back muscles of a pole vaulter, the barrel chest of a distance runner, or the reaching stride of a hurdler or high jumper? Talk it over with your coach and see what he advises.

My high school coach, Virgil Jackson, at Tulare, California, first got the idea of entering me in the Olympic Decathlon tryouts. But at the time, I'd never pole vaulted before and never thrown a javelin in my life. Weeks before the tryouts, I started practicing for both events. I got awful sick of that pole and that spear, but I kept at it and finally won my berth on the Olympic team.

Another thing I can't stress too much is training. I know the boys on college track teams never consider it time to go into training, because they never get out of shape. They train all the time. Smoking and drinking are out. And no carousing, no late hours.

If you plan to make coaching your career, the records you set in high school and college will help you get a coaching job. So keep training and practicing to win. It's something to work for.

Roadblock

By MARVIN L. DE VRIES

Storm and Dizzy expect trouble when their patrol car is stolen, and they get it!

At certain speeds, Patrol Car 44 had a slight shimmy. State Trooper Storm Allen complained about it for some time, and finally took it to the garage in town for repairs. The garageman hemmed and hawed and said he didn't know when he could get at it.

"Everybody wants everything done right away," he grumbled.

"We come first," Storm told him.

"All right, all right, I'll get at it first thing in the morning."

Storm gave him the whole day and went back for the car the next evening. The garageman looked surprised.

"It's back at the post," he stated. "Somebody picked it up this noon."

Storm frowned briefly. "Who did?"

"I don't know his name. He said he was new."

"We don't have anybody new."

"I don't know anything about that. He was all dressed up in a brand-new uniform."

"You know everybody out there, Pat."

"I didn't know this one."

Storm was puzzled, but it didn't dawn on him that there was something wrong. He went back to the post, but the car wasn't there. He asked every uniformed man on the place, but no one had gone to the garage to pick it up. It took time, but there was only one conclusion to come to. Patrol Car 44 had been stolen, and the man who had done

it had gone to the trouble of outfitting himself in a trooper's uniform to make it work.

Sergeant Christopher Drubb took it as an insult to the whole police force and blamed Storm. Storm was inclined to blame the garageman, but, wherever blame belonged, it didn't get back the car. The incident made a wry joke for the newspapers, but Storm couldn't laugh, and he couldn't find a trace of the car either.

Then, one wet foggy evening late in October, more than two months after it had been stolen, the car showed up on Tiplady Road.

Storm and his partner, Dizzy, had stopped at Charley's Luxury Diner in Anchor for a cup of coffee, and had spent probably twenty minutes there. Charley had hurried them away, because he hated fog and wanted them to get to the post before dark.

The stolen car came at them from behind. It was almost dark. Fog had settled down on the road, and Storm had his fog lights turned on. The car behind them approached at a reasonable speed. When it started to pass, Storm gave it room on the blacktop, but it wanted more than it got.

Storm muttered a protest and gave it a scowling look. Then he sat up straight. It was another state police car. Two troopers sat in the front seat. For a moment, he thought the way they were crowding him was their idea of a joke, but neither of them

85

looked his way. Then he saw the number, a big 44 painted on the side of the car, the same number as the car he was driving, and he knew what he was looking at.

It was the patrol car stolen from the garage in Lac du Bonnet, and the two men inside of it were probably fakes. They didn't look right. They wore uniforms, but anyone who knew a dishonest tailor could get a uniform. He gave dozing Dizzy a poke and stepped on the gas.

It was too late. The other car was a length ahead, and cut in on them before Storm could close the gap. Fenders clicked. Instinctively, Storm dodged, but he had already given them too much room. He hit soft shoulder mud and lost control.

As though tied to a rope, the car slewed into the ditch, and Storm couldn't stop it. It jumped across and cut a path through brush on the other side. It hit an obstruction of some kind and tipped on two wheels. It sideswiped a tree on the other side and caved in along the top. The lights went out. A tire popped. It lurched sideways going up a slant and started to tip. Storm swung hard, down the slant, and brought it back on all fours. Nose down, it dived into a blackberry patch and came to a jolting stop.

Storm's head whipped forward, and something on the steering wheel cut a gash along his jaw. Dizzy bumped his shoulder and barked his shins, but both men could move, and they moved fast back to the road, staring into the gloom.

The other car had disappeared in the fog. Even the sound of it was gone.

"Now what was that all about?" Dizzy demanded. He lifted a hand to his shoulder and felt for broken bones.

Storm told him what he had seen. Blood dripped from his jaw, and he held a handkerchief against the cut. He listened for other traffic but couldn't hear any. They might have a long wait before anything they could commandeer came past. He went back to the wreck and tried the radio, but it was dead, the panel twisted and sprung.

"No good," he complained, coming back to the road. "We need a telephone."

Dizzy said he knew where one was. He had seen wires running along a tote-road into the woods, and there was bound to be a house and telephone at the end of it.

"People by the name of Moore," he claimed. "I've seen the mailbox. It's up ahead somewhere. We can start walking, anyway. Maybe somebody'll come along."

It was a long walk. No cars came along. Dizzy limped, but he claimed his shins didn't hurt. He said he thought there must be something very queer going on.

86

"Those phonies! What d'you s'pose they're up to?"

"I don't know, but, for one thing, I think they tried to kill us. That wasn't an accident back there. They rammed us intentionally."

"Those phonies!" Dizzy muttered again.

It was pitch dark by the time they reached the Moore mailbox and turned onto the sandy tote-road. The telephone line got lost in the trees, and it was hard to follow the right road because forks branched out in all directions. Storm whipped his flashlight among the trees and made out the best he could, but at last the telephone line came to an end in a snarl of rusty wire buried under last year's leaves.

Dizzy picked up the frayed end and looked at it, and said: "No telephone."

"Maybe they've got a car we can borrow," Storm said, hopefully, and they went on.

A dog barked. At the next turn, they saw a house light, vague and shimmery as moon-glow, through the fog. The dog barked again, this time making a wild flurry of sound. A man called out a quick warning and silenced it. A moment later, the light in the house went out.

Dizzy and Storm reached the edge of the clearing and tried to get their bearings. It looked like a large pond, the tops of the trees closing it in. Storm hailed the house, but didn't get an answer. He moved his flashlight back and forth, looking for a building. They found a path and followed it until they reached a barn. An animal inside made a scared sound. An old pick-up truck stood under a lean-to. A chicken roosted on the box and went off into the night with a loud squawk when the light hit it.

"There's our car, anyway," Dizzy muttered, keeping his voice down. "If it'll run. I feel spooky. What's going on here? Where's everybody?"

Storm didn't have an answer. They followed the path in the opposite direction and reached the kitchen door of the house. Storm knocked impatiently. He thought he heard a stealthy sound inside, perhaps the scraping of a chair, or a cautious footstep, or even a hurried whisper flung across a room, but he wasn't sure. Perhaps it was only in his head.

Dizzy's spooky feeling was beginning to affect him. He knocked at the door again and called out who he was, his voice sharp and commanding.

This time he got an answer. It came from behind the nearby woodpile, a man's rough voice charged to the hilt with excitement.

"Both of you reach for the sky," it ordered. "I got me a rifle here."

"Well, put it up and come out of there," Dizzy blurted. "We're the police."

"Yeah, I know all about that," the man behind the woodpile jeered. "Now get your hands up. I'm not foolin'."

"Get some light," Dizzy muttered, disgustedly. "Look us over."

"For the last time, up with your hands, or I shoot an' I can shoot straight."

"All right, Dizzy," Storm warned in a low voice. "He might at that."

He raised his hands and Dizzy followed suit. The man behind the woodpile walked in and called for light. It came on from inside and poured out through the door glass.

"Your name Moore?" Storm asked.

"Yes," the man answered briefly, his voice cool and steady. A boy trailed him. "Take the rifle, Martie," Moore told him. "If they show fight, you know what to do."

He took their guns, and used Dizzy's handcuffs. One went around Dizzy's wrist, the other around Storm's. Then he herded them inside, and lights went on all over the house.

"We're looking for a telephone or car," Storm started in again. "We—"

"No telephone," Moore said. "Sit down there." He glanced at a clock on the table. "Martie, turn on the radio again."

There were two boys. Martie was the older. His eyes glittered with excitement. He didn't look afraid. The other one hung onto his mother's dress.

"You'll have to go to Anchor, Martie," Moore went on. "The battery's dead, but you can crank the truck, can't you?"

Martie nodded his clipped head and started for the door.

"Listen," Storm spoke up. "Why can't we all go? You can—"

"No," Moore objected. "I won't risk it. Go ahead, Martie. Get the sheriff, or a state trooper. Anybody you can find."

Martie went out, and the radio came on. It was tuned to the local station.

". . . can be sure that Brown's Baby Chick Food is scientifically balanced for healthy chicks. . . . And now, we bring you the latest bulletin on the robbery which occurred late this afternoon when men wearing state police uniforms got away with an estimated $30,000 from the Bank of Anchor. It has now been learned that the number of the stolen patrol car in which they escaped is forty-four. Charlie Townsend, proprietor of the Luxury Diner, states that he saw the car parked in front of the bank and thought it was the car of two troopers who had stopped at his place a little earlier. Both cars are marked number forty-four. It has not been learned which direction the bandits took out of town. Mr. Green, president of the bank, said he unlocked the door and admitted the robbers himself, thinking they were state troopers. It was past closing time but three employees were in the bank. All were bound and gagged, and the robbery was not discovered for some time. This is the first hold-up in Anchor since . . ."

Moore reached down impatiently and turned the knob to a short wave band. Storm's gun hung in his hand, but he was too far off to make a try for it.

Outside, Martie seemed to be having trouble getting the car started. Storm now knew that Moore thought they were the bandits who had robbed the bank, and he had gotten what he knew from earlier broadcasts.

"Listen, Mr. Moore," Storm insisted, as earnestly as he knew how, "this is serious. You're interfering with police business, and—"

All at once, Sergeant Drubb's voice came out of the loud speaker. Moore held up his finger for silence. Storm stopped talking and gave Dizzy a bleak look. His left arm and Dizzy's right one hung down between the two chairs they were occupying, the thin chain of the handcuffs holding them together.

Mrs. Moore sat on a chair across the room, the small boy in her lap now. She looked anxious, and a little concerned, as if she wondered whether her husband was doing the right thing.

Drubb was busy organizing a roadblock. This was always a pet project of his.

"They can't beat a roadblock," he always claimed. "Not unless they got wings."

It was like a checker game to him, with every patrol car on the right square, the quarry desperately hunting a loophole that couldn't be found. According to his present opinion, a place called Beaver Corners was the key spot. He used code numbers for his blockade, but Storm had them memorized and knew what he was talking about. He knew, too, that Beaver Corners was Patrol Car 44's assignment.

The bandits knew it, too, because they had maps stolen with the car. They knew there was a loophole, and that was where they were heading for.

"Step on it, boys," Sergeant Drubb went on. "Get there and hold it." He had a whole broadside of instructions, and then he spoke to Patrol Car 44. "You can take that tote-road cut-off between Tiplady Road and Beaver Corners," he told them. "Or are you past that?"

"We're past that, Sergeant," Storm heard the phony troopers reporting. "We'll get there." The voice didn't sound like Dizzy's, or his own, but Drubb didn't queston it.

"Oh, my," Dizzy groaned.

Once again, Storm tried to persuade Moore that they weren't bandits. "I know now where they're going to get through. That was them you just heard on the radio. We've got to get there before they do. You've got to believe me."

Moore scratched his head and began to look a little dubious.

"I don't know," he muttered, uneasily. "There was a report that they wrecked their car on Tiplady Road, but nobody says anything about that anymore. You two certainly look like you've been in a wreck. How did you get that cut on your face?"

"We were in a wreck," Storm went on. "That's why we're here. The car that was wrecked was ours, not the bandits'."

"The key's in my pocket," Dizzy put in. "You won't regret it."

Moore scratched his head again. "It's certainly a puzzle." He came toward them, and he looked as if he had almost decided to free them.

"I must say you sound like you're telling the truth. But if you aren't, I'd look awful silly letting you go. On the other hand, I can see it would be bad the other way, too. I don't know what to do."

Drubb started talking again. He sounded disappointed, but he announced that the earlier report that the bandit car had been wrecked on Tiplady Road about ten miles northeast of Anchor was true.

"They may have headed into the woods, or stolen another car. They may try to get a car at some farmhouse."

"You and your big mouth," Dizzy muttered to the radio.

Moore's jaw clamped shut. "Now I don't want to hear any more out of you," he stated, angrily. "Martha, you go see if you can do anything for Martie. He's having trouble."

He ducked down trying to look out the window. Storm flicked a look at Dizzy, then jumped. Dizzy came with him. They caught Moore between them and wound him up in a tangle, pinning his arms to his sides. His gun roared, but it did no harm. Storm jerked the weapon out of his hand. Moore quit fighting. His wife put her hand to her mouth, pushing back a scream. The little boy started to cry.

"Stay right where you are," Storm told her. "Nobody'll get hurt."

Dizzy got out the handcuff key and set them free. Moore stepped away from them, angry but careful. Dizzy's gun and the rifle were in the kitchen. He picked both up on the way out. Martie had finally gotten the light truck started. It was moving slowly across the yard. Storm and Dizzy ran toward it.

Martie must have seen them coming. He tried to pick up speed by shoving the throttle all the way down. The motor coughed and sputtered. The truck jerked and bucked, barely moving.

Storm sprinted to it and grabbed the door. "Go into the house," he told Martie. "Everything's all right. We'll be back."

It was an old ramshackle vehicle, but the motor seemed to be sound after it warmed up. At Tiplady Road, they turned right, away from the wrecked car. In spite of fog and drizzle, Storm's foot went down to the floorboard and stayed there. The road gradually slanted up, and they left some of the lowland fog behind. Dizzy watched for the tote-road cut-off Drubb had mentioned. The bandits themselves had reported to Drubb that they were going the long way around, staying on Tiplady Road until they reached the main highway, then cutting back on that toward the intersection at Beaver Corners. If it was true, it gave the two troopers a little leeway, to make the most of it.

They found the tote-road, and followed its snaky windings through the woods, but it was risky going. On one sudden turn, they jumped the ruts and took off into the woods,

dodging trees and windfalls until they found an opening and got back onto the road.

At another spot, they jumped a fallen log that threw them so high in the air there wasn't any traction left. Dizzy mumbled "Whew!" and "Wow!" and "My, My!" but finally closed his eyes and trusted to luck until they sloped down to the Beaver Corners intersection.

Storm parked the pick-up head-on toward the curving hill down which the masqueraders would come, and added some rails as a barrier.

Dizzy stayed in the pick-up to turn on the headlights when the time came. Storm went up the road and found cover in an angle of the rail fence. They didn't have long to wait before a car came down the curving hill. It came fast, headlights sweeping along the treetops until the curve straightened out. Then they bore down at the barricade. Brakes squealed. The car swerved. It came to a halt and tried to turn around. Dizzy switched on the pick-up headlights and headed for the brush. Storm could see him working his way along the fence on the other side toward the patrol car. A gun roared, and an eerie streak of flame from the patrol car pointed him out.

The patrol car backed and turned with a screech of tires and leaped away. Storm fired three shots and punctured a tire. The car jolted to a stop. The lights went out, but light from the pick-up still hit them. The men jumped down and bolted, one to one side of the road, one to the other.

The one on Storm's side headed for the rail fence. Storm ran toward him trying to close up the distance, but his luck ran out. He went down in a pothole, and his arm went elbow-deep into mud. His gun went with it. Gun-flame lanced at him, but he wasn't hit. He tried to fire a shot, but his clogged gun wouldn't work. He tried several times, then ran on again.

The pick-up headlights gave him an advantage over the bandit, but, without the use of his gun, it didn't do him much good. He slapped the weapon against his leg, trying to clear it, but it didn't help. Then the other man went down. He went deep, and Storm jumped him before he could pull himself out of the hole.

The jolt threw the man forward headfirst into the muck, but he twisted sideways far enough to get off another shot, so close to Storm's ear it deafened him. The gun barrel raked his cheek and tore open the cut he had gotten in the wreck. Storm caught hold of the bandit's arm and twisted the weapon from his hand. He spun it around and jammed it hard into the bandit's chest. The bandit cringed away and threw up his hands.

Dizzy was waiting at the patrol car. He claimed he had had an easy time.

"Just one shot, and my friend quit," he stated. "I didn't even hit him either."

They handcuffed the prisoners wrist to wrist, "Mr. Moore fashion," Dizzy said, and got them into the patrol car. The bank loot was in a canvas bag on the floor. Dizzy reported the capture to the post, but he didn't go into details. He said it was a long story, and they had a tire to fix.

"They got to grow wings to get through a roadblock," Drubb crowed. "I said it before, and I'll say it again."

"I'll bet you will, sergeant," Dizzy said, and hung the speaker on the hook.

Later, on the way back to the post, Storm yawned so hard he almost threw his jaw out of joint. He was dead-tired, and he got to wondering why a man pushed himself so hard.

Why didn't he stop at the easiest stopping place?—for instance, back there at the wrecked patrol car, or in the Moore house when they were both in handcuffs, or on the tote-road where, at the speed they were traveling, danger lurked on every turn, or later still, when his gun clogged and the risk of going on looked much too grave to run.

He was sure the answer had nothing to do with bank loot, or stolen patrol cars, or the small pay checks he got every two weeks, or anything at all that came from outside himself. He yawned again, and made a contented sound at the end of it. Maybe that was the answer. He sure did feel good.

The Straw Vote Machine

By JAMES W. ENGLISH

The Tailbone Patrol plans a publicity stunt which develops an unexpected boomerang

The old saying, "The bigger they come, the harder they fall," is no square talk. Brother, it's authentic! The Tailbone Patrol will vouch for that.

We were riding high, wide, and cocky as top patrol in Troop Ten, and bending everyone's ear with our self-admiring small talk, when we took our fall.

It started one night at troop meeting. Doc, our Scoutmaster, announced that Troop Ten was expected to participate in the Boy Scouts' nationwide Get Out the Vote campaign for the coming national election. Now, as Patrol Leader of the then lofty Tailboners —Mike Peterson's the name—I should have taken my cue from Doc, but I didn't. I just wasn't with this one, nor were the other Tailboners, and we talked most of the troop into our way of thinking.

"Aw, Doc!" wailed Toby, my overstuffed Assistant PL, who at all times is alert to the possible danger of being trapped into physical exercise. "You mean we gotta see that everyone in our voting precincts gets one of these Get Out the Vote reminders to hang in his window—or if no one's home, we hang it on the front doorknob?"

Doc nodded. "It's really quite simple unless you're allergic to work."

"But Phoenix is a growing city," Toby pointed out, not catching Doc's sarcasm. "There might be a couple thousand more doorknobs by next week."

"Yeah!" groused Tailboner Tommy Thompson. "And hundreds of new dogs, who'll forget they're man's best friend and try to ventilate the seat of your pants."

That's when Foxy Walker, PL of our nearest rivals, the Cougar Patrol, sounded off. "Doc," he said sarcastically, "it's obvious that this good turn presents insurmountable obstacles to our genius patrol, the Tailboners."

"Listen, Foxy," I snapped back, "if folks want to vote, they'll get to the voting places without us to remind them."

Foxy didn't say much else, for his entire patrol was siding with us. In fact, the whole troop was. But Doc cut us off curtly with the announcement that there would be a Green Bar meeting after troop dismissal.

That Green Bar meeting was short but far from sweet. Doc told us to imagine what this country might be like today if folks hadn't voted in years past.

"We need to get all Americans to vote," he said. And then he clobbered us—me in particular. "If some wise guys here think slipping Get Out the Vote door hangers on doorknobs is dull stuff, it's because they're too thick-headed to make something worthwhile out of this good turn. They're lazy, physically, mentally, and morally lazy."

With that, he stormed out of the Green Bar meeting.

"Wow!" exclaimed the surprised Foxy

Walker. "Doc sort of put it on us PL's to do something original with this good turn, didn't he?"

"Foxy," I replied dutifully, "for once you're making sense. I'd say the status quo on this good turn had better be fractured by next troop meeting, or some heads, meaning ours, are going to get cracked."

"Listen, Mike," he pleaded earnestly, "let's share any good ideas we get. It'll be for the good of the troop, and this isn't going to be an easy work project to sell to our patrols."

"I'll share this much with you right now," I replied. "Call this good turn a work project, and every Tailboner will be limping along on asthmatic cylinders. We hate work!"

After leaving Foxy, I stopped by the Palmcroft Drugstore, where, naturally, I found the Tailbone Patrol at work on chocolate sodas.

"Hey, Fritz," Toby called to the German refugee lad who's soda jerk on the night shift, "mix up some gooey stuff for Mike. He looks kinda down at the mouth."

Tommy Thompson, who'd been giving me the silent once-over, spoke up. "Okay, Mike. Let's have it! What happened?"

"Fellows," I said, "the Get Out the Vote campaign is on."

The uproar was so violent that Fritz fumbled a scoop of ice cream in mid-air.

"This is a democratic patrol, Mike!" Two-Bits Karsten, our watchdog treasurer and parliamentarian scribe, howled. "We haven't voted!"

"That's right!" yelled Toby, who momentarily forgot his ice cream.

So I told them how things were, and their faces got glummer by the minute. "And here's a lot of literature on the project," I added, tossing some papers on the counter.

The guys groaned.

Fritz placed the retreaded ice cream soda in front of me.

"Mike," he said, "tell these lazy braggarts what Doc means. They'll be protecting their American heritage."

"How come, Fritz?" several of us demanded.

"You guys know I wasn't born in the U.S.A.," Fritz said, "but I have my first papers and now I study for citizenship examination. It's a wonderful country!"

"Sure," interrupted Toby, "but why should we walk our legs off to get folks to vote? That's their business, isn't it?"

Fritz shook his head. "You have real freedom here. But you should have seen what it was like where I come from. Freedom! We got none. Opportunity!" He shrugged his shoulders. "Fear! Hunger! We got lots of that. Why? Because people forgot to vote and let a few crackpots vote themselves into office. The crackpots let the Communists take over our country and, too late, decent folks learned what the vote means. It means freedom, opportunity, happiness, life itself. Your Scoutmaster means you should protect your freedom by protecting the right to vote."

The Tailbone Patrol at long last understood the problem. Even Toby. He picked up the campaign literature, which I had dropped on the counter.

"I'm taking this stuff home with me, Mike," he said. "Got to put my brain to work and see if we can't eliminate the exercise from this good turn."

Next afternoon a sad bunch of Tailboners gathered at my house. Of course, I was more sympathetic than sad, for the doctor had just cut an ingrown nail from my big toe and I had orders to keep off my foot for several days.

"Honest, fellows!" I apologized. "This wasn't deliberate!"

"Why didn't you have him put a splint around your neck?" demanded little Billy Spears.

"Fellow Tailboners," called out Toby, who was putting in sack time on the sofa, "I think we can utilize Mike's extremely limited abilities. You see, I've figured out this good turn. There's no need to slip a door hanger on a single door or hike a single step."

"Boy, you'll never get a brain tumor," I snapped. "No brain!"

"Genius is seldom appreciated," observed Toby smugly.

"Okay," I grumbled, curious about his idea in spite of myself. "What's most on your mind?"

"The comfortable life, Mike. Good food, lots of rest, a place to ease the tired body."

"Never mind how you got into the awful shape you're in," snapped Two-Bits impatiently. "What's this miracle plan of yours?"

"Publicity!" purred the fat one. "Publicity for the straw vote machine. Now this morning as I sat in the Palmcroft Drugstore and ate an ice cream sundae. . . ."

"Before breakfast?" snorted Beans Roberts.

"Between breakfast," corrected Toby. "Well, I got to thinking about our good friend Fritz getting his citizenship papers next month. Did you know he's studying pre-med at the college in the daytime? Or that some of the doctors at the Palmcroft Medical Center are making a project out of Fritz? They're going to put him through medical school."

"Okay, society reporter," I snapped. "How'd you dig up the info, and what's it mean to us?"

The fat one looked at me and laughed. "Sure that hangnail wasn't between the ears, Mike?"

"Well, as I was saying," he added, turning his attention back to the Tailboners when I couldn't think up a quick answer, "Mr. Colton, proprietor of the Palmcroft Drugstore, told me this information, and in turn I told him of our problem. You see, I had figured out how he and Fritz and the business and professional men at the Palmcroft Shopping Center could help us. Mr. Colton liked my idea so much he's getting all these important people together tonight. Maybe he'll have a few others, too, like the judge who'll grant Fritz his citizenship, the city election commissioner, and a newspaper editor.

"And I'm rather proud of this next step," he added. "It was really psychic on my part —a realization that our PL would chicken out—so I invited them over here, Mike, tonight at eight p.m."

"You what?" I yelled.

"Never mind that," interrupted Tommy Thompson. "Let's find out what it's all about."

The Tailbone Patrol dragged our Assistant PL off the sofa, and after some roughhouse got the entire idea from him. And you had to hand it to Toby. This was a lulu, and it would really make the troop's other patrols look silly.

"We'll need an attorney to check city ordinances," I said. "I'd better call dad."

Beans Roberts was next on the telephone. "Pop's an electrician and this is some wiring job."

"My uncle is something or other in the carpenters' union," spoke up Billy Spears. "I'll bet he'll help."

That afternoon we ran up a telephone bill that bankrupted the Tailbone Patrol's treasury, but even Two-Bits was too excited to complain. And that evening our house was so filled with visitors that it looked like the nominating convention of one of the national parties. When the confab broke up, you'd have thought we had George Washington and Abraham Lincoln as running mates on our ticket, everyone was so enthusiastic.

Next day dad cleared all the necessary red tape with the city. The newspaper editor promised to break the story on page one Wednesday evening, which is troop meeting night. And Mr. Colton, representing the trades and professions at the Palmcroft Shopping Center, promised that a full-page announcement ad would be ready for Wednesday's newspaper.

A few more calls, placed by Beans Roberts' dad and Billy Spears' uncle, assured us of donated lumber, loudspeakers, PA system, banners, and all the carpenters and electricians needed to complete the job.

If, in those few happy days before the story broke, the Tailboners looked like the cat that'd swallowed the canary, just mark it down to ignorance, complete ignorance of the power of modern publicity.

I had my first misgivings as I read the story and ad in the Wednesday evening newspaper. Boy, we had the publicity. You see, the trades and professions at the Palmcroft Shopping Center were sponsoring a Get Out the Vote booth in their parking lot. The labor unions had erected the booth, and a PA system was piped into each store.

We had a stack of patriotic records, donated by a radio station. We'd taped a little speech by Fritz about what it meant to him to become an American citizen. The election commissioner had a plea for everyone to vote, and the judge handling Fritz's citizenship stated that just before election, Fritz would be sworn in as an American citizen in our booth.

And, boy, the Tailbone Patrol was mentioned all over the place, even gave our names, and that was what started me wondering if we weren't riding a ring-tailed comet on a non-scheduled flight.

The telephone started ringing. Folks congratulating us, folks wanting more information, folks saying they'd be over to sign our pledge books, folks out of our election precincts saying they'd be over anyway.

I left mom taking down telephone messages and slipped out to troop meeting.

First person I ran into was Foxy Walker, with a copy of the evening paper, and he was really mad.

"Thought you were going to share any bright ideas!" he snorted. "Instead of hogging all the glory for the Tailboners."

"If *I* had any bright ideas," I corrected. "This one was Toby's. Besides, you didn't report any brilliant strategy to me."

He turned away and I knew then that all he'd been able to come up with was the door-to-door canvass idea.

Well, if Foxy had been cooled off by what he read in the paper, the rest of the troop would have made the Antarctic seem like a friendly jungle paradise.

I gathered the Tailboners around me.

"Fellows," I said, "we've stirred up trouble. The phone's been ringing at the house ever since the newspapers hit the street."

"Ditto," muttered Toby and the others. "We need a switchboard."

"Brainchild!" I replied, facing my fat assistant. "I've a feeling this patrol is going to need a whole lot more than a switchboard. The troop's frosted at us, thinks it's a publicity grab, and the way those calls are coming in, I think we'll need all of the troop and then some to operate that booth."

Everyone looked at Toby, who for once was too nervous to take it easy.

"Look, fellows!" he pleaded. "I just think up these wonderful ideas. It's up to you guys to make 'em work."

Fortunately for the health of our Assistant PL, Doc called troop meeting at that moment. When we sat down after the Pledge of Allegiance, I noted that there were enough copies of the evening paper in evidence to start a couple of newsstands, and Doc had one in his hands.

"I see by the newspaper that one patrol has its 'Get Out the Vote' campaign in high gear. Mike, tell us what gives!"

"It's very simple," I said. "The publicity and the PA system bring people over to the booth, where they sign the roster for their election precincts. They pledge themselves to vote and we give 'em their 'Get Out the Vote' hangers. The precinct books are listed by streets, and we check the street numbers against the city directory to see if we have everyone. Those we miss at the booth we visit and give 'em doorhangers and a sales talk. We're out for 100% voting in our precincts."

"It's a swell idea," Doc said, "but I'm wondering how you're going to have enough 'hangers' to give to everyone who comes to the booth, since you expect folks from all over the city."

This problem I hadn't counted on. I got red in the face and turned to Toby. "Give, brain, I need details."

"And I'm wondering, too," Doc added, "how you're going to keep the booth open all day for three weeks and still stay in school?"

The troop started to laugh. "Oh, I wouldn't laugh," Doc cautioned. "The Tailboners are the only patrol who have done

anything about this good turn. What they've done is tops. The only problem is they seem not to have thought out their problem very thoroughly."

"That," I said under my breath to my squirming assistant, "is the understatement of the year."

"But, Mike," Toby whispered back, "all those adults backing us aren't dopes. Someone must have thought of these problems."

That stopped me, for he was right. Now dad, for instance, has a legal mind that doesn't let a lot of loopholes spoil a project. But if he'd thought of these problems, why hadn't he told me about them?

"Doc," I said, "the Tailbone Patrol would like a recess to make a telephone call."

I talked to dad on the telephone for some time, and when I hung up, I knew less than before I placed the call.

"Fellows," I said, "I got the snow job from my own dad. All he'd say is that the Tailbone Patrol has made such a reputation for carrying out our wacky ideas that he and the other men never questioned our capabilities. He said we've bragged about our great abilities so often that he is convinced."

Two-Bits waved a calloused fist under Toby's nose.

"Come clean, lamebrain, who suggested this idea to you?"

"It was mostly mine," he said meekly. "Mr. Colton just added a few points."

"Who started the conversation? You or Mr. Colton?" I demanded.

"Well, he asked why I was so down in the dumps and I told him about the Get Out the Vote campaign and he told me about Fritz, and the first thing you knew we had a project."

"If a guy comes by wanting to sell the Brooklyn Bridge, keep your hand out of your pocket," I snapped. "You were taken, and took the rest of us with you."

"But why us?" Toby demanded.

"Well," I added, "I seem to get the drift that some folks think we've been spouting off a little too much about being top patrol. Doc made a reference to it; dad certainly said as much. Even Foxy Walker wanted to share ideas, and Foxy isn't the type. Before, even when we're in trouble with the troop, they speak to us. Tonight it's the silent treatment. Know what? I think this is a put-up job."

"Well, let's go back and face the music," Tommy Thompson said. "Only, I wish I could tune in the troop."

Doc gave us a curious look as we came back in and sat down.

"What's the report?" he asked.

"No report," I replied. "The Titanic went

down, and so might the Tailbone Patrol."

Foxy Walker was on his feet pronto. "You Tailboners better not flub this one. Not after all that publicity. All the rest of the troop would get a bad name too."

Doc stopped other uncomplimentary remarks. "I'll call the Scout office tomorrow and see if you can have more Get Out the Vote hangers," he said. "Afraid you'll have to work the other problems out for yourselves."

Saturday morning it was a very nervous group of Tailboners who officially opened our Get Out the Vote booth. If a Tailboner has ever been humble, we were humble at that point. We were scared, too.

In the first half hour we handled over one hundred persons who stopped at the booth to pledge themselves to vote. Then the deluge started. Folks came in cars, they came lugging squirming kids, they parked bundles of groceries in our arms while they signed, they gave us doctors' prescriptions to run to the drugstore with while they stood in line. To tell you the truth, we ran ourselves ragged.

Toby, completely out of training for such physical exertion, was dripping wet. His Scout shirt looked like Monday's wash.

"Mike," he gasped, "who said this would beat peddling the hangers from door-to-door?"

"You, brain," I snapped, as I juggled two oversized sacks of groceries someone had parked in my arms. "And the day's hardly begun."

"Oh, you Tailboners haven't started to see the crowd yet," enthused an elderly gentleman next in line. "Why, that publicity downtown is the best I've ever seen."

"Publicity! Downtown?" I asked.

"Why, yes," the gentleman replied. "There are Scouts on every street corner with sandwich signs. You should read those signs!" For a moment his eyebrows knitted together as he tried to recall one. "Here's one. 'You've learned about the Tailbone Patrol's Vote Booth.' Then the next fellow's sign reads: 'In the newspapers or on the radio.' 'Well, we're the lamebrains who didn't

think up that nifty idea.' 'But we're lazy too and don't like to hike all over town.' 'So please hike out to their booth and save us blistered feet!' "

He laughed at the recollection. "They paraded down the street just like those funny shaving cream signs you pass on the highway, and folks all stopped to read what was coming next."

"That sounds like Foxy Walker and the Cougar Patrol getting even," Toby muttered.

A woman behind the gentleman shook her head. "Oh, nearly every troop in town is represented," she said cheerfully. "My son belongs to Troop 32, and his patrol worked the last two nights getting their signboards in order."

Beans Roberts, who had just arrived on the scene, grabbed the packages from my arms as I sunk into a chair.

"What's the matter, Mike?" he asked. "You look like you need first aid."

"I do," I replied. "A tourniquet around my neck."

Just then Billy Spears dumped a canteen of water on me.

"Break it up, you politicians," our mighty mite roared. "We haven't time for any heart attacks now. Look at our customers. One of you brains had better give before the police riot squad arrives."

I looked up and did a double, then a triple take. The entire parking lot was jammed with folks. It looked like the mob trying to get out of the stadium after a football game. Only, we were the exit, and we were most definitely a bottleneck.

Hurriedly I rounded up some cardboard and painted on the precinct numbers. We tacked these signs up, and then we circulated around getting people in the proper lines. It was still a madhouse, but some of the confusion was missing. All we needed was about four times as many Scouts; then we could have done a first-rate job.

I leaned against a side of the booth, trying to get up enough strength to check on the lines of people pledging themselves to vote.

Doc arrived about that time. "Having

lunch sent in?" he asked. "Not a bad idea. You seem busy."

"Doc," I said, "we aren't busy. We're snowed under."

"And we've been sabotaged," Toby replied. "All the troops in Phoenix are planning to get our records and see who in their precincts haven't pledged. The lazy dogs!"

"That's the way you fellows asked for it," Doc reminded us. "You made this a Tailbone activity, not a troop or council affair."

"So we goofed," admitted Toby. "And when we goof, we don't do it in any minor, piddling fashion. We really goof."

"We owe you and the troop an apology," I told Doc. "Not a little apology, a great big one. Guess we have a lot to learn about democratic processes, bending the will to the majority vote, playing it for the good of everyone instead of our own special gain."

"We should apologize to the entire council as well as the troop," Beans Roberts added. "How stupid can one patrol get?"

Doc smiled and waved to someone beyond the crowd. In a couple of minutes the rest of Troop Ten was on hand.

"I figured that four hours of this would cause the Tailbone Patrol to see the light," he added. "You fellows take your pizza pie over to the drugstore. Fritz has malts and hamburgers waiting. Troop Ten will take over the vote booth."

We were halfway through our lunch when Doc joined us.

"Tell me, Doc," I asked. "Who really thought up this idea?"

Doc grinned. "Mr. Colton and I had worked it out and cleared it with the council office. I'd planned to introduce it at troop meeting, until you guys poured cold water on the whole good turn. Then Mr. Colton and I decided to wait and see who came along asking for help."

"You and your original ideas!" Billy Spears growled, giving the fat one a dirty look.

"Then all those adults at that meeting knew the whole troop would participate after we got bogged down?" the amazed Toby asked.

Doc nodded. "You might say that the only really original idea was Foxy Walker's sandwich sign gag, which all the troops in Phoenix went for in a big way.

"Oh, yes," he added, "you fellows might like to know that the mothers' clubs of the council's troops are each taking the booth one day a week until the Scouts of Troop Ten get out of school. The troop will have the duty from 3 p.m. until closing time week days and all day on Saturdays. Okay?"

"It's wonderful, Doc," I said, and the Tailboners were yelling so loud that poor Fritz missed another scoop of ice cream in midair. But then, he didn't seem to mind. Why should he? He understood the meaning of democratic action all along.

Terror of Buccaneer Bay

By PASCHAL N. STRONG

An amateur sailor nearly wrecks the yacht club in his Crazy Lady when a hurricane strikes

That's what he was—the Terror of Buccaneer Bay. Strong men paled when he approached. Yet, to look at him you'd never guess that he was more dreaded in the anchorage than a hurricane.

He was about my age, eighteen or so. Tousled blond hair, tall and slender, a nose that went askew when he laughed, and—until that incredible Black Friday—a friendly half smile on his lips. His eyes should have warned me. They were the blue eyes of a dreamer. A dreamer with a sea-going urge. A dreamer who never had enough sea room. Sometimes I wondered if the whole Atlantic would have been enough.

I saw him first at the club dock when I was adjusting the jibstay of my Lightning for the coming race. I heard a cheery "Hello!" and looked up, and there he was.

"Hi," I said, wondering if he were a newcomer to the Buccaneer Bay colony, or just a visitor.

"Fine looking sailboat you've got," he said. "Are you a member of the Yacht Club?"

"Well, sort of," I admitted, taking another twist of the turnbuckle.

"Sort of? What do you mean by that?"

I looked up impatiently. But you couldn't get mad at that friendly smile. "I work around here each summer," I told him. "Helps get me through college. The fellows threw in a special membership without charge."

"My folks have rented the Murray cottage. I want to join the yacht club. I want to get a boat, too."

"No trouble in joining if you live here. What kind of boat do you want?"

"The biggest sailboat I can get for my money."

"Better learn to sail first," I said.

"But how do you know I can't sail?"

I laughed. "A sailor never calls a sailboat a sailboat. And a smart sailor never tries to buy the biggest boat for his money. He tries to get the smallest."

He looked at me as though I were crazy, so I explained. "Too much boat for your money means a rotten hull, poor rigging, and a bag of headaches. How much do you want to spend?"

"All I've got saved up. About two thousand dollars."

"Put half of it in a Lightning, like this sloop. Learn to sail and race it. It's more fun than a circus."

He shook his head, and I saw that dreamy look. "I want a seagoing boat," he said. He gazed out across the breakwater, toward the horizon. "I've lived inland. All my life I've wanted to go to sea." His voice faded as though a sudden vision of distant horizons had opened to him offering real adventure.

I told him of a shipyard across the Bay where he could buy secondhand boats. I didn't tell him what a shock he had coming when he discovered what a seagoing boat cost. And that was the last I saw of him for a week.

But it was I who got the shock.

I was doing a varnish job on a swank mahogany cruiser belonging to Mr. Steele. H. Maynard Steele. By this time I knew my friend's name was Archy Duval, and I guess he'd discovered my name, for he came down to the dock and said excitedly: "Hi, Bob. I've bought a boat."

"Swell," I enthused. "A Lightning?"

"No, a real boat." He saw the fire in my eye and added, "I mean, a real seagoing boat. A forty-foot sloop. She's a beauty! Her name's the Crazy Lady." He got that dreamy look again.

I went back to my varnishing. I hated to tell him what I knew. The Crazy Lady was a honey to look at. Spoon bow, trim lines, and a brand-new coat of white paint on her topsides. But everyone knew she was riddled with dry rot inside, that worms feasted on her planking, and that her auxiliary engine was an asthmatic old coffee grinder. And her rigging was rotten.

"What's the matter with her?" Archy demanded.

I told him. I had to tell him. I didn't want him to take the perforated tub outside the harbor and drown himself. But I sure hated to see the excitement fade from his voice.

He gulped and took it gamely. "Maybe you're right," he said soberly. "But she's mine, and I'm going to sail her until she goes under. Will you help me sail her back here?"

I helped him. I didn't want to, but I couldn't resist that innocent appeal in his blue eyes. We sailed across the Bay the next day. I explained the rudiments of sailing, tried to teach him how to handle lines—he would call them ropes—and when we approached the narrow breakwater entrance to our basin, I explained why he should lower sail and use the engine before zigzagging among the pleasure craft which rode at their

moorings inside the anchorage. When he made fast at a dock near his cottage, I begged but one thing of him.

"For Pete's sake, get a ten-foot dinghy and learn to sail before you take the Crazy Lady out."

"But you just taught me how to sail," he objected.

I shuddered. If Archy thought he could sail after one short afternoon on a flat sea with a ghosting breeze, there was trouble ahead. I explained to him gently that, come a spanking breeze and a seaway, the art of sailing had more booby traps than a mine field. He didn't hear a word I said. He was looking out to sea with that lost, dreamy look of his, and I knew that the sirens of the deep were calling him.

Came Friday. They still call it Black Friday at Buccaneer Bay. The boat owners try to forget it, but in nightmares it comes back in all its gory details. I had a ringside seat because Mr. Steele, H. Maynard Steele, was taking some friends for a ride on his cruiser and I was along as deckhand. It was a marvelous afternoon, the breeze dusting up whitecaps in the Bay, white sails scudding along the blue horizon, and a fleet of assorted craft riding happily at their moorings with no thought of the carnage ahead.

I brought Mr. Steele's cruiser, the Black Douglas, alongside the dock to take aboard his friends, and noticed that the Crazy Lady was not at her mooring. I figured that Archy and some of his friends were out in the Bay, and hoped he had a sailor or two aboard. While waiting for Mr. Steele, I took a gander through the glasses to spot the Crazy Lady. She was about a mile outside the breakwater, and even as I looked I saw her mainsail jibe violently around. I winced at the punishment her rigging took, and wondered what crazy idiot at the tiller would take such a risk with rotten gear.

And then I saw that the crew consisted of just one man, and that must be Archy. He was apparently headed in for the breakwater. Well, my hat was off to him for sheer, unadulterated nerve—I'd never have taken out a forty-foot sloop without at least one man aboard to help me—and I prayed that Mr. Steele and his friends would board the cruiser soon so we would clear the breakwater entrance before Archy approached.

Five minutes later we were under way, with Mr. Steele at the wheel. When I had coiled up the lines I joined him on the little flying bridge.

"Better keep an eye on that sloop heading in, sir. There's just one man aboard, and he doesn't know a sheet from a halyard."

Mr. Steele whistled. "You don't suppose he'll enter the basin under sail?"

I looked again through the glasses. "I guess not, sir. He's left the tiller and gone forward to douse sail. Oh, oh!"

"What's the matter?"

"His main halyard is snarled. He can't get his mains'l down."

"Then why doesn't the fool come about and get sea room? He'll be on the breakwater in a moment."

I put the glasses down. They weren't needed. We were approaching the narrow breakwater entrance from the inside, and the Crazy Lady bore down from the Bay. On her present course, however, she was headed directly for the jagged stones that flanked the entrance.

I saw Archy try frantically to get his mainsail down. And while he struggled, the Crazy Lady tore in toward the rocky breakwater with suicidal intent. Everyone on the Black Douglas held his breath when suddenly Archy, alive at last to danger, rushed back to the tiller. He gave it a yank, and now the Crazy Lady bore directly down on us, her bow wave curling like a foaming ploughshare.

Mr. Steele threw both engines in reverse and when our way was killed, he threw both in neutral, ready for any emergency. Though the breakwater entrance was narrow, there was room for Archy to clear us. But he was running square before the wind, and the leach of his mainsail was fluttering. If he backwinded the sail and jibed—!

He did just that. The boom whipped across the deck as Archy ducked wildly into the cockpit. The sloop careened around and tore

in for the kill. Mr. Steele jammed both engines full speed astern and avoided a head-on collision, but as the Crazy Lady shot by us the end of her boom carved a splintering white gash in the polished side of the cruiser.

Above the thunderous roar of Mr. Steele's anger, I heard Archy's voice in one frantic appeal for help. "What do I do?" he yelled at me.

"Bring her into the wind and cut your halyard," I shouted.

"Tell him to cut his throat," bellowed Mr. Steele.

Archy ducked below, presumably to find a knife. The Crazy Lady leaped joyously ahead, aiming unerringly for a ketch heading unsuspectingly for the Bay. Hoarse shouts of alarm from the ketch's crew brought Archy above, and not a second too soon. He seized the tiller in the nick of time to avoid more than a glancing blow, and took time out to shout his apologies across the sizzling atmosphere.

It was no time to apologize. The Crazy Lady was bearing down on an express cruiser riding innocently at her mooring. Archy discovered the fact barely in time to wear off violently, but he fouled the buoy, rode it under his hull, and when it bobbed up a few seconds later the cruiser was free to drift happily anywhere it chose. And from Archy's agonizing cry and his acrobatics at the tiller, I guessed that the mooring line had fouled his rudder.

By this time everyone in the anchorage knew there was a killer loose. Whistles tooted hysterically to warn the unwary. Unattended craft at their moorings could do nothing but wait stoically for whatever blows fate might bring, but those boats under way could and did scatter before the avenging scourge. The Crazy Lady, free of rudder control, charged about gaily from one tack to another. The speedboats sheered off, but she nicked two cutters as their crews were raising sail to escape, caromed against a couple of helpless yawls, clipped the top gear off a fisherman with a clean sweep of her boom, and chased a couple of Lightnings all around the anchorage.

The Black Douglas was closing in on her with Mr. Steele grimly determined at the wheel. "I'll sink him," he muttered. "I'll sink him if I go down with him." He looked at me. "Get that anchor ready, Lawson. When he goes down and yells for a life preserver, throw him that anchor. If you miss him, you're fired."

Mr. Steele wasn't fooling. His hates were few but fiery. Maybe he wouldn't actually have thrown Archy the anchor, but he was certainly going to run down the Crazy Lady if he could.

But fate intervened. Archy, convinced at last that he could do nothing with the tiller, had somehow found a knife and was slashing at the main halyard as we neared. The mainsail dropped in a billow of canvas that buried him in its whipping folds. A speedboat rushed in with a boarding party which lowered the jib, and Archy was towed to his mooring by grim-lipped men who said little but said that little very well indeed.

I went around to see him that night. I found him sitting silently on the edge of the dock near his cottage, looking across the moonsplashed waves toward his sloop.

"Don't say it," he said dully as I sat down beside him. "There's nothing you can add to what I've told myself."

"I'm delegated to bring you a message." I wasn't happy about it. "The membership committee of the Yacht Club held a special meeting tonight to consider your application."

"I bet they didn't have enough black balls to go around."

I nodded. They didn't.

Archy sat silently for a moment. "They tried to buy out Dad's lease on the cottage," he finally said. "Offered him double the money."

I looked the question I didn't want to ask.

"Dad said no!" I heard a note of pride in his voice. "Dad said we weren't running away. And he told me to stick to the Crazy Lady until I became the best sailor in the Bay."

"Will you stick it out?"

"You're darned tootin' I will." He stood

up suddenly as footsteps sounded on the dock. A couple of fellows from the club, strolling along the waterfront with their girls, were coming out on the dock to have a look at the moon. Suddenly they stopped sharply, and we heard them whisper together. They turned abruptly and left, but not before we heard one of them say something—a little too loudly—about the Terror of Buccaneer Bay.

"That's what you're up against," I told Archy. I wanted to get his dander up. I wanted him to stay and see it through. But I needn't have worried. His shoulders squared off and he looked like a young Viking facing the western ocean.

"I'll stick around," he said.

He did. He was cold-shouldered, ignored, and ostracized. No one was deliberately cruel, but Archy was new at the Bay, few people knew him or his family, so it was easy to pass him by. I saw him occasionally when I could get away from work, and I knew that the treatment was getting him down. Not for himself. For his parents. People didn't take them up, and Archy knew it was because of him, though his parents tried to make little of it. And he was on his sloop morning and afternoon. He'd chug out of the breakwater, hoist sail, and drive the Crazy Lady rail under in every sort of weather. He even had the old rigging replaced.

"I love that old tub," he admitted to me one day. "I love every rotten plank in her. I know she won't last another season, but I'll stick with her until she sinks."

Prophetic words! Fortunately for my peace of mind, I didn't know that I'd be with him when the time came.

The hurricane struck a week later. Everyone knew it was coming, of course, but not even the weather man could tell where the center would strike the coast. It looked as though it might roar in dangerously near the Bay. All the Lightnings and small boats were hauled up on shore and lashed down, but the larger and more expensive craft had to get under some lee or be destroyed. There was a safe lee across the Bay, where the land curved around in a hook, that gave protection against a blow from the sea. But if the wind came from the land, then the basin itself was in the best possible lee. No one would have to move.

So the sixty-four-dollar question was: Will the center of the hurricane strike to the north or the south of the Bay? If it struck to the north, we'd get the wind from the land and the boats could stay in the basin. But if it struck to the south, we'd get the full force from the ocean, and the little breakwater would be buried under a tidal wave of raging seas. And every boat in the basin would be wrecked.

All day long, as the clouds scudded overhead and the wind moaned around the eaves, the skippers of the threatened craft stuck to the radio for news of the hurricane. Everyone was prepared to take off across the Bay if the storm's eye were to come in from the south. And then, an hour before dark, the flash came over the air. The center of the hurricane would strike the south. The curved hook across the Bay offered the only protection. I seized my oilskins and started for the door. The telephone halted me. It was Mr. Steele. He wanted me to help him take the Black Douglas across the Bay.

"Sorry," I told him. "I'm going to help with the Crazy Lady."

The telephone receiver grew hot in my hands. I hung up. I knew he could get other help. Archy couldn't.

I found Archy at the dock, ready to cast off under power. His engine coughed spasmodically. "Want a passenger?" I shouted as I dropped aboard.

His look of astonishment turned to gratitude. "I sure do," he yelled above the wind. "Don't believe I could make it by myself."

He took the tiller and we eased away from the dock. The basin was a hive of windblown activity. Crews were rowing out to their moorings against a choppy sea, or making ready to get away from their berths at the various docks. The wind curved the waves into gray spume, and the rising swells from the ocean sent geysers of spray over the breakwater.

I cast a quick look around deck as we headed for the breakwater exit. Archy had learned much the last two weeks. Everything was shipshape. Lines were coiled, halyards made fast, and the sails tightly furled in stops under their covers. But I thought of the antique engine below deck and said, "Suppose I take off the sail covers. If the engine stops percolating around that breakwater, we'll need sail in a hurry."

He nodded agreement and I did the rest. Barring an engine failure too close to the breakwater, we'd be all right. I looked astern. Several other craft were under way, with the Black Douglas in the van, but we'd be the first one to clear out of the anchorage.

I didn't like the sound of the engine. It misfired as though there were water in the carburetor—not to be wondered at since bilge water covered the floor boards every time Archy missed a day's pumping. As we approached the opening between the two stone walls of the breakwater, I listened to the engine and my heart missed a beat. But the engine still chugged away. Spray from the breakwater, lashed into our faces by the wind, stung like shotgun pellets. The sloop's bow lifted skyward as she met the first swell of the open Bay. And then it happened.

The engine gave a weary cough and quit.

Archy and I sprang to the mainsail, tearing off the stops with feverish hands. As we worked I looked about anxiously. Wind and sea were carrying us back into the narrow breakwater entrance. Even as I leaped to the main halyard, I knew there was no chance of raising sail and making steerage way before we hit the south side of the entrance. Nevertheless I gave way on the halyard with a vengeance. The mainsail was halfway up when our stern grounded on a rock with a sickening thud. Now the sail was worse than useless. It helped the wind hold us on while each succeeding swell threw us higher and higher on the rocks under our keel. Then the bow swung slowly in, and we pounded helplessly, the hull writhing and shuddering at each smashing blow.

"Here comes the Black Douglas," shouted Archy. "She can throw us a line and haul us off."

The trim cruiser, slowed to half speed, was just approaching the entrance. Mr. Steele, H. Maynard Steele, was at the wheel, chewing thoughtfully on a large cigar. He watched us with more than ordinary interest. I held on to the main shroud and yelled for a line to pull us off. Mr. Steele slowed to quarter speed.

"Are you sure you can't get off?" he shouted.

"Look at us!" Every second counted, and he was asking foolish questions. "If you don't get us off right now, we're done for."

"Best news I've heard for years," he shouted back, and with a burst of speed the Black Douglas shot out into the Bay.

Archy and I stared at each other in unbelieving consternation. But just then Jack Stuart's powerful fisherman approached the entrance, and I knew Jack wouldn't let us down. He didn't. By the time he was abreast, his pal had a heaving line ready, and a second later the padded weight thumped aboard.

"Thanks!" I shouted as Archy hauled in the light line. A two-inch towing line was attached to it, and within seconds we had it aboard and fast to the bow cleat. Jack backed up as near to us as he dared to take up slack and then, with the line taut, he poured on the soup.

The water boiled behind his twin screws.

And as each wave lifted the Crazy Lady, her bow inched away from the shattering rocks. Soon only the stern was fast, and a moment more sufficed to free that. We were clear of the rocks, pointing obliquely across the entrance, when Archy, with a heart-rending yell, pointed down into the cabin.

I looked. I gasped. A hole big enough for a whale to come through had been punched in our starboard bow. And if a whale had been around he'd probably have come through. The whole Atlantic was rushing in. I turned around to shout to Jack to get his boat outside the breakwater before we sank, but it was too late. The Crazy Lady gave a sigh of frustration and settled beneath the waves. But the spirit of Black Friday was still with her, for her last act before she sank was to turn broadside to the entrance. She closed it like a cork closes a bottle.

Archy and I scrambled up on the shrouds. And Jack's boat was trapped inside the breakwater, with no chance of escaping across the Bay to the lee.

He threw us a line and we were pulled aboard his boat like a couple of drowned rats. He didn't say much. He took one look at the two dozen boats headed for the entrance and said, more in awe than in anger, "Never before has so much been done to so many by so few."

Archy took one look at the oncoming craft and said in despair. "They'll all be sunk by the hurricane."

"Go below, both of you," said Jack, not unkindly. "You'll find some dry clothes in the locker. I'll cruise around and tell the skippers to return to their moorings and do what they can." On second thought he added to Archy: "You'd better stay below where they can't see you. I'll tell them you're drowned. It'll make them feel better."

I remained below with Archy, trying to cheer him up. It wasn't much use. He was heartbroken. What he had done to the skippers on Black Friday faded into a pale nothing compared to what he had done today. We let him off at his dock, and then I went to the Yacht Club to help batten things down for the storm. The center was due to strike the coast about midnight, and no one could do very much except pray.

I won't tell you anything about that night. I want to save it for the end. But the next morning I went to Archy's house. Except for a few weak gusts and some scraggly clouds, the hurricane was over. Archy's mother told me that he had refused supper last night and gone to bed early. She added, "He was terribly nervous and unhappy."

I woke him up. It took a bit of doing, but I finally dumped him on the floor, bed-clothes and all. He stood up dazedly, and then wilted as he remembered what had happened. He started toward the window, then stopped as though unwilling to look upon the wreckage of the basin.

"Tell me the worst," he said glumly.

"I've got a message from some of the club members," I said. "You're being offered an honorary membership in the Yacht Club."

"I don't think you're very funny," he said. "Are all the boats sunk?"

"Only Mr. Steele's. It was blown ashore after he left it across the Bay. He's probably telephoning the insurance company now."

Archy looked at me queerly. "Am I crazy, or you?"

I laughed. "Brace yourself, my lad. The hurricane switched course at the last moment. It struck to the north of us. The wind hit us from the land. So every craft was safe in the lee. If you hadn't bottled them up, they'd all have been across the Bay—and sunk. And the skippers are plenty grateful."

Archy flung open the shutters. Every boat was riding securely at its mooring. Every boat except the Crazy Lady, whose mast reared up mutely from the breakwater entrance. A sudden smile split Archy's face from ear to ear.

"I couldn't have wanted a better end for her," he said.

It's the Ham in Them

By JOSEPH STOCKER

Come hurricane, or flood, or just a quiet evening, the ham operators keep on talking

The scene is the Northeast, with Hurricane Diane at her worst. Three hundred trembling youngsters watch murky water surging ankle deep over their island in the middle of the rampaging Delaware River. An auto appears on the far bank, but raises little hope. A passing motorist wouldn't have rescue equipment, and there is not enough time for him to go for help.

Strangely, the car remains where it stopped, but no one emerges. The waters rise and hopes sink. Then over the roar of the flood comes the steady whir of a squadron of helicopters.

Water was waist-high when the last child boarded a helicopter, probably still unaware of the key part the auto played in the rescue. For in the car sat a licensed "ham" with a portable radio; he had gotten through to Civil Defense officials, then waited to be sure rescuers found the right spot.

The scene is the Southwest earlier the same summer. A truck has plunged off a mountain road. Three people were badly hurt and a rancher brings them to Camp Geronimo, a Scout camp in Arizona. The camp doctor decides an ambulance plane from Phoenix is needed, and soon Scout Ed Burkhardt speaks tensely and earnestly into a mike:

"CQ, CQ, CQ, Phoenix; This is W7SUI calling from Camp Geronimo with an emergency! CQ, CQ, CQ, Phoenix!"

CQ means "calling anybody."

Ed flicks a switch and listens anxiously. "W7SUI from W7PMQ. Go ahead."

It was another ham in the Phoenix area. Swiftly Ed transmitted his message.

After that, things happened quickly. The Phoenix ham telephoned Scout headquarters. Headquarters dispatched an ambulance plane. The plane picked up the injured people at an airstrip near the camp, and, within an hour and forty-five minutes after the accident, they were bedded down in a Phoenix hospital.

Nothing Spectacular

Actually, of course, there was nothing very spectacular about Ed Burkhardt's feat of that day, and Ed himself would be the first to admit it. In much the same efficient and businesslike fashion, radio hams have been performing good deeds for humanity practically ever since the gadget was invented by the very first ham, a fellow named Marconi.

It needn't be concluded from this, however, that hams exist solely for the purpose of helping people out of whatever predicament they happen to be in. Hams are hams because of the fun in it. And the fun must be considerable, to judge from the fact that there are no less than 120,000 licensed hams in the U.S. alone and another 50,000 around the world.

Not a few of them are teen-agers, for amateur radio, unlike some other hobbies, is wide

open to young people. Indeed, Uncle Sam has gone out of his way to make the hobby enticing to the youth of America. Only a few years ago Congress passed a law permitting the Federal Communications Commission to license two new basic classifications of ham operators. They're called "Novice" and "Technician," and the only requirements are the ability to send and receive five words per minute in code, and some technical theory.

Uncle Sam Wants More

Uncle Sam was motivated, to be sure, by something more than a yen to help young people while away their time by exchanging "CQ's" and chit-chat with other hams halfway around the world. What he desired mostly was to create an ever-abundant pool of communications experts, ready to be called upon in case of a national emergency. But the result also was to set off a brandnew boom in amateur radio. And so today, even while commercial radio is still reeling from the impact of TV, ham radio is thriving.

Moreover, it seems to lend itself especially well to Scouting. Not long ago, for instance, Troop 510 in Chicago launched a formal training course for hams. It was the Scoutmaster's idea—he wanted to give his Scouts

107

an activity that would be a little out of the ordinary. He found a 24-year-old former Scout and licensed ham to serve as instructor. The Scoutmaster wasn't entirely sure whether the idea would catch hold or not. But he needn't have worried. On the first night, forty-five Scouts turned out for the course. Nine fathers turned out, too.

Rather obviously, therefore, age has no particular bearing on ham radio. One of the youngest hams ever to get his license was an eight-year-old Cub Scout in Pennsylvania. And in McAlester, Oklahoma, there are three newly licensed hams—a boy and two girls—who are just ten years old.

Whole families have taken to ham radio. The town of Cheney, Washington, boasts an all-ham family—mother, father and teen-age son and daughter (each with his own license and call letters).

It takes more than a license, of course, to become a ham. You'll need a radio rig of your own, which means a transmitter as well as a receiver. But it doesn't have to be expensive. With an assortment of old radio parts, some ingenuity and plenty of spare time, you can build your rig for very little money, and many an amateur has done exactly that.

I've heard hams tell about building their first rigs for as little as $2.50 to $5, although you'd better count on spending a bit more.

At the other extreme, though, there are amateurs who lay out enough cash on their equipment to outfit a 50,000-watt commercial station. One ham, for example, is said to have sunk upwards of $100,000 into his hobby.

You Start by Listening

For the fellow who wants to get into hamming and doesn't know quite where to start, SWL (for Short-Wave Listening) is as good a place to begin as any. You don't need a license to listen. All you need is a short-wave receiver (even the family radio will do if it is geared for short-wave as well as the conventional long-wave). After a spate of listening, you'll have the feel of the thing and possibly even get in a little practice at re-

ceiving code, providing you've done some boning-up on code in the meantime.

What's more, SWL will afford you an introduction to the curious gobbledygook employed by hams all over the world. You'll hear them chatting blithely about maximum plate ratings, grid bias, diodes, and superinfragenerators. (When two hams have nothing else to talk about, they swap information about their respective radio rigs.) You'll also hear them tossing back and forth what seem like totally meaningless chunks of alphabet. But they aren't meaningless at all. They're the international code systems which enable hams to surmount language barriers and talk to each other like American businessmen over the lunch table.

There are two such systems. One is a set of 43 "Q" signals. This should be used on CW (or code) only. QRL?—"Are you busy?" QRS—"Please send more slowly." QRA?—"What is your street address?"

The other system is a series of abbreviations. They're based on English but understood in every language. Examples: TNX—"Thanks." BCNU—"I'll be seeing you." DX—"Distance." 73—"Regards."

Thus a ham sending a message which reads, "QRU NW CUL 73," would be instantaneously understood to have said: "No more now. See you later. Regards."

The hams have even developed a vernacular applying specifically to themselves and their hobby. They use "ticket" for "license" and "work" for "contact" ("I worked 15 stations last night"). Some hams are "ragchewers"—they spend most of their time filling the air with small talk. Others, going about their business a bit more seriously, prefer to concentrate on "traffic," which is message-relaying.

Still others are "DX hounds." They like to see how many states, continents, and countries they can contact, how much distance they can get, and how many QSL cards they can collect. These are the flamboyantly decorated postcards which hams exchange to confirm their radio contacts. Recently I met a ham who had contacted 238 different countries and accumulated more

QSL cards (30,000 in all) than he had room for on the walls of his radio shack.

Message-relaying, by itself, is a sort of hobby within a hobby. In Peru, Indiana, an amateur radio hobbyist spends much of his time talking to the region around the North Pole. It so happens there are people up there —government personnel attached to bleak and remote weather stations located within a few hundred miles of the pole. All of them have families back home, and the Indiana ham serves as a one-man clearinghouse for messages between them.

His compensation? Only the satisfaction of maintaining a precious contact between human beings forced by circumstances to live far from each other.

Mighty Handy Guy

But it's in times of real trouble that the ham comes into his own and that people decide that he's a mighty handy guy to have around.

Up in New England they still tell of the valor shown by two radio amateurs—Wilson E. Burgess and George Marshall—in the big blow of 1938. It was a hurricane and tidal wave that killed hundreds of people and leveled thousands of homes.

The tempest roared in from the Atlantic on a Thursday. Burgess was at his job in a Westerly, Rhode Island, department store. Quickly he sensed that this was no ordinary storm. Gathering up an armload of batteries and wires from the store's radio department, he made for home. As he struggled up a wind-battered street, he ran into Marshall.

"All the telephone and power lines are down," Marshall screamed over the yowling gale. "The radio stations are knocked out and roads are blocked. We've got to set up contact with someone on the outside to try to get medical supplies in here."

They fought their way to Burgess' home. His transmitter was intact, but his antenna was down. So they rigged a makeshift antenna by wrapping several strands of wire around the house.

Burgess' first emergency call brought no answer. He tried another. This time he heard a feeble reply. It was a ham in New York. The New York ham relayed the call to another ham in Connecticut. A line of communications had been established out of the stricken town.

For the next three days Burgess and Marshall transmitted messages—more than eight hundred in all. They sent calls for food and drugs. They contacted relatives of victims and survivors. Burgess got only two hours of sleep in those three days.

By Sunday, power and communications facilities were restored. On Monday Burgess went back to work at his department store. That year the Paley Award, for the most notable contribution in ham radio to the American people, went to Wilson E. Burgess.

The legendry of amateur radio abounds in such instances of selfless service. In the Texas City explosions of some years back, it was an amateur operator who re-established communications with the outside world and brought in help. For thirty-six hours he stayed on the air, sticking to his key right through one of the earth-shaking blasts.

It was a ham who saved the day when a storm hit the lighthouse at Tillamook Rock, Oregon, knocking out its beacon, foghorn, and telephone. The ham, an assistant lighthouse keeper named Henry Jenkins, improvised a rig out of parts salvaged from an old radio receiver, plus some wire, bread wrappers, and a couple of brass doorknob plates. Thus he was able to send emergency warnings, via hams on the mainland, to shipping authorities, who, in turn, warned ships away from the treacherous and unlighted rock.

Not every ham exploit involves life-saving, of course. Often it's just a simple good deed, performed as a matter of course for somebody somewhere who is in need. So it was at Portland, Oregon, a few years ago, when a small girl stricken with leukemia expressed a wish for watermelon. Since that didn't happen to be watermelon time in Oregon, the hams got busy. They relayed messages along an impromptu transcontinental network all the way to Florida, whence two succulent watermelons were immediately dispatched to make a sick child very happy.

Along with fetching watermelons from Florida to Oregon and saving uncounted lives, hams have made some very notable contributions to the science of electronic communication. The average amateur is an inveterate and invincible experimenter. He's not satisfied merely to let a gadget do what it was designed to do. He must tinker with it, revamp it, and improve on it until it does everything except tie his shoes and bring in the evening paper.

Explained an official of the American Radio Relay League, the hams' parent organization in this country: "A ham's mind is always working at his hobby. He doesn't know when to quit, and the reason he solves so many problems and invents so many new devices is that he doesn't know what's impossible."

Ingenious Hams

The archives of "hamdom" are thus replete with stories of individual amateurs who sailed their air waves to new technological horizons. A mere ham, for instance, first convinced Westinghouse, many years ago, of the possibilities inherent in commercial broadcasting. It was likewise a ham who pioneered the use of short waves, till then considered useless. And when the Army finally bounced a radar beam off the moon, four out of the five experts conducting the experiment were hams.

"There's just no telling," said another big wheel in the ARRL, "what hams will uncover next."

But while they're uncovering new gimmicks, improving on old ones, and benefiting mankind in general, the hams also will be getting a whale of a lot of personal good out of their hobby. Amateur radio is like that—full of tangible values for the fellow who goes in for it.

It can be a steppingstone to a career—many an executive top-drawer engineer in radio and TV started out as a lowly ham. It's a short course—and a painless one—in geography and language. (Think of all the countries you talk to, half of which you probably never knew existed.)

And it's a perpetual lesson in good manners and ethics. For the amateur radio bands are twice as congested as Labor Day traffic, a continuous cacophony of thousands of competing voices and "dit-dahs." Without some kind of ethical code, there would be pure chaos. But the code prevails. It's simply: "Give the other guy a chance." And it works.

Ham radio is exciting, too. The amateur operator dwells constantly in that most intriguing and mysterious of all realms—the realm of the unknown. A flip of his dial brings him into intimate, over-the-back-fence contact with the world's farthest and strangest places.

As one ham has said, "You never know whom you'll talk to next. First you're talking to a Swede in the far north, where it's 35 below zero. Then you turn around and talk to a guy in Africa, where it's 130 in the shade. See what I mean? It's the unknown quantity."

Most of all, though, ham radio is a cement for world friendship. You can't help but feel a warm glow of affection for a fellow-ham you talk with every night, across an ocean and a couple of continents. His skin may be a different hue than yours, his way of life wholly alien to yours. But you can call each other by your first names and you know each other better than you know your next door neighbors.

I heard an avid ham put it pretty aptly.

"If amateur radio guys ran the world, there'd never be another war," he said. "Ham radio? It's the greatest friendship thing there ever was."

Thundermakers

By IRVING CRUMP

The Mountains-That-Walked were savage beasts who brought terror to Og, son of Og, on the homeward trail

Og, son of Og, crouched silently, studying the ground. There were wrinkles of worry on his forehead and dread in his eyes as he looked at the great footprints in the mud on the edge of the slough and darted fearful glances toward the tall, waving grass that fringed the swamp.

This boy of the cave people, who had so recently escaped from the tree people, after years of captivity, realized that there was a menace abroad in another way just as terrifying as the great apes. He knew that his life was in danger even as he squatted there trying to read the riddle in the mud.

The huge tracks were those of a Thundermaker, a Mountain-That-Walked, to mention only two of the many names by which the hairy mammoth was known to the cave people. But whether it was a family group, or a large migrating herd, which formed when they traveled from one section of the country to another, the cave boy could not be certain.

He had just come upon the tracks in the mud. There were many of them, and they were fresh. The makers of them had passed that way recently, perhaps during the time of darkness. The mud at the edge of the big footprint had not yet dried out and be-

gun to crumble as would have happened had the tracks been exposed to yesterday's sun. So the mountainous beasts with the shaggy hair, the tiny wicked eyes, the snaky trunks and the long, gleaming, up-curved tusks were not so long gone. They might indeed still be in the neighborhood. They could well be hidden in the tremendously tall grass, the plumed tops of which waved three times higher than the cave boy's head.

Young Og was trying hard to think, sometimes almost a painful process. He wanted to get back to the cave village where his father, Og, son of Fire, was the leader, and from which he had been stolen by the tree people so many years ago that he could scarcely remember when the ape mother had run off with him. The village was on the bank of a river that lay in the direction of the sunrise. But to travel that way the cave boy would have to cross that wide, grassy plain that skirted the edge of the big swamp. And to do that he would have to travel some of the trails that the hairy mammoths had made through the tall grass.

Suppose he met the great creatures while traveling one of those trails! The mere thought of it caused the cave boy to have a strange sensation at the roots of the hair on

111

his neck, while his heart pounded faster. Unless he could outrun the beasts and reach some kind of safety he knew he would be snatched up by a curling trunk, flung to the ground, and trampled to death under massive feet.

Young Og shuddered at the thought, and his eyes fearfully swept the wall of tall grass around him.

An erupting volcano had made it possible for Og, son of Og, to escape from the tree people. When, as a very young child, he had been stolen by an old mother ape to replace a baby she had lost, young Og had not been very popular among the anthropoids. They wanted to destroy him, and only the fighting prowess of the mother ape and her mate kept them from doing it. During the years that he was growing up, the ape people made repeated attempts to steal him from his foster parents and kill him because they superstitiously seemed to hold him accountable for any ill luck that befell their band of tree dwellers.

And when the volcano which towered above their valley home erupted, the apes were frightened into making a concerted attack on the two old apes in an effort to get at their human child. But in the furious melee in the treetops young Og found a chance to escape. And by floating down the river on a log and fighting off the tree dwellers with a flaming firebrand which he picked up from the ground, the cave boy managed to escape into a huge blanket of steam that filled the air where the lava from the fire mountain flowed into the river.

Young Og felt, as he made his way through the steam carrying the firebrand for a weapon, that he was moving through a fearsome place of swirling vapors toward the edge of the world. He was sure that at any moment he might step into space and disappear into a pit of monsters who were supposed to dwell in space. But fear of the apes drove him on, and he was truly amazed when the steam gradually thinned out and he found himself emerging into quite the same kind of country that he had come from on the other side of the area of steam.

It was rugged, rocky, treeless river shore, but it was sanctuary for the cave boy, for he knew none of the ape people would follow him through that barrier of weirdly twisting mist.

Breathing more freely, Og made his way down the river shore, finding food along the way; mussels in the shallows, snails clinging to the sides of the rocks, small fish caught in the landlocked pools, which he was able to grab with his hands, frogs, small turtles, and a variety of fare which both the apes and the cave people ate.

For a while he carried with him the hot and smoldering, but always diminishing, firebrand, for back in his memory were recollections of fire and its use by the cave people. In a vague way he knew that the use of fire marked one of the many differences between human beings and the creatures called the tree people. So he guarded his smoldering faggot carefully, making new fires each night by gathering driftwood and selecting a new firebrand each morning to carry with him.

But as careful as he was, he lost his fire. He stood the smoking brand up between some rocks while he tried to catch some fish in a pool left by the receding river. Forgetting to be careful, however, in his eagerness to catch his quarry, he made a great pother and splashed a lot of water around. Some of it knocked down the firebrand, and it fell into the water with a hissing sound. Though young Og frantically grabbed for it, he was too late. In that one careless moment, he lost his only instrument of protection and comfort.

It was a serious blow. For a while the cave boy was frightened. He crouched beside a rock and struggled to think. His mind went back the ten years or more that separated him from the time when, as a three- or four-year-old, he lived in the cave village with Og, son of Fire, and the cave people. And as he worked at this business of thinking, he was surprised to discover how many things he could recall about his people. He remembered that Og, his father, had a stone ax he carried in his belt, and a sharp stone

knife. He had a spear with a stone tip, a bow, and some feathered and stone-tipped arrows.

Most clearly of all, young Og remembered that his father had two black stones he called fire stones which he struck together and from which sparks flew. Og, son of Fire, trapped those sparks in some bark and wood punk and, breathing on them, made them break into flames. Thus did Og make his own fire.

Young Og decided that he was going to own all these things that his father possessed, but first he was going to have two of those black fire stones. So, as he traveled down the river shore, he constantly looked for pieces of stone that gave off sparks. Stone after stone he tested, and after a while he was pleased to discover that he had two which, when struck together, gave flashes of fire.

Then he found a thick growth of willows farther down the river and got some dried dead bark. For the better part of three days he worked and struggled to make fire. It was hard to trap those flying sparks and harder to fan them to flames. But after dozens of failures he finally succeeded in kindling his first fire, and he was tremendously elated. It gave him a great sense of achievement. His confidence in himself grew.

In his search for fire stones, he had found a sharp piece of flint that would serve as a knife, and another which made an excellent stone ax head. With tough willow bark and a stout shaft he made a rude but serviceable stone ax. With it and the stone knife sticking into the thong that held up the piece of bearskin about his middle, which was the only garment he had ever owned, he was as well equipped as any cave man ever had been until his father had found the secret of the bow and arrow.

His confidence in himself was almost boundless as he followed the river shore toward the southeast. But after ten days of traveling, suddenly the river swung toward the south, and then toward the southwest, and young Og realized that he was going in

113

almost the opposite direction from the way he wanted to travel. Far to the east he could see a blue line of mountains. It was beyond those highlands, he was sure, that the caves of his people were located in the bluffs along the river. So he must leave the river and head for the mountains.

The country had become softer and less rugged. To his right, young Og could see cattails and a great muddy slough in which grew tall, gaunt, weirdly shaped cypress trees laced together with hanging vines and bearded with gray moss. But edging the slough and reaching eastward and toward the north was a great plain of tall, plume-like, waving grass that the cave boy knew he could not traverse except by means of game trails. The tall grass was too thick for him to penetrate. But on the edge of the slough, where the plain and the swamp came together, the grass was not so tall, and Og felt that he might find a trail there. And if he could keep out of the mud of the swamp, he thought he could make his way eastward.

Confidently he started out and as he expected he found a trail skirting the swamp. Creatures of the wild came that way, and the path they followed made young Og's journey easier. He felt a sense of elation, and his confidence grew. In fact, he began to think that it would not be long before he reached those mountains on the other side of which he was sure his people dwelt.

But he had gone not much more than a fair walk when his confidence got a terrible jolt. The trail he followed seemed to be joined by other trails. Presently one, bigger and broader than the others, merged with it, and it was filled with giant footprints. This new trail was made by the mighty mammoths, the Mountains-That-Walked.

The great Thundermakers came that way; indeed some had passed not so long since and might still be close at hand. Perhaps they were watching him with cold little eyes from somewhere in the tall grass. Any instant they might come charging out at him with thunderous trumpeting to seize him in their snaky trunks or to try to trample him to death.

It was a fearsome place to be. As the cave boy crouched over the tracks and studied them and alternately swept with troubled gaze the wall of tall, waving grass that surrounded him, he found it hard to restrain an impulse to turn and dash madly back toward the river. Caution suggested that he clear out of there fast. But he knew that if he did, he would probably never find the courage to travel toward the sunrise again and he would never see his people. So, in spite of his fear, he restrained himself while he considered what to do.

The trail of the mammoths skirted the swamp for a distance and then seemed to swing in toward the center of the plain. Maybe at that point, he thought, he might find another branching trail, possibly one not used by the Thundermakers. The bend in the trail was just a short way ahead. Young Og decided to go at least that far. So gripping his stone ax determinedly, though he knew that weapon would be of small use against one of the giant creatures, he began to move cautiously down the trail, his restless eyes searching everywhere for danger.

He had not gone far before he came across discouraging evidence that the Thundermakers had traveled that trail not long since. The big footprints grew in number and there were fresh droppings in the trail. Young Og's courage weakened. He was sure that the great beasts were not too far away, perhaps even now feeding in the great meadow:

Suppose they should suddenly decide to come back along that trail! What could he do?

He was sure he could not outrun them, for, though huge in bulk, they were also capable of lumbering along with surprising swiftness. It would not be long before they would run him down.

The cave boy's eyes moved in the direction of the big swamp to his right. There lay his only possible salvation. He knew that the ponderous beasts were incapable of traveling through such a big slough. They were so heavy that they would bog down, and he felt sure that if he could reach any of those gaunt cypress trees he could probably climb beyond the reach of the creatures' snaky trunks. Then he could make his way through the treetops after the fashion of the great apes. So he resolved not to leave the vicinity of the slough no matter where the present trail led.

Soon he reached the bend where the mammoths' trail swung deeper into the grass country. As he hoped, there was a smaller trail branching off to skirt the edge of the big swamp. It was made by three-toed horses, small bands of which still roamed the country, though they were much larger now than their original ancestors.

Finding this branch trail gave the cave boy a sense of relief. There was no danger to be feared from these animals, for they were shy creatures who depended upon swiftness of foot to save them from their enemies.

Standing more erect and with fear diminishing, Og started along this new trail. It was marshy and difficult to follow, and often he had to flounder through hip-deep mud to get from one piece of firm ground to another. The horses did not mind this soft footing, for their three-toed feet were made to spread in soft earth and give them firmer footing. But these muddy parts of the trail were hard going for the cave boy, and now and then he had to pause on some hummock and catch his breath.

On one of these occasions he heard a strange rumbling noise that came to him from somewhere deeper in the tall grass. He was troubled by that sound. He could not identify it. He was sure it was not made by three-toed horses, nor did it seem to be any animal sound he could recognize. Cautiously but curiously, he crept forward, leaving the trail and venturing into the long grass in the direction from which the strange noise came. It grew louder, and as he parted the grass, he discovered its source with a sense of sudden alarm.

He was on the edge of a great tramped-down clearing in the wide meadow and in the clearing he beheld, with gripping fear, the largest herd of hairy mammoths he had ever seen. They seemed as many as the leaves on a tree, and that strange sound, like subdued thunder, he discovered came from their rumbling bellies as they tore up and ate great sheafs of sweet young grass that was growing up between the dried stalks of the old grass.

Og's fear almost paralyzed him. Yet he was fascinated, too.

Never had he seen so many of these great creatures. Nor had he ever been quite so close to them. There was a terrific number of cows and half-grown offspring. But there was one old bull who was bigger than any of the rest. He was the leader, and he was not eating as gluttonously as the other members of the herd. Instead, he moved about restlessly, his small eyes searching everywhere and his curling trunk constantly testing the air for danger smells.

The cave boy noticed, as he watched this huge creature, that his massive head and upraised trunk swung toward the point were he was crouching as his little eyes searched the tall grass.

Young Og's heart almost stopped, for he suddenly realized that the wind was from him toward the old bull and that the beast must have caught his scent. There suddenly became no doubt about this in the boy's mind, for the big bull began to move almost stealthily in his direction.

With pounding heart, Og tried cautiously and quietly to withdraw and reach the trail of the three-toed horses so that he could clear out of there fast. But even as he began to step carefully backward, suddenly the old bull mammoth caught the slight movement he made in the tall grass. With a thunderous trumpeting sound he alerted the rest of the herd, as he launched his great bulk into a tremendous charge.

There was a glare in his small eyes that boded ruthless destruction for whatever lurked in the tall grass, be it cave tiger or cave boy.

In panic Og fought his way back through the grass to the trail he had been following. Here he paused in a moment of uncertainty. But as more trumpeting sounded behind him,

and as the earth began to tremble under the heavy pounding of the entire herd following the old bull to wipe out whatever danger threatened them, Og knew that he must find safety immediately or he had not long to live.

His eyes fell on the nearest cypress tree not far out in the swamp. That was his only hope. Desperately he started down the trail heading for the reed-covered hummock at the end of which the tree grew almost by itself. As he ran, he was aware of the great bull, followed by scores of angry beasts, bursting through the tall grass to the edge of the slough.

Young Og was splashing through mud by

that time, trying desperately to reach the hummock. Once he staggered and fell in the slime, but he floundered swiftly to his feet and climbed out onto the higher ground of the hummock. Across this he ran, as loud trumpeting sounded behind him, and he could hear the threshing and splashing of the mammoths as they began to wade through the muck.

The cave boy realized, with sinking heart, when he reached the cypress tree, that it was not very big. One of those giant creatures could probably uproot it or break it down with his shoulders with ease. He looked desperately for a bigger tree. But there was none that he could reach in time. Indeed, it became a question whether he could even get safely up into this tree.

The old bull, with a number of other great creatures crowding behind him, was floundering through the slime to the hummock. And that small piece of earth began to tremble like jelly as they climbed up onto it and tried to reach the cave boy who was scrambling up into the branches.

It was a close call. Og realized it with sickening horror. The tip of the old bull's reaching trunk wiped across his muddy foot. If he had not pulled it upward with a cry of fear, the beast would have seized him and dragged him out of the tree. As it was, the brute trumpeted with the rage of frustration and wrapping his trunk around the tree he began to shake it so hard that Og had to cling fast with all his strength. He was sure that it would not be long before the angry beast would pull that tree down and finish him.

Fearfully, Og looked about for some way of escape from his predicament. Higher up he saw that long trailing lianas crawled across from the top of his tree to other cypresses farther out in the swamp. If he could reach those climbing vines, maybe he could travel across them, hand over hand like the ape people, to the next tree and so on through the swamp, always out of reach of the mammoths.

Despite the whipping of the tree as the old bull shook it, the cave boy climbed desperately upward. But as he reached the trailing vines in the top he became aware of a dull rending sound below him, as roots began to part and pull out of the mud. At the same time his tree began to lean perilously and he knew that the mammoths would soon have it down.

Even if he tried now to move across on the trailing vine, he would probably be pulled down with the crashing tree. There seemed to be only one possible way out of this situation. If he could cut a vine free and swing to the next tree by means of it, he would be safe. Otherwise, when this tree crashed, the mammoths would get him.

Seizing a stout trailer, he yanked his stone hatchet from the thong about his waist and began to hack desperately. He hadn't quite cut it through when the tree fell. But a sideways twist of the trunk parted the vine where he had been cutting it. Clutching it desperately, the cave boy launched himself into the air and started a wild swing toward the next tree as the cypress crashed.

The trumpeting mammoths fell upon it and, believing he was still in its branches, began eagerly to tread it down into the mud. But he did not linger to watch them, for the spectacle of their wrath was too blood-chilling for him to witness. Instead, he got away as fast as he could by means of the tree highway of the ape people. And he did not stop his panicky flight until the sound of the mammoths' angry trumpeting was lost.

Young Og never knew that in their terrible rage scores of the great creatures were bogged down in the swamp and lost their lives, all because they wanted to kill one lone cave boy. Nor could he know that eons later scientists would find the skulls, tusks and bones of these great beasts in the sun-baked mud of the old swamp and wonder how so many of them had perished in the same place and at the same time.

Amateur Sleuth

By ALAN HYND

Jimmy Campbell's shrewd deductions play an important part in this true story of the hired man who disappeared

For more than a year, Jimmy Campbell had done extra chores on his father's farm, and on neighboring farms, within fifty miles of Indianapolis, to get the money with which to buy every book he could find on the science of being a good detective. Jimmy wanted to be a detective above all else in the world. In fact he practically had his career planned at the age of sixteen. He intended to become a member of a big metropolitan police force and he hoped to become a real detective sooner or later.

So Jimmy took advantage of every opportunity he could find to read F.B.I. reports and otherwise become familiar with the techniques of the detection and apprehension of criminals.

Jimmy had definitely developed an acquaintance with the basic principles of crime detection—where to look for and how to develop fingerprints, the kind of questions to ask people who might know something pertinent to the solution of a crime, how to shadow people, and so on.

Jimmy knew that he would have to wait at least five years, until he was twenty-one, to join a police department—but he had no idea of just keeping his hard-won knowledge stored in his brain until that time. Not, that is, if there arose a legitimate opportunity to put it to use. Such an opportunity was to come to young Jimmy Campbell sooner than he had hoped it might.

Jimmy was kidded without mercy by his classmates in high school and by neighboring farmers and friends when they heard about his sleuthing ambition. "Hi'ya, Sherlock Holmes" was a favorite greeting he got at school. One of his teachers, when confronted by a classroom mystery, such as a misplaced book, would say, "We will have to put Detective Campbell on the job." Neighboring farmers, who had known his family for a couple of generations, wondered whether Jimmy had been seeing too many movies.

But Jimmy never was disturbed by any criticism. He'd just grin until his eyes were light-blue slits. He knew what he was doing.

There was one person aside from his father and mother (Jimmy was the only boy in the family, having two younger sisters) who thoroughly appreciated his ambition. That was Don Turner, the hired man. Turner was an open-faced big fellow in his twenties who had come to work on the Campbell acres a few years before and who had stayed on to be one of the family.

"Don't let that kiddin' get under your skin, Jimmy," he would say. "Let 'em call you Sherlock Holmes or anything else they want to. You stick to bein' a detective if you want to."

It was Don Turner himself who became a principal in Jimmy Campbell's first mystery.

One bright morning in July, when farm work was at its heaviest, Don Turner, who had fixed up quarters for himself over the milk shed, didn't show up for breakfast. Don must be sick, thought Jimmy. He told his father and mother he'd go and see. What he saw was an empty room and a bunk that hadn't been slept in.

Don Turner didn't own much in the way of worldly goods, but what he owned had disappeared. There wasn't a thing belonging to Don in his quarters.

"I'm surprised at Don," said Jimmy's father, who, when Jimmy hadn't returned to the house, had joined him above the milk shed. "I'd of thought that if he decided to go and work someplace else at least he'd have given me notice, especially at this time of year when the work's so heavy and help's so short."

Jimmy just stood there biting his lower lip.

"You always do that when somethin's on your mind, son," said Mr. Campbell. "What are you thinkin' now?"

What Jimmy was thinking, and he didn't hesitate to say so, was that Don Turner had not disappeared *voluntarily*.

His father grew slightly impatient. "Why, his bed ain't been slept in and"—the father waved an arm and encompassed the quarters—"he's packed up everything he owned and taken it with him."

"I can't explain it in words, Dad," said Jimmy. "It's just that Don wasn't the kind of fellow to do a thing like that. Those books I read—they teach you to size up a man's character. Don had a fine character; he'd never do anything sneaky." Jimmy looked around the quarters. "Please don't touch anything, Dad," he said.

Morgan Campbell stared hard at his son. "You'll have to prove it to *me,*" he said and walked away.

If Jimmy was going to work on the mystery of Don Turner's disappearance he would have to do it at nights, when he wasn't needed for chores on the farm—chores that would be doubly hard, now that Don was gone. All that day, while he helped his dad in the fields, Jimmy turned his mind back to conversations he had had with Don.

Don had been a taciturn sort of fellow, so the conversations had not been very enlightening. Once, though, only a few weeks before, Don had mentioned something about maybe getting married some day—to a pretty waitress who worked in the village.

Jimmy got an early bus to the village that evening. There were only two restaurants and a diner in the village, so his field of investigation was not great.

He went into the larger of the two restaurants first. He spoke to the cashier—a kindly man with eyeglasses. He explained who he was, further explained that Don Turner had disappeared, then asked the cashier if he would be kind enough to question the waitresses and find out if any of them knew Don.

One of the waitresses said she knew Don. "Did you know him very well?" asked Jimmy. "Well enough to maybe marry him some day?"

The waitress laughed. "No, not *that* well, young man. You should speak to Clara Markel in the diner on the edge of town. She's *very* sweet on Don and has been going steady with him."

Miss Markel was a charming girl of perhaps twenty-two, with soft brown hair and a candid smile. Yes, she admitted to Jimmy between serving customers, she was engaged to Don.

What was the matter with Don, though? Miss Markel was good and angry at him. He had had a date to meet her the night before, when she got through work in the diner at ten, but he had not shown up. And he had not communicated with her to explain his absence.

"I thought maybe I had got the nights mixed and that he would show up tonight," said Miss Markel to Jimmy. "But now that you say he's disappeared, why, young man, that's *serious*. We've got to do something about it."

Jimmy had learned that people often possess information of value in an investigation but don't think to mention it. Skillful questioning is, therefore, necessary.

"Would you mind telling me, Miss Markel," said Jimmy, "if you and Don planned to do anything special last night?"

"Well, something special and important was to *happen,* if that's what you mean. We were to become formally engaged."

"You mean Don was going to give you an engagement ring?"

The waitress nodded.

"May I ask how you knew he was going to give you the ring last night, Miss Markel?"

"Yes. Don said he would have the ring with him when he picked me up at ten."

"Did he say anything about where he was going to get the ring?"

"Now that you speak of it, he did say something about picking the ring up on the way to meet me."

Where would Don have picked up an engagement ring on his way to see his girl?

Jimmy had learned about deduction too. Don wouldn't have had the opportunity to do much traveling to get the ring between the time he had left the farm the evening before and the time he had been due to call for the waitress. Thus, he had probably planned to pick up the ring right in the village—at Arpel's, which was the only jewelry store in the immediate region.

Arpel's was closed for the night when Jimmy arrived at his deduction. But he went into a telephone booth, right at the end of the diner, and phoned Jonathan Arpel, proprietor of the store, at his home.

Jimmy's deduction paid off. Mr. Arpel said yes, Don Turner had been in about nine-thirty the night before to pick up a diamond ring that he had had on order for several weeks. Mr. Arpel had kept his store open after the usual closing time to wait for Don, who had come to town on the bus that arrived at nine-thirty.

"Could you give me more details about what the ring looked like?" asked Jimmy.

Mr. Arpel, to whom Jimmy explained why he was asking the questions, was glad to oblige. The ring had contained a blue-white diamond, weighing one and one-eighths carats, and had been set in white gold with a small emerald chip on each side of the diamond. The jewel had cost $385. Don, who had previously paid for it, put the box containing the ring in his pocket, and walked out of the Arpel establishment whistling. That had been about a quarter to ten.

Jimmy told Miss Markel what Mr. Arpel had told him. The information developed from the jeweler indicated that Don Turner had vanished, right on the streets of the village, between a quarter to ten, when he had left the Arpel store, and ten o'clock, when he had been due at the diner to pick up his fiancée. The diner was less than a ten-minute brisk walk from the jewelry store.

It seemed obvious to the young, unofficial sleuth that a crime had been committed—the crime of robbery. Somebody had known that Don Turner was carrying that valuable ring and had taken it from him. But where had the crime been committed, and where was Don Turner now?

Miss Markel had begun to cry and some of the patrons in the diner were wondering what was up.

"Don't worry," Jimmy assured her. "I'll find out what happened last night."

Jimmy had a feeling that he should report the whole thing to the police. In fact he intended to do so. But he wished he had more information to make sure Don hadn't had a last minute change of heart and run away.

Jimmy consulted his watch. It was only nine o'clock now. The last bus that would take him back to the farm left at eleven. He had two hours to devote to the mystery tonight; he would think a little longer, then call the police.

It seemed likely to Jimmy that Don Turner had gone direct from Arpel's store toward the diner. Jimmy went to Arpel's, which was on the same street as the diner, only closer to the center of the village, and began to take route he figured Don had taken. Halfway between Arpel's and the diner, he found himself passing through a block which would have been pitch dark at the time Don had passed through the block, and which was desolation itself.

There was a stretch of uncleared ground, thick with trees, on one side of the street, and on the other side was an abandoned metals factory. Very few persons had reason to pass through that particular block after dark.

The crime detection books had taught Jimmy to put himself in the shoes of possible suspects, the better to figure out what they had done. So now he put himself in the shoes of the person or persons who might have committed the crime. He decided first that the criminal or criminals were not strangers in the village. Rather, they (and Jimmy had the hunch that there had been at least two men involved in the crime) knew the village and its inhabitants. They had probably seen Don Turner picking up the ring and followed him. Had the criminals been strangers in town, lingering just long enough to commit a crime, they would not have been likely to follow one individual who made a purchase at Arpel's; they would have been more likely to rob the jewelry store itself.

All right, then. If the criminals were local men, the chances were they had slipped up behind Don Turner and knocked him into unconsciousness. In that way, Don would not have been able to see and recognize them. Jimmy's line of reasoning seemed to be corroborated by the fact that Don's quarters at the farm had been stripped of all his belongings.

Only local men would have known where their victim lived; the criminals would have gone to Don's quarters and stripped it to make it look as if Don's disappearance had been voluntary. Thus, with no suspicion aroused, they would have more time to cover their tracks and dispose of their loot in a pawnshop somewhere.

Jimmy stood there, in the deepening gloom of the desolate block, looking with mounting suspicion at the abandoned metals factory. He knew he should call the police, but something impelled him to go inside. He had covered the first floor, without results, and had descended to the basement when he heard a faint sound. It was, he knew, the sound of a human being, a man in pain.

That was how Jimmy Campbell found Don Turner. Don, the man who had told him not to waver in his ambition to be a detective, had been slugged about the head to within a whisper of death.

Jimmy raced out into the street and stopped the first man he found. He told the man what he had discovered in the abandoned factory and the man rushed to the nearest phone and called the county hospital. The doctors who came said that Jimmy had arrived at the factory none too soon. Don Turner had lost much blood; had Jimmy not found him when he did, it was doubtful if Don would have lived through the night.

Don was in no condition to be questioned in detail. He did say enough, however, to Sheriff Harold Cross to verify Jimmy's reconstruction of the crime. He had been hit from behind and knocked unconscious. He had no idea who had hit him.

Now that the case was in the hands of the duly-constituted authorities, Jimmy Campbell was out of it—almost. The ring turned up in an Indianapolis pawnshop the following day. It had been pawned by a fellow with red hair. That was all the pawnbroker knew about the criminal: he had red hair. Such a description could have fitted many people.

But Jimmy Campbell knew something the authorities didn't know. The criminals, in going to Don Turner's quarters and taking their victim's belongings to create the impression that Don had left voluntarily, had handled many objects.

Jimmy looked around Don's quarters, trying to figure out just what the criminals had touched and left their prints on. They had, he decided, touched the plastic knobs of a dresser where Don had kept his clothes; the dresser drawers, emptied, had been open when Don's disappearance had been discovered. A good thing, mused Jimmy, that he had asked his folks not to touch anything in the room.

Jimmy had developed fingerprints many a time with a fingerprint kit his dad had given him for a Christmas present. But this was too important a case for him to take a chance on; he would leave the development of *these* prints to the authorities. He informed his father of the potential value of an examination of the dresser drawer knobs and Mr. Campbell telephoned to Sheriff Cross. The sheriff, who himself had taken a course in crime-detection, at the F.B.I. in Washington,

went out to the Campbell farm and removed the drawers.

The knobs were heavy with prints—the prints of two men. Sheriff Cross sent the impressions to the F.B.I. Laboratory in Washington, where the prints of countless thousands of men with criminal records are on file. Back came the answer: The prints were those of William (Red) Hawkins and Ed (Big Ed) Wilkinson, men with criminal records who lived only two miles from the village where the crime was committed. Both Hawkins and Wilkinson had been released from prison less than a year previously and had been presumed to have reformed.

On the basis of the prints developed on the knobs turned over to the sheriff through the sleuthing of Jimmy Campbell, Hawkins and Wilkinson were picked up at their homes. They denied their guilt.

The pawnshop proprietor in Indianapolis, however, made a positive identification of William (Red) Hawkins as the man with red hair who had, the day after the crime, pawned the ring taken from Don Turner. In the face of the identification, Hawkins confessed, implicating his partner, Wilkinson.

Wilkinson had been in the Post Office the morning of the crime when Arpel the jeweler had received the ring through the registered mails, opened it and remarked to the Postmaster that Don Turner was calling at his shop for it that night.

Both men were sent to prison.

Don Turner recovered and returned to his work on the farm. A year afterward, Jimmy Campbell fulfilled the first step toward his life's ambition by taking and passing his examinations for patrolman. With his patrolman's experience, he now stands on the threshold of achieving his goal—becoming a detective.

Sea Trap

By E. L. BABCOCK

Surrounded by a school of giant fish, a skindiver struggles to keep his battered skiff afloat

The boy came out of the inlet in the ghost-light of dawn and turned north in the ocean, his boat a fourteen-foot skiff. There was no sign to him that this still and cool morning was not to be as many such mornings. Had there been, because of a fear, old and lurking in him, he would have turned back.

Here off the south Florida coast the Atlantic lay in flat summer calm, the surface a luminous glassy gray, with no movement or sound inshore save the wake and tat-tat-tat of the outboard. Only at a point far out on the horizon were there dark dots of other boats, the fleet of commercial fishermen after the king mackerel. For a moment the boy looked out at the fishing boats, at the whole expanse of the sea. Then he looked away, his face tightened and emptied of expression.

He was a Conch, of a swarthy-skinned people, part British, part Spanish, and perhaps part Negro, who crossed from the Bahamas in the young years of the century to form fishing villages on the Florida coast. In the way of his people, he had planned the sea as his bread and his beloved. But now that the time approached to take his place among the fishermen, he was plagued with the contradiction that had been in him for as long as he could remember. For as he loved the sea, he also shrank from the watery vastness and the unknown depths, a shrinking born from the memory that long ago his father had been lost at sea.

Because of this he was a target for scorn among his people. On the fishing docks he was a laughingstock and outcast, and when as now he looked on those who fished the deep ocean, he turned his own contempt on his shrinking. But it stayed, tormenting and foolish in him.

Close to shore he took the skiff north, passing a cluster of beach-side cottages where people slept and would go on sleeping for hours now on this Sunday morning. After a mile he came to where the water was broken by dark rocks. This was a reef of coral formation common to the coast. From the beach the reef ran out like a jetty southward for a hundred yards or so at an acute angle to shore. A small triangular cove was formed within, and the boy took his boat into it through the entrance that was the open base of the triangle between reef tip and beach.

When the wind was light and from the west all night, when the ocean was in flat calm, the boy came out like this into the cove to spearfish. He came because he was drawn to the sea as a moth to a candle flame. There was a need in him for the sight and sound and smell of the Atlantic. He chose the cove because he thought of it as a place protected from the deep ocean.

He cut his motor. With a small splash that broke the morning stillness he dropped anchor at a point halfway between reef and beach, in six or seven feet of dark water that

123

cleared as the light increased. From habit he checked wind and tide, and it was in doing so that he first saw the dark movement in the sea a mile or so out beyond the reef.

The darkness was stirring, widespread and strange, beneath the surface of the water, and it seemed to have a shoreward motion. The boy peered at it through the early light, puzzled. His mind could only call it seaweed or tide rip, although it was not quite like either. But then his attention left it, drawn back to the cove and his purpose, for a good-sized fish flicked the surface near the skiff. He took up his speargun and loaded the simple weapon.

The barbed arrow, fitted into a groove along the top of the wooden frame, was propelled out by a rubberband sling and trigger mechanism and was retrieved, with or without quarry, by an attached heavy fishing line rigged on a reel on the gun's underside. The boy fitted a mask of glass and rubber over his face and lowered himself into the sea that differed little in temperature from the summer air, the speargun held against him.

He swam on the surface toward the reef. In the east the sun rose behind horizon clouds. But there was light enough to see beneath water, and the boy dove where the reef wall began its rise. Through the gray-green underwater he flutter-kicked slowly over dark gray rocks broken by an occasional formation of surprising brick-red.

These were deeply creviced rocks rising in stepped ledges from the sand ocean floor. They were the haunt of the grouper and snapper the boy sought, but were not rocks to anchor to nor climb upon. Their barnacle-crusted planes were like the sides of a grater, lacerating to the touch.

The boy saw with surprise that there were bonito in the cove. The fat green and silver fish streaked above him just beneath the surface. His mind was a storehouse of the lore of fish and sea, and he searched through it for explanation of this. Bonito belonged not here but to the deep ocean out beyond the wall of reef. Never in all the times he had spearfished had he seen bonito in shallow, sheltered water such as the cove. Also,

the bonito moved in a darting panic, when among the bottom fish of the cove they should have no natural enemies. His swimming slowed, his mind nagged by the small strangenesses of the morning.

He spotted then the ponderous brown bulk of a grouper, not large but a satisfactory prize. The arrow streaked, trailing line. The boy retrieved it, holding the impaled and flapping fish above him as he surfaced. At the boat he freed the arrow, tossed the grouper into a gunny sack and turned back in toward the reef.

As he sucked in air to dive again, he faced south and the ocean beyond the cove entrance. Suddenly he let his breath go. In a swirling turn he reached the skiff and dropped the speargun into the hull and climbed aboard. He stood upon the center seat and stared south.

He saw that his eyes at water level had not deceived him. The strange dark movement he had marked earlier in the open sea was now but little east and slightly south of the cove. Clearly now it was neither tide rip nor seaweed, and he had not before estimated its size as so great. It moved shoreward like a dark stain spreading beneath water. It came rapidly, and with a zigzagging that could bring it inside the reef into the cove. It was, the boy knew, what had driven the bonito into the cove. Fear touched him, bringing with it an urgent desire to leave the cove.

He dropped to his knees and pulled at the anchor line, but he was not in time. The water of the cove entrance was filled with the moving darkness, and the cove was invaded before the anchor was aboard.

The boy gaped into the water, the anchor line gone slack in his hands, as within seconds the dark movement approached the boat and passed around and beneath it. Through a standstill of shock he made out forms, large and swift-swimming. He saw then that this was a school of tightly packed great dark fish, likely a hundred or more and of a size outlandish in the small cove, huge fish that swam with a driven purposefulness, not feeding. He remembered the

fleeing bonito and knew that they had only believed themselves pursued. The intent of this dark massive school was not food.

In the next moments the intent became clear. As at a signal the spearhead of the school swerved toward the cove shore. The fish began splashing rolls. Black whale-like bodies arched above water, some longer than twenty feet. The rolling took the first onrush of the school into the surf that lapped the beach, water far too shallow for the school. Thick dorsal fins and swollen bulbous foreheads floundered in the surf. Heavy black tails cracked the shallow wash. Yet the fish made no attempt to veer away from the beach. Deliberately the vanguard thrashed on, onto the sand where, once exposed, the black bodies no longer contorted. They became queerly still, wet black hides gleaming in the light.

At this the boy knew them, and his shock left him in the excitement of recognition.

He knew these fish from tales told long ago by his father and from time to time by others of the fishermen, not from his own experience. Few men had known them like this. These were the blackfish, the black whales, small for their species, that some called pilot whales or pot heads. They lived commonly and in great numbers far out in the ocean on the east side of the Gulf Stream, seldom coming in close to shore. But at times they came—whole schools of them came to beach themselves like this, and once beached they died from the parching of their bodies by sun and wind. These were animals driven to their deaths by some strange instinct which men do not yet completely understand, a primitive act, left over from the dimness of time. Two years before the boy

had heard of such a school beached at St. Augustine.

But why had this school come into the small cove with its short beach? Why had these fish not beached on the endless stretch of sand beyond the cove to north and south? Only the zigzaging as the school approached shore accounted for it. Mere chance.

Roughly the boy was jarred from speculation. The skiff shuddered abruptly, violently, then wallowed, and he was thrown to his knees. The hull, he realized with a fresh shock, had been stoutly rammed. He pulled up against the rocking boat. He saw around him what he had missed in his wonder, and in the morning coolness a sudden sweat broke out on his body.

He saw that many blackfish still swam about the boat and that these had begun a quickened rolling, now seemingly directionless. These were fully half the school, a crowding of the great fish, far too many to swim freely in the shallow confines of the cove. The heavy black bodies collided, and so the boat had been struck. The rolling was growing to a frenzy that thrashed the sea.

Now he saw the reason for the frenzy. The short cove beach was covered completely by the inert bodies of the first of the school, and these still-swimming fish were blocked from beaching. Their rolls were not as directionless as they appeared, but were a thwarted turning out toward the reef wall and from there a renewed and powerful lunging shoreward again and again in futile attempts to beach.

None turned back toward the cove entrance and the free beach beyond, and with a sick certainty the boy knew that none would. These were animals in the pattern of mass instinct, unswerving follow-the-leader. They would keep to their futile struggle to beach within the little cove. Blinded by instinct, they were trapped in the cove.

And as they were trapped, he was trapped. Surrounded by the thrashing school, the boat had been rammed once, and in the growing frenzy it would be rammed again. How long before the skiff would break up? Then he would be alone in the water, and his body would fare no better than the boat. He would be struck until he was drowned in the maul of fish.

He felt a choking fear in him that brought him to his feet in the rocking boat, searching the triangle of cove for an escape.

To the west of him the cove beach was as blocked to the boat as to the swimming fish. He dared not even move in closer to shore into more shallow water, for the most violent rolling of the school was in there. To the east the wall of reef was no refuge but another danger. There the boat could be sunk most quickly of all if driven on rock by the lunging of a blackfish, and the boy's flesh shrank from the remembered feel of barnacled rock.

He saw he could only try directly to reach the cove entrance and the free water beyond. That course lay through the thick of the school, but he was without choice. Desperately he began to haul at the anchor line.

But the hauling became a senseless tug-of-war. The rope burned back out through his hands as the blackfish struck it. The boat was rammed for the second time, this time from beneath, and rocked wildly. He was wasting his time and strength on the line, the boy saw in his desperation. With the fish knife from the sheath at his waist he cut the line, and the boat drifted free in the school.

He turned to the outboard. The motor spluttered and caught, and the boat moved under power.

He began a jagged tight-watched course toward the cove entrance. When the rolling fish came toward the boat, he veered sharply, at times turning in complete, tight circles. His progress was scant and dismaying in the churn of the school.

The sudden unseen lunge of a blackfish caught the hull from beneath, a heavy but glancing blow at the stern. The boat skidded sideways, and the boy's breath made a labored sound in his throat as he heard the motor race crazily and felt the propeller spin free and powerless.

Without looking, he knew the shear pin was broken.

Beneath the seat he kept spares wrapped in tinfoil. Clumsy in the wallowing and his driven haste, he unfastened the motor and lifted it into the boat. But before he could replace the pin, the boat was rammed with a direct and sickening impact. There was the crack of splintering wood. Water gushed through the laid-open curve of hull.

He had nothing with which to stop up the hole. In the swirl of water that covered his feet he could not even make out the size of the damage done by the fish. With the pail kept aboard he began to bail in frantic rhythm until he saw the uselessness against water that rose rapidly above the seat. The fear in him swelled to panic. Wildly he threw over the motor and can of gasoline. But in minutes the boat was completely awash, the water floating his body full-length, belly-down in the hull, his hands clutching the sides that were a bare inch out of the water.

Under him the hull settled. But the skiff did not sink, and he realized that the hull would ride that way for a while. Its shell would be his last shield against the fish. Through the sound of his heavy breathing he wondered, though, why he bothered to count on the boat.

The frenzy of the fish around him had increased. Further collision would come soon, and collision, now that the hull was all but submerged and without stability, would capsize it or smash it beyond floating.

He was filled again with the dreadful knowledge of how it would be in the water without the boat, how it would be to have his body struck again and again by the blackfish.

He would drown here in this familiar cove not ten yards from shore.

A physical sickness swept him, and for

seconds he felt nothing else. Slowly the sickness receded, and it seemed a draining of all feeling from him. Curiously now he felt little at all, only a numbness. In his foolish floating position, hands gripping the gunwales, he waited with almost a listlessness for the final blows of the blackfish on the shell of the boat.

The blows came. The school rocked and splintered the hull. The planking listed sharply. The rolling of the blackfish came now nearly over the washed gunwales. The boy's arm was grazed by the coarse black hide of a fish, and his arm bled. He felt the sharp sting of salt water on it.

At the pain an anger rose suddenly in him. His body twisted. Doubling up his legs, he kicked savagely at the fish. As he did, his thigh struck an object that floated beside him in the boat. In his anger he freed a hand and grasped the thing. It was the speargun. He felt a scornful surprise that he had not thrown it over along with the motor and gas can. He pushed it from him.

But the feel of the gun stayed in his hand and in his brain. A thought possessed him. A fantastic thought. Yet was it any more fantastic than this that had trapped him?

Caught between panic and anger, his brain turned over the thought. It was this: He could not fight the huge fish themselves, but it was not the fish—not of their free will—that had trapped him; this thrashing frenzy around him was the working of instinct, and if he had to fight anything, it was this.

His body became still in the hull. The beginning of a plan came to him. His hand reached out and took the speargun.

Cautiously then he worked himself to one side of the skiff and held to the gunwale with his armpit, trying to maintain the balance of the hull. With his freed hand he checked the gun. It was loaded from his last dive, the barbed arrow in the groove along the top of the frame, the reel of heavy fishing line below.

Carefully, he curled himself against the submerged hull, knowing clearly now what he would try.

The drift of the boat was east toward the reef, into the boiling outer turns of the school. As a blackfish rolled in an arc that brought it crashing against the washed bow, the boy aimed the speargun. The arrow hissed through air. The barb sank home in the body of the blackfish below the dorsal fin. But the drag was set too tight on the reel of the gun.

As the fish plunged away, the line broke.

For a sickened moment the boy did not search in the hull for other arrows. He carried others, but the likelihood that they had not been lost through the broken planks was small. Finally he made himself search with one hand and his bare feet. Under the lip of the stern seat he felt one. He wrenched it to him, hooked monkey-fashion between his toes.

He held the gun between his drawn-up knees as he rigged the second arrow. While he worked, the boat was struck and spun crazily in half-circles. At times he could do nothing but cling to gun and boat in the motion, unable to pay heed to the precarious balance of the hull. He was not capsized, but he knew such luck would not hold. He had little time left to rig the gun. Little time for anything. He put the reel on the free spool, and finally he was ready again.

The roll of a blackfish came at the boat, and the boy aimed. The arrow sank in the dark body beneath the dorsal fin in a fleshy part as before. The fish lunged away, and this time the line went out with it. The fish rolled on shoreward oblivious to the barb in its flesh, oblivious to all but the instinct to reach the beach.

At the barrier of the beached fish, the speared one swerved back out toward the boat and reef in the pattern of the school, readying to lunge shoreward again. The boy could only watch it. As long as the rolling went on, he could do nothing more. With a pounding heart he played the line, knowing that it could be cut or hopelessly tangled by others of the school.

As he felt a little slack, he reeled in, striving to keep the line just taut between boat and fish. He felt more slack and his heart bounded as he felt the fish become still.

He tightened the drag on the reel. Deliberately then he worked the line with jerks as strong as he could muster and still maintain his hold on the boat. He felt the fish stir, and he jerked with all his might on the line, praying as the barb tore at the flesh of the animal.

The fish began to swim, slowly at first, then with a sudden rise of power. It was a swimming different from the shoreward rolling of before. It was the run of a fish aware of pain, a fish in flight.

With a fierce thrill the boy knew that so far his plan worked. Through the pain of the embedded barb, he had roused the blackfish from the trance of instinct. But it was only half his plan. With a surging of breath he let out more line.

The boat began to move as the fish moved, towed by the speared animal, as a speedboat might tow a submerged surfboard, and the boy clung as he would have clung to a surfboard. Discovering its confinement, the fish, aroused, circled the cove in darting runs. The boat circled heavily behind, a dead weight on the line.

Intently the boy played the line that could still tangle into slack uselessness or break from the weight of the boat. With it he worked to avoid others of the school but not with success. The skiff was struck again and again. The blackfish towed finally a shambled skeleton of hull that could not float beyond another blow.

Then the fish broke from circling. There was a run northward toward the rock-bound apex of the triangle of cove. Then—southward.

The boy's breath exploded from him. "Find the way out," he said aloud and hoarsely. "Find the way out."

The fish ran south through the churning school. It gained the water of the entrance in a harassed escape from the cove, towing the wrecked skiff behind. The boy was pulled free of the cove. For fifty yards due south beyond the entrance he was pulled before he remembered to cut the line.

He rolled from the hull. He found himself in five feet of water, the speargun clutched in his hands, and he made a half-swimming way to shore. On the beach he dropped with closed eyes, his body trembling with exhaustion, his hands digging into the good coarse sand beneath him.

Finally he raised himself and turned back toward the sea. He looked at the vast Atlantic, and he felt his fear, old and lurking. But against it he put the knowing of what he had done this morning. He had pitted his brain against a violence of the sea as blind and unlikely as he would ever know—and he had triumphed.

He gazed on the whole of the ocean, the uncertain and unknown waters, and he did not turn away. He thought of fishing the vast and deep Atlantic, and he did not turn away.

El Berty Rapido

By WILLIAM F. HALLSTEAD

Outnumbered five to one, De Cabeza outflanks his enemy but can't outsmart his ally

We were flying across the southern border of Honduras at five thousand feet. I never thought the old boiler factory would go that high, myself. The day was perfect; the only clouds in the Central American sky were high wispy cirrus. The sun beat the wild country below us with shimmering heat, but up where we flew, it was cool. Then the rattling engine of our open cockpit biplane stuttered, skipped, and suddenly the day was not so perfect!

I looked around at Berty, piloting in the rear cockpit. He was peering over the side through his big goggles, so I looked down, too. There was a little town not far ahead. I saw the small cluster of white buildings, a dirt road straggling down from the hills, but I didn't see any airport.

The Kinner engine was growing rockier every minute. I caught Berty's eye. He gave me one of those tight grins of his and shrugged. This was just his meat! The nose of our plane dropped below the jagged horizon as we made a long curving dive toward the distant village.

Maybe you've heard that the old-timers in the aviation racket had to be smart cookies. This pal of mine was a smart cookie and then some. All this happened in 1931, just four years after Lindbergh flew the Atlantic.

It was the year there was a revolution in Peru, Great Britain suspended the gold standard, and the Perth Amboy Title Company in New Jersey built an airplane called the Bird.

I met Berty Linnaker at a little one-horse airport near Lancaster, Pennsylvania. I was working part-time as engine-greaser and wood-butcher for bread-and-butter money; Berty was working on his dad's farm and spending every nickel he earned on flying instructions.

He was a tall, skinny blond kid with sharp blue eyes and a pointed nose; would've looked more at home on a pinto pony than in the cockpit of the birdcage Curtis-Jenny we used for training.

Berty was nineteen and a nut for travel—how big a nut I had no idea until one morning early in May. He bounded into the rickety frame hangar. "Hey, Jim! Drop your cleaver and let's go to the Gulf of Mexico."

And I thought he was kidding.

"There's an airplane dealer getting started in town," he went on, "wants me to fly one of his planes to the Gulf and back. We get the trip—he gets the publicity."

An independent twenty-one, I closed my tool kit, and that was the end of that job. And it would have worked out okay if Berty wasn't so crazy to eat up mileage.

The Bird was delivered in two days. It was a beautiful ship, cream with red markings: NC 94V. The pilot's cockpit was behind a big open compartment where three passengers could park.

We set off looking like fugitives from silent movies in tight riding breeches and turtleneck sweaters. Leather helmets and huge goggles topped off our rigs.

I sat in front crammed between the luggage, and Berty flew from the rear cockpit. I read the engine manual from Lancaster to Raleigh; between Carolina and Birmingham, I looked over the manufacturer's construction book. After we reached New Orleans we had to sit out two days' rain. I had run out of booklets by then, and I had time to realize what had happened. We'd made the Gulf!

It had been such a short haul that when Berty jumped out of the hotel room chair and blurted out another stroke of ingenuity, I automatically said sure.

"We're gonna do that dealer one better," Berty yelped. "We'll take the crate to Panama."

That's how we found ourselves over this valley near the Honduras border one June morning—with engine trouble.

My heart was hammering on top of my throat as Berty aimed the Bird toward the little town ahead of us. We were losing altitude like a penguin. But Berty knew what he was doing; he had a field picked out. It was a large plot a mile outside town, and as we sank lower, I saw it was a cornfield. The crop was about a foot high.

There was no altitude to spare, so Berty dived straight in. As we settled, I spotted a bunch of people running toward us from town. This scene was blotted out by a knoll that rose up past us as we plowed into the corn. The soft earth killed our landing roll. Berty cut the switch.

He lifted his lean body from the cockpit. He'd shoved his goggles up on his forehead, and his face twisted in a grin.

"Best landing I ever made south of Mexico!" he announced.

I didn't have time to think up an answer. A great yo-ho and whooping welled over the hill, and a row of wild faces appeared on the crest of the rise. In five seconds, we were surrounded by rabid men, women, children, and dogs. They danced around us in a frenzy and brandished pitchforks, clubs and knives.

The kids tossed dirt clods. They yammered away in a machine gun lingo; even the dogs barked a strange way.

Berty and I gave up explanations or just *trying* to be friendly. We retreated to the Bird and tried not to be unfriendly. It was a hard thing not to be, because one little kid picked up a rock and bounced it off the rudder. Berty looked at the hole and groaned.

All the kids got the idea. Stones came like hail. The Bird was going to be shredded, and we'd have a crop of bruises ourselves. Then all activity stopped.

Berty looked at me and gave that little deadpan shrug. Our welcoming committee was staring up the hill. It was so quiet you could hear a pebble drop. I heard the kids drop some.

A lumbering black horse stood on the slope. On it, in a snappy green uniform, sat a huge man. He wore a monstrous black leather pistol belt. The pistol was in his fist like an unmounted cannon. He led his charger down the slope and shouted at the crowd.

"Vaya, vaya!"

They fell back and he rode toward us. I made a sort of bow and tried a little Spanish. Very little.

"Uh . . . *mucho gracias, amigo,*" I struggled. "I . . . uh, that is, we didn't mean to—"

The horseman held up a silencing hand. He was a stocky fellow with a square jaw, natty mustache, and a big round nose.

"Oh, no," he said. "I know you did. I am speak the American very good. I am in charge of this town, Jalagua. Capitan Dolor De Cabeza, I am." He swept off his visored military cap and bowed over his pistol.

We bowed back. The crowd liked this.

"You must excuse the people," De Cabeza went on, "but they do not understand. You are stranger and who is strange is to them from Montegro."

"Montegro?" I said.

De Cabeza's heavy face tightened, and his bulbous nose turned an angry red. "You are not from Montegro, is it?"

"Gosh, no," Berty said. "We ain't even met him."

The captain relaxed. "He is not a he, Señores. He is a village. Like this one of Jalagua."

He spurred his horse and rode slowly around our plane, inspecting it carefully. "You have papers, eh? The official papers? Allow me to see your official papers, Señores!"

"Papers?" I began. "We haven't—"

Berty stepped on my foot. "One moment, Capitan," he broke in.

I knew Berty, so I kept quiet. He ran to the plane, rummaged around and returned. "Our papers, Capitan." He handed over a batch of documents.

The capitan shuffled through the stuff with a happy smile. He jammed his revolver back in its holster.

"What did you give him?" I whispered.

Berty said, "Shh."

The officer handed the papers back one by one. I looked over Berty's shoulder. The registration certificate for the Bird, passports, Pennsylvania driver's license.

"Bueno!" cried De Cabeza. He handed Berty the engine manual. "Excellent papers!" He paused, then cried, "Señores! With me." He pointed toward town.

"Whoa!" said Berty. "We'll fix our ship and go."

We started for the Bird. De Cabeza whirled his horse between us and the plane. "No, Señores! There is the damage—this field."

The whole corn crop was flat. We'd knocked some of it down, but that mob had really completed the job.

"Come, Señores," the captain insisted.

"But the plane," Berty protested.

"The machine will not be touch. I, De Cabeza, will make the order."

The crowd closed in, looking black. So what else could we do? We went—hoping to chew up el capitan and spit him out.

"I tell you something," Capitan De Cabeza said that evening. "We have the fine jail. You owe for the corn, and for this I could lock you in the jail." His eyes gleamed shrewdly. "But, if you have money—"

"You mean pay a fine?" I asked.

"Si. That is it, a fine."

We were sitting in a barren room in a cold, plaster one-story building called the Barracks. The capitan lived here. There was a cot in one corner, a table where we sat, and several chairs. And something else: a rack full of gaudy, spotless uniforms of every color and cut. All De Cabeza's.

"All we've got is our luggage," Berty said. "That and the plane."

"As you say, Señor, as you say." There was something scheming in his tone.

Berty got mad. "Listen here, I'll call our Honduras embassy, and—"

The capitan laughed. "This is not Honduras. It is Republic El Vadora. You have no embassy in El Vadora."

There was a long silence.

"Señores," De Cabeza went on, "when I study the American by mail, I read of airplanes. It is good for war, no?"

Berty shot me an uneasy glance.

"I make the proposition," De Cabeza said. "You fly war for me; I let you out of jail on bail."

"War!" I said. "What are you talking about?"

"I tell you. There is a general in town of Montegro who wants to capture Jalagua! General Cara De Hierro, the Ironface. This De Hierro, he invades Jalagua day after tomorrow. This my scout sends me word about before he is captured."

Berty asked, "Well, how 'bout your army? Call them out."

"My army? He was the scout De Hierro captured. I never need an army before. I, De Cabeza, am the army now. And De Hierro," he added sadly, "he has an army five times as big as mine."

"Which is why you want our plane," Berty concluded.

"Si! We bomb the Ironface and his motorized and save Jalagua."

"What's this 'motorized'?" I asked.

"He have a machine who moves like the breeze," De Cabeza explained. "Secret weapon called a Ford. General De Hierro, he believes in speed. He says, 'Army that moves fastest *always* win'."

Berty had been doing some thinking. "Okay, Capitan," he said. "We stop De Hierro, you let us out. Right?"

"*Si, amigos, si!*" He exploded into violent laughter, then suddenly sobered. "Come, I lock you in jail until the day of invasion."

That, I thought, was a dirty trick.

We got permission for me to work on the plane next day while Berty sat and worried. By nightfall, I had the Bird in smooth running order. The trouble had been a simple matter of too much intake valve clearance on number two cylinder.

Fifteen minutes after dawn the following morning, Berty pulled a spare helmet down over the capitan's head and bundled him in the front seat with me and the baggage. I took him aside just before we started the engine.

"You're not actually going to get involved in this fool thing, are you?"

Berty grinned. "I know what I'm doing. Just hang on."

Whatever he did had to be done fast. We had just four hours of fuel left. The five-cylinder Kinner roared a mighty war cry as we bounded across the field tossing corn high in the morning air. Berty hauled back the stick, and we leaped from the ground and picked up altitude.

The capitan leaned over the side and saw Jalagua grow smaller. He turned and I saw two huge goggle lenses, that bulb nose, and a jaw-splitting grin. He liked this.

Berty climbed almost to seven thousand, following the dusty road through the mountains toward Montegro. He flew to the east of the northbound route, hanging in the sky between the sun and the road. We'd be hard to spot from the ground.

We'd been in the air half an hour when De Cabeza grabbed my arm. Ahead to our left lay a town of white buildings like those of Jalagua. It was larger and sprawled up the side of a low mountain like a carpet of sugar cubes. Montegro!

The plane rocked violently. Berty pointed off to the west. Down on the threadlike highway I spotted a tiny dust plume. De Cabeza saw it and waved his arms. The engine's blast died as Berty throttled back and banked the ship in a long glide toward the road.

We rounded a bend in a hair-raising skid, and there ahead was a narrow, flat clearing. A stream once, it was now dry hardpan. Berty chopped the throttle, and we didn't drop more than fifty feet before the wheels hit with a scrubbing sound. Berty scrambled to the ground before the prop stopped turning.

"C'mon, Capitan," he ordered. "Ain't got much time."

De Cabeza clambered out on the wing walk and hopped off. I got out, wondering just what was going on. I'd thought we would make a pass at De Hierro's five-man army and maybe try to scare them back home. But here we were in a lonely arroyo with the motor shut off.

"This way!" Berty called.

We followed him up the bush-studded side of the canyon. The capitan was gasping as we neared the top. I was kind of done in myself. Berty caught my elbow.

"We'll stay here, below this ridge."

I raised myself another foot, and there below us stretched the Montegro road. Berty had spotted this setup from the air.

"Okay, Capitan," he said. "Remember the plan I told you this morning and make it snappy."

"Plan?" I asked. "What plan?"

"Didn't have time to tell you," Berty answered. "Don't have time to tell you now."

De Cabeza climbed over the top of the rise, ran down the slope paralleling the road, and trotted out on the highway. I crouched below the ridge like Berty and waited. We didn't wait long.

Off to the north, there rose a clatter like a foundry during rush hour. In three minutes, an open 1928 Ford touring car swung in sight. It rammed along at at least thirty miles an hour and kicked up an impressive dust trail.

Peeking through a mesquite bush, I saw five assorted soldiers. There were, in the rear seat, two flint-faced guys flanking an officer. The officer sat in the jouncing car as if he had a wooden backbone. His arms were folded across his chest. A visored gray military cap rode his eyebrows, and his chestful of medals flapped in a colorful glitter at every bounce. His clean-shaven face was expressionless. This, I guessed, must be General Cara De Hierro, the Ironface.

Two men held down the front seat. The soldier on the right pointed a rifle straight up like a shotgun rider on a Wells-Fargo stagecoach. He was a mean-eyed fellow of about twenty-four. The other, the driver, was a mass of muscle with a head to match. He wore a great mustache that trailed back under his ears. Suddenly, the driver spotted Capitan Dolor De Cabeza standing at attention in the middle of nowhere.

He tramped the brakes. The big machine skidded sideways and rocked to a halt, straddling the road. The dust cloud caught up with the speed merchants and swallowed the scene. From inside the tan fog came a deep Spanish rumble.

"Que hay?"

The choking dust settled, revealing Capitan De Cabeza holding a rigid salute and attempting to blow the dust off his eyelashes. General Cara De Hierro had risen to return the honor. A rapid exchange of Spanish rattled up and down the road.

The Montegran general's surprise changed to unconcern. That gave way to impatience. He tapped his driver on the shoulder with his gloves. With a lurch, the Ford clanged past Capitan De Cabeza. He leaped aside.

When the Ford was out of sight toward Jalagua, the capitan trotted up the incline to us, and we all scrambled back to the Bird. On the way, De Cabeza puffed a report of his conversation with the enemy general.

"I tell the general turn back before it is too late.

"De Hierro says, 'Impossible. You have nothing to stop me—I am mobile.'

"I tell him, 'I give you warning. I am more mobile than you. I move like the wind. I will surround you.'

"De Hierro says, *'Que es eso?* What is that. A capitan orders a general? *Vaya!* Out of the way! He who moves fastest always wins. I move.' "

"Playin' right into our hands," Berty said.

I didn't get it. "What do you mean? He didn't stop for long."

"Stick with me," Berty ordered and climbed into the Bird. De Cabeza leaped in the front seat and rammed his head into his helmet and goggles. He was having a great time. Berty yelled, "Contact!" and I yanked the steel prop.

There wasn't any wind in this low spot. Berty just ruddered the plane around, and we boomed down the stream bed. Rocketing into the air, Berty didn't climb until we were miles away from the road; then he stuck the nose in the sun and up we went.

The next landing place wasn't a field or even an old creek bed. We passed the dust cloud far to the left and Berty cut back over the road after we drew ahead. The town of

Jalagua wasn't far off. If De Hierro was to be stopped, it had to be soon!

I was sure Berty knew what he was doing. I hoped he did because we were dropping lower and lower and still no landing field. Then—plop! We had landed on the road. Berty kicked left rudder hard, and we jounced off the highway, down a ravine, and around a bend. Craziest ride I ever had.

"We've got to get back to the road and cover our tire tracks," Berty warned.

We dashed to the dirt highway and messed up the marks the plane's wheels had made. And we finished none too soon. General De Hierro's car was almost on top of us as Berty and I hid behind some boulders, leaving De Cabeza in the middle of the road.

This time, the driver rammed the brake pedal to the floor. The touring car stopped like a rock, throwing the Ironface from his seat. He picked himself up, spouting a lot of Spanish. Then he fell silent as all eyes zeroed in on the grinning De Cabeza.

The driver let out his breath suddenly. *"No, no! Imposible!"*

The rifleman gasped. *"San Domingo!"*

Capitan Dolor De Cabeza shouted one victorious word. *"Mobility!"* And that did it.

De Hierro's jaw gaped and he sat down like a blownout tire. Slumping in his seat, he gave the driver a dazed order.

His mustache drooping, the soldier tramped the accelerator, swung around. The dust cloud grew again, but now it headed back to Montegro. General Cara De Hierro's invasion force had been hoodwinked into bloodless retreat!

Dolor De Cabeza was overcome with joy. "I have done it! I have the war won!" He doubled over with laughter.

Berty gave me kind of a bitter grin. *"He did it."*

"Now," De Cabeza said, suddenly recovering from his laughing fit, "now you fly me to Jalagua. I see what sentence I give you for the damage of the corn crop."

Berty wasn't grinning any more. "Why, you said you'd let us go if we turned back De Hierro."

"No, Señor. I mean I let you go *on bail.* And bail is over." The officer drew his big pistol.

We took off from the road in a nice easy climb, then Berty made a couple of quick circles, and I lost all track of ground points. This hop was longer than the others, and Jalagua had been only a few miles south. At last Berty throttled back. There was the town and the farms below us. I was surprised that he'd given in this easily, but, after all, what else could he do?

The Bird floated into a big flat field and rolled to a stop. The capitan rose—and froze.

"Eh? Señor! This is not Jalagua."

"Huh? Well, now, I'll be doggoned," Berty said. "You're plumb right, Capitan. Derned if it don't look like Montegro off there. I must've got lost."

"Aiee!" De Cabeza squealed. "And De Hierro is driving toward here!" He aimed the revolver at Berty. It must have looked like the mouth of a tunnel. "To Jalagua we go, or you go nowhere, Señores!"

Berty didn't bat an eye. "Didn't know you had a pilot's license, Capitan. She's all yours." He put a leg over the side. "Jalagua is that way." He pointed.

De Cabeza turned pale. "A moment, Señor. I—I—"

"Tell you what I'll do," Berty said. "I'll fly you to Jalagua for a price."

"A price? This is what you call the kidnaping!" But De Cabeza lowered the pistol. "What is the price?" he whispered.

"One cornfield," Berty said happily.

"Cornfield?"

"Yep, and it's already paid in full. I'll take your gun for the time bein', Señor."

Heading toward Jalagua, I couldn't hold back that grin that kept working on my mouth. De Cabeza's eyes slid my way. His little mustache twitched, his bulbous nose turned a wonderful red, then his face split wide, too, and he roared!

And Berty, the smartest cookie of them all, his shoulders were shaking up there in the pilot's seat. And it wasn't from the vibration of that old Kinner engine!

Smart Baseball

By PAUL RICHARDS

Some first-hand tips from the manager of the Baltimore Orioles

Smart baseball will win you a lot of games, unless you get too smart for your own good. Many young sandlot teams try to duplicate the tricks and plays which they have seen on major league diamonds and run into trouble because they lack the skill and experience. So make sure you are not trying more than you can handle when you get tricky.

It is one thing to watch and admire the smoothness of the Cleveland Indians' pick-off play at second base, when the pitcher turns suddenly and fires the ball right at the bag to find the shortstop waiting there for the throw. It is an entirely different matter for the average amateur to duplicate this kind of play.

It took dozens of hours of practice, even for the professionals, to get that play down pat. Yet I have seen occasions when even these topnotchers messed it up. Imagine what might happen to young players who casually decide to try that pick-off play on the spur of the moment!

More important than trickiness for smart baseball is a thorough knowledge of the rules. Get hold of a copy of the Official Rules Book and read it through at least once. You will be surprised at some of the things you find. Many fans who see dozens of major league contests each year remain hazy about the workings of the infield fly rule, or the differences between hit-and-run and run-and-hit plays.

I suppose it's all right for spectators to be vague on such points, but when you are out on the diamond or in the coaching boxes, a knowledge of the rules and of sound baseball strategy will often save the game.

Newspaper stories of big league ball games usually feature smart plays when they occur. Almost every week there is some outstanding, smart piece of strategy which the writers play up in their accounts of the game. It may be the old hidden ball trick; trapping a bunt to start a double play, instead of settling for one out; letting a long foul fly drop safely in the late stages of a game in order to keep a winning run from scoring from third after the catch; trapping a short fly in the outfield in order to make a play at second base, thus retiring a fast runner from first and putting the slower batter on base instead.

This last trick was a specialty of Tommy Henrich, one of the smartest-thinking outfielders in the game. This is a dangerous play and should be attempted only by real experts. The way Henrich did it was to bluff a catch, then trap the ball at the last moment, usually to catch the runners on first and second going the wrong way.

Another piece of smart baseball, which Henrich and many other outfielders learned, is to bluff base runners into holding their bases on sure hits. On a Texas Leaguer which the outfielder knows he cannot possibly get to in time for a catch, he charges with arms outstretched as though he were going to make a routine grab. The base runners, naturally, are forced to hold up momentarily to make certain that it will not be caught and they can sometimes be forced at second or third base. At the very least, this play prevents them from taking an extra base on the hit.

A different kind of bluff which has an important role in major league outfield play is faking a catch on long drives which will hit high on the outfield walls. Dixie Walker, formerly the pride of the Dodgers, made a fine art of this maneuver. With a runner on first and a high drive hit to right, Dixie would stand at the base of the wall tapping his glove casually, seemingly in perfect position for a simple catch. At the last possible moment, he would spring away from the high wall and get the ball on the rebound as it caromed off from 15 or 20 feet up on the wall, far above his reach. Many times during his career, he bluffed runners into holding their bases until it was too late for them to do anything but take one extra base on what should have been a base-clearing blow.

The Hit-and-Run Play

The hit-and-run play is a gamble. The main idea of this play is to advance a runner from first all the way to third base on a hit. A secondary motive is to avoid the possibility of a double play if the batter hits an infield grounder. The danger lies in the chance of the batter missing the pitch, having a pitch out called, or having the batter line out—any of which could erase the base runner.

Like all percentage plays, you should know when it is proper to call for the hit-and-run, and when it is poor strategy. Generally speaking, it should be tried only if your team is not behind by more than one or two runs. On getting the signal, the runner will break for second with the pitch. The batter's responsibility is to meet the ball in order to protect the runner.

Since the runner is going, either the shortstop or the second baseman will be dashing toward second in order to cover for the catcher's peg. This leaves a gap in that side of the infield for the batter to punch the ball through. The base runner should listen for the crack of the bat, then look for the coach or the ball, so that he can retreat to first if it is a fly ball which might be caught.

When your first batter gets on base, it is often smart baseball to sacrifice him to second so that he will be in position to score on a hit by any following hitter. The sacrifice will also eliminate the possibility of having your base runner knocked off in a double play.

With a runner on second base and no one out, the percentage play, if you want one run, is to sacrifice him down to third so that he can score on a fly ball to the outfield or on an infield out. Naturally, it helps a manager in such situations to have a bunter of high caliber up there.

A play which many young players neglect is the squeeze. It is beginning to come into its own again. There are two kinds of squeeze plays. One is the running squeeze in which

the runner on third base breaks for the plate with the pitching motion and the batter lays down a bunt any old place so long as he does not pop it up. The runner will score because he has already started and is practically on top of the plate when the ball is bunted. This play should be tried only when there are fewer than two outs.

A second type of squeeze play is called the safety squeeze, in which the runner on third does not break with the pitch. He takes his normal lead so that he can retreat to third if the ball is missed. As soon as he sees the batter hit the ball, he breaks for home. It is the batter's job to bunt toward that side of the infield which is playing deepest. The runner and coach on third must be alert when this kind of play is attempted.

Heads-up Baseball

What sports writers sometimes call heads-up baseball is often nothing more than an application of the Scout Motto "Be Prepared."

When a big league catcher sprints down the line with the batter on an infield grounder, he is furnishing insurance against a bad throw to first. Should the ball get past the first baseman, the catcher will be there to retrieve it immediately and prevent the runner from getting an extra base on the overthrow. Of course, the catcher will not go down if there are men on the bases. In such a case it is more important for him to protect home plate.

When your center fielder sprints a couple of hundred feet to back up an adjacent outfielder, that is smart baseball. A good outfield will back up all throws to the bases. The right fielder should back up first on bunts and pegs from the catcher. He also backs up second base on throws from the third base side of the infield. The left fielder backs up third base in the same manner that the right fielder backs up first.

The center fielder should back up second base on attempted steals for, if the catcher's throw is wild, the center fielder can prevent the runner from taking third on the overthrow.

Some things which are considered smart baseball are just plain common sense. For instance, if in the ninth inning, there is a runner on third base with less than two out and a tie score, you can move your outfielders in a great deal. If the batter should hit one over their heads, it does not matter because a long fly will enable the runner to score from third anyway. However, should the batter hit a shallow fly ball, it is possible to make a catch which might otherwise be out of reach and, more important, it will place the outfielders in position for a good throw to home should the runner try to score after the catch.

Some Cleveland Specialties

There are fancy trick plays which come under the heading of smart baseball, but only if you don't get too smart for your own good.

The Cleveland Indians came up with the "Boudreau Shift" on Ted Williams. As you know, Ted is a strong pull hitter and the Indians decided to swing their defense far over to the right, giving Ted the whole left side of the field to hit at. In this exaggerated shift, the second baseman was playing deep on the grass, the shortstop came over to play just about where the second baseman normally stands, and the third baseman got almost halfway between second and third.

The first time Ted saw this shift he stepped out of the box and almost broke his ribs laughing—but it stopped being funny pretty soon. The big slugger ignored the gaping hole in left field and tried to drive his hits through that overweighted right side.

Often enough he did smash a ball through, and, of course, there is no defense against a ball hit into the bleachers. But, this defense soon began to take sure hits away from Ted. There seems no question among sports writers that it has cost him many base hits over the past few seasons.

Another Cleveland specialty in the way of trick plays was the pick-off play on second base, which I have mentioned earlier. This is a play in which the pitcher and shortstop take a sign from the catcher—possibly after the shortstop first has flashed one to the catcher. As soon as the catcher gives his sign, both pitcher and shortstop begin counting. On a prearranged count, say "four" or "five," the pitcher whirls and throws directly at second base. In the meantime the shortstop has started a mad dash for the bag a count earlier and arrives to take the ball and put it on the trapped runner.

Fakes and Bunts

Smart infielders may work the hidden ball trick once in a blue moon, but there is almost no excuse for the base runner to be caught off. No runner should take a step off the base until he has seen the pitcher toe the rubber. If the pitcher toes the rubber without having the ball, it is a balk.

It is smart baseball on the part of infielders to make fake dashes every once in a while toward a base off which a runner is taking his lead. These dashes have the effect of making the runner start to retreat. If you can get the runner going back toward his base when the ball is hit, it will cost him those valuable two or three extra steps which might make the difference between an extra base or an out.

Playing a bunt often requires intelligent, fast thinking. A bunt which is rolling down the line should be allowed to continue rolling if it is immediately obvious that the runner has it beaten out. The bunt may roll foul at the last moment. On the other hand, if you know that you can get the runner easily, pounce on that ball in order to keep it from rolling foul.

Stealing signs, or anticipating certain plays such as a sacrifice or a hit-and-run will enable the catcher to call for a pitch out. Base runners tip it off by mannerisms. On receiving the sign for the pitch out, the pitcher makes his throw far enough outside the plate so that the batter cannot reach it. The catcher jumps out to the side and takes the ball in perfect throwing position for a peg down to second or first in an effort to nail the runner.

There is a type of pitch out which is very hard for the offensive team to guard against. Where there is a runner on first and a sacrifice is expected, the first baseman charges down the line as though he were trying to field the expected bunt for a play at second. The second baseman dashes for first base and the shortstop for second base. Meanwhile, the pitcher throws a wide curve to conceal the fact that it is a pitch out. The catcher takes the ball and pegs down to first base, which is covered by the on-rushing second baseman for a neat pick off. Of course, if the runner is on his way for second, the throw will be made to the shortstop.

Some General Hints

Whenever a defensive player takes a step to complete a play, a base runner is also advancing a step toward his base. Make your throws immediately without wasting time.

Outfielders should throw the ball low so that it may be cut off if desirable. The throw should be made to the base ahead of the runner—seldom behind him.

Run out every hit at top speed, even though it looks like a sure out. Hustle on every play—offensive or defensive. Hustling will win those close games.

One of the best ways to avoid mistakes is to figure out in advance what you will do if the ball is hit to you. Keep your mind on the game.

Practice hard to overcome your weaknesses and study other players.

Read and know the rules thoroughly.

Kit's Big Decision

By WILLIAM B. McMORRIS

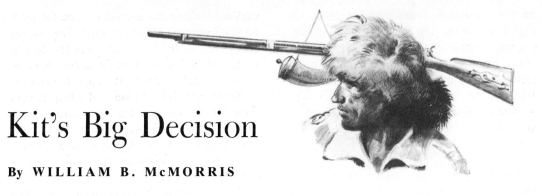

On his first trip West, Kit Carson was a greenhorn among mountain men

It was a morning like many other mornings in Franklin, Missouri, in 1826. Through the streets of the town rolled giant canvas-topped wagons pulled by big-boned Missouri mules that snorted rebelliously as they threw their weight against stiff collars. Men shouted greetings and good-bys punctuated by the crack of a teamster's lash. There was dust and excitement everywhere. Another caravan was taking the trail to Santa Fe.

This morning, just as he had many times before, a sixteen-year-old boy named Kit Carson stood in a Franklin saddlemaker's shop and watched the wagons pass. He saw the caravan's captain astride a sorrel pony galloping up and down the wagon line. Once in a while he would catch sight of the sun-blackened figure of a trapper in greasy buck-skins, traveling with the caravan as a hunter. Sometimes Kit saw boys no older than himself, their faces flushed with pride and excitement at being part of the wagon train.

Then Kit would turn slowly back to the saddler's bench and begin mending harness or repairing a saddle. His mind would not be on the work. Kit was a bound apprentice, obliged by law to earn his keep while learning the saddler's trade, but in his heart he was outward bound with the caravans for Santa Fe.

Later in the day, men would enter the shop and spin yarns while Kit and David Workman, the saddler, repaired a rig or took orders for a new one. The customers might be traders who would tell about the towns of Santa Fe and Taos and trips deep into Mexico to reap a thousand percent profit on calico, blankets, cutlery, and canvas. Kit liked to listen to their business talk, because once in a while they spoke also of Indian raids or buffalo herds.

Best of all, Kit liked to listen to the trappers who came to the shop. These were proud men who spoke with scorn of "town men" and "city fixin's." They were the mountain men, "half grizzly b'ar and half panther." When they talked of some scrap with Blackfeet or Comanches, Kit would gaze longingly at his battered Kentucky flintlock and see himself fighting shoulder to shoulder with these men in some forested canyon of the Rocky Mountains or along the Green River or perhaps "forted up" on a swell of grassy prairie. In Kit's dreams, his every shot "fetched" an enemy.

Those were the visions Kit had. Visions brought to life every day by the trappers, while in the streets of Franklin, the rumble of wagons was a constant reminder to Kit that the parade to the West was leaving him behind.

We don't know how long Kit nursed his dream of going West. Certainly he gave it careful thought. It was a rough, dangerous trip to Santa Fe. Kit had no money and no clothes except the ones he wore. He knew that, once started, there could be no turning back. Go or stay. It was a big decision, the biggest he'd ever have to make.

Kit figured and planned. Finally, one August morning he made his choice. Kit picked up his rifle, slipped out the door of the shop and down to the Franklin ferry. He crossed the Missouri, hiked a mile or two west, and walked into the wagon camp of Charles Bent, trader to the Mexicans and Indians and captain of a caravan readying for the West.

"Cap'n," Kit said, "I want to go to Santy Fee."

Bent, tall and muscular, looked down at the short, bandy-legged boy. The captain's first impulse was to laugh. Then he saw the confidence in the boy's eyes, the work-toughened hands, and the hard-muscled frame. The boy was a likely looking lad. Besides, Bent needed somebody to herd the "cavvy" —spare horses, mules, and cattle—that traveled in the wake of the wagon train.

The captain and the boy talked business for a few minutes and finally Bent grinned, "Git a blanket from the wagon, Kit. We leave at sun-up."

The Kit Carson whose big decision took him West the next day with Bent's caravan was far different from the Kit Carson of history and legend. He was just a ragged frontier boy who had never traveled any place after his parents had brought him from Kentucky to Missouri at the age of one. In short, he was the greenest greenhorn.

Kit didn't know about the skittishness of the half-green horses in the "cavvy." He'd never faced the pure cussedness of mules. He couldn't understand the placid stupidity of oxen that would mire themselves at a stream crossing and die without a struggle. He learned the hard way, just as a thousand greenhorns before him had learned.

It was an exciting life for the young greenhorn, for prairie travel was like being released from prison.

Then came a grimmer lesson in his prairie education.

It began when a teamster named Broadus needed his rifle in a hurry. All rifles in the caravan were kept loaded as protection against Indians. Broadus, however, wanted to shoot a wolf. The teamster snatched his flint-lock muzzle first, from one of the wagons. Something snagged the trigger. The rifle exploded. The heavy ball shattered the teamster's arm.

There was no doctor with the caravan, but all the experienced plainsmen knew what had to be done to save Broadus' life. The arm would have to be amputated.

But the teamster wouldn't hear of it. He clung to the hope that somehow his arm would mend. It didn't. In three days, racked with pain and fever, Broadus was pleading for someone to cut off the shattered limb.

The men of the caravan hesitated now. Broadus was already half-dead. The operation might kill him. Nobody wanted the dreadful responsibility.

The greenhorn cavvy-herd saw the pleading in Broadus' face. Still none of the experienced men spoke up. Kit could not bear to see the man die as long as there was a chance for life. Somewhere within himself, Kit found courage he did not know he possessed, the courage to speak up.

"I'll do it," he said.

Some historians say that Kit Carson actually performed the crude prairie surgery, but it is more likely that the experienced men, shamed by the courage of the boy, performed the operation themselves.

At any rate, it was done. The arm was cut off, the stump cauterized with a white-hot wagon bolt and spread with grease.

The patient was tough. He lived.

Kit never forgot this incident in his first prairie adventure. In later years he mentioned it often. The teamster's accident had shown Kit the price the wilderness could exact for an instant's carelessness. After this tragedy on the Santa Fe Trail, Kit's great courage was always tempered with common-sense caution.

As the wagons rolled on down the trail to Santa Fe, Kit stored up more knowledge. He watched the trappers and saw how they always slept near their weapons. When the caravan cut Indian sign, beyond the Arkansas River, Kit noticed that the mountain men

sat back from the campfire at night, out of the circle of light that could silhouette them as targets for an Indian raider. Kit imitated these moves until, unconsciously, he became a small copy of the trappers, always wary, always poised for action, his rifle never far away.

By the time Bent's caravan reached Santa Fe, Kit felt he was ready to join the great fraternity of trappers that roamed the Rocky Mountains. He was in for a surprise.

Trappers were mighty slow about accepting a greenhorn. Besides, most of the mountain men had settled down in Taos for the winter or were "holed up" in some natural park in Colorado. Kit was left in a strange country to fend for himself.

The money he had made as a cavvy-herd for Bent vanished rapidly. Kit went to Taos and wintered there with an old trapper named Kincaide whom he had met in the caravan. Kit learned to speak Spanish in Taos and met Ewing Young and other trappers who wintered in the town. Spring came at last. Kit had no luck with a trapping job. He was still too green for the mountain trail.

Back to Santa Fe he went. It was a black time. Kit was as hungry as the first grizzly in spring. He had to find work. The only job open was one as teamster on a wagon headed East. Kit hated to do it, but his stomach made the decision. He had to eat. He started with the wagons for Missouri.

About halfway out, his stomach filled but his heart sinking at the thought of returning to the saddler's shop, Kit took a new lease on his big decision. A westbound wagon train hove into sight. The westbound was short a teamster. Kit forfeited his pay, threw over his job, and headed West with a new employer.

This time Santa Fe was kinder to him. Kit landed a job in the southern mines. Later he hired out as an interpreter with a trader heading for Chihuahua. Kit was making his own way, but he never forgot the mountains and the trappers.

Two summers later he was back in Taos to try again when a band of Ewing Young's mountain men straggled into town. Their furs were gone, some of the men were wounded, and all of them were hopping mad. Seemed that the Apaches' hearts were bad that summer. It wasn't safe for small parties to venture out. Ewing Young needed more riflemen in a hurry, or he'd miss out on the early season trapping.

As Young recruited new trappers, he thought of Kit Carson. The kid was only nineteen, but he didn't "scare none," and he could hit what he shot at. Young asked Kit to go along.

Kit, 'lowing as how he wasn't doing much else at the time, guessed he could make it. Behind this casual front, Kit was as happy as a bear in a honey tree.

On the trail, he worked hard and learned fast. He had the makings of a trapper and more. When the Apaches pulled a sneak raid, Kit stood as cool as any veteran, placing his shots where they counted. He displayed the same kind of quiet courage he had shown on the Santa Fe Trail. That was Kit, soft-spoken, cautious, but when it came to a dangerous job, he never backed down.

Kit's ability in the mountains was not wasted on Ewing Young. Young took the better half of his crew of trappers and pushed on across Arizona into California. Kit was picked to go along.

It was a wise choice. Kit was the one who recovered horses stolen by Indians. When the Indians left them unguarded, he rounded them up and drove them back to camp. Kit also helped rescue the party from the clutches of some treacherous Mexican officials.

As a result of his "proving up" the first time out, Young recommended Kit to Tom (Broken Hand) Fitzpatrick, a great mountain man and part owner of the Rocky Mountain Fur Company. Fitzpatrick hired Carson on Young's say-so. Kit never again had to hunt for a job.

Kit's Missouri dreams had come true. Now he was a trapper. The other men slapped him on the back, called him "old hoss" and "child" in a tone that showed he belonged. They included him in their yarn-spinning sessions, listening when he spoke.

Kit now claimed full right to the title of mountain man. No one knew better than Kit how hard it was to win that honor.

Kit Carson's career was launched now. Even in his Missouri dreams, Kit could not have visualized the fame he eventually won. Before long, his name would be linked with amazing deeds both real and legendary. Nowadays no one can write an honest history of the West unless the name of Kit Carson appears somewhere.

Soon after Kit became a mountain man, he turned to "free trapping" with a band of his own followers. Of all the mountain men, the free trapper held the pinnacle of fur trade society.

During this period, Kit won the title "Little Chief" from the Arapahos. He fought a spectacular duel in Wyoming with a thug named Shunar. On the plains of Colorado, he and eight comrades fought off three hundred Comanches.

After the collapse of the fur trade, Kit met John C. Fremont and led the "Pathfinder" across the Sierras to the conquest of California. During the Mexican War he walked barefooted for one hundred and thirty miles to bring aid to a detachment of American infantrymen. Before long, journalists of the day began to tell the country what every trapper already knew about Kit. Kit became a national hero.

After the Mexican War, Kit was still a young man, but he wanted to retire. He and his Mexican wife settled down on land that later became a part of Philmont Scout Ranch in New Mexico. While he was "retired," Kit risked his life dozens of times to save people he did not even know. To a friend or a stranger, Kit always stood ready to lend a hand.

His fame would not let him rest. Everyone needed a man like Kit Carson. He was made Indian Agent to the Utes and gave up his home in the Philmont region.

When the Civil War came, Kit was made brevet brigadier general in the Union Army. Most of his time was spent keeping Indian tribes in order while regular Army garrisons were sent East to fight the Confederacy. Kit did the job assigned. He and his soldiers, mostly volunteers, took on the Apaches, Navajos, and finally the combined strength of the Kiowa and Comanche nations.

The Apaches and Navajos were soundly whipped—for the time being anyway—and Kit took a split decision from the mighty Comanche-Kiowa federation, something nobody else ever did.

Those battles were the last. Kit Carson died at Fort Lyon, Colorado, in 1868. Until the day he died, Kit always seemed a little embarrassed by the fame he had won. Everyone of that time who wrote about him spoke of Kit's modesty and friendliness.

Considering his amazing feats, we could forgive Kit if he had boasted a little. He had the right.

But it was a right Kit Carson never exercised. Perhaps the reason was that Kit could remember a time when a greenhorn saddler's apprentice made the big decision of his life and came West with his dreams. That memory kept Kit humble.

The Sinker

By GORDON D. SHIRREFFS

Henry flunked the swimming test so many times it looked as if he would sink the Patrol as well

Henry McNeill pulled off his sweatshirt and eased himself down the ladder at the side of the pier.

The water was warm but there was a brisk chop from the late August wind sweeping across Little Green Lake. Henry had been a sinker since Troop 17 had arrived at the Council camp almost one month ago. Every day he had tried to swim the fifty feet that would advance him to the Beginner's class. Camp was almost over and he was one of two sinkers left in his Troop.

He looked up at the pier. His elder brother John was on the lifeguard tower. John was the best swimmer in the Troop, an Eagle Scout and Leader of Henry's Patrol, the Foxes. He had been disgusted with Henry ever since camp started. For weeks he had tried to coach Henry, but with little success.

Henry looked out at the bobbing white floats fifty feet away. He had never passed the halfway mark. A swimmer was splashing and wallowing toward the floats. It was Phil Greenberg, a Tenderfoot Scout like Henry and a member of the Eagle Patrol. He was the other sinker left in Troop 17.

Phil was fifteen feet from the floats. Some of his Patrol mates stood on the beach and yelled at him, "Go on, Greenie! Keep going, kid!"

Henry smiled to himself. Phil had never passed beyond thirty-five feet. Henry lowered himself another rung. He would shove off when Phil let his feet down and waded solemnly to shore. But today Phil did not quit at thirty-five feet. He struggled on. He had ten feet to go.

"Keep going, Greenberg!" It was Henry's brother John. Henry looked up at the tower. John was watching the swimmer with keen interest. He wanted the Troop to have a one hundred per cent record of swimmers for the season, something no other Troop in the Council had been able to do.

Phil was five feet from the floats. Henry closed his eyes. He couldn't watch this.

"He made it! Good old Greenie! Ten more points for the Eagles! *Yaaaaaaaaah!*"

Henry opened his eyes. Phil was hanging on to the float line and grinning from ear to ear. The Eagles and the Foxes had been running neck and neck all month for the final standings in the Troop's Annual Camper's Award for Patrols. The Crow and Beaver Patrols were running a poor third and fourth.

Chuck Bryan, Assistant Patrol Leader of the Foxes, lay flat on the pier with his head close to Henry's.

"Listen, kid. You've *got* to make it! This may be our last chance to tie the Eagles. We need those ten points to do the trick. You can do it."

Henry looked up at his brother but John was looking out over the lake. Henry brushed back his cowlick. He leaned forward

146

and shoved hard with his feet. At first the panic didn't bother him. Ten feet, twenty feet, and at last he reached the halfway mark.

No one was yelling at him to encourage him as they did for Greenie. He closed his eyes and chugged hard with his arms. Henry opened his eyes. He had drifted sideways. He spit water out of his mouth. He had passed his old mark but now fear traced the length of his spine with an icy finger. He was farther out than he had ever been before.

The water must be over his head here. He slowed his churnings. He grew tense all over.

"Keep going, Henry!" It was Chuck Bryan's agonized voice.

Henry floundered around. "It's deep here! I'll drown!" he yelled. He struck out for the pier. "I'll drown! I can't make it!"

John cupped his hands in front of his mouth. "Oh, put your feet down!" he yelled.

Henry dropped his feet. The water was up to his armpits. John flapped a hand in disgust and arched cleanly off the tower in a perfect swan dive. Henry waded slowly ashore. Phil Greenberg was drying himself on the beach.

"I made it," Greenie said proudly.

Henry nodded. Where before he and Greenie had been pals despite their different Patrols, now it was different. A vast chasm had opened between them. Now Greenie was a *Swimmer*.

Greenberg waved proudly at John who was now sitting out on the fifty yard raft. John waved back as Greenie ran up the hill toward camp.

Henry got his sweatshirt and walked slowly up the hill. He had never been one to push himself but he *had* helped the Fox Patrol with their imposing record. He guessed he would be Second Class when he got back to the city. He had passed Scout Spirit and all of the Scoutcraft Requirements. He had not had a chance to pass Scout Participation because he had only joined the Scouts in July, a month before coming to camp. But somehow his whole life at camp had narrowed down to his passing the Beginner's Test.

Just a few days before he had realized with a sickening feeling that the ten points he would earn for his Patrol by passing the test would probably make the difference in the final standings for the Award.

He passed several Scouts on the way to his tent. They spoke to him but he knew it was more out of politeness than friendship. He had never made friends easily.

His brother John was always in the middle of a group. John had qualified for five Merit Badges at camp, won the difficult Nature Study Contest and won all but three events in the swimming meet. John alone had accounted for almost a third of the Fox Patrol's points.

Henry reached his tent and changed into his uniform. He was due at a handicraft lesson taught by Tom Allan, the Troop's Assistant Scoutmaster. But he didn't want to tell Tom he had flunked the swimming test again. He ducked out under the back of the tent as he heard someone coming up the path. He slipped behind a clump of birches and ran silently for the gully that led to the lake.

"Henry! Henry!" It was Tom Allan's voice, but Henry kept on going. He reached his hideout. It was a brushy spot on a narrow headland looking out over the lake. Below him he could see the T-shaped pier and the rowboats bobbing at their floats.

He reached into his pocket and pulled out a length of rope and a worn booklet. It was about knots, both simple and intricate. Henry began to tie knots. His first week at camp he had determined to master every knot in the booklet. Somehow it took his mind off his troubles.

After tying all the knots he knew, he shortened the rope with a Chain Knot and put it in his pocket. It was time he went back.

First call for Retreat was sounding when he entered his tent. His tentmates were putting the finishing touches on their uniforms to stand Retreat. Chuck Bryan looked curiously at Henry.

"Tom Allan was asking for you, Henry."

Henry nodded and went to his bunk.

Chuck came over to him. "Where were you?" he asked, but not unkindly.

"Took a little hike."

Chuck shook his head. "That's against the rules."

"I know it." Henry sat down and changed his sneakers for shoes. He could sense the feeling in the tent. The other boys talked steadily but now and then they glanced at him.

He liked them all but could call none of them his buddy. There was Candy-Bar McGivern, a First Class Scout who was an archery nut, and Roy Zilski, a top-notch handicrafter. George Benson, who had passed his First Class test in record time and who was Troop Scribe. Sid Goetz was a whiz at first aid and Norris Reiss was an expert at woodcraft.

Henry was the weak link in the chain.

"The Eagles have us coming and going now," Ed McGivern said gloomily as he peeled the wrapper from a candy bar.

Norris Reiss nodded. "Two more days of camp life and not much chance now to catch up with them."

Chuck Bryan kicked at the tent pole. "Tonight at the songfest they'll tell us about the last contest to be held tomorrow afternoon. Whatever it is, we've got to win it. The winning Patrol gets ten points. If we take it, we tie the Eagles. Then they'll have to toss us for the Award."

"I wouldn't want it that way," said George Benson softly. "We should have won easily. If Henry had only made Beginner."

"Forget it, George," said Chuck swiftly. He glanced at Henry. "Let's fall in, fellas."

The Fox Patrol marched down toward the parade ground. John was at their head. Sid Goetz was just behind John and was carrying the Patrol flag. It was an honor to carry the flag. The Scout who had made the best record for the day carried it at Retreat. Sid had just qualified for his third Merit Badge in as many days.

The Foxes passed the Eagles who were lining up before their tent. Fred Meade, Eagle Patrol Leader, waved casually at John McNeill. Standing behind him proudly was little Phil Greenberg holding the Eagle Patrol flag. He shook it at Henry. Henry smiled briefly and then looked straight ahead. In his weeks at camp, he had never carried that flag.

After mess Henry walked down to the beach. The distance *looked* so short between the pier and the floats. Yet when he was in the water it seemed like the English Channel. Henry pulled the rope from his pocket and began to tie knots.

There was a big fire being kindled down the beach for the songfest. The Troop was gathering on the side of the steep bluff overlooking the lake. Henry walked slowly up to the highest tier. The Fox Patrol was grouped fifty feet below him. Tom Allan was between them and the Crows. He looked up and beckoned for Henry to come down but Henry looked away.

The sooner he got home the better. But he had to stick it out for two more days.

The Scouts began to imitate their Patrol calls. The "caw—caw—caw" of the Crows echoed across the lake. The shrill "kreee" of the Eagles followed. The Beavers clapped their hands sharply. John McNeill stood up and the quick bark of a fox carried across the silent lake and died away on the far shore. Some of the campers looked back at him in admiration and clapped their hands.

The Scouts began to sing. "Old Mac-Donald Had A Farm" was followed by "My Darling Clementine." "Ivan Skivitsky Skvar" was thundered out. But Henry lay on his back and watched the ice-chip stars glitter against the dark blue blanket of the sky. They were singing the Troop song when at last he got up and started back to his tent.

He heard someone walking behind him when he reached the top of the bluff. It was big Tom Allan.

"Wait a minute, Henry," he said.

Henry leaned against a tree. Tom sat down on a stump. The big white S on the front of his college sweater showed clearly in the darkness.

"Don't you like to sing, Henry?"

Henry pushed his cowlick back. He shrugged. "Sometimes."

"But not tonight, eh?" the Assistant Scoutmaster smiled.

Henry nodded. He pulled his rope out and began to tie knots.

Tom crossed one leg over the other. "You're letting this swimming get you down, kid. You haven't had much fun lately. When you first came to camp, you worked hard at your Second Class Requirements. You were good at handicraft too. There's a half-finished pair of moccasins up at the handicraft shelter you haven't touched for a week. I missed you at my class today."

Henry tied a Stevedore's Knot and then a Sheepshank.

Tom watched Henry's hands. "You can take swimming lessons back in the city at the 'Y'. Then you could be a First Class Scout before camp starts next year. Some of the older boys are planning to start an Explorer outfit. We'll need younger fellows like you to take over Patrols and other duties here in the Troop."

Henry shook his head and tied a Double Carrick Bend. Tom leaned forward and watched Henry tie the bend. "You *are* staying in the Troop and coming back to camp next year, aren't you?"

"Not if I can help it," Henry said bitterly. He tied a Slip Knot and then a Figure Eight.

Tom got to his feet. "Where did you learn to tie knots as quickly as that?" he asked in surprise.

Henry looked up quickly. "I don't know. I just like to tie them."

"Can you tie any more?"

Henry nodded. He swiftly tied a Square Knot, a Mast Head, and a Sheet Bend.

Tom watched him closely. "You wait here, Henry." The Assistant Scoutmaster trotted toward the singers. Henry could hear Mr. Stanley, the Scoutmaster, making an announcement. In a few minutes Tom was back with Henry's brother and Chuck Bryan.

"Tie some more knots as fast as you can, Henry."

Henry's fingers flashed through half a dozen knots.

Chuck Bryan whistled. "You're in, kid. We sure can use you tomorrow."

"Tomorrow—why?"

Tom gripped Henry's shoulder. "Tomorrow afternoon the last point contest takes place. Mr. Stanley told me this morning that it was to be knot-tying. But it was just announced to the Troop now."

"We wouldn't have had a chance against Joe Gordon of the Eagles," Chuck said

quickly. "He's the best I've seen until now."

Henry looked at his brother.

John frowned. "We can't take a chance on Henry. He gets rattled too easily. You can see it when he swims."

"He won't get rattled," Tom said, "I'm not trying to tell you how to run your Patrol. But Henry should have this chance to compete. I think Chuck agrees with me."

Chuck flashed a quick smile. "Sure thing. It's to be a three-man team. Roy Zilski, Henry, and Yours Truly. Henry can replace Sid Goetz. Sid will be just as happy; he told me he didn't have a chance."

John shrugged. "We don't have a chance against them anyhow, so I guess it doesn't make much difference."

Henry didn't sleep well that night. Tom was just trying to get Henry to be one of the boys, he thought; something Henry couldn't do himself. An owl was hooting somewhere in the woods in back of the tent when at last he fell asleep. He had a curious dream in which he was entered in a knot-tying contest in water up to his armpits. His fingers were all thumbs and the rope was coated with molasses.

The next afternoon he trudged to the knot-tying clearing. There were peeled poles on which to tie hitches. Ropes of all sizes and lengths hung over the poles. Chuck and Roy were already there practicing. Henry sat down and watched them. Chuck was pretty slow but Roy wasn't too bad. The teams from the Eagles, Beavers and Crows arrived. Joe Gordon was a slim kid wearing a Star Scout badge. He eyed the Fox team closely and looked curiously at Henry. Joe didn't practice either.

When Mr. Stanley arrived, the clearing was surrounded with the campers. The Scoutmaster walked into the middle of the clearing.

"Scouts, this will be the last contest of the season. The winning Scout will get ten points for his Patrol. We will use the elimination system to cut down the field. The contestants will tie the Tenderfoot Knots for speed. The last man in each case will drop out automatically." He looked at the contestants.

"I'll name the knot and blow my whistle for the start."

Mr. Stanley held up his arms for silence. "Sheet Bend," he called and blew his whistle.

Twelve pairs of hands went into action. Joe Gordon finished first and stepped back from his pole. Roy Zilski was next, and Henry finished a second after Roy. A freckled-faced Scout from the Crows dropped out.

Roy won the Clove Hitch. Joe Gordon took the Two Half-Hitches. A Scout from the Beavers took the Bowline.

The eight remaining boys lined up again. Tom Allan came up behind Henry.

"You can do better than that, kid. You're not trying."

They tied the Stevedore's Knot, Figure Eight, Square Knot and Timber Hitch. When they finished the second round, Henry was the only Fox left. Joe Gordon and Paul Rose of the Eagles were still in the running as was a red-headed kid from the Crows.

Henry looked over at the Fox Patrol. Chuck Bryan came over to him and put his arm around Henry's shoulders.

"I didn't know you were this good, kid. The next round is tough, but you'll make it; you just have to make it!"

Mr. Stanley held up his hands for attention. "We're whittled down to the finalists now, Scouts. The next part of the contest calls not only for speed but knowledge of knots as well. Each contestant will name a knot; all four boys will tie it. If they do not know the knot, they will automatically drop out. Each Scout will get three points for first place, two for second, one for third. The boy with the most points wins for his Patrol."

Sweat trickled clammily down Henry's sides. Joe Gordon wiped his hands on his shirt.

"Some kid, Joe Gordon! Eagles! Eagles! Eagles!" the Eagle Patrol chanted.

Mr. Stanley looked at Paul Rose and nodded.

"Double Carrick Bend," said Paul.

Mr. Stanley blew his whistle.

Henry's knot hit the ground a half second

before Joe Gordon, who was followed by Paul Rose.

"That's the stuff, Hank!" yelled Chuck Bryan.

Henry felt warm all over. In his whole month at camp no one had ever called him Hank.

"All right, Red," called Mr. Stanley to the Crow.

"Sheepshank," said Red.

The whistle blew. The redhead's knot hit the ground a half second ahead of Henry's. Joe Gordon was third.

"Joe Gordon," said Mr. Stanley.

Joe looked warily at Henry. "Pipe Hitch," he said quickly.

Joe stepped back from the pole first. Paul Rose was second and Henry was third. The redhead slapped the side of his head in mock disgust and walked out of the clearing.

Mr. Stanley raised his voice. "Henry McNeill and Joe Gordon six points each. Paul Rose three points."

"Come on, Hank!" a familiar voice yelled. Henry looked around. It was his brother John waving frantically at him. "Come on, Hank! Show 'em!" John looked around proudly at his Patrol mates. They were all on their feet now.

"Your knot, Henry," Mr. Stanley said.

Henry cleared his throat. He couldn't think of a knot to tie. He looked helplessly at Tom Allan. Tom shrugged and held his hands palms upward.

"Taut Line Hitch," Henry said weakly.

The whistle shrilled. Henry stepped back from his pole just as Joe Gordon let go of his hitch.

The Fox Patrol exploded. They rushed into the clearing and some of them hoisted Henry to their shoulders.

"Some boy, Hank!" they shouted.

Mr. Stanley blew his whistle. "Scouts, this ties up the contest for the Annual Camper's Award. It looks like the Fox and Eagle Patrols will have to toss for it."

That night Henry happily showed some of the boys in his Patrol the really intricate knots he knew.

"Why didn't you stump those Eagles with a Mast Head Knot or something like that, Henry?" asked Roy Zilski.

Henry pushed his cowlick back. "Because they wouldn't know them, that's why. It wouldn't be fair. A real Scout wouldn't do that whether he won or lost."

Roy grinned. "Kid, whether you beat Joe Gordon or not on that last knot, you'd still have won as far as I'm concerned."

Later that evening Henry went down by the lake and looked out at the bobbing floats. Then he walked slowly up the hill to the wall tent where Tom Allan bunked. The Assistant Scoutmaster looked up from the letter he was writing.

"Come in, Hank. Congratulations on winning today."

"Thanks, Mr. Allan."

Tom leaned back. "Camp is almost over for this year, Hank. It makes you feel kind of lonely."

"Yeh," Henry said.

Tom smiled. "Anything on your mind?"

"Mr. Allan," Henry said swiftly, "the Foxes don't want to toss for the Award. Whether we win or lose, we wouldn't feel right."

"It does take the edge off it," agreed Tom.

Henry stuck his hands beneath his belt to keep them from shaking. He was a Patrol hero now. His brother had let him carry the Patrol flag at Retreat after winning the knot-tying contest. He could rest on his laurels now. He had heard a school teacher say that once. But he wasn't sure he wanted to.

"Can I try for my Beginner's Test once more?" he asked quickly.

Tom nodded. "The camp rules say you can try until the morning of the last day at camp. Tomorrow is that day. We pack up, strike tents, and load the truck for the trip to the railroad tomorrow afternoon. Yes, you can try tomorrow morning."

That night Henry hardly slept at all. It was a cool night but he had plenty of blankets. Still he was cold. The mere thought of going down to that lake in the morning and swimming all alone froze Henry's marrow.

He was silent at breakfast and while the

boys packed their gear. They folded the cots and took them to the storeroom. Henry helped them clear the baggage from the tent and stack it for the truck. He was helping strike the tent when Tom Allan came.

"All right, Henry," Tom said.

Henry rapidly stripped off his slacks and shirt. He had put his trunks on before breakfast.

"Where you goin', Hank?" asked Norris Reiss.

Henry didn't answer. He hurried down the trail with Tom.

John was on the lifeguard tower. Mr. Stanley was sitting on an overturned boat. John waved his hand at Henry. Henry got down the ladder into the water. Tom Allan lay down on the pier with his head close to Henry's.

"*You can do it, Hank.* Take your time; there's no hurry. Don't stop until you put that clincher on the floatline."

Henry nodded and shoved off. For the first thirty feet he swam slowly. Then he looked back over his shoulder. A wavelet slapped him in the face. He lost rhythm and sank. He thrashed frantically. It was the same thing again. He was panicky. He closed his eyes and kicked desperately but his nose and mouth filled with water. He coughed, sank again and then thrashed wildly.

"Relax, Hank!" It was John. "Count your strokes!"

Henry took a firm stroke.

"Give it a Sheet Bend!" cried John.

Henry took two more firm strokes. "Steve-dore's Knot, Buntline Hitch, Fisherman's Bend, Lineman's Knot," he said aloud, stroking with each name. He sank again.

"Throw a Mooring Hitch on that float line!" Mr. Stanley yelled from the beach.

Henry thrashed his feet. He lifted his tired arms and thrust hard at the water. His left wrist hit something. His cowlick hung wetly in his eyes, blinding him. His right hand struck something. He opened his eyes and reached out. His hands closed on the fifty-foot line. He sank down and his legs and arms trembled. He looked back at the shore. Mr. Stanley was running up the hill path shouting, "He made it! He made it! A one hundred per cent record of swimmers for the season! Not a sinker left in the Troop!"

John was doing a war dance on the pier. Tom held clasped hands over his head and shook them at Henry. *Well, the Foxes had the Annual Camper's Award now. That last ten points had put them ahead of the Eagles.*

Henry clung to the line and let the waves ride him up and down. He relaxed and suddenly felt for the first time as though the water would help him swim. He had fought it when it wanted cooperation.

"What's the matter, kid? You too tired?" yelled John. He stripped off his sweatshirt and poised himself for a racing dive.

Henry shook his head. He gulped a big mouthful of air and struck off for the pier. He was going to swim back if he had to name every knot he ever tied.

"Studding Sail Hitch," he said with the first firm stroke, "Top-Sail Halliard Bend."

Blood on the Ice

By JIM KJELGAARD

The little Arctic fox follows the polar bear, and Agtuk follows the fox

The dull eyes of the polar bear could discern only what was beneath his black nose. But his nose told him that the quest must continue. The cold wind that swept in from the north carried no scent of an open lead and therefore there would be no seals. The polar bear sat down, bracing his huge body with his ponderous front paws, and looked behind him.

Though it was high noon, the ice upon which he sat was revealed as a dim, almost gray sheet that here and there was broken by a tiny ridge. There was no sun, or light, except when the aurora borealis flashed its weird radiance. The polar bear was looking for his constant attendant, and for the past ten days his partner in hunger. Presently he saw him.

The little white fox sat ten feet away. In the gloom his eight pound, thickly-furred body was a warped image that seemed to shimmer into and out of the frozen background. The fox's bushy tail was curled about his hind legs, and the steady wind that whipped out of the north ruffled his fur. He lifted a front paw, held it against his body a moment, and put it back down on the ice. The fox warmed his other front paw.

The polar bear turned, and took one step toward the tiny creature. Like a slithering ghost, the fox glided ten feet farther back and again sat down. For almost a month he had followed this bear, always maintaining his distance and proper respect.

The first day the fox had attached himself to his huge host the bear had stalked a seal at an open lead. Crouching close to the ice, he had covered his black nose with his front paws and pushed himself forward with his hind ones. Absolute master of such hunting, the bear had at no time looked like a bear, a killing machine without peer. So perfect was his camouflage that he had seemed another ice hummock, a pile of snow, a part of the frozen pack upon which he hunted. The basking seal had had one split second to know fear, then the bear's sledge-hammer front paw crushed his back. After the bear had eaten his fill, the fox had darted in to feast on what remained.

For fifteen days they had enjoyed such abundance. The bear had killed a seal every day, sometimes stalking them beside open leads and sometimes killing them in the water, and both he and the fox had eaten well. But in the following five days the bear had killed only one seal, and two days afterwards had back-tracked forty miles to eat the frozen skin, flesh, and bones that had not been worth eating before.

The fox's last meal, ten days ago, had been only the iron-hard chips of skin and flesh that remained after the bear had fed. In that five days, and their single kill, the ice pack had shrieked and groaned. It was a tortured monster, moved by the wind and the slow-flowing but inexorable water. The leads had closed, and the seals were breathing through their blow-holes beneath the ice. The land of plenty had become one of starvation.

The fox had followed the bear westward through a nightmarish-place of weird shapes and shadows. It was neither land nor sea, but an endless desert of ice from which all life had fled. The polar bear, lord of the arctic and master of all in it, was a puny thing when pitted against so vast a space.

And all the while the north wind blew over the pack. It was a cold and pitiless vagrant that had wandered throughout the earth's frozen tip and seen all the cruel grandeur of tremendous, unviolated nothingness. It understood the futility of these two creatures that had blundered into its domain, and it enraged the polar bear.

Had his belly been full, no wind could have disturbed him. But his belly was empty. Pinching hunger was a thing with life, an invisible being that walked on the ice beside him and mocked him with the wind's voice. The polar bear reared suddenly, and whipped his paws about. But the wind merely split on either side and keened past.

Equally hungry, the little white fox was not equally desperate. The polar bear was a lone thing, a monstrous steel and whipcord creature whose strength was his only salvation. Dimly within himself he felt that that strength was pitted against something stronger, and he was frustrated because he was unable to combat it. But the fox was a little thing. In winter, when the gulls were departed, there was nothing on the ice pack that he could kill even if he encountered it. He had no strength, but turned that of the bear to his own devices. Bears always made kills and eventually this one would do so. So long as the bear walked before him, the fox knew that he would eat. He was not alone.

The bear rose to go on and the little fox padded after him.

The day did not pass. Rather, it blended into a deeper and thicker gloom, an undulating, velvet-like blackness that clung with smoky fingers to the ice pack. The arctic night was a solid thing, a live animal that fought desperately for life and seemed to find in its tenuous hold a hope of life enduring. The bear and the fox strode through it. But their lives combined were only a speck of consciousness striving through an infinite emptiness, a ripple in a sea of loneliness. As living things, the continuance of the spark that actuated them depended upon their ability to find, and kill, and eat, other living things. But except for themselves there was no tangible life here in the vast frozen reaches.

Still the bear fought on, a ghost-like wraith in the arctic gloom. His small head swung constantly, always in the wind, and his black nose moved as he snuffled about for the scent of that one thing which would be different from all the rest. Strength was a mighty factor, one that had never been de-

155

feated before. It could not be conquered this time because it was all-powerful. He could continue until the scents that the wind carried to his questing nostrils became transformed. Sooner or later he would have to smell the salty, flavorful tang of an open lead. Wherever there was open water there would be seals.

But the hunger that had assumed shape and form still walked beside him. It was much nearer than that other shadow, the arctic fox. And it was terrifying because the bear knew that he could neither fight nor walk away from it. It had neither pity nor mercy.

Even if they had existed, the bear would not have known how to accept either. Born in an ice-sheathed cave twenty miles inland, he had drunk coldness and savagery with the milk that flowed from his mother's dugs. He had lain in the cavern, a helpless, mewling thing, when the arctic wolves had come. His mother had met the big, white, long-fanged things, clubbed them with her paws and slashed them with her jaws until five lay dead about the cavern and four had fled fearfully into the snow-spattered barrens. Then she had entered the cave, and the cubs had fed from her blood-spattered teats.

The bear arose, and again slapped futilely at the howling wind. The gaunt and haggard specter that had emerged from his belly was very close beside him now, walking with long strides as he plowed through the arctic night. He turned again to look at the fox.

Ever since, as a yearling cub, he had broken away from his mother, he had been followed by foxes. Within his ponderous brain there was no clear realization of what they meant or why they followed him. He knew only that they were there, and when he killed a seal to which he returned later their scent was always about it. They had eaten of the seals that he killed and left as carrion on the floes.

Many times they had been impudent, dashing in even while he fed to snatch choice tidbits from his very jaws and make away with them. He had tried and failed to catch them. The little white foxes moved as swiftly and smoothly as the water itself. His paws had always slapped down upon the places where they had been.

But the foxes were fashioned of flesh and warmed with blood. The bear's nose told him that, and the new awareness of the little white fox was slowly instilled into his brain. He had never eaten—save for his mother's milk—anything except seals, and until he had grown as hungry as he was now it had never occurred to him that anything else was good to eat. But the new awakening to other sources of food set his mouth drooling and his tongue lolling.

Without breaking stride the bear whirled about and cast himself backwards. Invariably the little fox followed him on the left and about ten feet behind. The bear knew that, and when he lunged both front paws slapped down on the fox's accustomed place.

But the fox was not there. There had been no time to think of the bear's lightning-swift pass, but inborn senses that a thousand generations of his ancestors had developed were razor-keen. A split second before the bear's flashing paws had cracked down upon the ice, he had rolled sideways. Now, with his tail curled about his legs, he sat twenty feet away. Like an inquisitive kitten he watched his mighty host. He knew that the bear would have killed and eaten him. But that inspired neither fear nor resentment because the fox understood such actions. He himself, if he were able, would gladly kill and eat anything. The spur of hunger was a sharp one.

The little fox barked, softly and appeasingly, and watched the bear with calculating eyes. Again, he pressed both front feet against his breast and put them down on the ice. He was ready to spring from another charge if one came. But none did.

As though it was irresistibly attracted by some magnet set deep in the north, the bear's head swung that way. He turned his body, and tensed every muscle as his black nose probed for more of the faint story he had scented.

At a shuffling lope he started into the darkness.

A mile and a half to the north, Agtuk, the Eskimo, was walking across the ice pack. Twenty hours ago he had eaten. True, his meal had been only a few leathery shreds of seal skin. But they had stilled the gnawing pain in his shriveled belly. Now he had nothing to eat and could look forward to nothing.

But he still had hope. It was not the soaring hope that had been his six months ago. The arctic day had reigned then, and a few minutes of gray twilight at midnight had been the only symbol that there ever was a night. Agtuk had started north with Einar Larsen, a great man and explorer who had conceived the vision of land lost somewhere in the arctic sea. Agtuk had been very excited because no man had ever been where he was going. When he came back, and told of his journey, he would be the greatest man of his village.

However, though the last faintly-lit spark of hope refused to flicker out, Agtuk's reason told him that he was never going back. The first three months on the ice had been easy ones, marked by soft living. Einar Larsen had known things about the pack that even the Eskimos had never discovered.

Hundreds of miles from land he had chiseled holes in the ice and harpooned seals through them. They had filled their bellies recklessly. Even the seven dogs, working hard and pulling the sledge every day, had grown fat.

Then, suddenly, there were no more seals. They had eaten the provisions on the sledge. Reluctantly, but of necessity, they had eaten the seven dogs and the skin thongs with which the sledge runners were bound. For a month Agtuk and Einar Larsen had been fighting their way out of the wind-swept desolation toward the shore and safety. They would have won their fight, too, but Einar Larsen had sickened. When they left what remained of the sledge he had been able to walk only one mile a day. The last twenty-four hours he had walked less than a quarter of a mile, and Agtuk had carried him another five hundred yards before he awakened to the realization that he had a dead man on his back.

Agtuk had drawn the other man's parka close about his face and left him under the shelter of a towering pressure ridge. He had taken the .38 Magnum that Einar Larsen had worn in a holster at his belt and plodded on. The next morning he had eaten the last handful of seal skin, and sat for a long while in the shelter of a pressure ridge.

While sitting, he had taken the .38 from its holster and looked at it. It was a shiny gun, with a smoothly-working cylinder that contained as many cartridges as could be put into a rifle. And it had all the power of a rifle. Agtuk himself had seen Einar Larsen shoot a basking seal with it, and when they came upon the seal its back had been shattered. Most seals, when struck with even a rifle ball, would still slide into the water. But this one hadn't moved.

For a very long while, sitting with his back braced against a pillar of ice, Agtuk pondered the gun. It was a wonderful thing, a great and beautiful thing that he himself would have given a year's catch of furs to have as his own. Of course he could not have it because it still belonged to Einar Larsen, and if Agtuk reached land it must be given to whichever of the dead explorer's friends could prove himself most worthy of it. Agtuk thrust the gun back into its holster and went on.

He walked calmly, serenely, ignoring the pinch in his belly and the biting wind that drove freezing cold through the minute pores of his skin parka. A man must walk that way if he was to consider himself worthy of carrying such a gun. He must not be tormented by petty fears. Einar Larsen had walked in such a fashion, and it had been very painful for him to do so. He, too, had known that he would leave his dead body here among the floes. But his spirit had had noble clay from which to spring. The dark day merged into night, and Agtuk grinned.

The aurora borealis flickered across the ice pack, lighting it up like a pale moon. Agtuk staggered, and sank down.

From the first, the bear had known that he was on the trail of a man. But he knew men, he had met them paddling their skin kayaks and seen them on their whaling ships. And he was positive that they were not nearly so agile or so hard to catch as were the little white foxes. When Agtuk fell, the bear was so near that even his dull eyes witnessed the act. Drooling, making impatient little whining noises, the bear hurried to the motionless man. He opened his great jaws.

Then there was a sudden roaring smash not born of the eternal ice or conceived by the howling wind. The bear stiffened, as though in surprise, and all four legs grew taut. But he stood only for the barest fraction of a second. The bullet, shot into the roof of his mouth, had smashed his brain and torn the top of his head off. Quietly the bear collapsed on the ice.

Agtuk rose, gravely and deliberately, and knelt to lap up the hot blood that ran in little rivulets from the bear's smashed skull. It was surprising how food, any food, could re-create strength within a man. But he must hurry now, the bear would be frozen hard very soon. Still gravely, but swiftly, he cut from the hot carcass such strips of meat as he needed and rose to go on.

A man could meet death as a man should. But it was no part of a man's creed to die if dying was not necessary. Certainly, when the aurora flickered and revealed a bear twenty feet away, no one could condemn a man, or call him a weakling, because he fell on the ice and lured that bear to where it could be shot. Anyone would know that, in this arctic desert, bears would be hungry enough to come to the lure. Agtuk walked serenely into the darkness.

As soon as he was gone the little white fox came forward. It was all part of the plan. He had known that he would eat if he followed the polar bear far enough.

158

Easier Ways to Better Grades

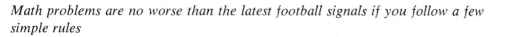

By STANLEY PASHKO

Math problems are no worse than the latest football signals if you follow a few simple rules

Can studying be made painless? Well, you can't get around the solid facts that studying is work. But so is football practice or rebuilding an old car.

What's the difference between the fellow in trouble with a geometry assignment and the same one eagerly absorbing complicated football patterns or tracing a wiring system? Maybe another boy is a dud at schoolwork but a whiz at solving contest puzzles. Why can he read *Annapurna* in one sitting and take a week to learn a few paragraphs about the economic geography of Tibet? If you knew and understood the answers to such questions, it might help boost your own grades next term.

First of all, efficient study needs organization. On the football practice field, the coaches have allotted so many minutes for calisthenics, so much time for dummy tackling, so much for running through plays, and so on. Everything is done systematically to get the maximum benefit out of the time available. Do you follow the same procedure with your study schedule? Probably never occurred to you to do it this way.

Actually, any student who devotes all of his school study periods to working on lessons has the biggest part of his learning problems licked right there.

But most students need extra time. They would be smart to follow the system used by the football coach. They should have a regular "workout" at the same time each day.

The hour right after dinner would probably be the one least missed. Right after school, you like to play outdoors, or practice a sport, or just have fun. In the cooler months there is little enough daylight left after school. Later in the evening there will be the radio, television, movies, Scout meeting, and other interesting things to take your time.

If you really study in your workout hour, you will find it's enough. It's important not to let anything stand in the way of your work during this time. No radio, no conversations, all the tools you need at hand, no excuses for dawdling or dividing your attention should be tolerated. If you start right out working hard, you will soon "condition" yourself—you'll have the habit of getting to work as soon as you sit down in this regular place at a regular time.

Now, there is the question of when certain things should be studied for maximum efficiency. A football coach will get the calisthenics in first to warm up the players' muscles and because they are the least interesting part of the practice period. He will then have the mechanical practice, such as blocking, tackling, punting, stance, and so on. Finally, he will give the team the most interesting part—running the plays or scrimmage. If he had reversed the procedure, it would close with the most half-hearted demonstration of calisthenics you ever saw.

Just as athletic coaches have studied practice procedures, psychologists have studied learning and made tests of study habits. For example, their findings seem to indicate that a person can memorize best in the morning. It follows then that your chief memorizing work should be done in the morning study period, while written work and reading assignments could be saved for the afternoon study period and the evening work session.

One psychologist found that after a student has memorized something, it is a great help to have him repeat it a few times just before going to bed. The lesson seems to stay with the student much longer.

Other experiments indicated that the best way to memorize a long speech, poem, lesson, or acting part was to read it through thoughtfully from beginning to end, over and over again, rather than learning it one line at a time. Test groups who read the subject matter from the beginning to the end required less time to memorize it because they understood it better than those who tried it a line or a paragraph at a time. But it is important to try to repeat the material after each reading. This is the part that really helps you to remember it.

The Engineers Know

Time study engineers and other practical psychologists have broken down the principles of learning to basic laws. The first law for successful study or achievement is *interest* in what you are doing or *desire to learn*.

The reason the football quarterback could learn his intricate play patterns easily, while muffing simpler math problems, is that he was vitally interested in the first and only mildly interested (if at all) in the second. It follows that you have to make yourself interested in what you have to learn. But how?

The best way is to try to find some way in which your lesson ties up with your own experience. To get interested in geography, you might look over a stamp collection and try to see how the stamps picture life in the various nations.

If you are reading *Ivanhoe,* imagine you're a movie producer trying to decide which movie stars you would have cast for the different roles. If you tell the teacher about this, you may start a lively class discussion (and arguments) that will make the story mean more and help you remember it the rest of your life.

You can devise similar ways to interest yourself in the subjects with which you have most trouble. If you can learn to motivate your own school work in such ways, you can become the outstanding student in your class. Knowledge and interest form an endless chain. As soon as you begin to learn facts about anything, interest automatically increases.

The laws of learning also show that frequency, recency, and intensity are important study techniques.

Frequency or repetition is what the quarterback does when he practices a hand-off until he can perform it automatically. It is also what a typing student does when he practices certain letter combinations until he can do them fast and accurately.

Recency is the reason the quarterback has to go through a great deal of relearning next fall. He has lost some of the skill during the off-season just as a typing student loses some of his speed after a summer lay-off.

Intensity is the desire to learn in order to win football games, in the case of the quarterback. As far as the typist is concerned, he will get intensity into his study if he needs money badly and knows that he can get a good job as a typist when he graduates from school.

Reviewing is an important aid to successful studying. If you are taking notes in class and make outlines of the work you have covered, you have a wonderful tool for reviewing. Past lessons should be reviewed regularly—but quickly. It isn't necessary to devote a lot of time to such reviews—after all, you have already learned this stuff. All you want is to make sure it sticks with you.

But don't expect reviews to take the place of study. You wouldn't expect to be able to buzz through the Morse code a few times as a review and have that help you pass the Amateur Radio Operator's License test unless you have already mastered the code by serious study and practice. It is the same way with school.

You will go a long way on the road toward better grades if you can make a good study schedule—one which you can maintain, not an ambitious one which is impossible and which you will drop after a few days. Make it a realistic one which you are *sure* you can follow conscientiously. If you have overestimated your work capacity, cut down on the schedule until you find one which you positively can maintain. Then keep at it.

A sample work schedule might look this this:

Ten minutes before leaving for school for planning the day.

Morning study period for memorizing language lessons or recitations. Try to use it for working on a subject which you have been assigned earlier that very morning.

Afternoon study period for reading assignments and working math problems, also for short compositions which need no research.

Evening study hour to clean up everything that is left for tomorrow's assignments. Rest of time to work on notebooks and long range big school projects.

A few hints which have helped other students to get better grades are:

1. Practice reading for speed so that you will be able to get more work done in a shorter time.

2. Start off each school term working twice as hard as you thought you possibly could. The momentum of such a start can make an honor student of you.

3. In examinations, do all the easy problems first. Then tackle the hard ones in order to give them your best attention—free from worry that you will come to the end of your time with part of the test unanswered. If you finish early, *don't hand in the paper immediately*. Go over it as often as you can, doing each problem as though you are first seeing it. You'll be surprised at the errors you can catch.

4. Be a good listener. Just sitting and listening honestly and intelligently is a big help in most classes.

5. Try to vary your subject matter in your study hour. For example, work fifteen minutes on a reading assignment, then tackle a composition which has to be finished, then memorize your language lesson or review it. You will find it more interesting than spending the entire period on one topic.

6. First work on the subject which seems most difficult or dullest to get it out of the way while you are still fresh. Save the easiest subject for the last part of your study period.

7. Take notes and make outlines in your notebooks, keeping a separate notebook for each subject.

8. No radio, television, or conversations while you work.

Only Fighters Are Wanted

By DAVID B. PARKER

The general needed a military escort through Indian country but he wouldn't take a dog as a recruit

The big dog galloped easily alongside the lead horse, just ahead of the dust cloud kicked up by the fourteen blue-shirted cavalry troopers who cantered behind. His tan and black hair was overlaid with the gray dust of the plains, but his head was up, his ears alert. Often his head cocked sideways toward his master.

Lieutenant John Leigh twisted in his saddle. The party of Indian warriors who had ridden parallel to their course for the past hour had stopped on the crest of a ridge. Sitting easily on their ponies, they watched the small escort platoon. Leigh spoke to the big dog.

"Not more than forty of them, Mike," he said. "They won't attack."

Leigh raised his right hand. "Trot! Column of two's!" The troopers behind him slowed, closed up, and moved smartly toward the small wagon train which was slowly moving toward them across the small valley.

Leigh led his column in a wide arc, Mike close by his horse's off forefoot, and drew up beside the general, who rode a big chestnut at the head of the train. Leigh's gloved hand snapped to the brim of his hat in salute.

"Lieutenant Leigh reporting, sir, with your escort. Colonel Chester's compliments, and it is three days' ride to Fort Hope."

The general returned his salute. He was a small, thin man, his nostrils pinched, his full beard flecked with gray. His reputation as a fierce Indian fighter had already, two years after the Civil War, spread throughout the regular army. Returning from Washington to take command of the Wyoming Territory, he had elected to ride with the small train of settlers who were heading up the Bozeman Trail. He eyed the lieutenant keenly.

"Very good, Mr. Leigh." The general's voice was brittle. He asked abruptly. "You saw the Indian party on the ridge ahead?"

"Yes, sir."

"You would have done well, Mr. Leigh, to have dispersed them before reporting to me. Your duty is to provide protection to myself and the others in this wagon train."

"It is a small party—I did not think them dangerous, sir."

"You thought wrong, Mr. Leigh. Disperse them at once."

Leigh turned his horse to give the attack orders to his troopers.

"One moment, Mr. Leigh." The general spoke sharply. He gestured toward Mike, who stood between their two horses, looking up into Leigh's face. "What is this dog doing here?"

"He is my dog, sir," Leigh answered. Mike's tail wagged slightly as he sensed he was the subject of his master's words. "I brought him from the East—he is the first Alsatian in the western plains, sir. I've trained him to accompany me on campaigns."

163

Leigh leaned down and spoke quietly to the dog. *"Circle right, Mike."* Mike walked around the rear of his horse to stand close on the off side.

"Very amusing, but this is no country estate, Mr. Leigh," the general snapped. "Find another place for the dog as soon as we reach Fort Hope. Only fighters are wanted in my command."

The general turned away. Mike put his forepaws on his master's stirrup, his nose touching Leigh's dusty boot.

"Down, Mike," Leigh said softly. ". . . Sergeant Crest! Have your men check their arms and gear. We'll make a running attack." He wheeled his horse and touched spurs lightly to the horse's flank. "Trot—ho-o-o!"

At the double-noted command, the squad left the wagon train and trotted forward. Mike galloped after them until his master turned and shouted, "Stay there, Mike! *Stay!*" Mike halted and stood disconsolately as the troopers moved rapidly away.

Half a mile away the Indians waited on the ridge-top. As Leigh's squad approached, they closed behind their chief who led them, first at a walk, then at a trot, obliquely down the flat slope toward the oncoming soldiers.

Leigh raised his left arm. "Left front into line! Gallop—ho-o-o!"

The Indians turned straight toward the thin line of cavalrymen and spurred their horses into a full gallop. The two bands raced toward each other, the Indians shouting their fierce, high-pitched yells of combat and firing wildly. The first volley from the cavalry cracked out two seconds before the two groups crashed into each other at full speed.

Mike, watching intently, could not see what was happening in the thick dust that surrounded the melee. But he heard the wild yells of the Indians, the shouts of the troopers, the sharp cracks of pistols and rifles, the screams of wounded horses.

The big dog looked back at the halted wagon train, but the noise of the battle pulled him forward. He broke into a run, straight toward the writhing mass of dust, gunpowder smoke, horses, and men.

He had almost reached them when the Indians, broken by the tough close-in fighting of the veteran cavalrymen, began a disorganized retreat. Leigh led his squad—smaller by three men now that one trooper had been killed and two others had had their horses shot beneath them—in a hot chase. They raced up the valley until the Indian ponies, carrying less weight, pulled away and entered a sparse wood at the bottom of the foothills. Leigh halted the squad, assembled them, and turned them back toward the wagon train.

Leigh had not seen Mike as the dog raced behind them in the short chase. The squad was picking up the two dismounted troopers when he saw Mike a hundred yards up the slope, just as the Indians, rallied by their chief, broke out of the woods and swept toward them.

Quickly the cavalry formed to meet the charge, and the Indians, knowing they could not break the tough group of seasoned fighters, though the soldiers were outnumbered two to one, veered off before Leigh gave the command for the first volley. But Mike was directly in the path of the galloping, yelling red men.

Leigh spurred his horse forward, and Mike saw him coming. The racing Indians trained their running fire on the single horse and rider who had so foolishly left the main body and rushed toward them.

Leigh galloped forward in a wide curve, close to the Indians. In a moment he was parallel to them, between them and Mike. His revolver blazed at the enemy not ten yards away as he jerked his horse to a skidding stop and wheeled back toward his squad.

"Come, Mike!"

The familiar voice brought a single roaring bark from the dog. He kept pace with his master's horse as they raced back, while the Indians swung into the shelter of the woods again.

Sergeant Crest saluted as the lieutenant rejoined the squad.

"I think that's the last of them, sir, for a while," he said calmly. His stolid face

164

showed no surprise at his commander's wild dash to save a dog.

"Form the squad, sergeant, and we'll move to the wagon train at a walk."

The train was on the move again ten minutes later when the cavalry rejoined it. Leigh saluted the general and would have dropped behind, but the general called him up.

"Mr. Leigh!" The general's voice snapped out for the whole command to hear.

"That was the most foolish exhibition I have ever seen! I will have that dog shot and you court-martialed if he causes the slightest disturbance to military discipline again. I repeat my former command, sir—you will dispose of him at the first opportunity."

The wagons creaked westward through the long afternoon. Lieutenant Leigh and his thirteen cavalrymen from A Troop, 4th Cavalry, scouted for the wagon train, and the general had no more words for them that day, except for a sharp reprimand of a trooper who flicked a burnt match into the tinder-dry prairie grass.

This was the first mission for John Leigh, graduated from West Point too late to see action in the Civil War. But his troopers knew their job, and they did it. Escort the wagon train. Twenty-two men, ten women, eight wagons, and sixty horses—moving west, building America. Keep them from surprise attack, defend them if attack comes. Your job is over when you get them and the general safely to Fort Hope; another platoon will take them from there.

One of the wagons was manned by soldiers—artillerymen, with scarlet stripes down the sides of their breeches. Inside was a new type of howitzer to reinforce Fort Hope's defenses. With the small, heavy little cannon were its boxes of case-shot ammunition.

Mike was close by his master whenever Leigh was with the wagon train. When the cavalry moved out to the front or flank to scout the area, Leigh's stern command, "Stay, Mike!" kept the dog beside the jolting wagons.

At high noon next day their scouting turned up something really big. Leigh came back from the reconnaissance they had made a mile to the front—came back with the horses stretched to a full stomach-to-earth gallop.

"War party coming behind me, sir! At least a thousand. This is the main body, I think."

Not a muscle in the general's face moved. "Very well," he said. Briefly he scanned the ground around them, then pointed to a slight rise a quarter of a mile to their left. "We'll make corral there, Mr. Leigh. The wagon circle will be twenty yards. Animals inside, in groups close to the wagons. Prepare barricades. On the double!"

Leigh turned the head of the wagon column sharply to the left, and the pioneers urged their tired horses into a trot. But they were only halfway to the selected defense area when the Indians came into view around a knoll. They trotted toward the wagons in open order, in a dozen ranks of over a hundred front.

The general yelled, "Corral here!" He grabbed the reins of the lead team himself to steer it into a circle. The Indians spurred their horses to a gallop. Ahead rode their chief on a magnificent bay horse.

As the Indians thundered over the knee-high, brittle prairie grass, Leigh ordered his troopers to dismount and form a firing line before the wagons. Three cavalrymen, acting as horseholders, led their mounts inside the rapidly forming wagon corral. At that moment, while the warriors were still out of firing range, disaster fell.

An axle on the last wagon broke, and as the wheels folded up against the wagon sides, the rear end of the wagon crashed to the ground. The horses pulling it were jerked to a stop. The wagon was isolated from the corral a hundred yards beyond. It was the wagon carrying the howitzer and its ammunition.

Leigh saw the cannoneers jump from the wagon and run toward the corral. He knelt, pistol in hand, in the center of his little line of men, until the Indians were almost upon them. "Fire!"

The sharp, accurate volley burst into the

faces of the charging warriors. An instant later, with new cartridges in their barrels, the soldiers fired again. Horses and men went down, but the Indians closed their ranks and swept on. Another volley, and the chief was knocked from his horse. Screaming wildly, the Indians swerved to the right, pouring arrows and musket balls into the wagon corral as they swept past.

Leigh led his men at a run into the meager safety of the corral. Mike was close at his heels as he posted his troopers behind the wagons and grain sacks hastily dumped on the ground for barricades. The general was leaning against the tailboard of a wagon, glaring at the Indians.

"They'll be back in a moment," the general said, without taking his eyes from the war party. "That first charge was impromptu —they hadn't expected to run on us so soon. After the next charge, we'll go for that howitzer."

Leigh glanced around the perimeter of their pitifully weak corral. The barricades were being reinforced, the women helping the men calmly. A wounded settler lay propped against a wagon wheel; his face was pain-racked, but he held his rifle firmly and asked for a grain sack for a firing rest. Leigh touched Mike's head a moment, then looked back at the Indians.

The warriors were in full war paint, colorful and hideous. They wore moccasins, cartridge belts for their muskets, and eagle feathers in their long black hair. They sat their horses easily without saddles or stirrups. Around the waist of one of them was a brilliant scarlet silk sash, taken from some cavalry officer's body.

A new chief had re-formed the Indian ranks, and now he loosed a wild whoop and broke into a fast gallop. The whole horde thundered behind him with gathering momentum.

Leigh and Mike heard the hard, dry voice of the general. "They'll try to ride us down in the first rush. Not a shot until I give the command!"

The Indians fired as they charged, a crescendo of musket and pistol shots. Bullets smacked into the wooden sides of the wagons and ripped the canvas covers. Mike flinched involuntarily at a heavy thud against the grain sack in front of him.

Soldiers and settlers were calm and silent. Their rifles pointed steadily toward the onrushing mass. The Indians were all but on top of them when the general roared the command to fire.

The terribly accurate volley struck down a score of horses and riders. Leigh leaned over his barricade, shooting deliberately round after round from his revolver. Mike quivered, his shoulder leaning hard against his master's leg, but he did not flinch again.

When another two strides would have crashed the warriors against the wagons, the deadly bullets from the defenders broke them and they split apart, streaming past the corral on either side. They poured close-in fire as they passed, but so great was their speed that their shots went wild.

But in the respite after they swept by, Leigh saw that the defenders had suffered heavily. Four men and one woman killed, over a dozen wounded. The general surveyed the wreckage around him and then called to Leigh.

"They'll ride us down soon, Mr. Leigh. We have to get that howitzer. Take five men and horses and drag the piece into the corral."

Leigh picked Sergeant Crest and four others, and they mounted their skittering horses.

"Stay here, Mike!" he commanded, and then led his men in a wild dash between two wagons out of the corral.

The Indians were waiting for them. They knew the isolated wagon's precious cargo and dashed toward it to cut Leigh off. Only halfway, Leigh saw there was no hope of reaching the disabled wagon. The defenders in the corral could not give even supporting fire, as his small detachment was between them and the Indians.

"Counter gallop!" he yelled, and they raced back to the corral with Indian bullets flying after them.

With dusty sweat pouring down his face,

Leigh stood again beside the general. Mike's tongue touched the back of his hand.

"We'll rescue the gun tonight," the general said. "Meanwhile, we'll keep the savages away from it with aimed fire."

The warriors rode past the crippled wagon, but steady, accurate shooting from the defenders kept them from dismounting and harming the howitzer. Baffled temporarily, they withdrew and formed for another charge against the corral.

The charge was furious, and although it was split again at the last moment, two more were dead inside the corral and Sergeant Crest had an arrow through his right arm.

Leigh talked to Mike.

"On the next rush, or the one after, they'll get us. They know it—they're taking their time about forming for this one."

Leigh stood up, watching the Indians on the far side of the wagon. A faint breeze cooled his cheek. Suddenly he looked down into Mike's eyes.

"Mike! There's just a chance—and it's up to you, boy!"

He whipped his knife from his belt and bent over one of the grain sacks. Swiftly he slashed down the length of the sack, and jerked its contents onto the ground. He ripped again with the knife, then twisted the coarse, heavy cloth until it resembled a piece of rope about four feet long. He tied one end of it to a ten-foot length of picket rope. He sprang up into one of the wagons and jerked the wooden cork from a kerosene keg. It took only an instant to soak the burlap with the pungent fluid. Then he jumped

back to the ground and squatted down in front of Mike.

"It's a tough assignment, Mike," he said quietly.

He took a long sulphur match from his saddlebag and struck it on a wheel rim. He touched it to the kerosene-soaked cloth which burst into flame and spewed dark, oily smoke. The far end of the picket rope, to which the burning cloth was attached, he held in his left hand.

"Mr. Leigh!" The general was standing over him. "What are you trying to do?"

Leigh looked up from his squatting position. "The breeze is right, sir. It's our only chance to get the howitzer."

The general looked at him, and then at the dog, understanding the plan. He was doubtful of Mike, but he did not speak. Leigh put his mouth close to Mike's ear, his right hand around the dog's shoulders.

"The rope game, Mike," he whispered urgently. "Obey!" He put the end of the picket rope between Mike's teeth. The flaming burlap strip lay on the ground behind the dog's shoulder. The oily smoke blew over Mike's face, but he looked up unflinchingly into his master's eyes.

Leigh stood up and pointed between two of the wagons. "Go, Mike—GO!"

For an instant the dog looked at Leigh, sensing his urgency. Then, his teeth gripping the rope firmly, he dashed out of the corral, straight toward the Indians. The flaming end of cloth trailed behind him on the ground.

The Indians saw the big dog running to-

ward them, mysteriously dragging fire behind him, but they could not at first understand the purpose behind this strange sight. Then, as the dry prairie grass caught fire, and the breeze fanned the flames, hot and fierce, toward them, they knew. With wild cries, those in front spurred their horses forward.

Mike was past the howitzer wagon now. Over the Indians' screams and the gathering fusillade of shots aimed at the dog, Lieutenant John Leigh's voice roared a command.

"Left, Mike! LEFT!"

Mike swerved to the left, his speed so great that the arc was wide, bringing him ever closer to the warriors. Behind him, the fires were raging now, making a crackling wall of flame.

Mike circled behind the howitzer wagon, was lost to sight. He raced into Leigh's agonized gaze again, far out on the plain in the waving grass. His flaming wake was a solid line of fire. The breeze was light but the grass was high and very dry. The gathering flames sucked in air, towered high, and moved more rapidly outward, away from the corral, toward the Indians. Only three Indians could force their singed horses through them; they galloped madly toward Mike.

Those in the corral breathlessly watched the dog, racing in a shower of arrows. Spurts of dust from scores of rifles marked his course. In another moment, the three pursuers would ride him down.

"Come, Mike! COME!"

The big dog heard the voice he knew. He swerved again and ran toward the corral. He was bleeding from a bullet graze, but now there was almost a perfect semi-circle of grass fire around the howitzer wagon. As he ran back, an arrow from one of his pursuers hit his shoulder and knocked him down.

He rolled completely over, but as though it were part of his stride, he came back on his feet at a dead run. Just then a volley from the expert riflemen of A Troop dropped the three Indians. Mike dashed between the wagons back into the corral. Leigh saw the arrow dangling from the dog's shoulder as with a yell of command he set himself and half a dozen soldiers to leap on their horses and gallop out to the howitzer wagon.

Tender hands pulled the arrow from Mike's shoulder, and the dog stood, panting, too exhausted to follow his master.

The breeze pushed the grass fire swiftly outward. The fire spread backward, too, but more slowly upwind, and by the time they reached the howitzer wagon, Leigh and his men had lifted the stubby little cannon off the wagon bed, thrown a rope around it, and were dragging it back to the corral.

In a few seconds they had the howitzer set up between two of the wagons and loaded it with an eight-pound shot-filled ball. Then the soldiers waited until the warriors had moved out of the path of the prairie fire and formed for another charge from a new direction.

The first round really did the trick. The ball exploded over the heads of the Indian mass, spewing a hundred grape-size shots into horses and riders. The Indians hesitated; the charge stopped before it had begun; a second burst broke them. Many of them had seen the "gun that shoots twice" and knew they could not fight against it. A single Indian jerked his horse around and galloped away from the corral, away from the terrible gun.

In another instant, the whole war party was running away.

Leigh took his eyes from the diminishing cloud of dust and knelt beside Mike. The arrow wound was painful but not serious. Leigh heard the general's voice behind him.

"Well done, Mr. Leigh. We will break corral and move out. Have the howitzer ready in the lead wagon."

"Yes, sir." Leigh turned to pass the order on, but the general had something else to say. "About your dog, Mr. Leigh. You will remember my saying that only fighters are wanted in my command. My feeling about that is unchanged. But your dog has proved himself a fighter, and he will stay on the rolls of A Troop."

Home on the Range

By B. J. CHUTE

A couple of wise guys who can't fry water undertake to cook a meal for the boss

Jeff Abbott parked the lawnmower against a tree and spoke to the hammock. "Get up, useless. It's your turn."

The hammock stirred and said, "Go away."

Jeff sighed, took hold of the ropes and tipped it neatly upside down. His brother Tommy popped forth and landed sprawling on the grass.

"Ups-a-daisy," said Jeff brightly and settled down in a patch of shade.

Tommy said, "I hope you're sitting on a wasp." He hauled the lawnmower into position and leaned dreamily on the handle.

"Quit stalling," said Jeff.

"I'm not stalling. Jeff, won't it be wonderful if Dad gets that job?"

"You'll still have to mow the lawn," Jeff pointed out realistically. "And anyway it's no good worrying about it until Dad gets back home tomorrow night."

"*With* Mr. Wilson," Tommy reminded him. "If I was Mr. Wilson, I'd make Dad manager of the Wilson and Arnold branch store here without even thinking about it."

"Well, Mother's planning a slap-bang dinner, and there's nothing like a good dinner to make a man feel mellow, especially Mother's fried chicken. One taste of that, Mr. Wilson'll make Dad vice-president."

"I'll settle for manager."

"I'll settle for you mowing the lawn. It's rising around your ankles."

Tommy sighed and was about to start work when the front door opened and their mother came out, wearing a blue housedress and an anxious expression. Tommy waved to her companionably.

"Have a hammock," he invited.

She declined with thanks, but crossed the lawn to join them.

"Your Aunt Dorothy just phoned. Uncle Jim fell down the basement stairs and sprained his ankle."

"Gee, that's tough! Anything we can do to help?"

"That's just it. Dorothy has a bad cold and the twins are behaving like wild Indians. She wanted to know if I could drive out and spend the night with her, and I said I'd call back."

Jeff got to his feet. "Of course you'll go. She can't possibly be expected to manage alone."

"You're sure you don't mind? You'll have to make supper out of scraps, I'm afraid— I'll shop for Mr. Wilson's dinner tomorrow morning."

"Don't give us a second thought," Jeff said airily. "I'll keep an eye on the house, and little Thomas will mow the lawn."

Little Thomas permitted himself a low

passionate growl. Mrs. Abbott said, "The laundryman will be coming. Oh, and Jeff, they've promised to send a man to look at the stove. The back burners don't light right."

"Back burners," Jeff repeated. "Okay. Now you go and call Aunt Dorothy and tell her the Marines are coming."

By the time they had seen their mother off in the family car, Tommy and Jeff were feeling highly competent and domestic. Tommy shot through the lawnmowing and, when the doorbell rang, Jeff welcomed the laundryman hospitably and retired upstairs to sort sheets and towels.

The doorbell rang again.

Jeff shouted down, "Tommy, if that's the man to fix the stove, tell him it's the back burners." Silence answered him. "Tommy?" More silence. "Hey, Tommy! Who is it?"

A hollow voice rose from the front hall. "Telegram," said Tommy. "From Dad."

Waving two bath towels, Jeff hurtled down the stairs and met Tommy coming up. Wordlessly, Tommy put the yellow envelope into his brother's hands, put his head into his own hands and sat down on the bottom step. Jeff opened the telegram:

> Plans changed. Flying down. Will arrive tonight with Wilson. Expect us dinner about six o'clock. Love.

"Tonight!" There was a flopping sound as Jeff landed beside Tommy. "Good grief! What do we do now?"

"Phone Mother and tell her to come home."

"Thomas! We can't. Nowhere to catch her. And she couldn't get back in time if we did."

Tommy thought a moment, then nodded gloomy agreement. "Well, how about wiring Dad and telling him to change his plans?"

"They'd have left by now." Jeff clutched his hair. "This is awful. Mother had everything planned to give Mr. Wilson a super-deluxe dinner, and now . . . Tommy! I've got the solution. *We'll get the dinner.*"

"You're mad," said Tommy.

Jeff consulted his watch and ignored his brother. "It's not four-thirty yet, and they won't be here until six. By that time, we'll have a delicious dinner all ready to welcome Mr. Wilson."

"Mother said there was only scraps for our dinner. You can't feed Mr. Wilson on scraps."

"Listen, chum, if Mother was home she'd cook up something, wouldn't she? She's always making something out of nothing. Well, we can do the same. You want Mr. Wilson to be happy, don't you?"

"For Pete's sake! Of course I do."

"Very well, then." Jeff seized his brother and pushed him kitchen-wards. "The first thing we do is plan a menu, starting of course with soup." He found a cookbook and dived into "Soups." "Four pounds chicken—one cup chopped clams. The things people think of! Tommy, look in the cupboard and see what kind of canned soups we've got."

"How about cream of mushroom?"

"Fine. We just heat that. Now, for the main course . . . beef roulards, veal shortcake, roast chicken. H'mm." He changed his tactics. "Tell you what, we'll pick our vegetables first. What have we got?"

"Bag of peas. Six potatoes. We could have baked potatoes."

Jeff, who had been voyaging dangerously among the meats again, shook his head. "We shall want the oven."

"We shall?"

Jeff nodded solemnly. "I've decided on a corned-beef-and-rice casserole, if we have any corned beef. Take a look, will you, Thomas my boy?"

"I suppose," said Thomas my boy between his teeth, "that you're being executive. Oh, well." He investigated the cupboard again and came out waving the corned beef.

"Now, find an onion and some tomatoes. The casserole takes thirty minutes, so it should go in the oven about five-thirty." He licked his pencil and made a note. "This is going to be easy. Soup, casserole, peas, potatoes—I think mashed would be nice. Let's see, potatoes on at five-twenty, peas at five-forty, set table at five-forty-five. . . ."

"Trains stop only on signal," said Tommy. "Passengers with baby elephants must leave their trunks in the baggage car."

"Hush," said Jeff. "Now, for dessert, we want something fancy. I think cake would be nice."

"I thought you were in the oven."

"That comes later. The cake will be out by the time the casserole goes in, which is why I have the timetable you were so rude about. Don't apologize."

"Who's apologizing?"

Jeff listened. No one was. He returned to his menu. "There's a recipe here for chocolate roll that sounds delicious. It's like a jelly roll, only it has whipped cream inside." He spread the cookbook out on the table. "I'll start that, and you do the casserole. First, you fix the rice and tomatoes."

"How much rice?" said Tommy resignedly.

Jeff referred to his cookbook again. "Four cups cooked rice. That would mean four cups uncooked rice, I should think. You just put it in water and boil it." He got down on his knees and started prowling around the saucepan cupboard. "Do you think Mother

has a jelly-roll pan?" he inquired from its depths, added something about darkest Africa and then gave a happy yelp. "Ah, got it!" There was a tremendous crash, rather like two armadillos locked in mortal combat, and Jeff came out hastily backwards with two muffin pans and a whole troop of small custard-cups pursuing him hotly. He had, however, the jelly-roll pan in one hand and the casserole in the other, so there was triumph on his brow as well as a sieve.

Tommy said, "The rice is on. Do I skin the tomatoes?"

"I suppose. Let's see, six tablespoons of cake flour. Tommy, what's cake flour?"

"Flour you use in cakes, I should think."

"Brilliant deduction," said Jeff ungratefully. "Flour's flour," he decided, measured six tablespoons, added cocoa, salt and baking powder, and then discovered he was supposed to sift the mixture three times. This seemed pointless and enraged him, and by the time he was through the third sifting the air was cloudy with flour dust. It cheered him enormously, on emerging, to discover that his brother was knee-deep in tomato skins. "There must be a better way to do that,

Tommy. You're not getting anywhere."

Tommy, who knew a better way, offered Jeff the knife. Jeff backed off and made noises appropriate to a man who is very busy with a chocolate roll.

"Three-quarters cup sugar," said Jeff, measuring like mad. "You know, Tommy, this is all quite simple. I hope Mr. Wilson appreciates home cooking."

Tommy was trying to arrange a separation between his nose and a large piece of tomato skin, and his reply was slightly blurred, as if with anguish.

"Four eggs," said Jeff cheerfully. "Beat egg whites stiff but not dry. H'mm, that's odd. You beat the yolks separately. Tommy, if you were an egg . . ."

Tommy put down his knife in exasperation. "I've got enough tomato skin on me to be a tomato," he said crossly. "Look, Jeff, can't I just cut 'em up and dump 'em into the sauce-pan?"

"Dump away," said Jeff. "I need you." He was holding an egg in each hand and staring at them. As Tommy came over, he outlined the problem in simple terms. "The recipe says to separate the yolks and whites. I'm in a very receptive mood if you have any suggestions."

"Sure," said Tommy with frightening clear-headedness. "I've watched Mother do it a hundred times. You simply take an egg, like this, and tap it against the side of the bowl—OOPS!"

"Have another egg," said Jeff hospitably, and added with admiration, "Who would ever have believed that a little egg with no feet could run up a person's sleeve so fast? Can I help you, pal—a vacuum cleaner or a bathtub or something?"

Tommy, between clenched teeth, declined aid and mopped himself up austerely with a dish towel, then held out a stern hand for another egg. "I merely hit it a little too hard," he said, cracked this one more skeptically and let the white trickle out slowly. "There. Now, grab the yolk before it skids."

Jeff automatically reached out his hand, palm up. Tommy dropped the yolk into it.

This time it was Jeff who did his speaking between clenched teeth, and by the time Tommy found a bowl for the yolks he was in a clearly fragile mood. Tommy tried another egg, and its yolk crept in with the white. In the next few minutes, they learned an astonishing amount about adhesion. When at last four yolks and four whites had gone their separate ways, they were both exhausted and Tommy staggered back thankfully to his rice which was beginning to bubble.

Jeff began to beat the egg whites to the tune of "Danny Boy." "Lookit the purty white mountain peaks it makes," he invited, admiring his handiwork. "Tommy, it says here to fold in the sugar. How do you fold in sugar?"

"I'm busy," said Tommy, who didn't know.

"I guess it just means stir." Jeff dumped in the sugar, stirred briskly and took a taste. "Umm, delicious. How are your tomatoes doing?"

Tommy poked one with a fork. "I think they're holding their own." He leaped as the doorbell rang. "Maybe that's another telegram, saying they're not coming."

"It's probably the man about the stove." He watched Tommy go, returned to his egg whites, then broke off as the phone rang. "Too many bells in this house," he said grumpily and went to answer it.

The phone call was from a neighbor. The doorbell had been pushed by a vacuum-cleaner salesman. When the cooks returned to the kitchen, they were greeted by a strange rich scent.

"My tomatoes!" Tommy shrieked and grabbed the saucepan. The bottom layer had turned a melancholy black and was clinging sulkily to the pan; the top layer was in its original state.

"Put 'em in another saucepan and start over again," Jeff advised, glanced at the clock and added, "Jeepers, we've got to hurry." He combined his eggs, added vanilla and dumped in the flour mixture all in one dump. This turned out to be a grievous error. The flour took a cordial dislike to the eggs and humped itself up in a series of hillocks. Jeff, wielding a spoon, would whack one hillock into place, only to see another rise behind it, and when, inspired, he tried to correct the situation with the egg-beater, the egg-beater bogged down in the batter. With the aid of two spoons, a knife and his fingers, Jeff finally got the batter loose and decided that the lumps would bake themselves out in the oven.

He began to issue instructions like an overwrought general. "Tommy, line the jelly-roll pan with waxed paper and grease the paper. You'd better hurry," he added. "I think the lumps are gaining on me." He hit them fiercely on their heads with his spoon, then glanced over his shoulder to see how Tommy was getting along, caught sight of the stove and gave a horrified howl.

"Tommy—LOOK!"

Tommy looked. The rice was boiling over.

Sequestered there in the saucepan of water, each separate little grain had been hard at work, swelling triumphantly. Now the time had come when the overcrowding became acute, and rice poured out over the sides of the pan in a tremendous white waterfall, inundating the stove, sweeping heedlessly over the burners and cascading to the floor.

It was a stupendous and stirring spectacle. People travel thousands of miles to see Niagara Falls; great natural events like the San Francisco earthquake become historic. Here, in the Abbott kitchen, the whole world was ricebound, and the majestic beauty of the show should have held Jeff and Tommy in hushed appreciation.

It didn't.

Jeff shouted, "Get a bucket!"

Tommy yelled for the Fire Department.

Jeff howled, "Do something!" and Tommy howled right back "What?" which was a good question.

It was Jeff who finally thought of turning out the fire. The flood began slowly to subside, leaving rice fields and swamps.

Jeff paddled back to his brother and eyed him severely. "What did you measure that stuff with? A bushel basket?"

"It's four cups full, like you said," Tommy defended himself. "It's not my fault if only

four cups full makes a full-scale blizzard."

"Well, clean it up," said Jeff morosely, then looked at the clock. "No, don't. I need you. Is the waxed paper greased? Where's my spoon? Where's . . . ?"

"Stop roaring," said Tommy soothingly. He shoved the pan under his brother's nose and Jeff poured in the batter, arranging the lumps as neatly as possible. Together, they put the finished product reverently into the oven, trying to avoid trampling on rice.

"Bakes twelve minutes," said Jeff. "Don't let me forget it. Now, where are we with the corned-beef casserole?"

"Well," said Tommy, in a masterpiece of understatement, "we have the rice."

Jeff, who was standing on one foot scraping rice off his shoe, conceded the truth of this statement. He drew a deep breath.

"From here on, everything's much simpler. You put the corned beef and rice into the casserole, make a sauce with the tomatoes and some onion . . ."

"What tomatoes?"

"They're not well?" said Jeff anxiously.

"Some are burned, and some are raw. We cater to all tastes."

"Well, put the raw ones on the bottom and arrange the burned ones where they won't show." He seized the casserole and began alternating corned beef and rice in a chef-like frenzy. Tommy peered into the cookbook to see what came next and suddenly announced, "You should have greased the casserole first."

Jeff gave the cry of a wounded hippopotamus. "Now he tells me! Well, it's too late. Here, you take your tomatoes now, Tommy, add salt, pepper, Worcestershire sauce and onion. Go find an onion and chop it."

"*You* chop it," Tommy suggested winningly.

"No, you. I'm busy." Jeff pointed indignantly at the clock. "Now I've forgotten what time the chocolate roll went in." He opened the oven, gazed inside and gave one of those wounded howls which were becoming a trade-mark with him. "It hasn't even begun to— Oh."

"Difficulty?"

"We forgot to light the oven."

"Then I suppose," said Tommy profoundly, "that it didn't bake."

"My boy, you're an absolute genius." Jeff lit the oven in some bitterness of spirit, suddenly remembered the potato problem and dived for the cookbook again. "Peel and boil for twenty to thirty minutes," he read. "Tommy, you peel things so nicely . . ."

"No." Tommy, who was sobbing quietly over his onion, was in no mood for more responsibilities.

Jeff retired into the potatoes, and almost at once he began to understand what his brother had been through with the tomatoes. The devotion of a potato to its peel is a very touching thing, and after about ten minutes of the most earnest endeavor it began to seem to Jeff that it was cruel to separate them. He gave up trying to peel thin and started peeling thick. This resulted in a splendid pile of potato peels and six miniature white marbles. He impaled one of these on the point of his knife and turned it around, examining it intently from all sides. "Look, Tommy, isn't Nature amazing?"

Tommy looked up with wet eyes and blinked. "What's *that* thing?"

"That," said Jeff informatively, "is a potato. I have six of the dear little, wee little things." He sighed deeply. "Tommy, do you think we need potatoes with all that rice?"

"Potatoes," said Tommy, who was a good brother, "are very fattening—onion's chopped, Jeff. What do I do with it now?"

"Mix it with the rest of the stuff and pour it over the corned beef and rice."

"I hope Mr. Wilson likes rice," said Tommy, mixing his sauce artistically. "A man who doesn't like rice is going to feel awfully out of things in this house. There—now what?"

"Now, it goes into the oven. Great leaping lemondrops, the chocolate roll!" Jeff leaped for the stove. "It's been in there at least ten minutes too long."

"How does it look?" said Tommy.

"Well . . . It has a lot of strange little bubbles on top, and in the middle it seems sort of depressed. Do you think it's done!"

Tommy joined him and peered. "Reminds me of that rubber mat on the porch."

"Are you insinuating . . . ?"

"No, no, of course not. Just a sudden mood of reminiscence." Tommy scowled at the chocolate roll. "You know, Jeff, I think you'd better take it out. It's five-thirty already and the casserole has to go in. And, anyway, if that roll gets any browner it will be black."

"You put things so nicely." Jeff took the pan out of the oven and made another grab for the cookbook. "F' Pete's sake!"

"Now what?" Tommy shoved in the casserole, closed the door and turned alertly to his brother's aid in what appeared to be yet another crisis.

"The roll's supposed to be turned out onto a towel, dusted with confectioner's sugar. I call that very eccentric. Get me a towel and some sugar, quick."

Tommy obeyed. Jeff sprinkled the towel with sugar and then turned his cake out onto it. "Now," he said, "we roll it up and wrap it in the towel, working rapidly." He worked

rapidly, producing a neat, professional-looking roll.

"Jeff," said Tommy quietly.

"Looks nice, doesn't it?"

"It looks very nice," said Tommy, "but I think you've made two slight errors. In the first place, you didn't take the waxed paper off . . ."

"Oh," said Jeff, rather blankly.

"And, in the second place," said Tommy, "when it says roll up and wrap in towel, I think it means that you roll it up first and *then* wrap it in the towel. The way things are now, you've got the waxed paper and the towel where the whipped cream goes."

"So I have," said Jeff. A respectful sort of pall settled on the scene, but then the natural optimism of the Abbotts reasserted itself. "Well, look at it this way. It has to be unrolled when it's cool enough to put the cream in, and at that time we merely zip off the towel and the paper in one brisk motion."

"I hope you're right."

"Of course I'm right. Now what have we got left to do?"

"Shell peas, whip cream, set table and . . ."

The back doorbell rang suddenly.

Jeff and Tommy leaped in duet. "If that's the man about the stove at a time like this," said Jeff, "I shall boil him in a saucepan and wrap him up in the chocolate roll." He strode to the door and flung it open dramatically.

A small man with a black bag clutched in one hand looked at him meekly and said, "Is this the Abbott house?"

"We expected you hours ago," Jeff said fretfully as he held the door open and followed him into the kitchen. "It's the back burners, but I guess you'll have to wait a few minutes before you fix them, on account of the stove's sort of busy."

The little man looked doubtful. "But I . . ."

"We won't keep you waiting long," Jeff assured. "You just sit down in this chair."

"Jeff," said Tommy in a hoarse stage whisper, "the peas aren't shelled yet. If we don't get them on pretty soon, we'll have to eat them for dessert."

Jeff clutched his brow and turned despairingly to the stove-man. "Look, can you shell peas?"

"Peas?"

"It's very simple," said Jeff apologetically, "and you'd be doing us a big favor." He put a bowl and the bag of peas onto the little man's lap and gazed at him trustingly. "I have to whip the cream and Tommy has to set the table, and if we don't get the peas on we'll really be in the soup."

"Soup!" Tommy yelled, catching the key word.

"Oh, murder! Get a can-opener and another saucepan." Jeff rushed around like a neurotic beetle, explaining as he rushed. "You see, the trouble is that my father's bringing a man home to dinner, and my mother's gone to visit my aunt who has twins and a husband with a sprained ankle and a cold. Well, *she* has the cold and her husband has the ankle." He paused to make sure this was all quite clear. The little man nodded dazedly, and Jeff went on. "So, this man that my father's bringing home is the president of the Wilson and Arnold stores—Tommy, where's that saucepan?"

"In your hand."

"Oh. Well, Mr. Wilson is thinking of making my father manager of the branch store here, so we're trying to get a nice dinner that will impress him. There's nothing like a good dinner to make a man feel mellow, and our aim in life is mellowing Mr. Wilson. He's probably a crab by nature," Jeff finished cheerfully. "I'd better whip the cream."

Tommy, table-setting, came out of the dining room. "What china shall we use, and where's the salt-and-pepper shakers?"

"Use the best, we want to be impressive. I don't know where the shakers are." Jeff whirred his egg-beater like a helicopter. "Put some water on to boil for the peas, will you, Tommy? And while you're there take a look at the casserole."

Tommy filled a saucepan, put it on the stove and then opened the oven door. He gasped, "Wow, that's hot" and backed off, looking pensive. Then he poked it cautiously with a spoon. "Jeff, you remember what the cookbook said about greasing the casserole? Well, the book was right."

"It stuck?"

"The rice," said Tommy precisely, "appears to have formed a thin coat of cement across the bottom. It would make a marvelous tennis court."

Jeff pondered this melancholy news-bulletin. "We'll serve it from the top," he decided resourcefully. "Tommy, this cream won't whip."

"Are you sure?"

"Positively. I'm beginning to have a vague feeling that Mother orders special cream for whipping." He gave the egg-beater a disgusted shake and splashed cream on the floor. "How can we have a chocolate-cream roll without cream?"

"How about spreading jelly on it instead? After all, it's second cousin to a jelly roll."

"I never spread jelly on a second cousin," said Jeff, "but we can try." He undid the towel around the cake and proceeded to unwrap. To say that cake, towel and waxed paper had become devoted to each other would be to understate the case. The paper clung to the bottom of the roll, and the towel clung to its interior. The cake itself, discouraged by the way things were going, peeled off in chunks.

Tommy tried hard to think of something reassuring to say, but there was a quality about the cake that defied comfort. "We could spread the towel with jelly," he offered. "Some towels have a very delicate flavor."

Jeff glared at the object he had produced. It was a sort of a chocolate towel, richly frosted with waxed paper. For anyone with a taste for towels and paper, it would make a most delectable and unusual dessert.

"Tommy," said Jeff.

"Yes, old man?" said Tommy in a hushed, respectful voice.

"What would you say to burying this quietly in the garbage can?"

"It would be kinder," said Tommy.

"That's what I thought." Jeff lifted the ruins solemnly and started toward the garbage can, then put his foot squarely into the cream he had splashed on the floor. There

was one moment when it looked as though Jeff would successfully defy the laws of gravity. In that moment, he grabbed for support at the stove-man's knee.

The stove-man's knee had a bowlful of shelled peas sitting on it. There was, therefore, a double crash—Jeff falling (with cake) and bowl falling (with peas). The peas, gladsomely released, scooted all over the kitchen floor. The cake only got as far as Jeff's lap.

He sat there on the floor, thinking long hard thoughts.

Tommy started to his rescue and then stopped, sniffing. From the oven a thin spiral of smoke wound its way out into the room.

The afternoon had trained Tommy to think fast in an emergency. He seized a potholder in one hand, turned off the oven with the other, drew the casserole out and eyed it somberly.

Jeff looked up from the cake in his lap. "There goes your tennis court, Tommy," said Jeff.

"There goes our dinner," said Tommy.

They looked around the room. They had mushroom soup and, if Tommy could find the salt-and-pepper shakers, they would have salt and pepper. Otherwise, their dinner now consisted of a well-burned casserole with a paved floor, a bowlful of shelled peas racing from door to window and a chocolate roll which Jeff was still sitting under.

The stove-man got down on his knees and began silently to follow the peas around the floor. After a moment, Tommy joined in.

Jeff rose and began scraping his trousers.

The swinging door from the dining room opened suddenly. Jeff stared for a moment, then shouted "Dad!!" Tommy, who had been trying to coax a pea out from under the refrigerator, looked up and echoed the shout.

Mr. Abbott got as far as "Hello, kids" and then saw the kitchen.

Called Jeff, "Where's Mr. Wilson?"

"Isn't he coming, I hope?" said Tommy, seeing a ray of light.

"Mr. Wilson?" Their father stopped staring at the kitchen and stared at his sons. "Didn't he . . . ?"

At that moment, the stove-man crawled

out from under the table, clutching a handful of migratory peas.

Mr. Abbott gave him one unbelieving look. "MR. WILSON!"

Jeff said "Oh, no" in a soft stricken whisper.

"Good evening, Mr. Abbott," said the pea-fancier, getting to his feet.

Tommy, two jumps behind on the plot, said alertly, "This isn't Mr. Wilson, Dad. This is the man to fix the stove." It then dawned on him that his father was in a better position to recognize Mr. Wilson than he was, and a quiver went over him like a ship meeting up with an iceberg.

Mr. Abbott gulped. "I had to stop off at the office, and I told Mr. Wilson to come on ahead and— What happened? Where's your mother?"

Tommy in a small voice explained about Aunt Dorothy. "So Mother went there," he finished "and Jeff and I made the—the dinner, and when the stove-man came we asked him to shell the peas because we were so short on time . . ."

"You asked Mr. Wilson to shell the peas?"

"We didn't know he was Mr. Wilson, we thought he was the stove-man."

Jeff said unhappily, "Gee, Dad, we're awfully sorry. We were just trying to make things nice."

Mr. Abbott put his arms over his sons' shoulders. "It's all right," he said. "We'll clean up this mess and go to a restaurant." He turned to Mr. Wilson. "I've got those reports you asked to see, sir. If you want to . . ."

Mr. Wilson shook his head. "It won't be necessary," he said crisply. "There's a plane back in about an hour. I'm taking that."

Mr. Abbott pulled his sons a little closer to him reassuringly. "I'm sorry you feel that way, sir," he said.

"Nothing to be sorry about," said Mr. Wilson. "I'm a man of quick decisions, that's all, and there's no sense hanging around once I've made up my mind. I'm too busy." He leaned over to scrape a smashed pea off his shoe and added, "I'll send you the contract to sign first thing in the morning."

"The—contract?"

"As manager." Mr. Wilson nodded. "Just what I want. Man with the kind of kids who'll put in a whole afternoon's hard work trying to fix things up nice for their father's guest. I knew you were a good business man, Mr. Abbott, but I take an interest in my managers' homes too. It makes a difference to me what their sons think of them."

"We—" said Jeff and Tommy.

"—and what they think of their sons," said Mr. Wilson.

"I—" said Mr. Abbott.

"Exactly," said Mr. Wilson. "And now, if I might just have a cup of coffee before I go . . ."

Jeff and Tommy looked at each other. "I'll boil the water," said Jeff.

"I'll measure out the instant coffee," said Tommy. "Very carefully, watching the teaspoon for any false moves. Cooking is *so* simple."

Jeff nodded solemnly. "Given plenty of time, a lot of space and absolute quiet, Mr. Wilson, I think we should be able to produce one cup of coffee."

"Two," said Mr. Wilson. "One for me, and one for my new manager."

Jeff gave him an appreciative look. "I'd like to know who said too many cooks spoil the boss," said Jeff. "He sure was wrong."

The Big Boss of Africa's Night Life

By WALTER J. WILWERDING

A man-eating lion looking for a bedtime snack is proud, sure, and powerful

Although my camp was near the Equator, I hugged the fire that evening. Even on the Equator, it is cold at seven thousand feet on the slope of Mount Kilimanjaro in East Africa. I shivered and listened to the sounds of Africa's awakening night life.

The raucous calling of galagoes came from the tall rain forest trees that surrounded my camp. A lone hyena moaned and whooped on the open veldt below. And from about two hundred yards away came the loudest sounds of all—the roars of the big boss. A lion was announcing the opening of the night's hunting. Soon there was a furious thundering chorus.

Anyone who has been at a zoo during feeding time knows about the noise that lions can make. They roar just as lustily before their feeding time in Africa. Few experiences can be more awe-inspiring, more spine-tingling than listening to the wild roaring of lions on the prowl in an African night.

There were many lions near the camp of my expedition to paint African animals, and we were serenaded nightly. Usually, the roaring began at about ten and kept up at intervals until one o'clock in the morning. Then about four a.m. we would be awakened by a final roaring as they returned from the hunt.

Our camp was situated not far from a rock-studded hollow in dense bush country.

Lions like places like that, as they provide protection against the hot sun during the heat of the day. Though the lion is a hot country animal, he often lives in high altitudes where the nights are cold and he does not like it too hot during the day. When the sun is high, he does not tarry in places without good cover.

I knew about this lions' lair in the bushes, since I had been down there to look it over. Naturally, I came loudly knocking. My native bearers made a racket by shouting and beating bushes with their spears as we approached. It was a wicked place in which to go calling on lions, and I held my rifle in readiness. Dense bush surrounded us, and we could see but a few feet ahead. But the lions retreated before the din of our coming to take refuge in the cool forest above.

So it was that I came to the place where the lions lived. Their fresh tracks were in the sand. Dried grass was flat where they had lain. There was no litter of filth or bones anywhere—the lions were good housekeepers.

One night a lion came visiting our camp. "The boss" is very bold and seems to be disdainful of man after dark. My natives slept in a grass-thatched hut at the rear of the camp. Standing beside this hut, the lion roared mightily. Awakened by the sound, I sat up and reached for my rifle. Then it occurred to me that a man-hunting lion would come in stealthy silence and would not come advertising his presence.

I put the rifle back on its rack and went back to sleep.

Frequently, we used a trail that ran between the forest and the bush country. But the lions used this trail too, for they like well-beaten paths and will always use them in preference to going through the thick of things. Several times, I encountered lions that were lying in the bushes near the trail. When very close to the trail, they would just get up to walk deeper into the bushes. This could only happen in the daytime, as the lion is very sure of himself after dark, and won't give way.

My Hair Stood on End

This same trail provided one of the most hair-raising experiences of my life among wild animals. I was walking down it in inky darkness, except for my flashlight. Suddenly I caught the bright, round orbs of a lion's eyes, which shone like twin planets in that velvet-black background. An angry, throaty growl warned me, "Keep away! Keep away!"

I was really more startled than frightened. To be thoroughly frightened, you have to have time to think things over and realize your danger. This happened suddenly, and I remember that I was only a bit annoyed.

The lion was at a bait that I had tied to a tree-stump near the trail. I had tied a dead buck here and had expected to watch over it from a machan, or tree platform, that the natives had built for me. Delayed by these preparations and with my dinner, black night had overtaken me before my departure from camp. The lion had come to his dinner early, and so we had both arrived at about the same time. I had hoped he would wait until the full moon rose, but I had failed to mention this in my invitation.

It would have been dangerous to shoot at those blazing eyes, for, had I wounded him, he would have been all over me in one jump. I yelled at the top of my lungs and, at this unexpected turn, he tore a forequarter off the buck and bounded off into the bushes.

Breathing more easily, I continued to the tree and climbed into the machan. I had some nasty business in mind for that lion. In fact I intended to make a rug out of his skin. Had he been aware of this, he might have settled with me when we met in the trail. As it was, he did a very good job of saving his skin.

As the moon rose, he rushed out of the bushes, growling hoarsely, tore off more meat and hurried to cover. Shooting in moonlight is poor at its best, and a rapidly moving target does not improve it. I hadn't fooled him at all. He knew I was in that tree, and he did not trust me. I hadn't a chance to fire a single shot.

After that, I sat up nights to watch for lions. My luck was usually about the same. They looked up at me, grabbed at the meat, and ran with it. I know they saw my slightest movement and apparently could hear the rustle of my clothing. As a sporting way of hunting lions, this machan hunting rates very low. Also it is a most uncomfortable way in which to spend a night. You can't climb down and return to a comfortable cot in camp—not if you are in your right mind.

Because a lion always feels very sure of himself after dark, he will boldly enter a camp or settlement whose activity he will shun during the day. While camped at Amboselli, my guide told me that a whole pack, or pride, as they're called, of lions had come into camp the night before and lain down within a few feet of one of the huts.

Clarence Wilson, my safari manager on my second trip to Tanganyika, had a startling experience one night when he lived near Tanga. Hearing sounds out on the veranda, he opened the door to see who was there. A lion was there, standing on the veranda and looking at him. Very quickly, Wilson closed the door in the face of his visitor.

A Lion for Escort

At that time, a missionary told me of a young lady who had come to his mission station and decided to take a walk in the moonlight. She had gone but a short way

before she saw a lion walking along the path toward her. Startled and frightened, she nevertheless kept her head, turned about and quietly walked back to the house. The lion kept pace with her beside the trail all the way to the house.

These things can only be explained when you realize that a lion knows he is boss at night. Anything from anteater to zebra is easy prey.

On another expedition, when I was camped in the Rau Forest near Moshi, there were many lions in the forest, but they did not advertise their presence by roaring. So close to a settlement, they have learned to keep silent.

These lions preyed on the buffaloes in the forest. One evening, a hunter from Moshi came to hunt buffaloes. He shot one toward dark and decided to camp nearby and then dress out the meat in the morning. All night, he and his natives were busy chasing lions away from the buffalo. A fire was kept burning, and all were busy throwing firebrands at the lions. The moment vigilance was relaxed, the lions were back at the meat.

Lions don't worry much about campfires. There are many cases on record where man-eating lions have jumped over campfires to kill people.

The father of Wilson, my safari manager, had a very unpleasant experience with a lion one night when working on the Uganda railroad, not far from Tsavo where the famous man-eaters gave the workers such a fearful time.

One dark night, a native came running to tell the elder Wilson that a lion had just killed and made off with one of the work donkeys. Taking his rifle, he told the native to take him to the lion, not realizing that a native takes orders literally. This one had been told to take his employer to the lion and, walking ahead with the lantern, he did exactly as told. Holding the lantern aloft, he pointed down and said, "There!"

To his surprise, Wilson saw that the lion was directly in front of him and that the native was already back of him.

Crouched over the dead donkey, the lion now rose to his feet, reared up and placed one paw on each of the startled man's shoulders. Giving a push, he sent Wilson down on his back. Before the man could recover from his surprise, the lion turned, picked up the dead donkey in his jaws and loped away.

Apparently, the lion was only concerned with eating his supper, so he had pushed the man aside and gone his way.

The Man-eaters of Uganda

Man-eaters are something different, unless one considers it from a primitive angle and regards man as the lion's legitimate prey. Not only are man-eaters exceedingly bold at night, they can be ranked as among the most dangerous animals on earth.

Often, man-eating lions are old or disabled lions that no longer can hunt and kill other animals. Finding men easy to kill, they turn to man-eating. It's just a matter of survival to them. They must eat, so they hunt the prey that is easy to catch.

Occasionally, normal lions will take to man-eating in places where game is scarce. There is now such a place in Uganda where the game has been thinned out by hunters and where many lions have taken to hunting men. It's a big stretch of wild country and not a good place in which to be found after dark.

Some years ago, not far from Tanga, on the Tanganyika coast, a lioness and her four grown young terrorized a native district for a long time. Game was scarce, and the lions took to killing the natives' cattle. Succeeding one day in killing a herder who foolishly tried to defend his herd against them, they fed on him and soon turned to killing natives. Boldly, they entered villages at night to tear at the doors of huts. They even climbed upon the huts and clawed their way through the grass-thatched roofs. Natives fought them off with firebrands.

All attempts to hunt the lions down and kill them proved futile. These lions were not old and sickly and had little trouble avoiding hunters.

A Lost Child

One evening, a native woman sent her little girl to a hut next door to borrow live coals to start a fire. When the child failed to return, the mother called to the woman next door and was told that the child had not been seen. Taking firebrands, the natives searched the ground and found that the child's footprints stopped near the footprints of a big lion. The animal apparently had been standing quietly outside the hut and had picked up the child as she emerged from the hut.

Lions very frequently hunt in gangs, or prides. I have rarely come upon lions hunting singly. Often there are six or seven in a pride and one that I came upon recently in Uganda consisted of sixteen lions.

A friend of mine living on a plantation in Tanganyika told me of a terrific racket he heard one night not far from his bungalow. There was growling, roaring, and bellowing. Next morning, he went to investigate. He found the remains of a big buffalo bull and evidence of a terrific fight that had taken place before the bull was pulled down. From the lions' tracks and the marks on the bull, he figured that four lions had attacked the buffalo, some clinging to his sides, others on his back, while one attacked his throat.

A buffalo bull is very tough and puts up a furious fight. It is doubtful that one lion can successfully pull one down, so they gang up on these old tough ones.

Two summers ago, I saw a buffalo bull with his tail missing and limping on one hind leg. He had apparently been attacked by a lion and had come out of the fray alive, but a bit the worse for wear. How the lion fared, I do not know, but I have an idea that he didn't look too good either.

In the summer of 1953, I was out looking for lions, not with any idea of shooting them, but to get pictures. My native guides knew how to find them for they knew that prides of lions like to lie near the edges of rocky ravines that are overgrown with bushes and trees. From such a place they can see far. It is easy to retreat into the wooded ravine when disturbed, and it is also quite easy to stalk game from such a retreat. So we searched the rims of these ravines and found three separate prides of lions.

Naturally, we did our searching toward the end of the day, for lions rarely show themselves when the sun is high. Just before the sun went down, the lions lay about in lazy groups, sleeping, washing themselves like house cats, or rolling over on their backs with paws up. As soon as darkness began to set in, they became restless. Then they looked far off at herds of grazing game. It was time to be off on the hunt.

As we watched these regal beasts from a safe distance, they rose to their feet to stalk into the gloom. Away they went, with great shoulders working at every stride; proud, sure, powerful and leaving no doubt about who was boss of the African night.

The Airtight Case

By PASCHAL N. STRONG

It was young Richard Barrett's job to let the air out of an airtight case

"Stephen Rawlings!" Brief excitement rippled over the courtroom spectators as the prosecution called its star witness. Richard Barrett, assigned by the court to defend young Joe Meadows, placed an encouraging hand on his client's skinny shoulders.

"There's the chap who'll set you free," he whispered, pointing toward the unkempt figure shambling up to be sworn.

"Who, him?" Joe looked at his lawyer as though he were crazy. "Why, he's out to get me. And they already got enough evidence to send me up for twenty years. My fingerprints on the oar handle, the ten dollar bill they found in my pocket. They got an airtight case. That's what I heard the people back there say. An airtight case."

"Maybe we'll puncture it and let the air out."

"But you gotta puncture Rawlings first," protested young Meadows. "He's going to swear he saw me jump from the boat to the dock just before he found Lawson lying there in the cabin."

Barrett nodded. He looked nearly as young as his client, and he felt shaky with nervous excitement as he listened to the clerk swear the witness to tell the truth, the whole truth, and nothing but the truth. Barrett couldn't do anything about his youthful looks—he had just graduated from law school a few months ago—but he could do something about his nervous feeling. He concealed it admirably behind a façade of nonchalant calmness. For a moment he glanced at the thin, freckled-faced, eighteen-year-old youngster whose freedom depended on his efforts, and then he concentrated on Rawlings, just taking his seat in the witness chair.

He knew that when Rawlings arose from that seat, Joe Meadows would either be free or would be doomed to spend the best years of his life behind bars.

For a fleeting moment his mind went back to the one little flaw in Rawlings' previous testimony to the grand jury. One little flaw, one small discrepancy that had furnished him with the clue to the solution of the case. But was he lawyer enough to exploit it properly—to tear apart the rugged net of circumstantial evidence which the prosecutor, in all honesty, had woven around an innocent boy?

The prosecutor, smiling and confident, knowing that his case was won, approached the witness chair. An expectant hush fell on the courtroom, so that the rustling of the wind in the live oaks, the distant cry of a seagull over the salt marshes, floated in on the warm autumn air. The prosecutor was not too tall, and not too stout, and he was endowed with a rich baritone voice that had won many a case with its hypnotizing effect on juries. His eyes were honest and frank, and it was generally believed that he wouldn't prosecute a man unless he believed him guilty.

Now he addressed the witness in a friendly,

companionable voice. "Tell the court your name, occupation, and place of residence."

Rawlings shifted awkwardly in his seat, folded his large, not too clean hands, twisted his jaw to make room for something he was chewing, and said in a sandpapered voice:

"My name's Stephen Rawlings—I guess most folks call me Catfish Rawlings. Reckon you might say I'm a profess'n'l fisherman. Leastways I keep boats for hire down at Palmetto Landin', an' sell bait, an' take out fishin' parties."

"And your place of residence?"

"Right close to the dock at Palmetto Landin', where Sapelo Creek heads up from the marsh. Reckon y'all know where that is."

Yes, thought Barrett, every man on the jury knew Palmetto Landing, where the Georgia mainland ended in a fringe of live oaks and palmettos, and the green marshes stretched out to the sea islands that fronted the Atlantic. And every man on the jury, he reflected unhappily, had already built up a mental picture of the happenings at the Landing in the early dawn of two months ago.

"What," asked the prosecutor, "were you doing just before daybreak on the morning of last August eighteenth?"

"I was down at my boats. Figgered on goin' shrimpin' to git some bait for the day's fishin'."

"Did you see anything unusual at the dock?"

"Yessir, I saw the Marsh Queen tied up alongside. That's Gur Lawson's workboat. He uses it to git back an' forth from the Landin' to Sapelo Island."

"Why were you surprised to see the Marsh Queen there?"

"Waal, I thought Lawson had shoved off the night afore. He'd come in to git the payroll money for the Island, an' most usually he shoves off soon after dark. 'Cose, I wasn't knownin' then that he couldn't git his engine started."

"Confine yourself to the questions, please. Now tell the court exactly what you saw as you approached the dock."

Catfish Rawlings, knowing that all eyes were focused on him, crossed his legs de-liberately, studied his mud-stained brogans as though in an honest effort to recall every single detail, then favored the tense crowd of spectators with a smirking grin which revealed crooked, tobacco-stained teeth.

"Waal, sir, jest as I got near I saw someone jump from the Marsh Queen to the dock an' take off for the woods like a scared rabbit. Then I—"

"Excuse me. Did you recognize the man who jumped from the boat to the dock?"

"Sure did, sir. I rec'lect sayin' to myself, 'Now why is young Meadows scamperin' off in sech a hurry? An' what's he got doin' on the boat anyway?' Yes, sir, I sure recognized him."

"Was it daylight at that time?"

"Not much daylight—sorta a half light. But I could see it was that Meadows boy—him that's sittin' there by young Mr. Barrett."

A muted, ominous buzz of tongues welled up from the courtroom as though everyone had suddenly put his unspoken thoughts into a whispered exclamation of "Guilty!" This was the final link in the chain of testimony which the prosecutor had forged to drag the defendant off to the penitentiary. Barrett felt his wrist suddenly gripped by the thin hands of the trembling boy.

"It's a lie!" Joe's voice was hoarse—half

whisper, half sob. "He's lying, Mr. Barrett! Can't you do anything about it?"

Barrett gently removed the hand that gripped him so terrifyingly. "Easy, Joe. Our turn will come."

The prosecutor, having waited for the time required to let the damaging testimony sink into the minds of the jurors, resumed his questioning.

"Now tell us what you did after you saw Meadows running from the boat."

Rawlings looked longingly at the brass spittoon near the jury box as though he'd like to try his luck with the tobacco squid working between his jaws. But he thought the better of it, recrossed his legs, and said:

"Waal, sir, I figgered somethin' funny must be goin' on, an' I reckoned I better have a look aboard the Marsh Queen to see if Lawson was okay. I went aboard an' took a look in the cabin, an' there was Lawson, slumped halfway out o' his bunk, an' I sure figgered he was dead, the way he looked. An' there, on the floor beside him, was part of an oar. There it is now on that table, the handle part, the part that had Meadows' fingerprints on it."

Barrett jumped to his feet. But abruptly, in the very act of shouting "Objection!", he stopped. The prosecutor waited expectantly. The judge peered at him over his spectacles, ready to sustain the objection.

Barrett sat down as abruptly as he had arisen. This was too much for the judge, who considered it as much his duty to instruct young lawyers as to see that the accused received all rights due him.

"Is there no objection from counsel?" he asked mildly.

Barrett arose. "No objection, your honor."

The judge regarded him condescendingly. "Then the court objects. That part of the witness's testimony dealing with fingerprints will be stricken from the—"

"May it please the court—" Barrett's voice was urgent. He wanted the right to deal with those fingerprints in his cross examination. "May it please the court, the defense requests that the testimony be received in its entirety."

The judge shrugged his shoulders. "The court hopes you know what you are doing, Mr. Barrett. The witness may proceed."

The prosecutor, wondering what Barrett was thinking of, addressed the witness.

"You say you saw Lawson slumped on his bunk, and the oar handle on the floor. What did you do then?"

"I figgered he was dead, an' I saw some blood oozin' from his head, so I run back to the house, got my jeep, an' went into town for the sheriff. Reckon I broke a speed law or two. The sheriff an' Doc Walters come back with me, an'—"

"How long did it take?"

"Not more'n half an hour, I guess. Waal, sir, the doc said that Lawson wasn't dead, an' sure enough he brought him to his senses, an' Lawson looked around an' saw his pay-roll money was all gone. I told the sheriff 'bout me seein' the Meadows kid runnin from the boat, an' we went up to his house, an' his Pa and Ma was jest gettin' up, an' Meadows was sleepin' like a log in the back room. We woke him, an' the sheriff searched him, an' found a brand-new ten dollar bill in his pants' pocket—the same bill the bank man said come from the payroll. Guess he musta hidden the rest an'—"

Barrett jumped to his feet. "Objection, your honor." He knew it didn't really matter whether this conjecture was left in the testimony or not, but he didn't want the court to believe he was a complete ignoramus.

"Sustained," drawled the judge. "The witness will confine himself to things of which he has personal knowledge."

185

"Continue, Mr. Rawlings," directed the prosecutor.

"There ain't much more to tell. The sheriff arrested Joe Meadows—how his Pa and Ma carried on!—an' I reckon y'all know what the fingerprint man found on—"

"Never mind that," interrupted the prosecutor before Barrett could object—which he wouldn't have anyway. He studied some notes in his hand to make sure that every point had been covered, and then, with an air almost of sympathy, said to Barrett:

"Your witness."

Barrett rose slowly from his table. For a fleeting second his gaze rested on the agonized faces of the simple, scrawny, elderly couple whose son was being tried for armed robbery and attempted murder.

They were both dressed in their Sunday clothes, as though somehow hoping to influence the jury by thus showing that Joe came from decent people. But the shiny blue serge hung scarecrow-like on the man, and the outmoded muslin dress merely emphasized the gaunt, haggard look of the farm wife. Only in their faces, etched with suffering, eloquent with appeal, could one see the inherent decency of the family whose only son was faced with imprisonment and disgrace.

Barrett gave them a faint smile of encouragement, and walked slowly toward the witness chair. It was only a few steps, but in that interval he rapidly reviewed the salient points of the testimony of previous witnesses —testimony more than enough to convict the boy.

Meadows' fingerprints on the oar handle.

The discovery of the ten dollar bill in his pocket—a bill which the local bank teller identified as one of a series issued to Lawson.

The incriminating testimony given by Catfish Rawlings.

Lawson was no help to either the prosecution or the defense. He had testified he had been struck down in the dark, while asleep; but Joe Meadows' fingerprints on the oar handle shouted the identity of the attacker to the world.

Yes, he mused, an airtight case, if ever there was one. An airtight case—so far.

But he knew the weak point in the state's case, and it had led him to the one tangible bit of evidence he could produce to prove Joe's innocence. As he stood before the witness chair he glanced back briefly at the object wrapped in old burlap under his table. By itself it was not sufficient to overcome the strong presumption of guilt raised against the boy. But, if he could first prove that Rawlings was lying, then that hidden item under the table would explode on the minds of the jurors with the impact of a bomb.

Silence, eager and tense, hung over the courtroom as Barrett faced the witness. For a moment he fixed his eyes on the unsavoury figure, clad in soiled blue denims, staring at him brazenly. But as Barrett gazed at him steadily, almost contemptuously, the man wilted visibly, squirmed, crossed and recrossed his legs. But still Barrett said nothing. He was recalling to mind all he had learned of the art of cross-examining a hostile witness. The trap must be concealed by innocuous questions. If the witness had lied, he must be persuaded to repeat the lie over and over again until he was irrevocably committed. And in this special case, Barrett knew that he must somehow work his client's account of what really happened into the questioning of the witness. Fortunately, he could ask leading questions, he could guide the witness's footsteps to the pitfall without objection from opposing counsel.

When he finally spoke his voice was quiet, encouraging, almost as though Rawlings was a friendly witness.

"You get up pretty early to go after bait, don't you, Mr. Rawlings?"

"Guess I do," rasped Rawlings belligerently. "I gin'rally go after shrimp 'bout low tide."

"Must have been pretty dark when you went out on the morning of August eighteenth, wasn't it?"

Rawlings grinned his teeth-yellowed grin. He wasn't going to be tripped up so easily by this smart alecky lawyer.

"Reckon it warn't so dark," he said. "Not sun-up, maybe, but light enough to see a man by."

"So you could really see him jump from the deck of the boat to the dock, eh?"

"That's what I said."

"Just wanted to make sure. Does the Marsh Queen tie up at Palmetto Landing very often?"

"Every time Lawson makes a trip from the Island. Once-twice a week."

"So you know his habits pretty well. You know when he draws the money for the payroll and all that?"

Rawlings' gums worked a little while he examined this question for a possible trap. He looked hungrily at the brass spittoon.

"Sure I know when he draws the payroll money," he said defiantly. "All the folks around here know that. But if you think that I—"

"I'm not thinking anything," said Barrett. He looked thoughtfully up at the pine ceiling, as though trying to reconstruct some picture in his mind. "By the way, wouldn't the tide swing the boat out from the dock a little—so a man might have trouble jumping from the deck to the dock?"

"Don't reckon so. Hardly a jump at all. Did it myself with no trouble."

"You must be a pretty good jumper."

Rawlings looked at him contemptuously. "It don't take a good jumper to do that. I rec'lect I just stepped from the boat to the dock, after I went aboard and saw what happened."

"I see. You distinctly remember stepping from the deck to the dock. Well, I guess if you could do it someone else could too. Do you have a hard time making a living?"

The prosecutor was on his feet. "Objection, your honor. Irrelevant."

Barrett wheeled toward the judge. "May it please the court, I am leading up to a point that may be vital. I assure you it will deal with a matter testified to by the witness."

"Objection overruled," said the judge. He wished he had appointed a smarter lawyer to handle the accused's case. Seemed like that young Barrett was just clinching the arguments for the state. Not, he reflected, that the state's case needed much clinching.

"Do you have a hard time making a living?" repeated Barrett. "I mean, you have to be pretty careful, don't you. Can't afford to throw away anything you might have some use for later?"

"Sure can't," agreed Rawlings readily. "Guess everyone knows I'm the most savingest man there is."

"Well, I'm glad to know you save things," purred Barrett. "Guess your eyesight is all right too, if you could step from the boat deck to the dock without thinking much about it."

"A blind man coulda done that. An' anyway there was plenty o' light."

Barrett stepped back to his table and reached for a paper bound book.

"I ask the court," he said, "to take judicial notice of the accuracy of the tide tables in this pamphlet issued by the U.S. Hydrographic Office. As you will see, it gives the times of high and low tides all along the Atlantic Coast."

The judge examined the book perfunctorily.

"Judicial notice taken," he said. He wondered if young Barrett had something up his sleeve after all.

Barrett opened the book at a premarked page and handed it to the witness.

"Please read the time of the evening high tide off Sapelo Sound, Georgia, on last August eighteenth."

Rawlings squinted at the page, and read laboriously: "High tide at ten-five p.m."

"High tide at five minutes after ten at night," repeated Barrett with emphasis. "There's a time lag of about forty-five minutes for the tide at Palmetto Landing, isn't there?"

"Guess so," agreed Rawlings. "It was high tide just afore eleven that night."

"And so it'd be low tide about six hours later, wouldn't it? Say about five in the morning—about daybreak."

"Why sure. An' that's when it was low tide."

"And low tide is about eight feet lower than high tide, right?"

"Jest about."

"And at high tide, the deck of the Marsh Queen is just about level with the dock, isn't it?"

"Jest about."

Abruptly Barrett's manner changed. His words shot out with the staccato effect of machine gun bullets.

"Then you lied when you said you saw Meadows jump from the boat to the dock about daybreak!"

Rawlings stared at him, jaw dropping. Barrett didn't give him a chance to answer.

"At daybreak it was low tide." Rat-tat-tat came the bullet-like words. "The deck of the boat would be eight feet below the dock! A man leaving the boat would have to *climb up* to the dock. He couldn't jump or step from the boat to the dock. So you were lying, weren't you. You didn't see him at daybreak!"

"I—I did see him then." Rawlings' voice was suddenly high-pitched, shaky.

"You said you stepped from the boat to the dock yourself. You said it, didn't you?" Faster, faster, the words came, giving Rawlings no time to think. "You said you stepped from the boat to the dock. *And you were telling the truth then.* You stepped from the

boat to the dock at high tide! At eleven o'clock the night before. That's when you first went aboard, wasn't it? At eleven o'clock the night before!"

Rawlings squirmed and spluttered and looked wildly at the prosecutor for assistance. The prosecutor jumped to his feet, but the judge gave him a slight shake of his head and he took the hint and sat down. Barrett bore in again.

"It's true you went aboard the night before, isn't it? You've proved it by your own words. Now isn't it true that you slugged Lawson and took the money? You don't have to answer that one—it's self-incriminatory. We'll let the facts answer for you. But isn't it true that when you left the boat—at high tide—at eleven o'clock that night, you saw Meadows, passing your house on the way to his house. He saw you too, didn't he? You thought Lawson was dead. You were trapped! He'd testify against you when the robbery came out. That's right, isn't it? He was passing the dock just then?"

"No, no!" Rawlings' voice was almost a scream.

"So you had to act fast. You had that oar handle in your hand. You called him and said you wanted him to make you a new pair of oars. You made him put his hands around the handle so he'd know what size to carve them—and to leave his fingerprints. You gave him a ten dollar bill from the payroll in your pocket to pay for the oars, didn't you?"

The prosecutor could stand it no longer.

"I object, your honor," he shouted. "The witness is not on trial. These questions, these statements, are—"

"Overruled," ordered the judge tartly. "Possibly you're right technically. But I must give defending counsel great latitude. Proceed, Mr. Barrett."

Barrett drew a deep breath. He glanced quickly at the jurors, the spectators. Every man and woman was leaning forward, hungry for each word. Barrett knew he had hit the bull's eye. Rawlings was a trapped liar. Now for the *coup de grâce*. He changed pace as suddenly as before. His voice was flowing honey as he smiled down at the writhing witness.

"You said you were the most savingest man in the county, Rawlings. Said you never threw anything away. Suppose you had part of an oar—the lower part. You wouldn't throw it away, would you? If you threw it in the creek, someone might find it floating around. You might burn it. But why burn good wood in summer when you could hide it under the house and burn it in the stove in winter?"

"I—I don't know what you're talkin' about."

"Don't you?"

Barrett strode back quickly to his table, reached under it and pulled out the burlap wrapped object. He tore off the burlap as he walked back to the witness. A gasp burst from the spectators as he revealed the lower part of an old oar.

"Look at this, Rawlings. See these initials carved in the oar? S.R. Stephen Rawlings. Your oar, isn't it? The oar you hid under your house to save for the winter stove. That's where I found it."

The prosecutor was on his feet again. The oar hadn't been properly introduced as evidence. But as he jumped up his eye caught the wild, exultant hope on the faces of the scrawny couple. He hesitated. He studied Meadows doubtfully. He looked at Rawlings, who was staring at the oar as though at a ghost. And then he sat down again, grimly.

Barrett stepped to the prosecutor's table and picked up Exhibit A, the oar handle which had clubbed Lawson into near death. He fitted it to the sawed-off end of the old oar.

"Look at this, Rawlings! It fits perfectly, doesn't it? Your oar—your oar handle. Look at it! Look at it!"

Rawlings staggered to his feet. He gave a crazed, trapped look around the courtroom, saw the open door behind the witness chair, and with an inarticulate cry made a dash for it. The stout arm of the bailiff seized him as he reached the door, and the judge pounded for order as the courtroom, jurors and spectators alike, leaped to its collective feet.

When the tumult subsided, the prosecutor stood before the bench.

"May it please the court, the state asks that the case against the defendant be dismissed."

The judge removed his spectacles and looked with wondering respect at Richard Barrett. Then, as though suddenly hearing the prosecutor's request, he said drily:

"The state could hardly ask for anything else. I presume the court will have another case on its docket soon?"

The prosecutor looked at the driveling Rawlings.

"The court will—with change in defendants, however."

"Case dismissed," ordered the judge.

Barrett didn't remember too much of what happened after that. It looked as though everyone in the courtroom was slapping him on the back at once. He did remember Joe's burning look of gratitude, and the joyful sobs of the muslin-clad woman who threw her arms around him, but most of all he remembered the words of the prosecutor who fought his way to him through the crowd.

"You saved me from a terrible thing, Barrett. I'll be eternally grateful to you. I need a new assistant, you know. I wonder if—"

Barrett laughed. "Can't talk about it now," he said. "I've got a date with Joe. We're behind on our fishing."

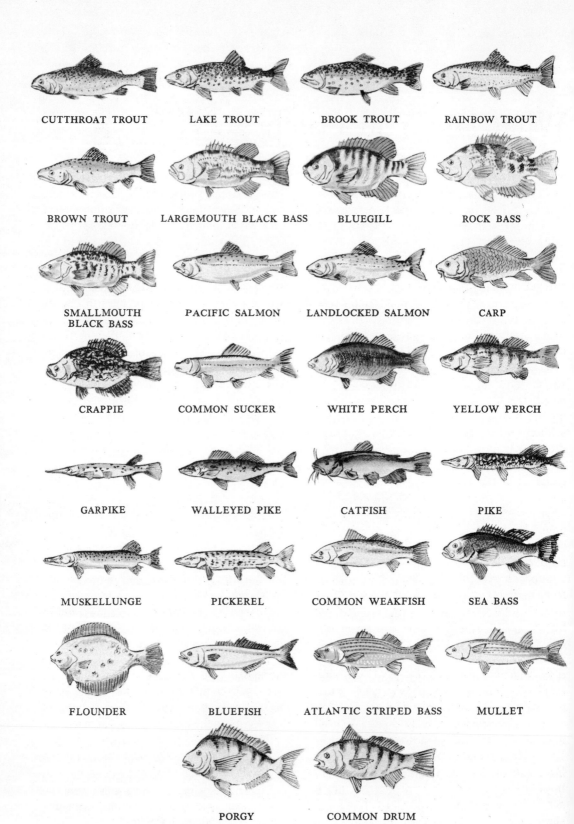

CUTTHROAT TROUT   LAKE TROUT   BROOK TROUT   RAINBOW TROUT

BROWN TROUT   LARGEMOUTH BLACK BASS   BLUEGILL   ROCK BASS

SMALLMOUTH BLACK BASS   PACIFIC SALMON   LANDLOCKED SALMON   CARP

CRAPPIE   COMMON SUCKER   WHITE PERCH   YELLOW PERCH

GARPIKE   WALLEYED PIKE   CATFISH   PIKE

MUSKELLUNGE   PICKEREL   COMMON WEAKFISH   SEA BASS

FLOUNDER   BLUEFISH   ATLANTIC STRIPED BASS   MULLET

PORGY   COMMON DRUM

What Did You Catch?

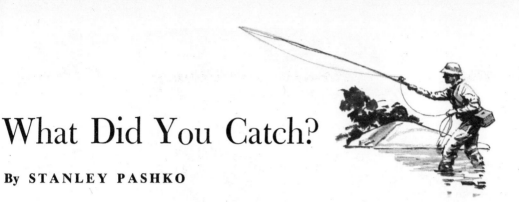

By STANLEY PASHKO

It's more fun fishing if you can identify some of the most common specimens

Anglers are a perennially optimistic lot. Year after year, they return to cast their lures over the fish of their local ponds and streams. While waiting for a "strike" they dream of the better fishing to be found far away.

The surf caster who pulls in a 30-pound striper off Cape Cod thinks how lucky the Northwest "Isaac Waltons" are to be hauling in boatloads of salmon. The chinook salmon fisherman on Vancouver Island dreams of the Florida paradise where, in a crazy competition, bass were taken on lures made of bottle tops, kitchen spoons, pine cones, and other weird odds-and-ends— where one lucky rod-wielder took a 20-pound bass on a wooden salt shaker just as it came from the hardware store. And so it goes all over the land.

Suppose you got the chance to fish away from home? You may be pretty good on fish identification when it comes to local species, but are you sure of yourself when you get out to strange waters? The fish shown on the opposite page are the best-known and most widely distributed species. If you are familiar with these, you will have little trouble wherever you may find yourself.

It is a good idea to begin taking special note of any unusual catches you may make. Irving Crump, author of the Boy Scout Merit Badge Pamphlet on Angling, suggests that boys keep a record of big ones by drawing a silhouette or traced outline of the fish on a sheet of paper. This is done by laying the fish on the paper and tracing all around it with a pencil. The girth of the fish can be taken with a tape measure and listed, together with the weight and other pertinent statistics, on the bottom of the sheet. Note what bait you used, where you caught it, what time of day it was, what the weather conditions were, and anything else which you think may help to make you a better angler.

At all times be a good sportsman. Remember the sad truth that man is the chief enemy of fish. You can have your sport without plundering nature of the treasure which supplies you with that pleasure. Take home only a few fish—and a lot of fun. The streams of today cannot yield an inexhaustible supply of game fish. We must begin to take serious thought of conservation methods.

Of course, no sensible boy would think of angling until he acquired a license—if he lives in a state where a license is necessary —and learned the game laws of his state thoroughly. He should know just when he can catch certain types of fish, how many he can take, how long they must be, and what restrictions are placed on his methods of fishing.

These vary according to states, and the true sportsman each year gets in touch with the state authorities, obtains a copy of the game laws, reads and digests it thoroughly, and *lives up to the laws.*

Sabor's Shoes

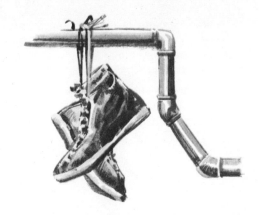

By JAY WORTHINGTON

Something besides a winning streak was on the line, and Mark was hot

The gym was a patch of bright light, as Mark Cheney followed Red Fessler to the side door. Dark figures were scurrying up the wide stone steps at the main entrance.

"Big crowd, for the opening game," commented Mark trying to sound casual.

"It's the winning streak," said Red.

"I guess so."

But Mark wasn't guessing. He knew it was the winning streak. The Panthers were on the spot tonight, with that unbroken skein of twenty-four consecutive victories hanging over their heads, like the sword of Damocles.

And right in the middle of the spot, taking most of the glare, was Mark Cheney. He was the *X*-factor, Mark knew. The question mark. The player who was supposed to take Joe Sabor's place this year.

It was a pretty spot, when you were starting your first game, thought Mark, as he held the door for his shorter, thick-set teammate.

Buz Bright and two substitutes were sitting on benches in the dressing room, talking. Mark and Red dropped their bags in empty lockers. They could hear the thumping feet of the Jayvee team, already up on the floor, above the sounds of the crowd and the hollow, lighter *thunk* of bouncing basketballs.

Buz Bright grinned at Mark's thin, solemn face, and pointed to the old pair of sneaks dangling from a steampipe that ran lengthwise along the little room near the ceiling.

"Think you can fill those shoes tonight, Mark?" teased Buz, good-naturedly.

Mark lifted his high, spare shoulders. "I'm not Joe Sabor," he said, simply.

"We could use Joe tonight," said one of the subs.

"Any team could use a man," spoke up Red Fessler, who was the Terrace School's captain, "who averaged twenty points a game."

Mark tried not to look at Sabor's old shoes. He wished that last year's manager had not tied them there by their laces, after the final victory, as a reminder for this season's players to carry on the amazing winning streak.

"Let's watch the Jayvee game," he said, abruptly.

The preliminary game had already started when they reached the Terrace bench. The junior Panthers were losing to Central's Jayvees, 10-6, at the end of the quarter.

Mark Cheney squirmed on the bench, wondering if this was a bad omen. Terrace's Jayvee players were all young and green, it was true, but that was a warning about the varsity team's reserve strength. The Panther first-line was thin. It was a tip-off, too, when a substitute like Mark Cheney, who had yet to earn his letter, was expected to fill the shoes of a star like Joe Sabor.

Mark was glad when the first half ended, although the Jayvees were still losing, 19-14.

He stood around in the dressing room with the other Varsity players, waiting for the youngsters to clear out. They went, at last, and the Varsity began to dress.

The Panther uniforms were all green, except for the gold trim on their shorts and the gold letters spelling TERRACE across the jersey fronts, and the big gold numbers on their backs.

Mark Cheney was Number Sixteen. Joe Sabor had been Eleven. Their numbers were different, anyway, Mark consoled himself as he pulled on one of the thick-soled sneaks. He was several pounds lighter and a half-inch shorter than Sabor, too, although his mother said he'd be taller if he straightened up.

The door opened. A tall, haggard-looking man entered, carrying a folded newspaper. Mark recognized Mintzer, sports reporter for the *Evening News*

"How do you feel, boys?" asked Mintzer in his raspy voice.

"We feel with our hands," retorted Buz Bright. "How do you feel, Mintzer?"

"I'm just waiting," said Mintzer, grinning.

Then the reporter unfolded his newspaper at the sports page, so the players could see the heavy black streamer:

PANTHER WINNING STREAK GOES ON LINE TONIGHT!

Mark and his teammates already had seen it, of course. The write-up had listed the scores of the twenty-four games in the streak, covering the season-and-a-half span of uninterrupted victories.

"You'd better be rooting for us, Mintzer," said Red Fessler. "You can use some more adjectives if we win."

Mintzer turned to Mark Cheney. "How about you, Mark? Think you can do it?"

"Do what?" asked Mark, his dark head bent over his laces.

"Fill those shoes." The reporter nodded toward the old sneaks dangling from the steampipe.

Mark hesitated. "I thought the team built up the winning streak, not one player."

"That's right. But three members of that team are still playing for Terrace tonight. The only important one who's been graduated is Joe Sabor. That makes you the key man."

"Does it?"

"Hasn't anybody told you?" The hoarse voice became almost taunting. "You'll be playing the pivot, just like Joe Sabor."

Mark didn't answer. He had knotted his

laces so hard that he had to untie them and start over again.

"Go watch the Jayvee game," suggested Buz. "Go do your job, Mintzer."

"That winning streak is my job tonight," said Mintzer. "That's why there's such a big crowd. They want to see if you can keep it going."

"Maybe you'd better talk to the Central team," said big Golak. "They might have something to say about it."

"You beat Central twice last year."

"We beat everybody last year," snapped Buz. "So what?"

Red Fessler said, more calmly, "You'd better go, Mintzer, or I'll have to tell Coach you're bothering the players."

"Bothering? Who's bothering?" Mintzer grinned, opening the door. "I only came down to wish you luck!"

"Thanks!" yelled Buz after him, with heavy sarcasm. "We should have put an assistant manager at the door, to keep away the buzzards!"

Yellow-haired Hahn, the fifth man, dropped on the bench at Mark's side. Hahn was a solid defensive player, but an ankle sprain had put him on the shelf early in the preceding season.

"I'm glad the pressure isn't on me the way it's on you," murmured Hahn. "I'd come apart at the seams."

Mark grinned weakly. There was a bond of unspoken sympathy between the two, since they were the only starting players who had contributed little to the winning streak. They were the ones who would make the difference, if the streak was snapped.

The minutes ticked away tediously, and the players became more silent as the zero hour approached. Captain Red Fessler bounced the new yellow basketball between his knees as he sat on a bench, staring at the floor.

They were all wound up, Mark knew. The school was already getting wide publicity. If the Panthers could extend the streak, finishing another season without defeat, they'd be famous. All of them. Red. Buz. Golak. Hahn. Yes, even Mark Cheney. . . .

And then, perhaps, sportswriters like Mintzer would write about the great Terrace team, instead of repeating over and over how many points Joe Sabor had averaged during the long winning streak.

The Jayvees thumped down the stairs, at last, perspiring and crestfallen.

"How'd it go?" asked Red.

"Three points! We almost caught 'em!"

"Good try!" said Buz Bright, trying to sound enthusiastic.

But Mark saw the network of nervous glances. As the second team goes, said the old superstition, so goes the Varsity.

"All right, hot shots!" snapped Red. "Let's go up there looking like champs!"

Mark tried to hang back as they reached the gym floor, but Hahn pushed him ahead of him. The crowd roared acclaim, as Red Fessler led the green-and-gold figures the length of the yellow floor. Red dribbled the new ball under the basket for a practice lay-up shot. The white net danced, and the crowd roared again.

Some of Mark Cheney's nervousness faded as the ball slammed into his hands and he pushed in his lay-up. They went around three times from each side of the basket, and then scattered for set-shots, foul-shooting, and other specialties.

Mark warmed up around the keyhole, practicing his pivot and hook-shot with his right hand, and going in for rebounds. He didn't try his left-handed shot, hoping to make the Central team think he couldn't hook from the left side. Joe Sabor had hooked shots from either side, a factor that had counted heavily in Sabor's scoring—and the winning streak.

Coach Hoff talked to the officials and the rival coach. Terrace's rotund, white-haired coach came over to the keyhole, after a few minutes. His red face was sober. Hoff was on the spot, too.

"How are you hitting, Mark?" he asked.

"All right, I guess."

"Take plenty of shots, right away," instructed Hoff. "Scare 'em. That will give our boys confidence, too. Sabor always did a lot of shooting."

"All right," Mark replied quietly.

Mark took his practice foul throws. He was feeling looser every minute, and wished the warm-up period could be longer.

But now the two gray-shirted officials were standing at the center circle, waiting. The players stripped off their warm-up togs and huddled. Coach Hoff leaned over the Panther circle.

"Watch your fouls," warned the coach. "The ref says he's going to call 'em close. He knows Central is itching to smash the winning streak, and he says he's not going to let the game get out of control. . . . Look out for their fast break, now, and—and good luck!"

Mark locked grips with his four teammates, in the last-second handclasp. The Central players were already in position, waiting and grinning, in their royal-blue jerseys and white trunks. The pressure wasn't on them.

The crowd boomed again, as the green-clad Panthers scattered to pair off with the blue-and-white figures. From that moment Mark Cheney was aware of the crowd's yelling only as a dim echo to the action, like an accusing jury.

Big Golak stepped up to the center circle to jump-off for Terrace. The yellow ball flashed into the air.

The towering Central center gained the tap, and the blue team flashed down the floor in a rehearsed play with the guard coming around.

The guard was Mark Cheney's man, but Hahn and Buz Bright were there, ready for anything. Buz blocked the play, and the ball moved around more cautiously, as the players slid into their assigned patterns.

Central tried a shot, missed. Big Golak grabbed the rebound, whirled, and passed off to Red Fessler. Mark galloped ahead to the keyhole, turned, and waited.

Hahn and Buz brought the ball across the center-line, worked it around. Red took it, promptly slammed a pass into Mark.

Mark pivoted to his left, but found a big blue figure blocking his hook shot. He dribbled away, pivoted again. He saw the basket, and aimed a two-hand shot. The ball arched nicely—but he'd been a fraction too strong.

The ball skidded over the far side of the rim, and Central recovered. Mark released his breath. Oh well, he'd try his left-hander next time. That would give them something to worry about.

Both teams seemed nervous. The first points were foul shots, one by each team.

Mark netted his first basket on a follow-up, after a teammate's miss. Red Fessler and Golak scored two-pointers, and the Panthers enjoyed a slim lead at the end of the first quarter, 9-8.

A fast break quickly netted two points for Central, however, and the blue-clad players pressed their advantage. Mark and big Golak fought grimly under the boards, but they were being out-reached by taller Central players.

Mark wasn't getting many shots. Not as many as Joe Sabor would have taken. The flashy Sabor had been a constant threat, keeping rival defenses unbalanced.

Nor could Mark net one of his left-hand tries, weakening the deception he had hoped to set up. He had worked hard on that left-handed hook, but it wouldn't come as naturally as the right-handed one. And he wasn't getting it off quickly enough, he saw, against first-line opposition.

Central was leading, 18-13, when Red Fessler asked the referee for time-out.

"This is it," Red told the green huddle. "We gotta stop 'em now, before they get away from us. We gotta stop 'em right here —or it's good-by everything! You know what I mean!"

Mark's bony hands tightened into fists. Yes, he knew. Their precious winning streak was in peril, because he wasn't playing like Joe Sabor.

The teams matched foul shots again. Then a pass came to Mark, near the keyhole. He faked to his left, and then wheeled to his right for a left-handed hook. He'd have to make that left-hand threat good without any question.

His shot went in. The ball slammed against the backboard and into the net, although he

He galloped on to his keyhole slot. The ball came across the center line, and Red promptly bounced a pass into Mark.

He faked left and right, this time, and then pivoted to his left and hooked a right-hander.

Swish!

The crowd yelled and the referee blasted his whistle. He'd been fouled on the shot.

He toed the free-throw line, fingering the ball, aimed, took a deep breath, and let go.

Swish!

A glance at the scoreboard, as the crowd roared, confirmed that the score was all tied up, 19-19. And he'd done it, with his three-point cluster.

His body throbbed strangely, wonderfully, as he back-pedaled on defense. A fiery something was spreading all through him, up his back, down his legs, out to his fingertips. He knew what it was. He'd heard about it. He even recognized it, dimly, from kid games.

He was hot.

His throat and lips were dry, and his lungs felt seared, but this was something different. His playing was hot. He felt as if he could suddenly move faster, think faster, and shoot better than any other player on the floor.

Central worked the ball around. They seemed to be pressing now. They tried to force a shot. Hahn blocked it, but committed a foul. Central netted one point and edged ahead again, 20-19.

Mark waited at the keyhole, confident, as his teammates brought up the ball. They were looking for him, trying to feed him, the way they had always done with Joe Sabor.

He slid around. There, the pass was coming, head-high. He grabbed it, passed off to Buz Bright. Buz faked a shot, slammed the ball right back at Mark.

He dribbled once, and pivoted toward the basket. He'd lost his man. He knew he would. He aimed a two-hand shot. He was hot. He couldn't miss, now.

Swish!

The crowd went *oooh!*—and the scoreboard winked Terrace out in front again.

had aimed for the rim. But it went in, and it counted two points.

He raced back on defense. He blanketed his man tenaciously, until he saw a shot floating toward the enemy basket. Then he whirled and, as the ball came off the board, he leaped high. His fingers closed around the ball. He ducked and spun, coming down, and dribbled to sideline safety, and passed off to Hahn.

Then, as a panicky Central team moved down the floor, the first half ended.

Mark Cheney's teammates were grinning, chattering, as they pounded into the hot little dressing room.

"You looked like a big leaguer, Mark!" yelped Buz.

"We can't lose," panted Red, "if you keep that up!"

Coach Hoff was smiling, too, but somewhat nervously.

"Keep your eyes open," he cautioned Mark. "They may try a different defense next half."

Mark nodded, and rested his back against a metal locker. He almost grinned, as he saw Joe Sabor's old sneaks dangling from the steampipe. He'd scored nine points already. Nine in each half would give him a total of eighteen, not far from Sabor's average of twenty.

But he wished the first half hadn't ended right then, when he was hot. What would happen now? Could he take up where he had left off?

He took a few warm-up shots when the team went back on the floor, and then wished he hadn't. He tried two left-handers and missed both. He was shooting at the other basket now.

Then the second half started, and it was like a new game. The Central players had cast off their temporary jitters and were moving with their earlier precision. They scored a quick basket to regain the lead.

Mark went to his keyhole slot, telling himself he could do it. He'd get hot again, and stay hot, until the Panthers had a big lead.

The ball soon came to him. His green-jerseyed mates were depending on him. That was obvious.

But now something was different. A tall blue figure had been drifting near Mark, standing almost in front of him. Mark had to grab and twist, to hold onto the pass. He glanced over his shoulder. His regular guard —a big fellow named Cogan—was right in back of him, as usual.

Central was using a different defense, as the coach had warned. They were using a floater, double-guarding him, the way some teams had tried to do last year, against Joe Sabor.

Sabor had laughed at such defenses, tying his rivals in knots with his deft ball-handling. Mark didn't laugh.

He froze. Then he passed out to big Golak. His teammates kept trying to pass it back to him, bouncing it, lobbing it. He dribbled away, finally, and tried a two-hand shot. The ball skidded off the rim and sailed out of bounds.

Mark called for time-out.

"They're double-guarding me!" he panted, in the Panther huddle. "You fellows will have to break it up! Take more shots!"

They stared at him with dazed eyes. They had thought everything was all right, apparently, as long as they got the ball to him. They looked stunned.

"O.K.," gulped Red. "You heard it, gang!"

They tried. They began to hit with set-shots, and Mark passed off to cutting teammates whenever he could. The system seemed to work, and the score remained close through the third quarter.

Central returned to its original defense at the start of the final period, leaving only Cogan to guard Mark Cheney.

Now, thought Mark. Now he could do it. He tried to tell himself he was getting hot again, the way he had been in that first half.

They were feeding him again, but it wasn't the same. His left-handed shots wouldn't go in, and the Central players were getting the ball on his misses. Cogan seemed to stop worrying about the left-handers, and concentrated on blocking Mark's right-hand hooks.

Mark fought to keep the Panthers in the game. He hurtled into the backboard battle, and committed his third personal foul.

"Watch it!" warned Red. "Don't foul out!"

Mark had tallied a single point on a foul shot, but he failed to net another goal until only three minutes remained to play. By that time the scoreboard read:

Terrace—41. Central—49.

The crowd was yelling almost without pause, sensing an upset. The air seemed about to split with tension. A mighty winning streak could be shattered, within minutes.

Mark's teammates fought with fury, as if suddenly aware that their danger was about to become reality. They closed the gap, in a brilliant spurt, to 51-47.

A pass came to Mark, with less than a minute to play. He faked left, faked a handoff, then turned left again and hooked a shot with his right hand. He missed.

Central recovered the ball, and that was the end. The rival team was content to freeze the ball. The score remained 51-47 until the final buzzer sounded, ending the longest winning streak in the history of Terrace's Panthers.

There were no hysterics in the dressing room. The freeze-finish had warned them. They slumped on the benches, exhausted, the crowd's shuffling a dull thunder overhead.

"Well, that's it," said Red, bending over his laces.

Mark leaned against his metal locker, staring at the ceiling. An old pair of sneaks, dangling there, slowly focused in his eyes.

"It was my fault," he said.

"No," said Buz, after a moment of silence. "If Joe Sabor carried the rest of us along on that winning streak, then it's time we stopped getting a free ride!"

Mintzer, the sports writer, stepped hesitantly through the doorway, and looked at them with sad, dark eyes.

"I was pulling for you, fellas," he said. "I'll tell 'em how you went down—like champs."

Red tried to grin. The others didn't try. Mark thought about that last shot he'd missed. If only he'd made that one, and one other—

Two more figures entered—Coach Hoff, and a tall, dark young man wearing a big gold "T" on his unzipped green jacket. The latter reached the center of the room before he was recognized.

"Joe Sabor!" gasped Buz. "Did *you* see that game?"

Sabor nodded, smiling. "It was a great game, fellows."

Red said, "We killed your winning streak, Joe."

"Not mine," said Sabor. "Those things can't go on forever, anyway."

The ex-star walked over to where Mark Cheney was staring at the cement floor. He slapped Mark's shoulder.

"You looked good, Mark. You'll make a real player."

"Me?" Mark looked up, suspiciously. "I didn't do anything—not like you would have done, I mean."

"Are you kidding? You scored **twelve** points in your first game, didn't you? Do you know what I did in my first game?"

Mark blinked. He hadn't thought about it.

"I scored six points," said Sabor, "and got thrown out on personal fouls, and we lost the game. I didn't even have a left-handed shot then. . . . Remember, Golak?"

"That's right." Big Golak nodded. "You were terrible, at first."

The other players were moving around, looking alive again. Mark began to unlace his shoes, realizing a little what had helped to make Joe Sabor such a great player.

Sabor reached toward the steam pipe. He yanked down his old sneaks and dropped them on the floor.

"You don't need these," he said. "You're a new team. You'll be starting another streak, maybe next week."

"Don't say that!" groaned Coach Hoff. "I want to get some sleep, and enjoy my meals again!"

The players yelped, and began to head for the showers. Hahn stood up, across the room, grinning at Mark.

"Come on, Varsity," said Hahn.

"Coming."

But Mark hesitated. He eyed Sabor's old sneaks, lying on the floor, close to him. He reached out, pulled one of them on his right foot. Then he grinned foolishly, as he saw Sabor watching him.

Sabor nodded, and winked. It was a perfect fit.

Yellow Dust Madness

By GORDON D. SHIRREFFS

A young Apache trails two white men who fight foolishly for the yellow dust called gold

The Arizona sun beat fiercely down into the little canyon, streaking the face of Pa-nayo-tishn with sweat as he knelt on the burning sand. The brass of the empty cartridge case he had found was hot against his fingers. He studied the flat, sandy floor of the canyon.

A white man must have left the case there, and it had been fired from just such a carbine as Pa-nayo-tishn wanted. It was a fine gun that shot seven times without reloading, of a kind that he had deeply coveted many times as he loitered about the white man's towns and forts.

A lizard scuttled out from under the mesquite bush and stared unblinkingly at the young Apache called Pa-nayo-tishn (The-Coyote-Saw-Him). Then a brown hand shot out, and Pa-nayo-tishn wrung the neck of the little desert dweller and dropped it into his food pouch.

He had been on the trail for three days—three thirsty, burning days—since leaving the *rancheria* of his clan of the Chiricahuas high in the mountain meadows. The finding of the cartridge case deep in his own country was a good sign from the *Kan,* the gods of his people. He had sworn to find a man with a gun like that and take it from him for Pa-nayo-tishn desired to be known as a great warrior. With a fine weapon such as he sought, he could raid deep into the land of the little men to the south. He would become a brave high in his clan.

What better test of a young warrior than to find and, if necessary, kill a white man and take his carbine that shot many times without reloading?

Pa-nayo-tishn glanced at his mare. The horsegut waterbag slung over her withers held barely enough water to last until he reached the stream on the far side of the hills rising before him. He fingered the smooth cartridge case, knowing that it must have been dropped recently, else the wind-driven sands would have covered it from sight. He slipped the brass cylinder into a fold of his garment and stood up.

Leading his mare toward the mouth of the canyon, he found a pile of horse droppings. He raked quick fingers through them. They were still slightly moist. The white man was but a few hours ahead of him.

Hours later in his trailing, he had constructed a mental picture of the man ahead of him. A big man on a big horse. A white man who was trying to move through the heat-shimmering hills as stealthily as one of the Tinneh. Silently and unseen.

Pa-nayo-tishn had also found a second set of tracks later in the day. Tracks of another white man, afoot and leading a heavy-laden burro. He was ahead of the big man and had left traces of his tapping on rocks. He was one of the crazy whites who hunted through the land of the Tinneh for the soft yellow metal that drove white men mad.

Many such as he had fallen to the Tinneh because the hunt for the yellow metal had sealed their eyes to danger. The Tinneh hated them.

Pa-nayo-tishn rode into an arroyo and up it to a little valley close beneath the hills. Purple shadows were creeping down the hillsides, and the sun was behind the mountains. He heard the subdued music of a stream as it rippled shallowly across the smooth stones of its bed. The white men had camped there a day apart. There was plenty of sign. The ashes of the second man's fire were still warm against the earth.

The Indian picketed his mare and piled great handfuls of grass for his bed. He ate sweet roasted mescal and the cold roasted heart of an antelope he had shot with an arrow several days before. He drank deeply at the stream and then quickly built a small wickiup. Twirling his fire-sticks, he lit a fire of dry wood and then heated stones from the stream bed. He pushed the heated stones into the wickiup with a branch from a cottonwood.

Throwing his blanket over the shelter, he stripped off his moccasins, buckskin kilt, gray calico shirt. He entered the wickiup and closed the blanket behind him. He threw water on the heated stones. The steam soon caused rivulets of sweat to break out on his body. The *taachi,* sweat bath, sometimes brought visions while one was asleep. These visions often gave wise counsel to young warriors on the trail.

When he began to feel sleepy, he threw aside the blanket and ran down to the stream. He plunged into a shallow pool, gasping at the shock of the cold water. Then he trotted up to his bed and rolled himself into his blanket, to sink almost instantly into a deep untroubled sleep.

The faint hoot of an owl awoke the young Indian hours later. He had seen no vision in his sleep. He sat up and listened. The melancholy cry was repeated. He threw off his blanket and arose. *Bu,* the owl, was a harbinger of ill-omen. Death or misfortune followed closely behind him.

Pa-nayo-tishn dressed quickly. He led his mare to the stream and let her drink her fill. He refilled the horsegut canteen until it was swollen with water. He slung his lance over his shoulder and rode out of the valley. With a muted chant to the Gods of Darkness, he threaded his way toward the mountains to the east and south. A cool breeze swept toward him as he left his campsite to the lonely vigil of *Bu.*

When the first pale fingers of the Sun God touched the high peaks, he was well into the jumbled mountains. It was easy to follow the trail of the two white men. He did not want the first man. The other man—the man with the gun—was a warrior like Pa-nayo-tishn, and fine quarry.

The day moved slowly. He saw antelope several times but did not stalk them. There was plenty of roasted mescal in his food pouch. He had all the water he needed.

Several times he touched the *chalchuitlhl* hanging at his throat. It was a good fetish: the lightning-riven twig of an oak. He had found the twig the first day on the trail after a great flash storm that had filled the arroyos brimful of rushing, angry water. The finding of the fetish had led to the finding of the cartridge case, and that was a wonderful happening.

Later in the day the trail grew faint, and he lost it altogether in a maze of jumbled rock covered with scrub oak and manzanita. It was a place of wild towering cliffs hanging high overhead. The *Kan* had played great games here in the early days of the world, hurling great rocks about and shattering the living rock.

Perhaps *Bu* had spoiled his luck. It would be hard to pick up a trail here. He quirted the mare into a deep cleft beside the trail. Before it grew dark he scattered handfuls of *Hoddentin,* the sacred meal of the Tinneh. It was a gesture to appease the gods. Then he slept again.

At dawn, a cool breeze swept down the cleft and rustled the trees in the canyon. He led his horse out of the cleft and cast about for several hours. His luck had changed again, for he found a wad of the brown leaf the white men chewed. It was lying part way up the mouth of a tortuous canyon branching off to the south. There was now but one way for those ahead of him to go—straight into the heart of the great range towering before him. A great, chaotic mass of rock covered with trees and thorny brush.

In the middle of the afternoon, the Indian picketed his mare in a shallow, grass-carpeted canyon. There was a rock pan of water within reach. He painted his face with red ocher and drew two white bands across nose and cheeks. He pulled on his buckskin battle shirt painted with the symbols of the sun, lightning, moon, water beetle, and many other spirit signs to pray to in time of need. He cached his food bags and left the canyon armed with bow, knife, and war club. His man was not far ahead. There was no other place he could be.

Hours later, Pa-nayo-tishn lay on his lean belly on the lip of a knife-edged ridge. His bow lay strung beside him. He had bound a mat of bear grass about his head so that his head would blend with the ridge. He watched the twisted canyon below him. Long shadows of purple and black had begun to creep down the mountain sides. A thin thread of bluish-white smoke arose from the canyon and drifted off before the slight breeze.

Farther down the slope of the ridge beneath Pa-nayo-tishn lay a man. A big white man. He lay so quietly it had taken Pa-nayo-tishn some time to see him. The dying sun had sparkled for an instant on the brass trim of the carbine Pa-nayo-tishn wanted. The big man turned and looked upward at the sun. The light turned his beard into a dark, blood-red mass. It was a sign that Pa-nayo-tishn had good medicine, the Indian thought.

The big man crept slowly down the ridge. He moved silently for all his great size. Pa-nayo-tishn followed him. At last he could see a tiny *jacale,* a little cabin of upright poles plastered with mud. It was almost invisible, so carefully was it hidden in the mouth of a great cleft in the side of the ridge. There was a tiny leaping stream dashing out of the cleft.

The redbeard lay still, watching the *jacale.* His heavy carbine rested on the rocks before him. A small white-bearded man came out of the cabin and walked to the stream carrying an *olla.* He filled it with water and turned back toward the cabin. He glanced up at the towering peaks.

Why did not the redbeard make himself known to the other? Were they not white-skinned brothers?

The redbeard hunched over his carbine. The heavy roar of the weapon re-echoed flatly from the canyon walls again and again. A puff of smoke drifted from its muzzle.

The whitebeard staggered. He dropped the *olla.* The water glistened for a moment as it struck the earth. The whitebeard began to run. He ran swiftly for one so old.

The big man leaped to his feet with a shout and levered another cartridge into the carbine. The weapon roared again. The whitebeard jumped into the *jacale.* In a moment, he reappeared, running hard for the brush along the banks of the stream. His hands were full of little bags.

Redbeard bounded down the slope like *choddi,* the antelope. There was a long knife in his hand. The old man staggered into the brush. Redbeard crashed in after him. Pa-nayo-tishn shivered. There would be a lost soul wandering about the canyon that night.

When darkness drew its blanket over the mountains, Pa-nayo-tishn moved swiftly down to the cabin. Soon the moon would arise. There was a glow of light within the *jacale.* Pa-nayo-tishn passed quickly through the brush and cautiously circled the dead whitebeard.

The Indian moved through the brush and looked into the open window of the *jacale.* Redbeard sat at a tiny table. He was running thick fingers through a pile of yellow dust before him. In the white man's eyes sparkled the madness Pa-nayo-tishn had seen before when there was gold about. Suddenly the man scooped up the yellow dust and poured it back into the stained buckskin bags and thrust them beneath his dirty shirt.

Pa-nayo-tishn faded swiftly into the shadows and back up the ridge. He trotted steadily down the canyon through its shadows until he found just the place he wanted.

It was not too far from his horse. He could look down the narrow twisting trail without being seen himself. He slipped a pebble into his mouth to ease his thirst and then scattered *Hoddentin* to the four winds. He must wait patiently until dawn.

With the first gray traces of light, he re-strung his bow. He watched a hawk rise and circle slowly about down the canyon.

When the light grew strong and yellow, he heard the thud of hoof beats. Their low thunder soon echoed through the canyon. Pa-nayo-tishn notched a poisoned, three-foot cane shaft to his bow. The hawk sailed swiftly off before the wind.

The redbeard rounded a shoulder of rock. He was swaying in his saddle, singing and talking to himself. Such was the effect the yellow metal had on the white men.

Pa-nayo-tishn waited until the redbeard passed beneath him. The back of the white man was broad. Pa-nayo-tishn arose and drew the bowstring back to his ear. The sharp swish of the arrow was cut short by a thud and the hoarse grunt of the redbeard, who swayed and tried to turn in his saddle. Then he slid to one side and fell heavily to the ground.

Pa-nayo-tishn notched another shaft. He went down to the redbeard. The white man lay still. His mouth gaped open, revealing yellow, uneven teeth. Pa-nayo-tishn wrinkled his nose. The smell of the unwashed white man was not sweet.

He thrust a foot beneath the body and rolled it over. The buckskin bags fell out into the trail from beneath redbeard's shirt.

Pa-nayo-tishn unbuckled the wide belt from about the big man's waist. It was heavy with a small gun and many cartridges. He stepped to the horse. Thrust into a boot beside the saddle was the heavy carbine Pa-nayo-tishn had longed for. A thick belt filled with cartridges hung over the horse's withers. Pa-nayo-tishn was now rich indeed.

He looked through the saddlebags. There was food and a bag of the little brown beans the white man brewed to make black water. He found a fine hatchet and a good knife. He glanced at the redbeard. A skillful warrior that man had been, but he had let the yellow dust dull his senses.

Pa-nayo-tishn swung himself onto his new horse. Thoughtfully he weighed the heavy buckskin bags in his hands. The yellow dust would buy many fine things from the white traders. He could buy calico and cartridges for the fine gun.

Yet there was madness in the little bags of yellow dust. The blood of two men was on the bags. Perhaps the whitebeard spirit would come looking for his dust. That would not be good. Not even the riven oak twig would help then.

Pa-nayo-tishn drew his knife and slit the little bags one by one. He scattered the heavy glistening dust among the rocks beside the trail as he rode along. When the bags were flat, he hurled them into the brush.

With a low chant to the god Stenatliha he rode to the canyon where he had left his mare. He had food there, and Pa-nayo-tishn, as befitted a successful Chiricahua, must fill his belly for the long trail home.

Siren Song

By WALLACE WEST

An old cream separator was all Scoops needed to perfect his ultrasonic fire extinguisher

"Hey, Junkie! wait up!"

Jeffrey Smithers clenched his big hands. His lumpy jaw tightened. Could a fellow help it if his family was in the scrap business? But Jeff had learned by hard experience that it was useless to show how he hated his nickname. He waited.

"Where you heading, Junkie?" asked the slim, blackhaired boy who clattered down the high school steps and joined him. "Are you going to the field house?"

"Nuh uh," answered Laurel Creek's star athlete. "Coach called off practice so we could all go see the new fire truck. You coming, or not, Scoops?"

"Might as well." Scoops Traylor tried to keep step with his tall friend as they cut across lots and up the half-dry bed of the creek that gave their village its pretty, distinctive name.

"Suppose she's been delivered yet?" Jeff asked once as they paused for breath.

"I think so. I saw dad and the jeep heading for the firehouse half an hour ago. Personally, though, I don't care whether she ever comes."

"Why not?" Smithers stared down at him in amazement.

"Laurel Creek won't need a truck when dad and I get our ultrasonic fire extinguisher finished."

"What's an ultra-zombie fire extinguisher?"

"I said ultrasonic, Junkie! It's a souped-up siren you can't hear. Puts out a fire just like that." Scoops snapped his fingers.

"How big a fire will this silent dog whistle put out?"

"Well . . ." Scoops kicked a stone into the creek. "Just a little one right now, but . . ."

". . . but our new truck can throw 250 gallons of water a minute on a *big* fire right now." Jeff completed the sentence.

"That's not so much. Able Mabel can pump 750 gallons. And the Three Rivers pumper throws a thousand."

"Ours will have a 500-gallon water tank on her, though."

"That's all right for houses that aren't near water mains, I guess." Scoops made the mistake of shrugging his shoulders while wriggling through a barbed-wire fence. Jeff had to untangle him.

"Look!" shouted the long fellow as they came in sight of the firehouse. "There she is. What a beauty!" He made the last hundred yards in eleven seconds. Scoops' knees pumped like hot-rod pistons but left him far behind.

The truck in front of the brand-new red brick building was being mobbed by all of the children and most of the men of Laurel Creek village and township. What could be seen of it glittered with chrome and scarlet enamel. The Women's Auxiliary of Volunteer Engine Company Number 1 was serving soft drinks and coffee. Several wardens were keeping traffic moving on Main Street.

Scoops grinned when he saw that his father, Fire Chief Thomas Traylor, had got all dressed up in his uniform for the occasion.

"See those inch-and-a-half hoses mounted on reels at either side of her cab?" the chief was explaining to the crowd. "We can drive her right through a grass or brush fire while two men ride up there and pour water on the blaze."

"Gollies," Jeff whispered as he wedged himself close enough to touch a glossy fender. "You hear that, Scoops?"

But Scoops was not listening. He had walked once around the new piece of equipment. Then he had turned up his freckled nose and gone into the empty engine house. Now he was patting Able Mabel's battered radiator. He felt sorry for the old pumper. Seemed as if he were the only person who remembered how she had earned her name.

One windy September day three years previously somebody had been burning leaves without a permit. The blaze got out of control. Sirens screamed. People ran. Schools were let out.

For a time it looked as though the whole center of Laurel Creek would go. But the old pumper and her smoke-blackened crew managed to save everything except the hardware store. She was cheered to the echo as she lumbered back to the garage. That was when Mayor Horton dubbed her Able Mabel.

As the result of that fire, Laurel Creekers raised money to build a real engine house and finally to buy the new tank truck. Able Mabel was a has-been!

Or was she?

Scoops came ambling out with a crooked grin on his lips and a determined look in his black eyes. It was the look that made his mother cross her fingers; made his father wonder, on alternate weeks, whether his son was a budding genius or a blithering idiot.

"You've got another idea!" Jeff forgot all about the truck as Scoops wandered by without seeing him. "Quick! Go soak your head under that hydrant. Remember what happened last time."

"Wasn't my fault the spring on my apple picker broke," Scoops said and flushed.

"Or that the side of farmer White's barn was in the way when your gadget went into reverse and started to de-pick," Jeff reminded him. "It took us two days to wash off all that applesauce."

"You win, Junkie. But dad and I have a patent pending on an improved model of that picker. One of these days it will make us rich."

"You can say that again."

"Dad," Scoops called above the chatter of the crowd, "may I use the jeep?"

"If you will take it home afterward. I have to drive this thing back to Three Rivers. She has a bad leak in one of her pump gaskets. Time to break up this clambake anyway." The chief climbed into the truck's cab and started the motor. "Tell mother I won't be home till after dark." He waited until the wardens had cleared a path through the crowd, then roared away with bell clanging.

When Scoops climbed into the jeep, he found Jeff occupying half of the front seat. Instead of turning on the ignition he reached into his pocket and pulled out a cardboard box. Opening it, he studied what looked like an oddly shaped watch crystal.

"I'll bite," his pal sighed at last. "What is it?"

"A piezoelectric crystal. Dad brought it from the laboratory yesterday. It has a flaw. The Northern Electric people were going to throw it away. Guess it will do."

"Do what? Spot flying saucers?" Jeff was bouncing with curiosity.

"It generates about ninety million sound waves per second."

"That's a lot of sound waves. Those supersonics you mentioned, I suppose."

"Not supersonics, Junkie. Ultrasonics! 'Supersonic' refers to airplanes that fly faster than the speed of sound."

"Excuse me for living. But what good does it do to make sound waves so ultra that not even a dog could hear 'em?"

"You can make oil and water mix with ultrasonics." Scoops was showing off now. "You can pasteurize milk and sterilize the milk bottles. You can aim an ultrasonic beam at the sea bottom, listen to the 'echo' and find the depth of the water and even whether there are fish in it."

"Handy gadget to hunt whales with," Jeff teased him.

"A British whaler is doing just that . . . You can shake dirt out of clothing . . ."

"Traylor's Ultrasonic Washing Machine!" Jeff sucked in his thin cheeks and winked. "It will make another fortune for you."

"And," Scoops concluded, "you can put out fires."

"This I have to see."

"This I am going to show you—on one condition."

"Now comes the bite!" Jeff shuddered.

"On condition that you get your father to lend us a piece of junk."

"Not junk, Scoops! Call it scrap. Please."

"All right. Have it your way."

"What do you want *this* time?" Jeff grumbled as Scoops started the motor. "Last time it was the transmission from a Model T Ford."

"We must have moved ten tons of jun— of scrap before we found it," Scoops chuckled. "But, boy! How that thing could pick apples!"

"And de-pick 'em."

"What we want now is a big centrifuge," Scoops rambled on.

"Centerwhich?" Jeff was no slouch in physics, but his friend's quick changes of pace often left him gasping.

"Centrifuge. That's a high-speed spinner."

"Why not ask Northern Electric for one?"

"Lab centrifuges are worth their weight in gold, and they can only spin a fraction of an ounce of stuff. I need something big enough to fasten a fire siren to. Saaay!" Scoops eased the jeep onto the highway behind dozens of cars that were leaving the engine house. "A cream separator is a centrifuge. Its insides spin like mad. Would your father have a beat-up separator?"

"Oh, sure. But, if I may be so dumb, why spin a fire extinguisher?"

"It's the Doppler Effect." Scoops turned the car off Main Street. They bounced across the railroad tracks toward a lot surrounded by a high board fence. A sign on the fence read: "Smithers' Mammoth Scrap Yard. We Buy EVERYTHING And Sell Same."

They drove through a gate, turned left around a mountain of old rubber tires, squeezed between rows of sheds stuffed with baled paper or rags and chugged past busy shops where big metal castings were being cut into chunks with saws and acetylene torches.

"Doppler's Effect," Scoops shouted above the noise, "causes a sound to increase in pitch when the object making it approaches the listener."

"Is that what makes a train whistle go up the scale as it comes closer to you?"

"Go to the head of the class, Mr. Smithers. When the train approaches, it pushes more sound waves ahead of it and into your ears than when standing still. The result is the same as if the number of waves made by the whistle had increased."

"Sort of the way a boat heading into a storm hits more waves than if it were at anchor," Jeff agreed. "I understand that. But I still don't see . . ."

"Find me a cream separator and I will explain all," Scoops sighed as he stopped the car in front of the yard office. A thin little man in overalls came to the door.

"We don't 'ave it," the man said in a cockney accent. "Whatever it is you want, we're fresh out of it. I told you both last fall that—"

"Please, pop!" Jeff wiggled his bony knees from under the dash and went to Scoops' aid as he always did. "Don't act as if you sold watches. This stuff is just—just junk."

"Scrap!" his father yelled as though he had been stung. "Scrap is a five-billion-dollar industry. Scrap bought our new home. Scrap's going to send you to college. How often must I tell you?"

"I'm sorry." Jeff tried to look that way. "I promise never to say the bad word again if you help us out this one more time."

"Humph! You made that promise before." His father smiled in spite of himself. "Well, what is it you want?"

"Just a cream separator."

"A separator? Blimey! Next time it will

be a diving bell or a balloon. You'll find one in that shed." He went back to work, shaking his head helplessly.

An hour and six blisters later the boys dislodged a huge 1930-model creamer from behind other ancient farm implements, bales of metal turnings and similar toe-crushing objects. The thing had a leg missing but its insides still could spin.

They loaded it into the jeep and headed for Scoops' home. Jeff hung onto the separator for dear life to keep it from bouncing out. Scoops' ears burned as Laurel Creekers nudged one another and burst out laughing as they drove along Main Street. When he stopped for the town's one red light, someone suggested that he was kidnaping a robot's grandfather.

Things got worse when they passed the Northern Electric Laboratories where Thomas Traylor worked as head physicist when not fire chiefing. It was quitting time.

"Want that cyclotron calibrated, Scoops?" whooped a home-going technologist.

"Send us a postcard when you get to the moon," another chimed.

Scoops couldn't think of clever replies so he stepped on the gas.

"Mother," he called as he backed the jeep up to the door of a combination garage-workshop behind the big old-fashioned Traylor mansion.

"Yes, son?" A pretty, red-haired woman left her gardening and came toward them.

"Dad won't be home till dark. He had to take the truck back to Three Rivers."

"I've heard of golf widows," Mrs. Traylor smiled. "Guess I am a fire widow . . . Oh, hello there, Jeff. I didn't see you. What on earth are you hugging?"

"Just a cream separator, ma'am," Jeff said, blushing.

"Don't tell me you two are going into the dairy business! I hate cows."

"No cows, mother." Scoops patted her hand. "We're making a centrifuge."

"Really?" she said. "Would you like some sandwiches before you start?"

"Thanks, but we haven't time," said Scoops, while Jeff looked unhappy. "We

want to finish so we can show it to dad when he gets back."

"I'll bring them to you." Mrs. Traylor bustled away.

They wrestled the separator into the shop and propped it level with bricks. It was about the size and shape of a gasoline pump. On top was a big pan for the milk. Below that was an upright cylinder full of metal discs. Below *that* were the gear box, two spouts and a crank.

"Here's the setup," said Scoops, pointing to a work table that ran across the back of the room. At one end of it stood a Bunsen burner. An old-fashioned fire siren and an auto horn had been bolted to the other end.

"You see we have drilled a lot more holes in this siren housing. Then we put in a high speed motor. So, instead of making 15,000 waves, or cycles, a second, the old girl can now rev up half a million. Please keep your eyes on that fly crawling up the wall while I demonstrate."

Scoops flipped a switch. The siren grumbled. The tone crept higher as the motor picked up speed. It became an ear-splitting shriek . . . It was gone!

Not a sound disturbed the quiet of the shop but Jeff pressed his hands to his ears. The bones in his head seemed to be rattling against one another.

"Watch the fly! Watch the fly!" Scoops commanded.

The insect had stopped its crawl. It buzzed its wings awkwardly. It lost its hold on the wall. It was dead when it hit the floor!

"Traylor's ultrasonic death ray!" Jeff gulped.

"It only kills germs, insects and mice, sometimes, at point blank range," Scoops answered as he cut the power. "It uses so much juice that it costs a cent to knock out one measly bug.

"This horn is something else again," he went on. "I can focus its beam and see some fireworks." He tinkered with the horn for a while, lighted the Bunsen burner, clipped an odd-looking meter into place near the flame, and pressed a switch.

The horn merely shivered. Jeff thought it

had broken down. He changed his mind when all his teeth began to ache at once. Mrs. Traylor came in just then. She screamed and dropped the tray of sandwiches as the ultrasonics took effect.

The blue gas flame twisted and dodged. It did a sort of hotfoot dance on the burner tip. It split. It wasn't there any more!

Scoops stopped the horn and turned off the Bunsen. Jeff felt his jaw. Mrs. Traylor pressed her lips tightly together. But she did not scold as the boys helped her pick up the ruined sandwiches. Physicists in a house, she had learned, could do almost anything—and generally did! Also, she was never cross with Scoops because she felt a tiny bit guilty in his presence. When her son was born, she had just finished reading a novel by Sir Walter Scott. In spite of her husband's objections, she had insisted on naming the baby after *two* characters in the book. That, to put it mildly, had been a mistake.

"Pretty good," said Scoops, as he and Jeff got back to work. "The meter showed better than 50 million vibrations or cycles per second. But I want to hit 100 million. The N.E. fellows are working in that range. Dad says that, if I do so, I can make it put out a really big fire, maybe."

They worked like beavers for the next two hours. The sun was setting as they got their Rube Goldberg contraption working.

Finally Scoops turned the thing on and gave the separator handle a few spins.

The T-bar spun merrily, but the meter needle didn't even flicker.

They tinkered some more. Then Jeff grabbed the handle and cranked until the bar whistled through the air.

The needle swept across the dial. There was a ping and a spark. The meter read 90 megacycles before it overloaded.

"Let's ask your mother for something to eat now," Jeff suggested. "I'm starved."

"The man talks about eating!" Scoops threw up his hands. "Remember your Shakespeare, Junkie: 'There is a tide in the affairs of men.' We can't stop to eat now. We have to find a fire to put out."

"Where?" Jeff asked as he wiped some of the grease off his hands and face.

"Never mind. Let's get this thing back in the jeep and wired down."

"I wish coach hadn't postponed practice," Jeff sighed.

"Think what this can mean if it works right," Scoops dreamed out loud while they drove slowly through Laurel Creek's suburbs as the June dusk settled down. "The same siren that brings firemen sliding down their brass poles will be used to put out fires. Hang an ultrasonic on Able Mabel and we can send the new truck back."

"Ub glub!" said Jeff. (Mrs. Traylor had

waylaid them as they were driving out of the yard, so his mouth was full of one of her thick chicken sandwiches.) "There's your fire up ahead," he repeated after swallowing. "Someone's burning trash."

"That's Mr. Thompkins from the Lab. He just finished his new house and is cleaning up around it." Scoops eased the car to a stop behind a hedge out of sight. "O.K.," he whispered. "Limber up the artillery."

They aimed the clumsy, haywire rig as best they could. Scoops closed a circuit to the jeep's battery. Jeff started cranking.

The separator clanked and complained. Thompkins' neat little fire leaped, then faded to a pile of coals. The neat little man who had been feeding it yelped in dismay. His white shirt had turned black!

"Oh-oh," Scoops groaned. "I forgot about that. Ultrasonics make smoke particles cling together and fall to earth. I'll have to buy him a new shirt, I guess."

"Well, you've proved you can put out a fire," Jeff whispered. "Let's get out of here before we get into more trouble."

"That fire isn't *out,*" Scoops snapped. "It's still smoldering. Crank faster."

Jeff put his back into it. But so did Mr. Thompkins! The spinner complained worse than before. The little man, neat no longer,

scampered about gathering dry wood and pieces of tar paper. He heaped these on the dying blaze.

Fed with such combustibles, the fire did leap high for a moment.

Scoops joined Jeff at the crank. The blaze died down.

Mad as a hatter at these strange goings-on, Mr. Thompkins piled shingles, brush and whatever he could get his black hands on over the coals. Up went the fire.

Something had to give! It was the separator. With a long, scalp-tingling "Screee-eee" it stopped dead.

"What happened?" gasped Scoops in amazement.

"I think the spinner jumped its bearings."

"Maybe it just needs oiling," Scoops gasped some more. "Help me."

"No time. Look at that fire go. I'm turning in an alarm. It looks to me as though things are beginning to get way out of control. Look at that blaze go!"

Scoops did look as Jeff ran in search of a call box. Released from its ultrasonic damper, the fire was roaring fifteen feet high. Worse still, it was moving across the debris-filled yard toward the new house. Mr. Thompkins, arms outspread, danced helplessly in between.

210

Heart in mouth, Scoops grabbed an oil can and squirted madly. Able Mabel could never get there and hook up to a hydrant in time. And the tank truck, which could have come a-squirting, was in Three Rivers.

He tried the handle. It moved! He cranked for dear life. The huge fire died back a little, but not nearly enough.

There had to be a way to keep it from moving across those last twenty feet of yard. There *had* to be!

Scoops dived over the seat, got the jeep started after three fumbles, and shot it to the curb midway between the blaze and the house.

Vaulting the seat again, he jerked the reflector till it focused at the base of the creeping flames and resumed his cranking. Up. Down. Up. Down. The splintery handle put more blisters on his palms. The intense heat singed his eyebrows.

"Hey, boy! Come over here," he heard Mr. Thompkins shouting. "I gotta have help."

He didn't even look up. That was just as well. A rain of greasy soot was falling. It got thicker and thicker until he could hardly breathe.

Up. Down. Up. Down. Scoops risked a glance at the fire. It was stopped in its tracks, but it still blazed high. A piece of soot, feeling big as a blanket, closed both his eyes. He clenched his teeth and continued cranking.

From the south he heard the scream of a siren and the roar of a big engine. Good old Mabel! She'd be the hero again.

But another siren was coming like the wind from the north. That tank truck! Racing back from Three Rivers like the United States Marines. Poor old has-been Mabel!

Tears trickling from his closed eyes, Scoops cranked on endlessly. It was Thomas Traylor who finally pried his fingers from the separator handle.

"It was all my fault," Scoops told the firemen an hour later as they sat in the engine house drinking coffee. (Hot showers had made him and Jeff reasonably sootless.) "I should have waited for dad. Junkie warned me, but it all looked so simple. How was I to know?" He stopped in mid-sentence.

"How was he to know," piped up Mr. Thompkins, "that I would get mad at the fool fire and start piling tar paper on it? Wasn't anybody's fault."

"Better yet," chuckled Chief Traylor, "it was like the song those other sirens used to sing, the song that made sailors come closer and closer to the rocks until their ships were wrecked."

"There can be no doubt that the boys saved the Thompkins house, though," said white-haired Mayor Horton. "Neither of the trucks could have got there in time. I propose that, at its next regular meeting, Volunteer Engine Company No. 1 make both of them honorary members. At the next Town Meeting I also will propose that Laurel Creek appropriate some money for development of Traylor's Ultrasonic Fire Extinguisher."

"Gollies!" whispered the heroes as the firemen nodded and sipped their coffee.

"There is just one thing more on tonight's agenda." The mayor pulled solemnly at a bushy eyebrow. "The company must enroll new members under their correct names. I propose, therefore, that Jeffrey Smithers' nickname be forgotten in the future. As for you, Scoops, I don't believe I ever *heard* your given name. What is it, son?"

Scoops turned scarlet. He looked at his father. But the elder Traylor spread his hands as if to say: "Don't look at me. It wasn't my fault."

Scoops stood up. He took a long breath and stuck out his chin.

"My name is Ivanhoe Athelstane Traylor," he said and waited for the laugh.

"A good old English name," said the mayor, pulling at his other eyebrow.

The firemen nodded and sipped their hot coffee.

Twenty Below

By JOHN BARELL

They faced the greatest danger of the Antarctic—adrift on a crumbling iceberg

This story about the Antarctic reflects the young author's deep interest in polar exploration. Sixteen years old at the time he wrote this story, John Barell is the proud owner of four personal letters from Rear Admiral Richard Byrd and was the admiral's guest at the departure of the U.S.S. Atka for its Antarctic exploration.

As soon as the sledge reached the crest of a little knoll, the antennae and stovepipes of our partially buried city came into view. It was one of those unbearable Antarctic summer days; the temperature was up around 30°; the clouds overhead had formed into a thick, milky phenomena that blended almost perfectly with the horizon; and a shower of ice crystals was beginning to fall.

I could see a few of the men toiling in the large T-shaped pit which was to house our tri-motored plane. Others had started a smaller pit to hold our two tractors. I was in harness returning from an investigation of the base camp of last year's 1931 Swedish Antarctic expedition, which had wintered a few miles south of us; and because of the unusual temperature, the pulling had really been rough. As I drew up to one of the shacks, I unleashed the sledge dogs, took off the remaining supplies and the tent, and climbed down the observatory hatch into the meteorological station. Two buckets were already on the floor catching the drip of the melting snow.

As the summer night came on, the ice shower developed into a light, wet snow, and visibility was reduced to fifty yards. Water dribbled through cracks in the shack partitions and held up the painstaking operation of drying clothes. The night watchman began his tour of the cabins and of the conditions on the surface. I stayed up late talking with George Parker, second-in-command. George, a tower of strength, had a brain that was alert and ingenious. A better man couldn't have been found to meet the rigors of polar camp life.

We were discussing the camp's affairs. I was beginning to feel a little desperate about them. "George, how is the intermediate cache coming along?"

"The men are working themselves to the bone, commander. We're using four teams and twelve men, and there are still ten tons to be hauled up here. Then, too, that snow bridge across the large crevasse to the south of the depot is gradually giving way with the widening of the crevasse."

"Well," I began, "winter is drawing too close, and it won't wait for us to unload that place. Tomorrow we'll have to cease operations here and use the remaining members of the camp in the dump operations. It has to be finished soon."

"I agree, sir, but the conditions, you know, are terrible for sledging, especially hauling supplies, and they're terrible on those poor dogs. One died yesterday from sheer ex-

213

haustion. But it has to be done, as you say."

"Let's hope the weather breaks clear for us. The dangers of widening crevasses will increase in this warmth."

"How about the airplane pit?" George asked. "That can wait for a few days or even a week, can't it?"

"Absolutely. It's only March eleventh. The sun won't set for more than nine months. We have plenty of time for that, but both the hangar and the tractor pit must be completed by the twenty-ninth at the latest. Don't you agree?"

"This is your third polar expedition, Commander; you know more about it than I or anyone else—"

"But," I interrupted, "an expedition is above all a cooperative affair, George. Remember that."

The day had been a rigorous one, so we cut the talk short. Because we were the last ones to retire, George and I extinguished the fire and started down the underground ice passage to our shacks. Just as we reached the closed door of the cabin, we were jolted by a frantic cry down the tunnel.

I couldn't see who it was because the tunnel was pitch black, but we both knew it had to be the night watchman, Nat Christy. By the sound of his screech he must have discovered something disastrous in one of the shacks or on the surface.

"Commander! Commander! To the south—"

"Steady, man! What's wrong?"

"The ice is splitting—to the southeast—a large crevasse is opening up—thirty feet wide, four hundred yards long—half a mile from here!"

I stood there astounded. My mind whirled in that split second. What could we do? The camp—what would happen to it?

Wait. I knew as well as anybody else what we would do. This was the greatest hazard of wintering on the gigantic Ice Barrier. That you might awaken some morning to find that your base was a floating town— an iceberg—was the one great fear that all expeditions here had to face, but by the grace of Providence that had never happened. Shackleton in 1908 had abandoned

the possibility of wintering on the huge barrier because of the same threat we now faced. Tomorrow we might be floating in the Ross Sea! This meant death to all, as a drifting berg rapidly disintegrates under the impact of winter winds.

I was solely responsible for the lives of all the men, and the burden of the expedition rested on my shoulders. If something weren't done about this crevasse immediately, I would be technically responsible for the lives of all who were with me.

I had thought of this hazard endlessly, and with the aid of other veteran Antarctic men had arrived at the only possible solution. All vital supplies—food, clothing, tents, radios, and other valuable scientific apparatus—had to be hauled to an emergency base southwest of the camp—away from the vicinity of the widening crevasse. Once on this high ground about three miles from the camp, the expedition would be relatively safe. If the crevasse should widen enough to allow this part of the barrier to sheer off, at least we would not float away on it.

I gave orders as calmly as I could.

"George, wake all the men, and tell Myers to radio the cache party to start south as soon as possible. We need help right here. Send Demis and Hutch to the snowmobile upstairs. That'll be a lifesaver if it will only start. Nat, you come into the library; I want to make a map."

With an accurate map of the location of the crevasse and of our rescue camp, I started the men to work.

The next three hours were chaotic. Men were rushing here and there removing cases of food from the tunnels, repairing sledges, packing precious instruments, and finding parts for the tractor. I can gladly give thanks that I was in command of such a conscientious group of fellows.

But we could not prevent the oncoming disaster; we could only try to assure our safety from it. We would be far from a state of security and comfort in a retreat camp, for winter was quickly descending on us and any possible aid from the outside was cut off because of the lateness of the season. The earliest possible aid could not arrive until late December or early January. Morale would have to be kept high.

Men can easily turn against each other or resort to more drastic measures to relieve the terrible agony of living ten months under cramped conditions, with wet sleeping bags and clothes, the barest of essentials, and with bone-searching cold that is only partially relieved by stoves. It would be up to me and my staff to prevent complete destruction of the expedition; we would constantly have to assure all that they would safely survive, a tremendously difficult task under heartbreaking conditions.

All hope depended on our weatherman. If he could predict a change in the present conditions, he would be our deliverer. We needed a cold blast of air from the polar plateau. But the continuation of this terrible warm front for about three days was in sight.

Our twenty-three men and thirty animals, after forty days of grueling unloading operations, were near the point of exhaustion. The two tractors had rendered great service; they had succeeded in transporting forty tons of supplies to the camp. I was greatly surprised that not one of the crew collapsed during those early rush hours while our fate hung in the depths of that horrible fissure. Two mongrels, however, died right in harness from the terrific strain. The men were working at the utmost peak of their physical endurance, and as every single carton of food or clothing transported would help save us from a disastrous end, we were not able to halt this excruciating toil for one minute.

From 10:30 that night until 7 o'clock the morning of the twelfth, no one was idle; very few even stopped for a breath, let alone food or sleep. But even with all at work and with the greatly needed aid of the cache group and its tractor, we were only able to move one and a half tons to the southwest! Three people might be able to live on that amount for two and a half months. We needed a tremendously larger amount of supplies to survive.

Neither time nor fate was with us that day. The snow had stopped; the temperature had dropped to 28°. It had to go down to −20°

at least, but Ole, the meteorologist, could not yet see anything in the picture to cause him to change his forecast. The surface was still in a wretched state: soft, deep, and slow. It took one loaded sledge an hour and a half to make a round trip—a sad state indeed.

The snowmobile at the base was beyond nine-hour repair. As we could not lose the valuable services of Demis and Hutchinsen, I sent them to the depot tractor which was just starting south with another load. By 9:30 our expectation that this car would prove to be a lifesaver began to show light, for in two and a half hours it alone had moved three more tons to the rescue camp. It now looked as though we were going to have a better chance for survival because in one load it could carry enough food for one man to live through the approaching night. It was constantly on the trail.

On its fourth run it stuck in a small crevasse; its gas line froze and cracked. Demis and Hutch flagged a returning team, and told them to bring out a new line. They thought it would take only an hour to put it in and get the car on the road. We were now minus both our most precious possessions. The one at the base camp had two men on it, but it was still many hours from repair. Just as the team with the new gas line was pulling out, Petersen, the biologist, dashed in with a new report.

"The big crevasse is a mile and a half long, Commander!"

There could be no new strategy employed because of this report—only speed, speed, and more speed. I knew the fissure was getting wider every minute, but there was absolutely nothing to do about that. The only factor which would have any effect on it was the cold.

At 11 o'clock with only six and a half tons down south and the trail tractor still needing work, the thing I dreaded most happened. I was in the main building unloading some of the meat, and had stopped for a moment to watch the drops of water dribble down the walls into puddles on the floor. Pete Smith, our best and most experienced driver, suddenly stumbled through the open door and dropped practically at my feet.

I picked him up and laid him on a bunk and immediately called Doc. Pete looked terrible, and for a moment I was haunted by the thought that he might be badly injured. However, when the doctor came, he said it was nothing really serious that a complete rest of ten or more days wouldn't cure. The poor fellow had been working all the day before in the relays from the cache, had had no sleep last night, and had started in with the others here at 3:30 that morning.

The average person would have collapsed days ago if he had been in Smith's shoes, but Pete was one of those indomitable fellows who never stops working. He toiled nearly eighteen hours a day. In those last eight hours he said he didn't know what had held him up, but I knew it was more than willpower alone.

I then realized that this relay work had to be done in shifts, rather than by all, all at once. This would slow down the work, but it was humane, and I should have ordered it sooner. I put serious blame on myself for not looking after the men better. They were all of the type that would never tell you when they were exhausted.

The manpower was now only two-thirds its maximum, and we were moving at a snail's pace.

But by one o'clock the auxiliary radio, the seismic sounding apparatus, a great portion of the meteorology equipment, and all the surveying instruments were crated and on the surface, waiting transportation by the tractor. This was a tremendous achievement. At this time I took a breather from my duties to check the car on the southern trail. I was on skis halfway to it when I saw Demis and Hutchinsen slowly plodding through the deep snow toward me. Their story was that at first they had seen only the superficial wounds. Now they knew the snowmobile needed a complete engine overhaul, and that would take time.

Much of my calmness now departed. I began to show desperation, my courage slackened, and I felt some of that fear again. Both tractors were out, full manpower wasn't being employed, the temperature was varying only slightly, and the surface remained wretched. If only we could have used the big plane—but surface conditions prevented its take-off.

To move the valuable scientific gear, great care had to be exercised. Consequently, the pace was greatly slowed down. The dogs were dropping in their traces from exhaustion. They could go no farther. I called a halt to all sledge operations to and from the camp. It meant too much valuable time lost.

The crevasse was now four times its original length and branching out in other directions! All that in less than twenty-four hours. Certainly we had to continue; but if both men and animals were to outlive this crisis, rest had to be taken. Even so, the most time I dared provide was six hours.

During these six hours I could not rest, but kept right on carting and moving supplies. I felt it was my duty, even though I was just as worn out as the others. I hadn't lost my faith, but doubt was beginning to take its place. I found that I was blaming myself for the coming tragedy. After all, I had brought all these men down here, and it was up to me, as leader and most experienced of the expedition, to bring them back to civilization, two thousand miles away.

Torn from my work by this thought, I picked up the Bible and began to read, then to pray. . . .

"Commander!" Ole burst through the door with a resounding crash. "It will be more than 20° below in five hours! A new air mass is moving in."

I was too stunned to say anything. I knew what Ole had said would happen, for he was always right.

From then the temperature gradually fell from its high of 31°. Fifteen men practically sat on top of the thermometer watching the mercury fall—a sight which caused rejoicing. When it finally reached its maximum descent, the sky had magnificently cleared into a beautiful multi-colored sunset.

The dark, gloomy crevasse would now hold fast and within a few weeks would be all snowed in.

Cap Shott

By J. PAUL LOOMIS

Only Long Louis, king of voyageurs, had courage to battle the big river of a thousand thunders

The Grand Rapids of the Athabaska River roar on in the deep spruce woods, seldom heard now by men. Forty years ago the railway by-passed that turbulent section of the stream where thundering whitewater like the Brûlé and Rapids of the Drowned are small beside the Grand. Now, too, planes and winter tractor trains help carry the commerce of the north. The long canoe and bateau brigades of the fur trade cross the lakes and follow the swift rivers only in the memories of a few grizzled voyageurs.

But in cabin and by campfire, wherever men speak of great rapids, still echoes the name of Cap Shott.

He is a legend of daring. Yet perhaps the name would never have been coined and the man who wore it might long ago have been forgotten except for a boy at Methy Portage one July morning in 1863.

The northern summer sun was just above the spruce. Pungent smoke of breakfast fires, just extinguished, lay in blue skeins in the still air. An alert, white-breasted loon on the glassy surface of Methy Lake sent his shrill *I see he-he you!* to echo back from the walls of timber, and a bull moose, feeding on lily roots, lifted his dripping head. The *hommes du Nord*—men of the north, as the Hudson's Bay voyageurs from Athabaska called themselves—were starting back over the long portage.

Muir McEwen was struggling to get one of the ninety-pound bales of trade goods upon his back. He was a husky youngster of seventeen, strong enough, but he didn't know how.

Three months ago he had sailed from Scotland, an apprentice clerk of "The Company of Gentlemen Adventurers Trading into Hudson's Bay." Yesterday, with the yorkboats that had brought a year's supply of goods for many trading posts, he had arrived here at the height of land between the Atlantic and Arctic watersheds.

Today the yorkboats were already on the lake, returning to Fort Churchill with the year's take of fur. The trade goods—and Muir—were headed on toward the Athabaska with the *hommes du Nord*.

"Marche! Marche!" rang an order. The same voice stormed on in angry French.

Muir heard a surly reply, then the crack of a fist. He turned in time to see a tall young man whose black hair was bound by a red *fillet* knock down a hulking halfbreed fifty pounds heavier than himself, and then kick him vigorously.

Muir did not know that a moccasined foot is not likely to do much damage. Or that there were no rules to bush fighting. By his code it wasn't fair and he broke through the ring that had quickly formed, three-deep, of Canadians, Crees and mixed bloods, leaning forward under their heavy packs.

"Stop!" he cried. "Dinna' kick him again!"

217

Since no attention was paid to him, he struck with fists he had learned to use when, at fourteen, he went to work in a shipyard on the Clyde. His audacity brought an intake of breath from the watchers.

Muir rocked the tall man on his heels. But with the quickness of a lynx the voyageur recovered balance, struck—and Muir saw a starry blaze that blacked out. Then the branches of a spruce formed blearily above him through water that had been doused on his face.

He saw the tall man over him, heard him say: "Listen, stupid one! I am Long Louie Fassoneure, me. *Bourgeois* de brigade. That's boss. Eef you don't lak it w'en I punish a loafer—you look anoder way. You stay here now in de camp by Methy Lac. Don't leave it or you get lost. We come back 'fore dark."

Crouching before the pack he had thrown down, Long Louis lifted it upon one bent knee. He twisted his supple body to put the broad band of the tumpline over his head, then straightened with a heave. The pack was upon his back.

"Marche!" he said again and the hundred packers took the portage trail after him.

Muir gaped. *He* had been struggling to shoulder *one* of these bales. These men were each carrying two. Except Long Louis, who had *three* bales in his tumpline.

Muir walked to the landing and bathed his battered face in the cold water of the lake. His left eye pained and had swollen nearly shut. How could he sit here all day alone, chewing his anger at Long Louis? Besides, he had started out to pack!

By following the example of Louis, Muir got his bale upon his back. For a time he watched the trail ahead for the packers, sure he would overtake them. But jabs of pain began to point out to him muscles he hadn't known until now that he possessed. Sweat stung his eyes. He had to rest more often.

Yet on he went, uphill and down, across meadows where the midsummer sun blazed, through woods gloom where mosquitoes were a droning torment, over spongy muskegs.

Finally he was ordering himself: "Ye must go tae yon tree; then nothing matters!" And at the tree, "Now only tae yon log." So he stumbled into the camp at the Clearwater River and dropped his bale where thirty big birchbark canoes lay on the stream bank.

Louis rose from his lunch of roast meat cut from the juicy hump of a huge woods bison that one of his Crees had shot. It was a point of pride with the *hommes du Nord* that whether they fed royally on buffalo and moose or starved on suckers, they lived entirely off the country they went through. "Pork-eater" was a scornful term for greenhorn which they applied even to their own kinsmen of the brigades that set out from York Factory and Fort Churchill with English bacon in their boats.

"I tol' you to stay in camp," growled Louis, and Muir tried to brace himself for more punishment. "But to carry de pack fourteen mile de firs' tam you put heem on! An' not lose de trail on de mossy muskeg!" Wonder had broken the scowl of the *bourgeois*. "You are passenger, not voyageur. W'at for you carry de pack at all?"

"For the same reason I pulled an oar in the yorkboat," Muir answered. "I will na' loaf while ither men work."

"*Bon!* Fine!" cried Long Louis. "We got honner tons yet to portage. W'at your name?"

"McEwen."

"*McEwen!*" The word exploded from Louis. His large gray eyes glared in his swarthy face. "An' you go to Fort Chipewyan. You de son of ol' Douglas McEwen, chief factor there?"

"Nephew," Muir said, startled by the swift change.

"All de same. W'y you not tell me? This morning I try to teach you to mind your own business," Louis went on, "but you will tell de factor I give you de black eye an' he fire me—lak dat!" He clapped his sinewy hands. "Me, Louie Fassoneure, dat can outpack, outpaddle, outfight, ev'ry oder man in nord countree—fired because you weasel on me!"

"I bear tales tae *no* one," Muir said vehemently, but he doubted if Louis heard him through his crackle of angry French.

"All right," the *bourgeois* summed up, "while I'm still boss you *be* voyageur. You goin' pack till your ears hang down!"

Strong meat and strong tea gave Muir a start for the return over the long portage but it was all he could do to keep up with the packers' gliding, sag-kneed stride. He thought he couldn't get out of his blanket the next morning. But he made it and after breakfast, stood, packed and in line.

Long Louis saw him, and though he said nothing he pushed Muir's tumpline back from his forehead, which the boy soon found lessened the strain on his neck.

He saw Louis take the pack off one man and make him stay in camp because of a lame ankle; then soundly whip three others —at one time—when they rushed him because he ignored their complaints that they, too, were lame. And again he set the swift pace for the column while carrying once and a half the load of any other man.

Worse than the weariness, Muir decided, was the deadening monotony of the packing. Yet he endured the long day, was less tired the next. The fourth day he made the portage with *two* bales. Tired as he was that night, the headiness of having carried a man's load enabled him to walk up to the fire beside which Louis lounged.

"Why must ye," Muir asked bluntly, "drive the men—and yourself, too—like ye were fighting forest fire? Just tae show ye are boss?" Around them the talk stopped. "Have we not all summer for what we are aboot?"

"*No,* pork-eater!" Louis bounced up. "Only half of a short summer left, to get de goods down de Athabaska to Fort Chipewyan; down de Slave to Fort Resolution; down de Mackenzie to Fort McPherson. So we get tired, eh? So we rest sometimes? So, two thousand mile from here de freeze-up come, snap! De supplies don' get through to leetle posts up de Peel Reever, up de Laird. Hunters don' get traps an' blankets— don' ketch fur dis winter. Don' get lead an' powder. Mebbe starve. You work for Company," he finished; "you don' say, 'this job, she's hard!' "

Muir saw reason in that. And more distinctly than before he sensed the loyalty that all these men held for the Hudson's Bay, for which their fathers and grandfathers had worked. He felt that loyalty growing in himself, too. Felt it strongly enough to make him forget at least a part of his bitterness at Long Louis in a sharper resentment at the huge expense of Methy Portage to his Company. Expense in money and more precious time. It made him still more rebellious at the dulling toil this portage had demanded of three generations of his fellow Company men —and might demand of generations to come.

"Could ye not pack the freight wi' horses?" he asked.

"How you get *chevaux* here in canoe? Or across muskegs?"

"Then is there nae ither route? One that does na' make men intae animals."

"Yes! Send de goods from York Factory up de Saskatchewan to Fort Edmonton. On by oxcart to Athabaska Landing. Down reever from there."

"Why don't they?"

"De *Grande Rapide* of de Athabaska! Can't portage dat one, he's in canyon. An' nobody shoot *heem* by canoe!"

"Does that mean *you* could not?" Muir asked. "Ye do mony things nae one else can. If not by canoe, by bigger boat."

"Wait till you see heem!" said Louis. "Wait till you hear heem bellow lak a thousand thunders—de *Grande!*"

"But where is the grand voyageur? Long Louis, who can whip anyone else in the north! Would ye na', for a change, like to fight something *stronger* than ye are?" Then he leaped out of reach of the arm Louis shot out to cuff him for his impudence.

Louis followed him but a step. He stood staring into the shadows, listening. Muir could hear only a loon's haunting night-cry. But the set of the firelit features of Long Louis told Muir that his ears were filled with the unforgettable voice—with the challenge —of the great rapids.

"By gol'," Louis broke out, "a *beeg* bateau—lak you say—she might do it! Might run de right channel. De *rapide*," he explained, "is split by half-mile island. By gol', I'm goin' try! I been pack mule long 'nuff. Me an' all these men>"

"*Bon!* Fine!" Muir mimicked, for he had learned the value of a taunt to set the resolve of these volatile voyageurs. But already the mood of Louis had changed!

"Who," he asked in a dulled tone, "goin' give me *time* to go there an' build de bateau? Who goin' man de oars?"

"I'll help ye build it," Muir heard himself saying in a rush of earnestness. "I've worked

in a shipyard. I've rowed in boat races on the Clyde, as well as all the way frae Churchill."

For an instant Louis gaped. Then he threw back his head. "Ho, ho!—you hear it?" he roared to the whole camp. "De pork-eater, *he* will shoot de *Grande Rapide!*"

Muir's fists knotted and his cheeks felt scorched. But even deeper than his anger at the ridicule was his disappointment. For the joke that Louis had chosen to make of Muir's eager offer seemed to have scattered the big voyageur's plans to blaze a better trade route.

At last the portaging was finished. They loaded the big canoes nearly to the gunwales, and with Muir bending to his paddle with the rest in time to *chansons* from the France none of them had seen, the brigade glided down the Clearwater. Then down the calm lower portion of the Athabaska. Against

wind and rain on the ninety-mile Athabaska Lake they paddled along its wave-pounded shore to the defiantly set log buildings of Fort Chipewyan.

Muir was proud to meet his uncle, whose word was law in an empire of the north. He answered the many questions of home, then at his first chance he told the plan of Long Louis to end the Methy Portage route by shooting the Grand Rapids. Douglas McEwen's bearded lips straightened.

"Lang Louie must ha' been talkin' through his hat tae hear his wits rattle," he said. But he sent for Louis.

Long Louis entered, with a dark look at Muir. It changed to surprise when the factor, without mention of the black eye about which he knew nothing, asked the *bourgeois* if he truly believed he could shoot the great rapids.

"I'm coming to tell you w'en you send for

221

me," said Louis. "Wit' de right bateau, de right crew—yes."

"Can ye get men tae risk it wi' ye? And mind, I'm not asking ye tae drown yersel', nor any mon."

"I will go," put in Muir.

"Tush, lad, ye dinna' know," the factor said impatiently. "And ye are na' of this voyageur breed o' river rats." The rebuff hurt, but worse to Muir was the twist of scorn that came again to the lips of Long Louis.

In the end, Louis and four picked men did not go on north with the brigade. Instead they and Muir and Douglas McEwen paddled the factor's long, swift canoe back up the Athabaska. Above the mouth of the Clearwater they lined their craft up many white-maned rapids. These Muir studied in awe, but the voyageurs looked at them with dancing eyes. They left the canoe below the Grand.

With only small packs they could scramble up the steep cutbank and work along the rim of the canyon. Sober-eyed now, they stared into it. Yet as the voice "lak a thousand thunders" rolled up and over them, Muir felt his every nerve tingling.

Three miles above the rapids they made camp. There in the crisp days of northern autumn they hewed spruce logs into ribs and thwarts and planking. It was Muir who could most accurately swing a broadax— Muir who came to Louis with many apt suggestions on how to dovetail and dowel the strongest joints. But it was according to a design in the mind of "Cap" Long Louis, as his men now called him, that they built the huge bateau.

Sunrise was gleaming on the "ghosts' breath" mists which the frosty air raised from the river as they launched their craft. The men's shoulders hunched. It was not the hour for daring. They took up their oars. All but one, a man called Pierre Poisson, who, white of face, shook his head.

The fist of Louis drew back.

"No!" Muir caught that arm and jerked Long Louis around. That took a strength Muir had not possessed at Methy Portage.

But the packing, the paddling. . . . Louis glowered.

"The lad's right," said Douglas McEwen. "Ye canna' beat courage intae a mon. More like ye'll knock it out o' the others." The other three, indeed, were trading uncertain looks.

"So we're whipped, then?" Muir demanded of his uncle and Louis together. "After all this work—we'll go back tae Methy Portage! Not if ye'll let me prove I can pull a man's oar. I know the risk. But I'll take it—wi' Louis steering." He looked, by turns, straight into the eyes of the two men.

"Ye're the same tae me as ma ain son," the factor said with a strange gruffness. "But there's nae life in the north wi'oot danger. And naething kills the heart of a lad like *telling* him tae be afraid. I gi'e ye ma permission." He turned. "Do ye want him, Louis?"

Muir felt as though he were hung on the hook of Fort Chipewyan's great fur-steelyard, being weighed. Louis had scorned him twice. This time—

"Mais oui! But yes! At the nearest oar," Cap Louis said.

With a new set to their jaws, the other three oarsmen followed Muir to their seats in the bateau. Louis pushed off with his big steering sweep.

"Keep your eyes open, lad, And guid luck!" The factor's words were ordinary, but Muir would remember his tone. He watched his uncle disappear on the cutoff trail through the woods, swiftly, in order to be at the rapids when the bateau arrived. Pierre followed him, looking like a wet moccasin.

Where the river split upon the island, it plunged downward. Through the throaty roar that made the air quiver Muir heard a shrill, continuous scream. All his senses were tautened by it. He saw that the river divided willingly, without hurling itself upon the island. But he could not turn to see how it raged below the island's point. In the thunder he could not hear the orders of Long Louis. But he could see—and answer—the exultant laughter in Cap Louis's eyes.

The bateau shuddered as it met the first great combing wave. Reared. Leaped. Slapped down with a mighty splash into the chute below. Then she was yanked this way and that as though a gang of water demons had her by the keel. The powerful arms of Louis fought them on the steering sweep. Jerks of his head told the rowers to pull or to back water, as his eyes read the churning river ahead. And yet . . .

Bump! Grind! It was an unseen rock Muir felt beneath them. On it the bateau hung. The current boiled up her side. It was turning her. *Any* craft would swamp, beam-on!

The men pulled till their eyes stood out. They were pivoting the boat back to her course in the teeth of the river! And the big steering sweep in the hands of Louis snapped.

He would have gone overboard but for Muir's lightning leap and clutch. Muir's own oar, which he had jerked inboard even as he jumped, he thrust into the hands of Louis. For himself he caught up the spare oar that lay across the thwarts. Louis plunged his oar to the river bottom. He lifted the great bateau clear of the rock!

On they raced, leaping and yawing. Past the foot of the island. Through torn water where the channels came together again. On —till they were circling in a big eddy four hundred yards below. Here they made land. Here Douglas McEwen met them.

One of his hands fell on Muir's shoulder, one on that of Long Louis. A hand of Louis nearly took the other shoulder off of Muir. The voyageurs went mad.

"Hooray!" they yelled above the distance-lessened roar of the rapids. "Hooray for Cap Shott! Dat Long Louis, he shoot de *Grande Rapide!*" So, on an instant's impulse, they gave Louis the name by which he was known the rest of his life.

"Yes, ye did it!" shouted the factor. Then his lips tightened. "But ither than tae prove the daring in ye, *what of it?* It's nae trade route. Ye could na' bring a *loaded* boat through yon water alive."

Muir saw the triumph drain out of the eyes of Cap Shott. "It was w'at you call brave sport," Louis said. "But for nothing, I guess."

For nothing! Everything in Muir refused the thought. Not for nothing, with that surge in his blood! Not with that grip of Louis, welcome now, still on his shoulder! Clear as a stencil his mind saw all that he had seen since they neared the rapids.

"We could have landed on the head of the island," he said. "And ye can see that from the island down to this eddy there are no rocks. Louis could bring a loaded boat through *that.*"

His uncle's eyes drilled. "What ye thinkin', lad?"

"That the boats of a brigade could be unloaded where the river divides, then run through empty. The flat island is an easy portage for the freight. No oarsmen could land at the foot of it, but the boats would bring up, as we did, in this eddy. So if there were a way to get them back . . ."

"A *cordelle!*" shouted Louis. "De beeg towline! De men on de island tie one end de *cordelle* to a log an' throw heem in reever. De log, too, come to this eddy an' crew of de bateau ketch heem an' mak' de line fast. Those men on de island—lotsa men—tow de bateau back to be reloaded. Eh?"

Douglas McEwen considered this well. Then, "I believe ye can do it," he said. He turned to Muir. "Ye *do* keep your eyes open! Ye'll make a smart clerk, a keen trader, someday."

"Please, sir, I'd rather be a voyageur wi' Louis."

"I ken that," replied the factor. "But there are still rivers tae be explored, new trading posts for you as a Company officer to locate, while Lang Louis must be here every summer tae run the boats through yon rapids."

That was the way it was. For the next forty-nine years Cap Shott piloted every one of the hundreds of cargo boats that the Hudson's Bay Company sent through the Grand Rapids. His fame spread through the northland. It spread almost to the limits of the new trading country opened by Muir McEwen, who became a chief factor before his hair was gray.

Latch On!

By D. S. HALACY, JR.

Hitchhiking in the sky is the trickiest aerial act in a pilot's training

Lieutenant Bob Garrity squinted at the speck seven miles above him tugging its threadlike contrails and pressed the mike button.

"Skyhook, this is Hitchhiker One leaving target area. Stand by for hook-up." Scowling, he waited for the answer from the GRB-36 droning along at 40,000.

"Roger, Hitchhiker One. Skyhook ready and waiting for hook-up."

Bob put back pressure on the column and opened the Thunderflash's jet wide. The big RF-84 cocked skyward and the altimeter began to wind up. The sky over northern California was a Chamber of Commerce dream, its deep blue rich as a mountain lake with just a few wispy high cirrus to the west. It was a beautiful day, but the scowl stayed on Bob's rugged, young face. He was unhappy, and right now his expression wasn't much like that of the smiling guy on the poster outside the Air Force Recruiting Office.

Checking his oxygen, he tilted his head back against the rest and studied the big hook above the Thunderflash's canopy. Six times today he had threaded it into the loop of the "trapeze" in the bomber waiting upstairs. Operation Skyhook, they called it. That or "FICON."

Whatever you called it, Bob was fed up. He'd had it, and he was thankful this would finish up his stint.

The powerful recon ship he flew could nestle inside the belly of the special B-36, and the idea was that the bomber could lug the Thunderflash to enemy territory thousands of miles away, drop it off, and then circle at safe altitude while the recon mission was accomplished. Fifteen minutes ago Bob had dropped from the trapeze and dived on the target area staked out in the valley. The simulated picture-taking done, he was spiraling upward now to contact the bomber.

He rolled level at 40,000, feeling the slight thrill that still came after the terrific climb, and lined up on the GRB-36 waiting ahead. The contrails were huge boils of clouds, now that he was at their level, and he edged the Thunderflash along between them. The trapeze was waiting, and automatically he glanced again at his own hook.

Cutting power, he babied up until the open bomb bay was like a yawning cave above him. Bob had made hook-ups so many times he'd lost count, but the new boom operator was still green even after all the practice. With a grunt, Bob corrected fast, made contact, and felt the reassuring grip of the trapeze.

The sergeant running the boom made a high sign and grinned at Bob, and his voice came over the intercom.

"Hook-up completed, sir. Standing by."

"Uh, Roger. That winds us up for today," came the voice of the major up on the flight deck of the B-36. "Unless Hitchhiker wants to try another round just for the book?"

"Thank you, but no thank you, sir!" Bob

said tightly. "I've had mine. Ready for release!" He waved a brusque hand at the sergeant in the bomb bay and then set himself for the odd feeling that came with release. Under control, he dropped the Thunderflash into a dive and fled back down the miles for home.

He looked over his shoulder once at the shrinking bomber creeping across the face of the sky and grinned. *That's all, chum! This boy has other things to do tomorrow!* Twenty minutes later, he was striding into Operations, whistling happily. Leave had never seemed nicer.

"I'm back, Skipper," Bob cracked easily as he went into Captain Anders' office. "Skyhook complete. Next hitchhiking I do is in a gooney-bird for home!"

"Oh?" the skipper said, looking up to frown at Bob across the stack of paperwork that was always there. "I've got news for you, Lieutenant, and it isn't all good. You're flying again tomorrow."

"You're kidding, sir!" Bob said in panic. "You approved my leave—I've got a ride home in that courier ship. I told you how much I've been counting on it, Skipper!"

"Sorry, Garrity. What was it, a birthday you were going to celebrate at home?"

"Yes, sir," Bob said tensely. "The whole family—"

"You're twenty-three, Garrity. Too young for your wants to hurt you, and old enough to know better. Uncle works us twenty-four hours a day when he takes the notion; or didn't you read the fine print in your commission?"

"Roger, sir," Bob said, dropping his gaze to the floor. "So I fly tomorrow. What's the occasion that's so important?"

"Skyhook," the skipper said. "Six more runs, at least."

"Skyhook! But, Skipper, I'm checked out on that blasted trapeze! You know I've made—"

"You are," the captain said wearily. "I'd say you're the best trapeze artist I've got."

"Well, why do I have to go up again tomorrow?" Bob demanded, fingers squeezing tightly on the oxygen mask he still carried.

"Sergeant Thomas needs **more practice,** that's why," the skipper snapped. "He's a good man, and the major wants him checked out by the end of the week. Look, Garrity, I told you I'm sorry. I'm not going to argue the point with you. Report to briefing at eight in the morning. Understand?" His eyes glinted hard under the thatch of graying hair, and Bob swallowed and nodded.

"Yes, sir," he said, saluting briskly. "Eight o'clock." Then he spun on a regulation about-face and stalked out into the late afternoon. His face a mask of bitter disappointment, he headed down the line.

The faint, pulsating drone of the GRB-36 reached down from the sky, and Bob shot one glance at the contrails glowing red in the sunset and snorted. This was the thanks he got for doing his job well. Now there was nothing to do but call the folks and tell them to forget tomorrow's plans.

What had the skipper said? You worked twenty-four hours a day when Uncle wanted it. Leave wasn't important. All that counted was Skyhook and a dumb sergeant who was slow with the reflexes!

Seven times the next day he took the Thunderflash into the hook. Seven times with never a miss in spite of the brooding anger inside him. Grudgingly he had to admit that Sergeant Thomas had improved, but that helped little, and when the boom operator waved happily after the last hook-up, Bob didn't bother to answer the gesture.

He returned to base, and when the bomber landed and taxied to the ramp, Bob was waiting. They got the critique over, and he took the bomber pilot's praise with little outward indication. As he left the briefing room, Sergeant Thomas called him and trotted to catch up. The husky little man was grinning like a kid who'd learned how to ride a new bike.

"Thanks for sticking it out, Lieutenant!" he said. "Kinda hard to teach an old dog like me new tricks, and I sure appreciate your patience."

"Skip it, Thomas," Bob said. He was still bitter, and the man's enthusiasm rubbed him just backwards. "It wasn't my idea, anyway.

Did you know you messed up a leave for me with your thickheadedness?"

It was a rotten thing to say, and he could tell it hurt the man. The sergeant stiffened as if Bob had called him a dirty name.

"I'm sorry, sir," he said in embarrassment. Wetting his lips, he seemed lost for words then, but finally got out, "Thanks for helping me, though." Awkwardly, he turned and took off for the enlisted barracks. Bob watched him, half-ashamed of himself, and half-indignant. He turned away just as someone called his name from the briefing room door. It was Captain Anders.

"You're really sore, aren't you, Garrity?" the skipper asked, his eyes boring deep into Bob. "Jumping onto poor Thomas like that. The sergeant was really grateful; he thinks he's doing a job."

"I'm glad somebody does," Bob said before he could bite back the words. He knew he was saying more than he ought to, but he couldn't seem to control his temper.

"You don't think you are, Garrity?" The skipper's tone cut like a whip now, and he moved over to stand in front of Bob. "Maybe you'd like it better out of Skyhook, eh?"

"Frankly, sir," Bob said evenly, "I would."

"I'm disappointed," the skipper retorted, and the fire seemed to go out of him. "You don't show me much, Lieutenant, and I think we can do without you on Skyhook from here out."

"Sir," Bob said uncertainly. "I—"

"That's all, Garrity. Report to me in the morning."

Bob whipped up a salute, and then he was staring at the skipper's broad back as the man walked slowly toward Operations. Bob had made a slip, but what could he do now? There was only one thing to do, and that was take it, whatever way it came now. But there was misery in him as anger fought with shame and the feeling of failure.

In the end, he shrugged and went to the BOQ. He was getting out of Skyhook, and wasn't that what he wanted?

The skipper wasn't vindictive in the morning. Strictly business seemed to be his attitude. He motioned to a chair for Bob before he started talking.

"You're sharp, Garrity," he said. "Sharp enough not to take my word for anything. When I was your age, there were a lot of things I couldn't see. Bailout drill was one of them, and I learned what respect was the hard way."

Bob started to say something, but the skipper put up a hand.

"You figure Skyhook is just practice, a way to fill squares on the board over there. Well, I hope you're right. I hope the bell doesn't ring again. But meantime, we have to stay on the ball."

"Yes, sir," Bob said. "Do you have a new assignment for me?"

"Yes, unless you want that leave," the skipper said, reaching for a manila folder.

"I don't want it—now. I'll save it for the next special occasion!" Bob said pointedly, and the captain nodded, keeping his face sober.

"All right, Garrity. I've requested a new man from Wing to take your place in Skyhook. We've got an aircraft down at Biggs you can go pick up. Thunderflash that was forced down en route from San Antonio here. They have it repaired, and we need it."

"Yes, sir," Bob said, getting to his feet. "I'm ready to go now. Getting away from the field awhile might help."

"Good. There's a B-25 over in the transient section about to take off for El Paso. I'll call the tower and get you on. Good luck."

Bob saluted and went out. It was ironic that even this ferry job would be a Thunderflash, too, as if he hadn't had enough time in the recon ship! Sighing, he went by Personnel Equipment and got his gear. There was time for coffee with the B-25 pilots, and then they got upstairs and headed south.

The engineering officer at Biggs was pleasant and happy to be getting rid of the plane. He took Bob out to check it over in the afternoon, shaking his head wearily as he pointed to the hook.

"Attracts too many nosy people," he said. "I'm always hauling some joker down. They want to check that hook and ask a million questions about what it's for. I guess you know, eh?"

"Yeah," Bob said. "I know. You say it's ready to go?"

"Ready as we can make it. But stick around, Lieutenant. You just got here. Bingo tonight, and this mess has the best steak dinners you'll run across."

"I never won a thing in my life," Bob said, grinning weakly. "Might as well fly on back and get it over with. Frankly, I want to get rid of this monstrosity, too."

"You're the doc," the officer said. "I guess this bird will climb over the weather I hear is moving in."

Bob got a hamburger in the snack bar on the line and then filed a flight plan for the California base. The weather boys were agreeable.

"If you tool right along, chum, you can beat the storm. If not, you've got fuel enough to make an alternate. Don't hook that gadget on a cloud!"

"Don't worry," Bob told them. "That hook is strictly along for the ride. I'm done with the trapeze stuff. Thanks for the briefing, gentlemen, and come see us when you're in California."

He cleared the mountains in an easy climb-out after take-off and set a course. Night came like a black dye filtering through the air, and the world became the glow of the panel before him. Lights down on the deck winked out as the undercast scudded across beneath him, and he picked the Thunder-flash up on her blowtorch of blue flame to climb to thirty thousand.

There was plenty of time to think—to think and to wonder if he had been entirely wrong. The skipper had put his finger on it, when he said Bob thought they were playing games. What else was it? Anybody could tell you the B-36 was already obsolete, and what was the good in having crews trained to the fine edge the skipper wanted?

He gave it up at last, and got busy checking his position by radio. The Thunderflash was kiting along at a great rate—he would give it that much credit. Contacting the base, he got the weather and scowled. Not too bad, but not good either.

"Advise you start losing altitude shortly," the tower said, through the heavy crackle of static. "We've got a couple of big ones in the area running tanker rendezvous missions."

"Roger," Bob acknowledged, shaking his head tiredly. More squares getting filled up, he thought. "Air Force 795, out."

His shoulders ached from the straps, and his eyes were tired too. It would be a relief to get out of the blue and into the sack, but the thought of tomorrow was no comfort. What would the skipper come up with then, and how long would it be before Bob was transferred from the base? Leaning back, he eyed the shadowy bulk of the hook over his head and hated it conscientiously. If it hadn't been for Skyhook, he thought, everything would be fine.

At 1810, he decided it was time to start down. Reducing power, he flipped the radio and was about to call the tower, when the sudden flash of red stiffened him in the seat. Letting go of the mike button, he riveted his eyes on the panel to pin down the furiously winking warning, afraid for a single moment of panic that he was on fire.

Then he knew it wasn't the fire detector but the hydraulic boost pressure warning. Relief came fast, but right on the heels of it was the knowledge that failure of his boost system was almost as bad. With no boost, how could he land? Chill fingers of doubt began to pluck at him; not the near-panic of a moment ago, but the slow, considered realization of his predicament. Again he reached for the mike button and made the call he had to make.

"Hamilton, this is Air Force 795, en route your base with emergency. Boost system failing; over."

"795, this is Hamilton. Roger on your emergency. Estimate your position, and keep us advised. Over."

"Roger, Tower. I am approximately fifty miles southeast. Altitude 30,000. Pressure still dropping. Landing will be impossible."

"Roger, 795. Depress your tone switch, and advise if you abandon ship. We have alerted—"

"Air Force 795, this is Air Force 271. Skyhook, orbiting at 35,000 in your vicinity." The loud, calm voice broke into the call from the tower, and Bob recognized it for Major Pachek in the GRB-36! "795, are you Garrity, in a Thunderflash?"

"Affirmative, 271," Bob said crisply, brain racing desperately as his eyes flicked across the panel. "I have an emergency, so will you—"

"I understand, 795. Suggest you alter course for our aircraft, and hook on. Dropping a flare now, and think we have you on our radar."

A bright glow flared off the right wing, and Bob sucked in his breath as the major's plan hit him. The pilot must be crazy! At night, with his pumps failing—

"Negative!" he said tightly. "I've never made a night hook-up, 271. Too risky for you. Thanks, but—"

"We'll take the risk, Garrity," the major said. "And you've got no choice in the matter. Right?"

For agonizing seconds, Bob turned it over in his mind. The major was right, of course. With flaps, gear, and brakes out of commission, a landing was impossible. He'd have to abandon, and lose Uncle a half-million dollar aircraft. And there was the terrible chance that the empty Thunderflash might pile up in an inhabited area!

It seemed an age that the crippled plane hurtled north, and then, almost of itself, it seemed to come around to bear on the waning light of the flare. He pressed the mike switch, and heard his own voice, sounding strained and far away.

"Roger, Skyhook. Hitchhiker making approach for hook-up. And let's make this one count, sir!"

After that it was a tense nightmare. He had once thought he could make contact in his sleep, and now he found out what that would be like. Closing fast, he lined up with the GRB-36, not breathing until he saw the faint glow of light in the belly, and made out the shadowy outline of the trapeze waiting for him. For the first time that he could remember, he was shaky on the controls and knew it would be touch and go.

Nearing the boom, he matched the speed of the bomber and was sure he was set. Then he stiffened suddenly, and a wing rocked wildly upward. Choking back a cry, he tried to steady his nerves, sighing relief as the boom operator countered for Bob's mistake. A second later he felt the solid click and looked up to see the hook engaged with the loop. It was all over, and he cut power and reached up to open the canopy as the trapeze lifted him up into the bomb bay of the big plane.

On shaky legs he couldn't control, he walked along the catwalk toward the boom operator, wondering who it was he owed maybe even his life. The man was good, that last correction was all that prevented Bob from having to make another approach, and with the boost gone—

He recognized the little sergeant then, as the man moved from his controls and stuck out a hand in greeting. The heavy pound of the bomber's engines beat through the catwalk, and he could barely hear what Thomas said in his ear, as he lifted aside the oxygen mask.

"Hi, Lieutenant! Glad we could give you a lift, sir!"

Bob gripped the hand tightly, conscious of the cold sweat inside his gloves. He had learned a lot in the last few minutes. The skipper had been right; some things you had to find out for yourself. Bob had found them.

In the pressurized compartment he grinned at Sergeant Thomas and worked his shoulders tiredly. They were slanting down for the base now, with the crippled Thunderflash tucked in the belly.

"Sergeant, I don't know what to say, except that I'll buy you a cup of coffee when we hit the flight line!"

"Lieutenant," Thomas said, winking, "that's the nice thing about these big babies. We got our own coffee right back in the galley. Come on and be my guest!"

Flapjack Jenny

By VERNE CHUTE

The town marshal of Cloudburst was more worried than usual over one missing bank robber and $10,000 worth of banknotes

If anyone was still sleeping in Cloudburst it wasn't "Dustproof" Bentley's fault. He stood in the center of the desert town's wagon-rutted street spouting with indignation.

"Dang that lousy, flea-bitten, mangy, no-good rascal," he yelped. "Now where did she get to?"

Attracted by the disturbance, Ed Seeley, who never seemed to sleep, strode off the board sidewalk, his nickel-plated badge catching the first light of the dawn.

"What's eating on you, Dustproof?" he demanded.

The old miner pulled his eyes away from the blacksmith shop, where huge, age-old cottonwood trees stood around like shadowy ghosts afraid to go home. He peered into the town marshal's face before he answered.

"What I'm doin' is like always—a-huntin' for Jenny. Wherever she is she's in trouble. Jenny's always in trouble."

The tall lawman smiled a little and his hard eyes lost some of their bleakness.

"Maybe she's down the street waiting for Jim Williams to open his bank. You know she's got five hundred dollars coming for catching that Clary Outfit."

Dustproof snorted with indignation.

"Yeah, her and who else! All she did was smell flapjacks cookin' and lead us to th' bank robbers. I had a hand in that capture too, mister!"

"Okay, okay," laughed the marshal. "Any-way, I reckon that's what you're in town for —to get the money." The strengthening light showed the bleakness once more in his eyes. "There's one member of the bunch we didn't get. We think his name is Bevan and that he's got the balance of the loot. It's about ten thousand dollars and is likely hidden right under our nose." Before striding off up the street he gave a low-voiced warning. "Better not let too many folks know you're collecting that reward money this morning. There's some bad characters staying in town."

Dustproof patted his battered rifle and grinned after the lawman. Nobody was going to bother him. He started down the street to continue his hunt for his burro.

Neither he nor the town marshal had seen the small man crouching in the gloom between the two closest buildings. Now the man slipped out the back way to the alley, looked both ways, and then circled to reach the Chinese restaurant unseen.

Unaware of possible danger, Dustproof was lost in his own thoughts as he shuffled down the street. Neither he nor Jenny had been much of a bargain for Cloudburst, or for the Ord Mountains where he had his grubstake mine. Jenny's coat was matted and disreputable-looking, and Dustproof's jumper was worn out, his Levis able to stand alone. His felt hat looked as though it had been gnawed by a generation of pack rats, and his brogans were warped and patched to within an inch of their life.

But all that would be changed. When the bank opened, he'd be rich. A man of standing.

Passing the general store, he snorted derisively. It was in this store that he'd gotten his nickname when someone had said, "That Bentley, he's as free from gold dust as a frog is from hair."

Dustproof took to the wooden sidewalk now, clomping along it toward the end of the street. Two places left to look for Jenny: the livery stable and the Chinese restaurant. By virtue of her detective work, Jenny had won certain inalienable rights at both places.

Daylight was coming fast now. A coyote waiting on the hill above the town suddenly gave its banshee song to serenade the new day. Then the paintbrush of the sun was brightening the sky to salmon. And then it was racing through the pinks and reds until its fiery brilliance would wipe out all other color. To the north the flat-topped Ord Mountains took shape as though projected on a magic-lantern screen.

Dustproof didn't find Jenny at the livery stable so he went to Willie Lee's restaurant.

He peered through the open door first, sniffing hungrily at the smoky fragrance of frying bacon that twisted out to meet him. An ornate ceiling lamp flickered, showering its yellow light over the room in a losing fight against the hurrying daylight. Willie's first customer of the morning sat at a rough pine table across the room. The window at his side was open. A plate of syrupy flapjacks steamed in front of the man, who glanced up, knife in one hand, fork in the other. The man himself was small and wore a flat-topped plainsman's hat.

Dustproof stared. But he wasn't looking at the little man. His stark, wide eyes were held hypnotically on the open window beside the man. Framed in the open window was a long-eared visage—Jenny.

Jenny's big lips slavered and drooled. Her glassy eyes rolled with excitement. She was a burro with a one-track mind—and her mind was on flapjacks. The stack of cakes before her were golden brown, carefully buttered and syruped—a sight for a burro.

"Don't do it!" implored Dustproof, jabbering excitedly, pointing. Unfortunately, he was doing his waving and pointing with his old .45-.70 rifle.

The stranger misunderstood. In a flash he was out of his chair, his hand racing to his gunbelt. Dustproof hit the floor, sliding along it to a table. He came up without his rifle, but with his hands up over his head.

"Dad-blame it, mister," he sputtered indignantly, "I was only tryin' to help you." He shook his grizzled head sorrowfully. "Now it's too late. She done got 'em!"

"Wh—what?" The little man swung around. The shadow that had darkened the window was gone. The man's flapjack plate was empty, but a wide trail of sticky syrup led across the sill.

Dustproof lurched to the window in scandalized indignation. "Dang you, Jenny! Stealin' th' food of city folks!"

The man jerked him away from the window in time to see Jenny making off with the cakes. "I'll learn you—" he shouted.

His gun blazed fire, but Dustproof hit the man's arm upwards. The bullet intended for Jenny went for a ride off into the desert and Jenny romped to safety.

Smoke curling up from his gun, the infuriated man swung back to Dustproof.

Dustproof shrugged his shoulders. "Mister, she's no lady. But you shouldn't ought to go shootin' at her."

The little man howled with fury.

"I'll shoot me that pilfering jackass yet," he shouted. He leaned out the window, but Jenny was nowhere to be seen.

Willie Lee, his round Oriental face shining like a full moon, waddled out and pulled the table back from the window.

"Mo' better you sit here," he beamed.

Anxiously, Dustproof sought to explain. "Jenny didn't mean no harm. She jest thought them cakes were her'n on account of Banker Williams. Jenny gets her livery stable hay an' her flapjack toppin's free whenever she's in town. This is on account of th' job she done. Willie, put th' stranger on th' fire some more pancakes." Dustproof moseyed over and picked up his rifle.

Willie's close-cropped head bobbed affirmatively up and down like a busy cork in a catfish pool. He stopped slicing quarter-inch strips of side bacon. "I give him Jenny-burro flappy-jacks all leady." He began dishing up the flapjacks he'd cooked for the burro.

The stranger howled again. "Don't give me no burro flapjacks. Make a new mess. And some of that there bacon. And if you got any fresh eggs, fry me two; if they ain't fresh, make them scrambled."

Willie's head bobbed, his blank face beaming without expression. Pouring out three portions of batter on the hotplate of his cooking stove first, he laid slices of bacon in a pan. Into another, smaller, frying-pan, went two eggs that he beat hurriedly with a fork and shoved to the back of the stove. A huge pan off to the side held fried potatoes eight inches deep.

Willie dished up the three cakes he'd cooked for Jenny. When Joe Smith from the livery stable came in, Willie shuffled across the room with the plate. "You likee flappy-jack?"

"Likee," said the man. "An' a cup o' mud."

The stranger still had murder in his mean little eyes. He looked at Dustproof.

"What's that danged burro got them cakes coming for, anyhow?"

Dustproof straightened himself.

"Well, me an' her caught some bandits a while back; that is, she smelled 'em a-cookin' flapjacks down in th' ravine and me an' th' boys surrounded 'em. It was th' Clary Outfit. You likely heard about 'em."

The man's eyes turned cold. "No," he said with such a note of finality that Dustproof turned hurriedly away.

Dustproof moved back to the kitchen and regarded Willie from beneath his sunfaded brows. Willie watched him suspiciously.

Dustproof finally grinned a little self-consciously. "I'll have some of them flapjacks, too. An' a couple of eggs fried with spuds. I'll pay you after th' bank gets open. Jim Williams has got some money for me."

Willie beamed and nodded. But his words contradicted his facial expression.

"You no got money; no eat."

"Huh?" Dustproof flushed. "You know me. I'm kinda related to this burro what eats here steady when she's in town; she eats here an' down at th' livery stable."

Willie complacently stirred his fried spuds.

Dustproof exploded like a lantern fire. "You mean that four-legged critter of mine *can* get credit an'—I can't?"

Willie turned the stranger's flapjacks. "Bankie Williams say all the time fly flappy-jacks fo' Jenny—no say you."

There was a clatter at the table. The stranger yelled, "Hey, you! Leave that Chinaman alone till I get my breakfast!"

Dustproof said weakly, "I'll be a dirty polecat with two stripes down my back."

Willie shook his head. "Polecat no eat either without money or Bankie Williams say." He dished up the stranger's order and waddled out to the window table.

Complaining about man's injustice to man, Dustproof grumbled his way out of the restaurant, picking his empty teeth fiercely as he went.

On his way down to the cottonwoods where he'd left his blankets and wooden pack saddle, he met Marshal Seeley again.

"I got troubles till the bank opens," he complained. "That danged Willie is gettin' too big for his britches."

"Yeah?"

Dustproof told him what had happened, finishing with, "Th' small gent's got a mean disposition. Tried to shoot Jenny, he did. All she did was reach in th' window an' steal his flapjacks."

The lawman smiled faintly. He seemed at ease again. "He's the jasper I'm watching. Name of Bevan."

"He's still there," said the old miner in a conspirator's whisper. Then he grinned a little to himself. He looked at the sturdy building that housed the Cloudburst Bank.

"It won't be open till eight o'clock," he said, "so I might as well get over to the general store and get my supplies. If you need any help just call on me."

Ed Seeley nodded and lifted his hand and they parted. Dustproof went to the general store. At the porch, he stopped and looked down the sun-drenched street. The humor-wrinkles deepened around his eyes.

"That Jenny!" he chuckled.

Braced on her four legs, she was asleep in the warm sun. Ward of Cloudburst, she'd filled up with free hay and had had her toppin's at Willie's. Now she dozed, oblivious to flapjacks, banditry or the restless stir of men.

Inside the store Dustproof picked out his supplies. His list was modest, but he added a can of peaches and a couple of cans of salmon in case he had company. He told Old Casey, "Put th' grub in a couple of gunny sacks so I can swing it across my burro. I'll be back when th' bank opens."

He looked around and there was Bevan. The little man began looking at the pipes and tobaccos. Dustproof ignored him completely and started for the door. His next chore was the bank.

He mumbled as he crossed the street, "I'm seein' Mr. Williams first, and then I'm makin' that Chinaman fry flapjacks till I bust eatin' 'em."

Bevan came back to the door of the store and watched Dustproof go into the bank that Banker Williams had just opened. Then he turned, smiling evilly to himself.

When Dustproof plodded out of town behind Jenny, he wore a new outfit from clodhoppers to felt hat. Jenny herself had a new halter and a cotton lead rope. There were cartridges for the .45-.70 and supplies that would last a month.

Uncomfortably filled to the top with feed, Jenny groaned every inch of the way. She hated to leave Cloudburst. After the half-way mark to Ord Mountains was reached, she'd automatically started thinking of the steaming flapjacks she'd get the next day.

Dustproof was vigilant, sticking close to the rifle jammed through the ropes on Jenny's hurricane deck. Although Bevan had been at the general store when he was ready to leave, Dustproof had stalled around until the little man had ridden out of town ahead of him. Marshal Seeley was ahead somewhere on the trail.

"If Bevan's got the missing banknotes from the Clary robbery on him, Marshal Seeley will find 'em," he told Jenny.

The burro didn't stop grunting with each plodding step. A mile ahead Ed Seeley was waiting for them under the meager shade of a Joshua tree. Jenny plodded on to the shade and stopped. Dustproof pulled off his new sombrero and fanned himself with it and looked askance at the marshal.

The lawman looked worried. "I saw him, all right. But no luck. Too friendly, though. He said he figured I was suspicious of him for something or other and he *insisted* that I search him." Seeley smiled faintly. "I did. Nothing."

Dustproof leaned against Jenny, who

promptly leaned back. "I still think he's up to something."

Marshal Seeley wiped a hand across his tired eyes. "Bevan's the man, all right," he agreed. "And I think he's got those stolen banknotes hidden somewhere. If they're in Cloudburst he won't get far from town."

Dustproof shook his head sympathetically. "He goin' far?"

"Said not." Seeley mounted his horse and turned its nose toward Cloudburst. "He said he was just out for a ride—say, did you leave your own money in the bank?"

The old miner grinned at him. "No, I didn't, Ed. I kind'a like to look at it. But don't worry. I'm takin' a short cut I know up th' road a piece. An' I got th' old rifle."

"You better carry it then," advised the marshal, lifting his hand and riding away.

Dustproof looked after him. Then he prodded Jenny into motion. She went on, groaning as though she were being broiled over a slow fire.

"Yuh ornery bald-face," Dustproof complained. "Shut up or I'll get me a new burro. One burro is as good as th' next one. Yeah, an' a dang sight better." He added after a minute, "I got me my flapjacks in at Willie's, too!"

Jenny said nothing. She kept going, and when she came to the short cut, turned into it. A few Bar-17 cattle, ranging from the Mojave River to Old Woman's Springs, gazed stupidly at them, watching them pass. The trail began to rise.

When Jenny led the way into a grove of shaggy Joshua trees, Dustproof suddenly decided to take the marshal's advice and start carrying the heavy rifle. He quickened his step and was reaching for the rifle when a voice behind him barked: "Don't do it!"

Dustproof whirled about and went rigid. It was Bevan. His eyes were slitted and he meant business. A sneering smile was backed up by an ugly-looking six-gun.

Jenny showed her interest in the proceedings by bracing herself on her four legs and going to sleep. Bevan led his mount from a screening clump of mixed greasewood and yucca and dropped the rein.

"You did some nice traveling, fellow. Mighty glad to see you again, and I'm obliged for what you done for me."

"Huh?" cried Dustproof.

Bevan chuckled and came ahead to jerk the .45-.70 loose from Jenny's rigging.

Dustproof surged forward. "Hey!" he protested. "You can't do that!"

Bevan's face lost its smile. "Get back!" he ordered. "One word out of you and I'll ventilate you proper. And that goes for that flapjack-eating jackass, too!"

Dustproof muttered and moved back. Bevan holstered his gun, then jerked the lever of the rifle until he'd thrown the cartridges on the ground. Picking them up, he put them in his pocket. "Got any more?" he demanded.

The old man looked miserably toward the pack on Jenny's back. Bevan nodded, but he made Dustproof turn his pockets inside out to prove he had no cartridges on him. After he'd pitched the rifle off into a bed of cactus, he took Dustproof's canteen from the pack saddle and took a long drink.

His smile was as cold as winter ice when he said: "I'm moving on. Got a long way to go."

Swinging into his saddle, he jerked the burro's tow rope. Jenny woke with a start.

Scandalized, Dustproof had one vociferous protest left.

"Dang you, Bevan! Do you have to take Jenny an' my grubstake?"

"Ain't the grubstake I want most," the little man taunted. "It's that ten thousand dollars in banknotes."

"Huh?"

"It's in the bottom of one of them gunny sacks of groceries. I put the package of greenbacks in there myself while the store fellow was busy with another order. You see, I knew that smart alec deputy was watching outside the town for me. Now ain't that something?"

"Well, I'll be a striped horntoad!" cried Dustproof. "Hey, why can't you take th' money out of th' sack and let me an' Jenny go?"

"That would be nice," jeered the man.

"I'm already a little leery about what I hear about you and that jackass. I ain't taking any chances." He pulled his gun from its holster in a slow, deadly motion. "All right, now I'll take that fat purse I just saw."

Dustproof stared. "You can't do that!" he cried. "That's Jenny's an' mine! You can't make us poor again!"

Bevan slowly pulled the hammer back on his gun. Dustproof fumbled the purse out of his inside jumper pocket. The little man reached down and jerked the leather out of his hand. Then he dug spurs into his mount's flanks and the horse lunged into the old miner, knocking him down.

Bevan changed hands on the purse and slashed his quirt across the old man's face.

Only Dustproof's whiskers saved his face from an ugly cut.

The bandit looked into the purse, counting the money swiftly. Then he rode on his way, pulling the protesting Jenny after him. Dustproof sat on the ground and what he said after the bad man was no blessing.

After a moment, he got up and shook himself like a spaniel coming out of a duck pond. He rubbed a gnarled hand across his cheek, and his gesture wasn't entirely in reflection. He winced from the pain, but otherwise he was unhurt.

First he snaked his rifle from the cactus patch, then he hurried to the last turn he'd made in the trail. On the back trail, the Mojave Basin was laid out before him like a map. A blanket of heat-blurred gray was a dry lake, the green patches on the crazy-quilt of the basin were ranches. But the drifting cloud of dust that moved off at right angles to the trail was what brought a contemptuous growl from his throat. Bevan was making good his escape.

The sight galvanized the miner into action and sent him trotting down the trail toward Cloudburst.

"Marshal Seeley's got to know about this!" he ranted.

Two hours later, he heard the hoof beats of a fast-traveling horse coming from the direction of Cloudburst. His heart rose. In a few moments Marshal Seeley spurred into sight and threw himself from his blowing horse.

Dustproof had saved enough breath to blurt out his story. "So he's got the reward money of Jenny's an' mine," he summed up. "He's got supplies, an' it'll soon be too dark to track him down. But he's skirtin' th' dry lake. I could see that from higher up on th' slope."

"Nice going," cried Seeley. "A fellow in the general store saw Bevan fooling with your groceries. That gave me an idea that I wish I'd hit on sooner."

Mounting again, the marshal swung his horse off in the direction Dustproof had pointed to, then spurred out of sight. Dustproof almost grinned. Marshal Seeley knew every trail and short cut in the desert.

Jenny hadn't liked going off at a tangent from her accustomed trail up the slope. It broke her line of thought. Another thing she didn't like was being pulled along by her rope. In the first mile she'd been kicked at by the horse, and twice she'd laid her ears back and shot forward to nip at his hams. Bevan growled at them both but relentlessly spurred on, half-dragging Jenny after him.

The coming night was swallowing the long shadows of afternoon when Bevan came to a dry stream that ran into the equally dry lake. Crossing over, he moved along on the other bank. The arroyo became deeper as he followed it toward the distant rise. When he stopped some minutes later, he'd reached the

spot he wanted. There was a deep canyon between him and improbable pursuit.

Dismounting for a rest, the man tied Jenny's rope securely to an outcropping of rock. Having already retrieved the package of banknotes from one of the gunny sacks, he drew his knife to cut the ropes of Jenny's pack saddle and release the groceries. He would travel alone from here on.

"This is as far as you go," he said, and a cruel gleam came into his dark eyes. After the pack slid off the wooden pack saddle, he drew his gun. "All right, you glass-eyed she-fiend."

But he hesitated and didn't shoot. A pistol shot would sound a long ways in the evening air. In a moment more he'd lost his chance.

A clatter of horse's hoofs suddenly sounded across the draw. Marshal Seeley had arrived. The marshal went into swift action in the gloom, sending a bullet *zinging* off a rock beside Bevan, furrowing a groove in his horse's neck. Squealing in pain and fright, the horse galloped away into the sunset. Bevan exploded in anger. Crawling to the rim of the arroyo, he peered across. He suddenly snapped out a shot, but he got one in return. In the next moment he was falling back, holding at his chest. Bullet-shock held him transfixed for a moment. He was in a bad way, his horse gone, and in a few minutes the pain would begin. Unless he got the flow of blood stopped, he soon might be too weak to go on. His bleary eyes saw Jenny; she was his only chance. He began to crawl toward her in the gloom.

Jenny stood back on her haunches, snorting at him. But he followed the halter rope to her head. Holding her halter close, he pulled himself up on the pack saddle. Being a small man had its advantages, and he was able to wedge himself into the saddle and then turn Jenny off into the brush.

The burro found a path leaving the rim of the deep draw. She took it and thus gave the slip to Marshal Seeley. The marshal was left crouching in the brush on the other side of the arroyo, waiting for another shot at Bevan.

When Jenny stopped a half-hour later,

Bevan still had her pointed away from Cloudburst. He'd been able to stop the flow of blood in his chest, but the effort had left him weak. He tied himself into the saddle, knowing that he had to go on, to put as much distance as he could between himself and Marshal Seeley before daylight.

Plodding on through the night, Jenny soon found herself with an unconscious man on her back. No longer guided, she turned her nose back to the trails she knew best.

Daylight was just filtering into Cloudburst when Old Dustproof looked out the door of Willie's restaurant. The fragrance of coffee and flapjacks perfumed the dawn air, and every frying-pan that Willie had was filled with eggs frying and suckling noisily. A dozen horses stamped fretfully at the hitch-rack.

Marshal Seeley himself had gotten in sometime during the night and now had a posse organized. After the men had been fed, the marshal said quietly, "All right, men. You know who's riding with who. Let's get going."

The men gulped their scalding coffee and filed out, bringing some of the warmth and smell of the restaurant with them. Dustproof moved fretfully aside. He'd have to stay in town and wait.

It was full daylight now and there was no time to lose. Yet not a man of them mounted. They stood like men transfixed, staring into the street, watching a lone burro coming toward them.

No prima donna ever made a more timely entrance than did Jenny. Before the men's incredulous eyes, she plodded toward them, quickening her step when the smell of flapjacks reached her. Her big white nose stuck far out in front and her eyes rolled excitedly. Her big lips slavered and drooled. As though pulled by a smoky rope, she moved past the men to reach the side of the restaurant.

"Hey!" said Dustproof weakly. And then the men got their second shock. The bulging load on Jenny's back was the wanted man— *Wesley Bevan!*

Marshal Seeley came to life. "Somebody get the doc," he ordered. "The rest of you unload this jasper off Jenny's back."

He took two steps backwards and yelled into the restaurant: "Willie, put on a mess of flapjacks and make it fast. We got a customer out here who doesn't want to be kept waiting."

After they'd recovered his money and the banknotes belonging to the bank, Dustproof beamed and scratched his head. A great pride glittered in his old eyes. Then he said what later became famous words in Cloudburst:

"That Jenny! She went and brought him in, all right. But I'll never see how she got up on her own back to tie him right on to her pack saddle!"

237

Man of Courage

By ZACHARY BALL

His stoical Indian brother wasn't afraid—but it was Jimmy who had to go into the ring

The Seminole youth stepped out of the old sedan and stood on the sidewalk while his brother locked the car doors. A broad spread of moonlit lawn lay before him, with a concrete walk laid across it that led to the lighted auditorium. The parking lots, flanking the big building, were all filled and the parking boys were slicing the darkness with their flashlights trying to find space for late arrivals.

"They've really got a crowd tonight," Dave Tommie said from the other side of the car as he banged the door shut.

The youth on the sidewalk didn't answer. He was watching the crowds going toward the auditorium's main entrance. The night breeze fluttered a handbill someone had dropped, and spread it at his feet. He could read almost every word of it in the glow of the tropical full moon.

In huge letters across the top were the words, AMATEUR BOXING TOURNAMENT. And below the heading were several braces of names of the preliminary kids, and below that in bold letters, SEMIFINAL BOUT. Under this heading was his own name, Jimmy Tommie, and Chick Morgan.

Chick Morgan. Just reading the name sent stinging prickles of fear along the nape of his neck.

"Come on," his brother said, and they started across the dew-wet grass.

Not since he was ten had Jimmy Tommie been scared enough to want to start running and never stop until he was safely in his own bed in his own *chikee*. But that's how scared he was now as they approached the big building.

He filled his lungs with the feather-soft night air. The night was warm, as nights always were in Miami, the smell of night-blooming jasmine was on the air and cottony clouds, tinted by the glow from the city's lights, hung low overhead. But the Indian youth wasn't seeing any of these things because of the way he was fighting his fear. And he wasn't doing any better job of whipping the fear than he knew he was going to do whipping Chick Morgan.

They passed a group of loud-talking high school boys going toward the main entrance. They could have been guys from Jimmy's own school for all he knew, for he hadn't really seen them.

Why? he was asking himself. *Why did they have to match me with Chick Morgan? Why not someone else from Palm Avenue School? Anyone else.*

He hadn't seen Chick since they went to junior high school together, not since the day Chick gave him that beating down on the bay shore.

Jimmy Tommie liked going to the white man's schools all right, but he didn't care much about being on the boxing team. He would never have put a glove on if it hadn't been for his brother, who was an ex-Golden Glover. But Dave had been insistent about it, and ever since their parents had died, Jimmy had tried to do whatever Dave wanted him to do, just as if Dave were his father.

"Hey," Dave said as they approached the side entrance.

"What?" Jimmy asked.

Dave looked keenly at him. "Are you scared, kid?"

"No. Just a little nervous." And he knew his brother knew he was lying.

They went through the big door and headed for the dressing rooms. A roar came from the crowd out in the auditorium that sounded like a strong hurricane gust. That meant the first prelims were in the ring.

In the dressing room, Jimmy began getting out of his clothes, nursing a vague hope that by some miracle there might have been a last-minute shifting and he'd go in with someone besides Chick Morgan. But he doubted that there was any change in the matching, and at that very moment they heard a gang come in from outside and go down the corridor. He recognized Chick's voice, the loudest of them all. And hearing it, Jimmy Tommie's fear turned wet and cold within him.

While Dave was taping Jimmy's hands, he said, "A semifinal ain't so much. When you hear them yelling out there, just don't think about it."

Jimmy said nothing. And when he was in his robe, his brother said, "Stretch out and relax. I'll let you know when it's time." And he went out.

Jimmy didn't think he'd ever be able to relax again as long as he lived. He lay on the board table staring at the ceiling. *If only my brother had been a baseball player or something,* he was thinking. *Or why didn't I tell him the first time he said he was going to make a fighter of me that I didn't want any of it?* He became aware of a throbbing in his neck muscles and a tightness in his arms and legs that was like pulled leather. He simply must relax.

He forced himself to think about the Everglades where, during summer vacations, he often spent weeks without ever returning to his home village. He thought of how it would be out there tonight, the quiet, peaceful night silence, ruffled with the tiny silver-bell tinkle of tree frogs, the long moss swaying to the breeze, the icy stars drifting in the blue-black patches between clouds, the occasional drumming of a bull 'gator somewhere out in the velvety blackness of the river.

He tried hard to keep his thoughts on those things, but the heavy waves of sound from the audience out there wouldn't let his mind hold onto anything except that he too would soon be out there, and the crowd would cheer just like that when he lay stretched out on the canvas.

Chick Morgan was sure to be the favorite. He was like that. He hadn't fought any more amateur bouts than Jimmy himself had, but he had a way of tucking the fans into his pocket the moment he stepped into the ring.

The Seminole swiped his glove across his forehead and looked at the sweat on it. He was staring at it when his brother came back.

"It's about time to go," Dave said.

Jimmy said, "Yeah," and sat up. It didn't seem as if Dave had been out of the room thirty seconds.

Dave sat down and watched Jimmy, who was sitting there swinging his feet and thumping his mitts together. "Remember," he said, "don't even hear the hooting and yelling."

"I won't pay any attention to it."

After a minute Dave stood up and put a hand on Jimmy's shoulder. "Still nervous?"

"I'm okay."

Dave picked up his bag of towels and stuff and said, "There are two kinds of guys in this game, the ones with guts and the ones without. Let's go."

Jimmy followed him out the door. Jimmy was the taller of the two, but aside from that they were very much alike. Dave was wearing tan trousers and the traditional bright-colored *fokshigi* that most Seminole men wore instead of a shirt. Dave always wore one when he was in the ring with Jimmy. He said it was a good trade-mark for them.

Neither of them said anything as they walked down the aisle between the tall legs of bleacher seats toward the lighted ring, which appeared to be swinging in a haze of tobacco smoke. And as they approached the ring, something akin to panic began pounding at Jimmy's insides. He worked his fingers and could feel them squash inside his mitts.

Anybody would think this was the first time I ever had a pair of gloves on, he thought wryly, and wished that there never had been a first time.

The crowd had been fairly quiet, but now it opened up on a burst of clatter like sudden hail on a board roof, and Jimmy and Dave could see the referee counting over a prone form in the ring.

"That's the Bentlow kid, taking a nap in the resin," Dave said.

Jimmy watched the boy struggle to his feet. The crowd cheered wildly for him. Jimmy swallowed against the brick-dust feeling in his throat. They pushed up to ringside and sat in two folding chairs and waited for this last preliminary bout to end. Jimmy was aware that his brother kept watching him closely.

And once, when the crowd was making a lot of noise, Dave leaned over and said, "You got a sag in your shoulders, kid. Looks to me like you don't want to make this fight."

The words built a quivering sickness deep in Jimmy's belly. "I wouldn't be going in if I didn't want to," he mumbled stubbornly. He didn't look at Dave, but kept his eyes on the Bentlow kid up there taking his beating.

"Remember what I've always told you," Dave said. "The other guy is made of the same kind of bone and muscle you are. I've seen this Chick Morgan fight. He's no champion. But he's good. That's why I had you matched with him."

Jimmy looked at his brother. This was something he hadn't known. He tried to grin, but his lips felt as if they were smeared with dried glue.

"Oh, he's tricky, all right," Dave went on. "Watch him in the clinches. And don't let him get you to working it fast. Keep your head and watch for openings."

Jimmy pulled a big breath in and held it, then let it trickle out through his nose and said, "I'll try to work him over, Dave." Then awkwardly, when Dave said nothing, "Yeah, I'll try to unhinge him." And he waited for a helpful word, some little sign of encouragement, but his brother's attention was on the prelim fighters again.

But when the round ended and the next one got underway, Dave turned abruptly and said, "I don't think you'll last three rounds, the way you're feeling. You're scared limber on the outside and stiff on the inside. Relax, will you?"

The words, spoken calmly but unsympathetically, speared into the boy's listening consciousness.

"Don't get yourself all messed up," Dave continued. "Take a dive if you can't stay with him." And again he turned his bronzed face toward the ring.

Jimmy looked miserably around to see if he could see anything of Chick Morgan. He couldn't. Then he sat and watched the ring too, watched with his jaws clamped so hard together that they began to ache. When the action slowed up, he gazed over the crowd again. It looked like the most people he had ever seen in his life, and they were all bellowing for the sight of blood, the thing they had paid their money to see. While pretending to watch the currents of smoke twisting up toward the big lights over the ring, he studied his brother's stony profile out of the corner of his eye. And suddenly a wave of fury surged over him at what Dave had just said. And as the noisy moments went by, it built into a rage that added fire to the hot ball that still lay sickeningly in his stomach.

He didn't have to say a thing like that, he told himself. *After all, this fighting business was his idea. I never wanted any of it. I only went into it because he wanted me to.* Jimmy sat there fuming as the kids in the ring danced out into their fifth round. *One more,* he thought, *and then I'm in.*

There was a sudden loud burst from the crowd as the Bentlow kid went down again. And anyone could tell that they'd have to help him out of the ring. They did. And when the announcer was telling the crowd unnecessarily who had won the bout, Jimmy heard his brother say, "Come on."

Jimmy watched the Bentlow boy going toward the dressing rooms, a man holding to each arm. He watched until they were out of sight, then followed his brother up into the ring.

They were the first ones in. Dave helped him slip his arms out of his bathrobe sleeves, then draped it over his shoulders as he sat down. And Jimmy sat there looking along the rows of ringside seats, not seeing anyone.

A moment later Chick Morgan trotted up the steps at the corner of the ring, ducked through the ropes and ran toward Jimmy without stopping in his own corner. He was a thick-chested, square-faced, grinning youth with bushy eyebrows and a low-slung, shovel-like chin. Jimmy knew he was coming over to taunt him. But the crowd had mistaken the gesture for sportsmanship, and their applause rattled against the rafters.

Chick put out his gloves, and Jimmy stood up to acknowledge the greeting.

"Hi-ya, chief," Chick grinned. "How's the old redskin? We make big powwow, you and me, huh? You Sitting Bull, me Black Cloud. Black Cloud going to rain all over Sitting Bull." And he threw his curly head back and laughed.

"Nuts!" Dave said to him. "Go into your corner, punk."

Chick ignored him. "You look scared to death, kid," he said to Jimmy. "You must be remembering that day on the bay shore, huh?" And he laughed again. "Well, here we go again, just like that time." And he trotted across to his corner.

He hasn't changed a bit, Jimmy thought. *He's still the arrogant, show-off bully. And a better fighter than he was then.*

The mike was lowered from above the ring, and the announcer walked over to it.

"Ladies and gentlemen, as the semifinal bout of the evening—the Palm Island Club presents—eight rounds to a decision, two Miami lads who have both made good records on their respective boxing teams—in this corner the hard-hitting junior of Gulf

Stream High School and the only Indian athlete any school in our county can boast of, weighing 130 pounds and wearing yellow trunks—Jimmy Tommie!"

Jimmy stood up and made a slight bow to the crowd, not hearing the boos and cheers, but still hearing Chick's insults to his race and to his courage. He was still not hearing anything else when Chick Morgan was announced. And it startled him when the auditorium lights went out, leaving the ring in the brilliant down-shooting beam of the overhead lights. Dave had to nudge him when it was time to walk out to the center of the ring for instructions.

When it was over, they went back to their corners, and Dave slipped the robe from his shoulders. He swallowed hard against the dryness in his throat and wished the first round was over so he could wet his mouth. He gripped the ropes and bounced up and down, trying to loosen his tight leg muscles, keeping his head down so his brother couldn't see his face.

Then the bell rang and he moved out. Chick came dancing out of his corner grinning, making his play for audience approval.

Jimmy started it with two quick left jabs and a hard right that missed. Then he was on the canvas.

The ropes and corner posts of the ring, and Chick, and the referee made one slow revolution, then came to a stop.

Well, that wasn't so bad, Jimmy thought grimly. He had landed on one shoulder, and he froze there. Now he propped himself up and looked toward his own corner. Dave was staring at him, not a muscle of his face moving.

And in that moment Jimmy felt sorry for his brother. *I'm the one on the floor,* he thought. *But Dave's hurt more than I am. He thinks I'm letting him down and how bad he wanted me to make the Golden Glove tournament and go from where he left off when he had to go to war and got a hunk shot out of his back.*

He heard the count of eight and got up.

Chick, his grin wider than ever, lunged at him. Jimmy jabbed a left to the jaw, then threw it again as Chick came back from the first one. Then Chick was showering him with punches, hard ones, and he put his gloves over his face and pressed his elbows against his ribs. He stumbled inside and hung on until the referee pushed them apart. And that was when Chick, not smiling now, caught him with a shattering left hook.

Jimmy went down and lay there. His breathing was as dry as dust and he was very tired. But his mind was clear, clearer, it seemed, than it had ever been in his life. He took stock of himself. He was wet with sweat and there was a dull ache somewhere.

He rested on the count and got up again. This time, when he was on his feet, he moved quickly away. He kept it up, using everything that Dave had taught him. He used the ropes, changed speed and direction, and all the time kept snapping out his left at that square face, as grim now as a cypress stump.

Then, without even knowing where the punch came from, he went down again. This time the floor hit him hard, really hard. But the bell saved him.

Back in his corner, Dave worked him over, his hands moving swiftly and his lips tight. Down on the auditorium floor around Jimmy's corner a gang of kids were razzing and shouting insults. Dave yelled, "Scram!" at them, but they kept it up.

Dave was still toweling him when the ten-second buzzer sounded. He put his lips close to Jimmy's ear and said, "Look, you're not hurt. That guy's no better than you are. And I'm not saying that just so you'll stay out there and get your brains knocked out. If I didn't think you could whip him, I'd call it off. Now are you going out there and beat him, or not?"

The bell rang and Jimmy stood up. And it was like Dave had said, he wasn't hurt. He actually felt good. He moved out, then ducked away as Chick bore in swinging.

He's sore, Jimmy was thinking. *The guy is sore because I'm still on my feet. His pride is hurt because I was able to come out for another round.*

Then he became aware of something missing. Something was gone from him and he didn't know what it was. Suddenly he did know.

It was the fear. It was gone! And it had

left him cool and relaxed inside. When he realized that, he smiled and there was no glue stiffness around his mouth now. He saw a hard right coming, ducked under it, and kept smiling.

Hey, he told himself, *I'd better pay attention to what I'm doing, or he'll spread me out again.*

They settled down into a familiar pattern now. Jimmy kept jabbing with his left, kept jabbing, and he was smiling all the time. He wanted to make Chick think that was all he could do, just jab with his left. And when he abruptly changed to right-hand leads, he could read surprise in Chick's dark eyes. Then he went to body hooks, keeping in mind all that Dave had ever taught him.

The fans were taking note of his boxing now and were beginning to let him know they liked it. He didn't really hear them, but he could feel the effect of it through Chick's punches.

My stoical Indian brother, Jimmy thought.

When the bell sounded, Jimmy knew he hadn't taken the round, but there were more of them coming up. Six more.

"Better," Dave grunted, as he went to work on him.

And when the fourth round was over, Dave said, "You're even up now. I figure you've got two rounds apiece."

In the fifth, Jimmy was still pleasing the crowd with his boxing, but he was throwing his punches harder now. *I've got Mr. Chick Morgan wondering just how good I am,* he thought, pleased. And just before the bell he bore into Chick with a flurry of fast distracting feints, then dropped him with a right-hand smash that carried everything he could put into it.

Chick made it to his feet but had some difficulty in finishing the round. And now Jimmy had no more doubts, none whatever.

"Don't start getting cocky," Dave warned glumly. "You got three rounds to go yet, and as long as there's ten seconds of the last round left, you can get beat."

Jimmy said nothing.

But he had no more than reached the center of the ring at the beginning of the sixth when he knew that Dave's words had been correct. He was short with a left, then tried in his eagerness to follow it up with a right that missed and left him off-balance. And Chick took him with a right that seemed easily twice as hard as the hardest blow Jimmy Tommie had ever absorbed. He tried to fall inside, but Chick stepped back and hit him twice more before he went down on his face.

He didn't know he was down until he tasted the resin on the canvas. Now the ring was a speeding merry-go-round and he was in the middle of it. He tried to move, but his blood had drained off to some remote place, and his body was a nightmare of helpless weight. Finally he did manage to roll over, and the big lights flashed and swayed and dipped wildly overhead.

He rolled over again. He put both fists against the rough canvas and pushed with all his strength. And he knew what it must be like to be an old man, a man who is too battered by the years even to stand on his feet. He looked toward a neutral corner, and Chick was standing there, grinning again now.

Jimmy Tommie's tongue snaked out and wet his dry, bruised lips.

He again permitted himself the luxury of thinking how cool and peaceful it would be out in the Everglades tonight. And more than he'd ever wanted anything, he wanted to be out there this minute with the wooded stillness wrapped about him, away from these hot flashing lights, away from the sickening sound of the crowd and the sticky canvas that was clinging to him with its hot resin smell and wouldn't let him get up.

Listen to me, all Seminole men! This land of the swamp, it is for Seminole! All was given to Seminole by great Micco in beyond. We will not be driven from our home. Never! For Seminole is man of courage!

The words seemed so real that they startled Jimmy Tommie. It was as if they had been shouted at him through great hollow distance. He wondered if he had heard them spoken by someone in the past. He didn't think he had. But listening to them now, if he really were listening to them, put a great comfort upon him that was like warm rain in a forest glade. And beyond the words themselves, he had a flashing vision of straight-backed bronze-skinned men throwing their war cries on the air, their words tearing from their lips like thunder.

He yanked his mind back to reality. *I must be conked out and don't know it,* he told himself. But he had needed that thinking—that vision—for strength, for courage.

He thought he must have been lying there a very long time, and was surprised when he suddenly became aware of the referee's voice saying, "Four! Five!" Jimmy watched the shirt-sleeved arm rising and falling before him like a mechanical gadget. He tried again with everything he had to get to his feet. And just in time he did. Chick came at him again, boring in fast.

The referee stepped between them, took Jimmy's wrists in his hands, and wiped the resin from his gloves. And Jimmy was grateful for that moment that gave his strength a little more time to build up. Then the referee stepped away and Jimmy Tommie threw a left. He thought he threw it fast, but it looked like something in slow-motion. Still it reached Chick, and then they were in a clinch again.

While Jimmy was using up good strength, trying to break the clinch, Chick said into his ear. "Look, Pocahontas, you're washed out like an old sock. Why don't you just forget all about it and go on back to your tepee?"

Jimmy snapped out of the clinch, blood anger hammering through him. He began throwing punches at Chick's head. Then Chick was giving him blow for blow, and Jimmy had to work inside and hold on again.

"Better do like I said," Chick panted into his ear. "You just haven't got it, Indian. You did all right in your class, but you're out of your class now. Just like that time on the bay shore."

Jimmy Tommie barely heard what he was saying, for he was holding onto those other words that were still ringing in his consciousness, still being shouted at him through that strange, unearthly hollow distance: *Seminole is man of courage!*

With a mighty effort he shoved Chick against the ropes, snapped back out of the clinch and started throwing his gloves with a speed that surprised him as much as it did Chick. And out of the flurry, a left hook took Chick hard on the lower jaw. Then Jimmy landed more and more of them, one punch after another, because the hook had done something to Chick's timing.

Jimmy stood with his feet wide apart, snapping an endless volley of rights and lefts into that square, and now puffed, face. And with each punch he threw, he was remembering that day on the bay shore, remembering the insults he had taken from Chick Morgan tonight and back there in their junior high days. And Jimmy Tommie felt so good he could hardly keep from bursting into laughter.

Chick began to sag. And Jimmy leaned over him, still punching, never missing. When Chick's knees were no more than six inches from the canvas, Jimmy came in with one last hard right that twisted Chick over until he landed on his back instead of on his face.

Jimmy walked what seemed a mile across the ring to a neutral corner and watched the heavy-shouldered youth as he lay there unmoving, his head resting on his left arm. The referee counted him out.

At the count of ten, the crowd built a wall of sound all around the ring, and the referee hurried over and raised Jimmy Tommie's hand. So solid was the roar of applause that Jimmy wondered how he would ever be able to get through it to the dressing rooms. Then there was a lull while the announcer bawled Jimmy Tommie's name over the mike, and the gushing waves of wild sound washed in and lapped over them again. Jimmy went across the ring and patted Chick on the shoulder as the referee pushed the still dazed fighter toward his own corner.

Jimmy felt his bathrobe thrown about him, while he walked with his brother to their corner and climbed through the ropes. A policeman was there, keeping away teen-agers who were bent on stealing Jimmy's bathrobe. Then another officer opened an aisle to the dressing rooms. And Jimmy Tommie walked through the crowd, his head lifted into the noise. People shouted, "Champ!" at him in a good-natured way.

He stood under the shower all warm inside, not noticing his bruises, and when he came out he grinned through puffed lips at his brother. Dave, as always after a fight, was wearing an expression of typical Indian stoicism. Nothing was said between them until they were in the sedan and headed for their village; then it was Jimmy who spoke.

"Well, you thought I was scared," he said, "and you were right. You thought I couldn't whip him, but you were wrong."

"Yeah. You most near killed him. But you waited too long. You got to get over that. You don't want to wait until you're all in to do your fighting."

"He was all in, too."

Dave said nothing. Then after a long silence, Jimmy said, "He tried to talk me out of the fight in that last round. And you know, I learned something."

"Sure, sure," Dave said without expression. "You learned that when a guy tries to talk you down it's because he knows he's not able to keep you down with his fists. You still sore because of the razzing I gave you before the fight?"

"I'm not sore," Jimmy said.

Dave said, "I'll tell you something. A few years ago I went into the ring with a guy who had me like that, scared to death before he ever laid a glove on me. After the first round of that fight, my trainer called me every

kind of a yellow-bellied redskin he could think of. He got me so mad I forgot to be scared. That's what I was trying to do to you. But I guess it don't work so well coming from your own brother."

Jimmy chuckled. "Something worked."

Dave nodded. "I figured tonight I'd know whether you'll ever make a fighter or not. That's why I wanted you matched with Morgan. I wanted to find out. And I wanted you to find out, too."

Jimmy's swollen mouth twitched and made itself into something resembling a smile. "You know, I never realized until tonight how important in-fighting is. It's important, you know that?"

Dave nodded and said nothing, not wanting to break in on the youth's new-found confidence in himself.

When they stepped out of the car at home, Jimmy stood a moment looking up at the tops of two tall pine trees with the moon riding between them.

He said, "Say, Dave."

"Yeah?"

"How about a few days out in the 'Glades, some fishing, huh?"

"Suits me. But you've got a match in ten days."

"Well, just three or four days. How about going out tomorrow?"

"Then we'd better be getting some sleep." They started across the grassless compound toward their *chikee*. "Yeah, Jim, you made a fight of it tonight, all right," Dave said.

Jimmy laughed softly. "I'll be making a fight of every one of them from now on."

"I believe you will," Dave said, pleased.

The Mudhen, V.S.

By MERRITT P. ALLEN

As emergency "vet," The Mudhen cures a horse but lets loose a galloping nightmare

Sitting cross-legged on the grass of the back campus, Froggie Bates looked earnestly at the sky and repeated, " 'Breathes there a man with soul so dead who never to himself hath said—hath said—hath said—' Mud, what was it the guy said to himself?" He appealed to his roommate, known to the whole school as The Mudhen.

"It sounds like a horse," The Mudhen remarked, from his horizontal position on the ground.

"Naw! He didn't say, 'It sounds like a horse.' That doesn't make sense."

"Shut up!" The Mudhen rolled on his side.

"But, Mud, I've got to learn the thing before class tomorrow."

"*It is* a horse. I can hear it walking with my ear to the ground like an Indian."

"What's biting you? A horse walking with his ear to the ground like an Indian!"

"It's in the Bumble Bee's garden." The Mudhen got up with unusual speed. "We'd better see about it in case he is away."

"What harm will he do if he is away?"

"The *horse,* jughead, he'll ruin the garden."

They climbed the fence, edged through some shrubbery and came upon Mr. Beeman digging in a flower bed. He looked up and smiled in his usual friendly way.

"I thought I heard a horse walking," The Mudhen explained.

"What you heard was probably William Shakespeare," Mr. Beeman answered and went on digging.

"I—" The Mudhen paused and blinked. "I thought it was a horse."

"William seemed restless, so I tethered him behind the barn," Mr. Beeman said casually.

They hardly expected to find the Bard there, but just to put things straight they looked behind the barn. There, walking round and round a picket pin, was a fat little horse that looked lonesome and pricked up his ears with a pleasant expression.

"This is William Shakespeare," said Mr. Beeman, coming around the corner of the barn. "He belongs to my sister, who has left him with me during her vacation."

"Swell! I love horses." The Mudhen went over and stroked William's neck. "Do you object, sir, if I come over and see him once in a while?"

"Assuredly not," Mr. Beeman said eagerly. "You may take full charge of him, if you wish."

"Mud doesn't love him that much," Froggie said.

"Yes, I do too!" The Mudhen declared warmly. "I'll be tickled pink to look after him. Frog, go bring him a pail of water."

"Me!" Froggie snorted. "He's not my baby."

"Run along and get the water—that is, if you want some help with your math tonight," The Mudhen said sweetly.

"You can't kick me around that way!" Froggie cried. "I'll get the water because I like the horse, not because you told me to."

247

He walked away with an independent air.

So began their friendship with William Shakespeare. Why he was so called was never explained to them, nor did it matter. They, like most boys, had a fondness for animals and this one was fat and friendly and something different to play with outside of school.

When it came to caring for him, The Mudhen figured out what should be done and Froggie did it, for that was the way their perfect partnership worked. And it was all right with Mr. Beeman, whose interest in horses was nil plus the square of zero multiplied by ten.

It may be that Fate arranged this setup so that when it became necessary for Mr. Beeman to be out of town for a few days the horse would not be neglected. But if Fate left the cover off the grain bin that day, she was either downright careless or hopelessly dumb about the habits of horses. At any rate, William Shakespeare found the box open and ate three times as much grain as he was equipped to handle. When the boys went over to bed him down for the night, they found him inflated to blimplike proportions, sweating rivulets and breathing in a way that brought terror to the hearts of his friends.

"G—G—Gosh sakes! He's g-got the fi-flu," Froggie chattered.

"He's got the bellyache," said the practical Mudhen, pointing at the empty grain bin.

"Is that all?" Froggie looked relieved, for he had suffered that ailment and survived.

"All!" The Mudhen, who knew something about horses, gave him a look. "It's enough to kill him. Beat it to a phone and call a vet."

"But, Mud, they charge four or five bucks."

"That's cheaper than a dead horse. Scram!"

Froggie may have scrammed, but it seemed to the anxious nurse that a fossilized snail could have passed him on the first turn. Minutes masquerading as hours dragged by, while William Shakespeare groaned and sweated and finally lay down broadside on the barn floor. The Mudhen rubbed him with swabs of hay and begged him not to pass out.

"You've got to hang on, Willie," he implored. "If you croak I'll be in dutch with the Bumble Bee and he will be in dutch with his sister. No matter how punk you feel, you mustn't let us down. Please buck up."

But no vet came. Finally Froggie galloped in carrying an old-fashioned dinner horn and a huge pitcher full of liquid.

"Where's the vet?" The Mudhen shouted.

"Sick," Froggie panted.

"There are two in town."

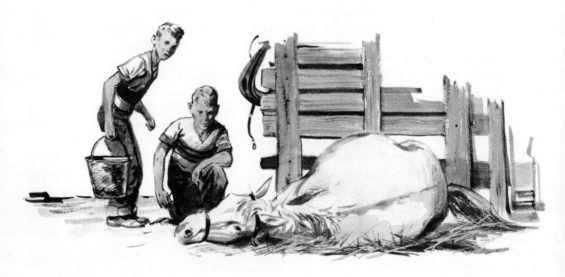

"The other one is away. I called the sick one again and told him it was a matter of life and death, for William Shakespeare has an awful bellyache. He tried to be smart and said the British Museum knows more about Shakespeare than he does, so I'd better call them."

"Didn't you tell him William is a horse?"

"Sure, soon's I got a chance to. He said a name like that was enough to give any horse a bellyache."

"And he isn't coming?"

"I told you, Mud, he's sick—sick in bed. But he said to give him, that is, to give William, a pound of baking soda in two quarts of water and exercise him."

"Exercise him!" The Mudhen gestured toward prostrate William. "How you goin' to exercise a horse that can't walk?"

"How do I know? I'm telling you what the man said. So I got the soda from the Bumble Bee's housekeeper and she found a tin horn for me and—"

"For pete's sake! What are you goin' to do with a tin horn?"

"It's not for tooting," Froggie assured him. "The vet said to pour the dope down William's neck through a funnel, but we couldn't find a funnel so Mrs. Stebbins said to use this horn. We poured some water through it and it perks."

Perking in the kitchen sink was one thing, but perking down the throat of William Shakespeare was something else. Rank amateurs though they were, the boys knew that the horse's powerful teeth could crush a finger like a stick of candy.

"But we've got to give him that medicine," The Mudhen said grimly. "Whether he lives or dies, we can't have folks sayin' we didn't try to save him."

"If he croaks, the Bears will kid us raw," Froggie prophesied.

The Mudhen nodded, well knowing the heathenish temperament of the rival fraternity.

"There must be a vet in some other town," Froggie reasoned. "I'll go ask the telephone girl to call—"

"Eureka!" The Mudhen interrupted.

"Is that the name of a town or a vet?"

"It's this." The Mudhen dived into a dark corner of the barn and came up with a stick about a foot long with a large hole in the middle. "It's a piece of busted ladder. We'll put it between William's jaws and stick the horn through the hole. If he bites, he'll bite the wood."

"Hot dog!" Froggie's tone paid tribute to genius. "They oughta give you a vet's degree or somethin'—like H.D.—horse doctor."

"Please." The Mudhen closed his eyes in pain. "V.S.—Veterinary Surgeon—not horse doctor."

Deceptively, under pretense of inserting a bit, they persuaded the horse to open his mouth and accept the stick. Gently they worked it back as far as it would go and ever so carefully pushed the dinner horn into the hole, its small end aimed down his gullet.

Then, naturally enough, they discovered that while William was in that position nothing would run down his throat. It would be necessary to get him on his feet, pull his head up by running the halter rope through a convenient ring in the ceiling and then, standing on the stairs, transfer the bellywash from the pitcher to the tin horn.

William was, or thought he was, too ill to resist, so eventually he stood with upturned mouth wide open.

"I'll latch onto the halter. You hop up the stairs and drench him," The Mudhen said, with a professional air.

"Do what?" Froggie gasped.

"Drench him. That's what vets call giving a big dose of liquid."

"Drench" was the exact word for it and Froggie was the exact drenchee. William inhaled about a quart of the stuff and then sent it back, propelled by a mighty cough and heave that first drowned Froggie, then knocked him off the stairs. The pitcher did not break because it landed on his stomach and emptied itself down his trousers legs. Intuitively The Mudhen leaped backward and let go the knotted halter rope, which flew up and smashed the electric light bulb.

"Are you hurt, Frog?" The Mudhen shouted.

But before the soggy Froggie could answer, the darkness was rent, shattered, pulverized by a blast of sound.

"Jeeeepers!" The Mudhen reeled backward, overtook the open feed bin and jack-knifed into it. The floor trembled as the ailing William bolted for the door, taking the fiendish noise with him.

"Where are you, Mud?" Froggie sounded terrified.

"Coming out of the feed box. What happened to Shakespeare?"

"I—I guess he exploded. It's all over me."

"But the noise? That was no explosion."

Just then it sounded again outside the barn, a terrific metallic bray that would have raised gooseflesh on a fencepost.

"Jumping bobcats! He's blowing the dinner horn, Frog."

"William Shakespeare?"

"That board with the horn in it must be stuck in his mouth."

"Oh, my gosh! What'll we do, Mud?"

"You mean, what will he do?"

"He's doing it."

He was, with gusto. All his life William had been a well-mannered horse, and it is no disparagement to record that he suddenly abandoned his former behavior pattern.

Why not? In itself a bellyache is hard to endure and when, in addition, one finds one's mouth filled with something that feels like a woodpile and sounds like the Last Trumpet, one is persuaded to get the heck out of there. So he galloped down the driveway and into the street, giving voice to what was probably the first equine horn solo.

Under ordinary conditions a stanch dinner horn of the old school can make itself heard for a mile, but when it is activated by the lung power of a panic-stricken horse its range becomes amazing. And so does its tone, which acquires not only enormous volume but a weird, unearthly note of alarm that might cause a stuffed crocodile to climb a tree. William Shakespeare made the most of his unsought opportunity by putting his four feet to the pavement in a way reminis-

cent of Paul Revere, or rather of Paul's horse.

Then something else happened. By one of the most remarkable coincidences in modern times, at the very moment of William's setting forth, the main electric line went flooie and the village became dark. And down the black street, hoofs pounding and horn screeching, went William Shakespeare like a messenger of doom.

"Air raid!" someone screamed, and the words took wing. "Air raid! Air raid! Air raid!" flew along streets, across gardens, over housetops. Somewhere someone snatched a phone and called emergency headquarters.

"Can you verify it?" the operator snapped.

"Don't stand there arguing. They've landed by parachute outside town. Grabbed all the cars, cut the wires, but a guy on horseback got through. Blow, you fool!"

The operator was still hesitating when a clatter of hoofs and a wild blast of alarm drew near and passed into the darkness. "That guy is a hero," the girl sobbed and threw the siren switch.

"Oh, my gosh!" Froggie caught hold of The Mudhen as the wail rose to high heaven. "They'll put us in the pedal fenitentiary for this!"

"Come on!" The Mudhen tugged at him. "We've got to hide that horse before the lights come on."

"You're nuts."

"Everybody is. Scram!"

They ran down the street, that was intermittently lighted by passing cars. By then police sirens were adding to the din and some misguided patriot was clanging a church bell like mad.

"I can't hear William any more," Froggie panted. "We're stuck."

The Mudhen stopped abruptly and pulled his partner onto a lawn.

"You know something, Frog?"

"Not a thing," Froggie admitted cheerfully.

"If that horse has any sense, he'll beat it home where the Bumble Bee's sister lives. That's just outside of town. Let's go."

"There'll be nobody there. She's gone visiting."

"We don't want anybody there except William. Come on! We'll cut through this garden to the back street."

A truck backfired a few feet away and from a window above them a woman shrieked, "That was a bomb! Get ready to jump!"

"Follow me, Frog," The Mudhen shouted.

"I can't see where—" Froggie's voice stopped with a smothered squawk.

"What the heck!" The Mudhen turned back. "What's wrong, Frog?"

"They dropped a parachute on me!" Froggie sounded underground. "Pull it off me, Mud, I'm smothering!"

The Mudhen groped until he found cloth, yards of it, a great blob that seemed to cover the whole lawn. It was heaving violently and from its depths came muffled cries and grunts. There was a sudden ripping sound and Froggie began to cough and sputter like a stalling motor. The Mudhen put out his hands and found the air full of soft floating, flakelike things.

"Feathers!" he cried, enlightened. "Somebody dropped a feather bed on you. Hey, you up there! Don't throw anything more down."

"I'm going to jump on the bed before the house burns down," the upstairs lady shrieked, as the old truck backfired again in the dark street. "They're bombing us!"

"Don't jump!" The Mudhen yelled. "There's no fire."

She caught the word "fire" and flung it around for all she was worth: "Fire! Fire! Fire!"

"I'll send in an alarm," a neighbor whooped.

"I've got my own hose hooked up," said a voice nearby.

There was a gurgle and a hiss as a vicious unseen stream of water hurtled through the night.

"Aooooow!" Froggie's voice rose and fell with a splash.

"Shut it off, you sap!" The Mudhen roared.

"I'll keep things wet," the man promised heroically.

He did, very wet, so wet that by the time the boys were out of range they made a piker of the proverbial drowned rat.

"Pft! Pft!" Froggie said.

"What ails you?" The Mudhen asked testily.

"You'd spit if you were plastered a foot thick with wet feathers."

"Snap out of it. We've got to find that horse."

"I hope he's dead."

"I don't. I'm responsible for him."

"Then you're responsible for all this mess."

"Shut up!"

They listened for a while to the wild sounds in the village, of which William Shakespeare and his horn were no longer audible parts. It was possible, as The Mudhen had suggested, that he had fled to his old home. Acting on that hunch, they made their way there and found him peacefully eating grass behind the empty house. Somewhere along the way he had lost his noise-making apparatus and also his bellyache. Stealthily, they tied him in an open shed and went back to the school, where their absence had not been noticed.

They spent the next day looking innocent and listening hard to various wild speculations as to what had caused last night's false alarms, but heard no word to indicate that the town guessed what it owed William. That evening, by devious back streets, they escorted him to Mr. Beeman's barn.

A few days later Mr. Beeman came home and hailed the passing Mudhen.

"I chanced to meet the veterinarian this morning," he said. "He told me you phoned him that William was ill while I was away."

"Yes, sir. The vet knows his stuff. He said exercise would be good for William and it cured him."

"Thank you so much. But I regret causing you so much bother."

"Don't mention it, sir." The Mudhen gazed thoughtfully at the sky. "It wasn't the least bit of bother to anyone."

Sacrifice Spurs

By CARL HENRY RATHJEN

He ate, slept, and lived in the saddle, fighting off thieves and fatigue, but his biggest
enemy was the news riding aboard a river boat

Dave Remy spotted the silver spurs in a Sacramento store window that California dawn of February 23, 1855, as he and old Jep Frey, his dad's ranch foreman, hurried down crowded K Street.

"Jep, look!" He pointed as gold miners and townspeople jostled by on their way to the riverfront. Jep Frey turned his gray head from the street jammed with stagecoaches awaiting the arrival of the steamboat from Frisco.

"Think you've earned them?" he asked.

Dave tugged his gaze from the spurs. Beauties. Just the kind that his dad, recovering from a horse's kick, had said he could buy if he proved himself man enough to get a good price for cattle in Sacramento.

"Yesterday," Dave began defensively, "you said that $12,500 in gold wasn't bad at all in these hard times."

Then he saw the twinkle in Jep's eyes. He started eagerly toward the store, but Jep grabbed his arm.

"You can buy spurs any time. It ain't every day we get to town to see the steamboat arrive from the big city. And look at all them stagecoaches waitin' to gallop to Hangtown, Auburn, Marysville, everywhere in the Mother Lode Country."

"You look," said Dave, his excited eyes on those spurs again. "I'll find you down on the levee."

But Jep hung onto his arm as the crowd shouldered by.

"Better give me that deposit certificate, son. Your pa's countin' heavy on that gold. And this is the kind of a crowd that pickpockets like."

The word "son" stung a bit. Dave spoke up.

"I was old enough to sell those cattle, Jep. Guess I'm man enough to take care of that gold certificate—and this, too." Dave patted the bulge of his wallet which had the five hundred dollars his father had said to bring home. "Besides, the certificate can't be cashed by anyone except me or dad. His gold is safe in the bank."

Jep studied him, then smiled.

"See you down at the levee then—man-size spurs and all."

Dave dashed into the store. He strapped on the silver spurs, though it would be a few hours before he, Jep, and the ranchhands got their horses from the livery stable and started home. As he proudly jingled out on K Street again, a boisterous group of miners jostled him. He quickly felt for the wallet's reassuring bulge.

He thought of Jep's warning. He'd heard stories too about pickpocketing. The hard times tempted people to be lightfingered. Gold miners were up against it because this

253

winter's scant rainfall had shut down placer operations. As a result, San Francisco business slumped. The East had had a hard winter too. So had his dad. But that gold deposit certificate was a windfall that would hold things together.

Dave suddenly didn't like the idea of getting into the thick of the riverfront crowd to look for Jep. Someone, smart enough to steal that certificate from him, might be clever enough to get it honored at the bank. His dad would surely lose the ranch then. So, reluctantly turning his back on the arriving steamboat, he strolled up K Street like a man too busy and important to be interested in ordinary excitements—until he reached Bremond's restaurant. Hey, he hadn't had breakfast yet!

Gravely, as befitted a man who had earned his spurs and would someday own one of the largest ranches in the Sacramento Valley, he entered and ordered—two stacks of flapjacks with sausages, a side order of bacon and eggs, fresh rolls and jam, coffee, two wedges of pie and a bottle of root juice.

With that man-sized meal straining his belt, he jingled outside. Everyone was now hurrying from the riverfront toward a crowd farther uptown. Dave wondered what the new excitement was about. Then hard fingers bit into his arm. Jep Frey glared hard at him.

"Where in blazes have you been? I've looked all over for you! What're you doing *standing* here?"

"I've been having breakfast," Dave began, puzzled.

"Spurs! Breakfast!" snapped Jep Frey. "Ain't you heard there's a run on the bank before it closes its doors?"

"The Adams Bank?" Dave gasped.

"What else would I be worried about?" Jep retorted, yanking him out of his daze. "If you'd been at the levee, you'd have heard that the panic from the East hit Frisco yesterday. It started a run—everybody runnin' to the bank, all at the same time, and drawin' out their money. All the Frisco banks are closed. The Adams home office there has failed, closed forever. And it's anybody's guess how long the Sacramento branch can stay open and pay out—"

Dave heard no more as he dashed ahead. His dad, the ranch, everything depended on that $12,000 gold deposit. With Jep shoving behind him, he fought through the crowd into the bank. He thrust the deposit certificate at a harried clerk, caught at the lapels by Jep's big fist.

"I can't!" yelled the clerk. "Wait your turn in line!"

The crowd agreed angrily. A miner called to Dave.

"You should have got here half an hour ago, kid."

A half-hour ago he'd been swaggering his new spurs into Bremond's. Dave couldn't look at Jep as they sought the end of the line. Outside. Down the street. Around the corner. Endless. Dave's heart sank clear down to those danged spurs.

"We'll be all day reaching the window," he groaned.

"If the bank's got any money or gold left by then," Jep glowered.

Dave felt like giving up that man-sized breakfast. He stared at the certificate, now just an empty promise to pay. . . .

"Jep! I've still got a chance! This is payable at any branch of the Adams bank. There won't be a run like this in Hangtown, Auburn, anywhere in the Mother Lode Country. Not yet anyway."

"The telegraph already flashed the bad news from here all over California," Jep growled. "Wait a minute!" he squinted. "There's not a chance in California. But, Dave, there isn't any telegraph line to Portland, Oregon! They won't know up there! So if we catch the ship Columbia sailing from Frisco this afternoon—"

Dave turned eagerly toward the river front.

"That wad of five hundred will take care of our passage," he agreed, patting his wallet. Then he stopped short, "Jep! The Columbia will carry the bad news *with* us! And the Portland branch will refuse to honor the certificate when they hear how everything's closed down here!"

Jep looked suddenly haggard, then spoke through his teeth.

"I hope you're satisfied with the price you paid for those spurs. Twelve thousand in gold *and* your dad's ranch!"

Dave blinked down at the silver spurs. Sacrifice spurs! They'd made him feel so grown-up, ready to take his place beside his father riding about the ranch. Riding . . .

"Jep, these spurs may save everything yet."

Jep laughed harshly.

"If you mean what I think—"

"I'll beat the Columbia by *riding* to Portland."

"You're crazy!" Jep exploded. "It's seven hundred miles!"

"You've called me a riding fool," Dave argued. "You've taught me how to ride, toughened me up."

"Not for seven hundred miles over mountains against time. You'd have to ride day and night for a week . . . *if* you could stay in the saddle that long—"

"I've got to," Dave cut in. "It's my only chance."

"It's throwin' the chance away! Take the Columbia, son. When she docks in Portland, we'll get to the bank ahead of the bad news and—"

"It'll be shouted ashore before we can get off her," Dave insisted. "Then what?"

"It's a better try than having you fold up somewhere in the mountains. You ain't made of iron. Gimme that deposit certificate. *I'm* takin' the Columbia!"

They turned as a steamboat whistle sounded. Then Dave raced for the river-front. Jep panted after him.

"Now, you're showin' sense, son. We'll—"

Dave sprinted as he saw a sternwheeler edging away from the wharf. Jep followed behind him.

"Not that boat, you fool! She's goin' up-river!"

Dave leaped wildly across water. His spurs

gouged planking as a deckhand caught him. He turned quickly and called to Jep on the receding wharf:

"I know it—I'll be waiting with the gold when the Columbia docks in Portland."

Jep gave him a hard look, then vanished into the crowd.

Dave paced as the sternwheeler thrashed its tortuous way up the Sacramento River. What had he jumped into with those blamed spurs? Seven hundred hard-riding miles. But the more he miserably thought about his pop's losing the ranch the more he knew he had made the only possible decision. Get to Portland *before*, not with, the bad news. He prayed that the Columbia was as slow as this creaking riverboat.

At last the old tub swung into Knight's Landing, forty-two miles upriver from Sacramento. Dave jumped to the wharf and cut short the greeting from old man Knight, his father's friend.

"I need a good *fast* horse, Mr. Knight. Will you sell me one?"

"You can't buy a horse from me, son." Dave turned away angrily. A fine friend! "But take my best mount at the head of the wharf."

"Thanks," Dave grinned over his shoulder. Excited, he startled the drowsing bay stallion. It reared into life, fighting his efforts to mount. Swinging up, he pricked it with a spur. The lunging stallion nearly threw him. His cheeks burned as everyone stared. Nice way to start the long ride to Portland, forgetting all the horsemanship Jep had taught him!

He calmed himself, then the horse, walking it a quarter-mile till it became accustomed to his weight. Then a quarter-mile of trotting. Another galloping. Trot again. Walk. Trot. Gallop again with the other forefoot leading this time. Give the horse a chance to stay fresh longer, keep from getting leg-weary.

Riding north through the hot, dry Sacramento Valley he glanced eastward toward the High Sierra draped with snow. Their ranch nestled over there in the foothills, its entire future dependent on a nest-egg of gold in Portland, nearly seven hundred miles away. Dave tugged down his hat brim as he spurred the stallion ahead.

Late that afternoon he rode the weary horse up to a ranchhouse huddling under towering eucalyptus trees. A young man and a woman, holding a baby, came out as he dismounted, patting the stallion.

"Sir," Dave requested, "will you sell me a horse and return this one to Mr. Knight down the valley?"

"Reckon I can," said the man. "But if you've ridden all the way from Knight's you'd better set awhile."

"Just in time for supper," smiled the young woman. Dave realized he hadn't eaten all day . . . not since Bremond's!

"Thanks, but I haven't the time. Now about a horse, sir."

After he saddled up while explaining his haste, the young woman handed him a package of food to take along.

"I'll pray that you make it to Portland in time," she said. As he rode away, he heard her speak to her husband. "I used to envy people who had money in the bank."

He traveled fast until darkness blotted out everything but the stars. He let the horse have its head and kept his eye on the north star . . . until it exploded into a thousand stars when the limb of a tree smashed him in the face. He clung to the saddle, fighting dizziness. He ought to wait for daylight to travel in this strange country. But the Columbia would steam north all night. He squinted into the darkness and urged the horse onward.

At dawn he roused a fat, grumpy liveryman in Red Bluff and made a deal to trade horses. Asking the man to call him in an hour, he burrowed into a pile of hay. He dreamed he was crawling toward a pile of gold, but someone hauled him back by the shoulder. He fought desperately.

"Easy, kid," a voice said. He opened his eyes to see the liveryman bending over him. "Hour's up," the man grinned.

Dave stumbled to his horse, put his foot in the stirrup, and felt no bulge in his hip pocket. He whirled.

"Where's my wallet?" he demanded, advancing. The man's hand dropped toward a gun. Dave dove, clamping on the wrist. The heavy liveryman swung him off his feet and piled onto him. Dave felt himself being pinned down. He got a leg clear, lifted it, then brought it down hard, driving a silver spur into the man's rump. The liveryman howled. Dave wriggled free, smashed him in the face and got the gun.

"All right, all right," the man yelled. "Here!"

Dave quickly checked the wad in his wallet and, most important of all, the deposit certificate. Mounting, he tossed the gun in the hayloft and rode away.

The sun climbed to the noon sky and hurled its heat into the Sacramento Valley. Mountains shimmered. Dust devils swirled. Dave's eyes smarted with sweat. Twenty-four hours since he'd left Knight's Landing. It seemed like twenty-four years. But here he was, still in this blasted valley, still in California. And the livery stable plug lathering out under him. How had he ever imagined he could make it to Portland in time to save his dad's ranch.

He goaded the wheezing nag to a ranch just south of Redding and bought a chunky pinto which the foreman said would "take the mountains ahead like they was the flats." That night, in black mountains hulking below snow-capped Mt. Shasta, he wished he had bought a coat along with the pinto. The moon hung like ice among brittle stars. Trees cracked in the sharp coldness. He ran beside his trotting horse in an effort to warm up. Back in the saddle he fought drowsiness.

He woke up, half-frozen, outside a cabin above a rushing river as a little grayheaded lady tried to get him out of the saddle. He tumbled off numbly and she steadied him into a kitchen warm with the odor of freshly baked bread. As he thawed out by the stove, he glanced out the window down toward the river where two men, probably her husband and son, were fishing. He shivered.

"W-what r-river is th-that?"

"The Sacramento, son."

He groaned. Just how long was that river? Was he ever going to get out of California and into Oregon? He asked about getting a horse.

"We'll talk about that later," she said, giving him a motherly smile. "You have some breakfast first, and then some rest. You're all tuckered out."

"I had my sleep on the horse," Dave replied, still shivering and trying not to think about a soft bed and warm blankets. She persisted, but tired as he was he wouldn't give in. Too risky. She was a nice old lady who'd think she was doing him a favor to let him sleep on and on and on—while somewhere off the coast the Columbia steamed northward for Portland.

"Then at least," she sighed finally, "you'll let me fix you a man-sized breakfast."

The cool mountains made for fast riding all that day. By nightfall he'd dropped into the valley north of Weed and hoped to keep up the good pace in flat country. Then wind blasted out of the darkness. The notorious wind of that area that could rip a farmer's seed out of the soil. Wind that could almost lift a man from the saddle and tear him away from a desperately needed crop of gold waiting in Portland. A wind that kept him continually battling the horse which wanted to turn tail and drift in the wrong direction.

Feeling battered and beaten from the blustering night, he rode on, and along toward noon of that third day he swayed into Yreka, still in California, but only twenty miles south of the Oregon border. He wanted to keep pushing, but what if he fell asleep in the saddle again and became lost in the mountains? He'd been lucky last night. So, after trading horses and ordering the new one to be saddled and ready to go in an hour, he reluctantly got a room in a hotel.

The bored desk clerk nodded vaguely when Dave asked to be called later. He'd better wake himself up. But how? He was so exhausted he'd fall in too deep for his inner senses to pull him out before precious time had been lost.

He stared about the shabby room. A decrepit bed. A rickety chair. The usual pitcher of water and basin. Battered bureau with cracked mirror. A candle in a bottle. Yawning, he saw the cord from the window shade. An inch or so from the top of the candle he cut a notch clear into the wick. Fastening the cord to the mirror, he strung it through the notch, touching the wick, and tied the other end to the handle of the pitcher balanced precariously on the edge of the bureau and only prevented from tipping by the cord.

Lighting the candle, he spread blankets and pillow on the floor below the bureau and plunged into darkness . . .

. . . until the candle flame burnt down to the cord and severed it. A flood of water doused his head. The pitcher bounced off his chest. He sat up sputtering and reached for his boots . . . and those silver spurs.

North of Yreka the road climbed, higher and higher into the Siskiyou Mountains while the sun dropped lower and lower. In the evening hush of the darkening mountains he was giving his horse a walking breather when he heard hoofs furiously pounding back around the last bend. At least a dozen or more horses. He frowned uneasily. Outlaws? A posse? A bunch out for a hilarious time? He couldn't mix in anything that might delay him.

He spurred into a shadowy clump of brush a moment before a sheriff's posse rounded the bend. As they charged by the sheriff raised his arm. They hauled horses back on haunches just up the road.

"Don't see his tracks no more, boys. Head back an' watch for where he turned off, th' danged horse thief."

Dave scowled, sliding his hand forward to his horse's nose to prevent it from whinnying. He remembered the shifty-eyed individual who'd traded him this horse, and got the better of the deal at that. He should have obeyed his warning hunches, but he'd been too anxious to get a fresh horse and keep going. Now he was riding a stolen horse, had been spotted on it, and the sheriff was after him!

If he rode out and tried to explain matters, it would mean hours of delay for a check-up. And another thing—frequently "hoss thieves" got no opportunity to alibi! Dave's throat felt dry and tight as the posse rode slowly back in the deepening darkness peering at the ground.

They missed the spot where he'd turned off. Dave sighed through clenched teeth. He'd wait quietly a few moments and then . . . Then he saw a deputy wheeling back for another look!

No chance of explanation now after hiding out. Dave drove his spurs home. His startled horse leaped out, hoofs clawing the road. The posse shouted. Dave streaked around a bend in the road. A long straightaway. He spurred desperately for the next curve as guns barked behind him.

The chase went on and on, neither gaining nor losing as bullets whined past in the straightaways. Sweeping into another straight stretch Dave, bending low in the saddle, saw a blur of white in the darkness ahead. A roadside marker. The Oregon border. The sheriff's authority would cease beyond that. But sometimes sheriffs ignored little legal points!

Dave spurred and lashed. His horse flattened its ears and streaked ahead. Guns blazed in the night behind him. His horse staggered, then pitched him past the marker. Dave rolled limply until his momentum slowed, then gained his feet and raced into the Oregon brush.

"Too late, men," the sheriff called out. "He's across."

"To heck with the line!" a voice retorted. "We've got him now! Laws ain't made for horse thieves!"

Despite the sheriff's commands a lone horseman rode into the brush. Dave crouched in the shadows. Horseless. Hunted. How would he ever get to Portland in time now, if at all? The rider searched closer, his six-shooter glinting in starlight. As he was about to discover Dave, Dave shoved up on the man's boot with all his strength, toppling him from the saddle. Dave grabbed the saddle horn and swung up as the horse darted ahead in panic. Off in the darkness he reined in and shouted back.

"Sheriff, I'm Dave Remy from the Circle R down in the Sacramento Valley. I didn't steal that dead horse. And I'm just *borrowing* this one. I'll send it back."

He rode into the night. Into Oregon. On his way again to Portland. A long, long way yet. But still on his way.

At Hungry Creek he met a man who was returning to California on a borrowed sorrel. They swapped horses and Dave rode the sorrel to its home corral at Bear Creek. On to Jacksonville for an hour's sleep and a fresh horse. Another night of walking, trotting, galloping. He ate, slept, lived in the saddle on long-legged, easy-gaited horses, chunky pounders, strawberry roans, chestnuts, bays, pintos. Trading a tired horse for a frisky one. Paying some extra cash if he had to. Anything to keep going.

The morning of the fifth day he fell out of the saddle in the little town of Eugene, Oregon. But an hour later he hauled himself onto a new horse. That night he couldn't keep his bloodshot eyes focused. His head bobbed and rolled as though on a swivel. He was too weary to run beside the horse to keep himself awake. Riding at a mad gallop to blow away the cobwebs and pound himself awake, he rode out the horse ahead of schedule.

"How far to Portland?" he murmured, blinking wearily at an innkeeper in French Prairie six mornings after he'd bought the silver spurs.

"Half a day's ride. But you ain't for it, son. Bet your eyes would burn holes in a pillow."

"Not now," Dave snapped. "Get me the fastest horse in town."

He'd have to push and get to the bank before it closed for the day. It wouldn't be open tomorrow if the Columbia had arrived in the meantime. Suppose she'd already made port? What would he do then?

At ten-thirty that morning he spurred his lathered mount to an auctioneer's corral in Oregon City, his eyes feverishly selecting a horse. And at noon he tossed that horse's bridle reins to a boy on the south bank of the Willamette River.

"Ferry to Portland, mister?" another boy called, standing expectantly by a rowboat. Dave shoved it into the river.

"Five dollars if you get me across fast." He squinted toward boats moored on the far side. "The Columbia in from Frisco yet?"

"No, sir. Ain't heard the cannon announcin' that she's comin' up the river."

Dave smiled triumphantly and relaxed a bit. The hot sun, the glinting water, the rhythmic creak of the oarlocks made him sleepy, terribly sleepy. He fought to keep his bloodshot eyes open just a little longer. He doused handfuls of water in his face, over his head. Blam! The cannon! He forgot sleep.

"Ten dollars more, kid, if—"

He grabbed the gunwales as the boy stood back mightily on the oars and nearly toppled him overboard.

"Golly, fifteen dollars!" the kid grunted. "That's more'n dad makes in a week. He'll think I'm a real man."

Dave stared at his spurs.

"Don't get cocky with a pair of silver oars," he muttered. "You might have to make a long hard row with them."

"Huh?"

"Keep rowing," Dave growled, glancing worriedly downriver.

He ran through the streets of Portland, but made himself *walk* into the Adams office, spurs jingling.

"The cashier's out to lunch," a young clerk began doubtfully.

"Where?" Dave demanded. A new voice spoke behind him.

"Something I can do for you?"

Dave handed the deposit certificate to a portly gentleman mouthing a gold toothpick.

"Have you any identification?" the cashier inquired, curiously studying Dave's travel-stained, tousled, bloodshot appearance. He leisurely verified the validity of the certificate, but then suspiciously looked Dave over again.

"Everything seems in order," he said slowly and pointed the toothpick at the certificate. "But there's something odd here. This deposit was made only six days ago down in Sacramento. And the Columbia isn't in yet."

"I rode here. Yes, all seven hundred miles," Dave explained, then went on quickly. "I have important business here, but I *missed* catching the Columbia. It wouldn't have been safe to carry that amount of gold overland with me."

"Quite true," the cashier admitted, but still he hesitated. Dave heard a horse galloping up the street. If he let this pompous bank official stall much longer . . .

"What's wrong with this office?" he snapped. "Haven't you got the gold to—"

"Of course, of course," the man interrupted, smiling reassuringly at eavesdropping customers. The galloping horseman went past the open doors. The official led Dave to a teller.

"Forty pounds of gold. Twelve thousand dollars," smiled the teller, tying the bag. Dave grabbed the bag from the teller and went out into the street just as a shouting mass of men converged on the bank.

"Hello, Jep," Dave smiled wearily at the familiar figure trying to push nearer the front. Jep stared unbelievingly as Dave handed him the bag of gold. He shook his head slowly.

"How did you do it, kid? Seven hundred miles in six days and nights! You must be made of iron!"

"More like iron that's melting now," Dave said, tottering to stay on his feet. Jep steadied him, then guided him down the street. Then, in a dim room, Jep was easing him down on a bed, swinging his leaden legs up. He heard Jep's voice from far away.

"Dave, do you want to keep them beautiful spurs on?"

"Uh-uh," Dave murmured, smiling sleepily. "I'm not going to be riding any more nightmares . . . not for a real long, long while . . ."

Jep's chuckle faded away as Dave sank luxuriously into the deep velvet blackness of sleep.

The Return of Private Kerry

By FRANK R. PIERCE

He was the best Army combat dog in Alaska, but his chances of finding his master were one in a thousand

Private Kerry was Private McGee's pet name for the carefully bred, highly trained dog he had been detailed to handle. In time they would constitute a man-dog team to serve where there were subzero temperatures. From sled dog and wolf ancestors Private Kerry inherited the resistance to cold and hardship. The Army had introduced other strains to improve the dog's response to training. At the present moment Privates Kerry and McGee, with other man-dog teams, sat in a plane as it roared over a rugged part of Alaska.

"It's another jump, Kerry," McGee said, his arm about the big dog. "We've done it before, and we'll do it again. You aren't scared, of course, but I am. So are the other guys, but it doesn't stop us."

Kerry bared fangs capable of snapping an enemy's leg bones and gazed fondly at McGee. He snuggled up a little closer and whimpered happily. McGee was the great love in Private Kerry's life and that was the main idea. He would do anything McGee ordered—attack or cease attack; play a little or maintain a dignified reserve.

The lieutenant in command peered down at the ground and said, "Let's go!" He disappeared.

Private McGee followed, with Kerry at his heels. As soon as the turbulent air stopped tossing McGee about, his eyes popped open in astonishment. He yelled, "What's going on here?"

Instead of dropping, he was going *up*. The plane was *below* him. He looked at Kerry, who was even higher. Obviously a tremendous up-current had caught the chutes and was carrying them aloft. McGee spilled some of the air from his chute and began dropping. The plane was miles away, but no more men were jumping. Apparently the pilot, realizing what he had flown into, had issued orders.

Kerry's training had been thorough, but he hadn't been taught the trick of spilling air from a chute. He saw McGee leaving him, and tried to follow the man, but his paws found only thin air. A feeling of utter helplessness filled the dog and he howled dismally, hanging limply from his chute.

Mountain peaks that had been above him were now level with his eyes. They were growing larger as they rushed toward him. Kerry couldn't know it, but a hundred and twenty mile an hour up-slope wind was carrying him toward the range. As he gained altitude, breathing grew difficult. He gasped.

Now the first mountains were directly under, and he was dropping, as the updraft leveled off. Below the dog, the icy fingers of glaciers clung to mountain passes, as if intent on stopping all movement in the great ice masses spread over the lower country. Many of the peaks, too wind-swept and steep to hold snow, stood out like black, broken fangs.

Kerry narrowly missed crashing into one, then he was over a river that split the range and drained vast back-country regions. There were gorges with thousand-foot walls where the river piled through them and the water was churned to a froth by the speed and boulders. The river disappeared and became a series of creeks that were crystal clear or murky with glacier water. Beyond lay a less violent country, but it was all hemmed in by mountains.

A glacier lay five hundred feet beneath the dog. Its snow bridges were mostly gone, and the crevasses yawned with their beautiful blue lips and their blue-black depths. Private Kerry struck the ice with considerable shock. The chute dragged him some distance; then his body jammed between ice hummocks.

An eagle, circling high, came down without wing movement, then went on. A hungry raven, wearing the black of death, flapped its wings heavily and circled in hopeful investigation. It dropped, and the feeble dog's jaws slashed and the raven lost some feathers as it rose.

Recovery from shock of impact was slow. Kerry whimpered and looked for McGee who had always been around. Presently Kerry howled—the eerie howl of his wolf ancestors. He squirmed from the ice and looked at the chute which had lost its air and was now nothing more than a flapping piece of silk.

Kerry waited quite awhile before he began chewing the shrouds. When he was free he walked slowly back and forth looking for McGee. He knew it was now chow time. Deep inside the dog stirred that instinct which mysteriously guides animals home over trails they have never known. He trotted slowly over the ice, tested a snow bridge, decided it was unsafe and continued his search for a trail. Presently he was back where he started from. He was on an ice island, completely surrounded by crevasses.

He tried the snow bridge again, and felt the snow give under his paws. He sat down and howled. As long as he could remember,

McGee had been around to help him with his problems.

He couldn't know at the moment McGee was glumly reporting, "Kerry went clean out of sight—like he was tied to a balloon. He probably died from lack of oxygen. Best dog in the bunch, too."

Night came slowly, but with increasing hunger pains. Private Kerry's coat served him well, for nights were bitter cold at this altitude. Around midnight he tried the bridge. This time the newly frozen crust of ice and snow held his weight. He moved slowly, ever downward, hour after hour. Again and again he thought himself trapped by crevasses, but managed to detour those he couldn't leap.

The glacier ended between two sheer walls. A dirty gray stream flowed over a bed of sand and gravel brought down by the ice. Private Kerry stood a long time on a block of ice peering into a pool thirty feet below. Twice he half turned to retrace his steps, yet he knew nothing but ice lay behind him—ice broken with crevasses where a slip meant a plunge that he instinctively feared.

He looked for Private McGee, whimpered anxiously, then jumped. He dragged himself from the pool, his coat heavy with sand, waited until the water ran off, then shook himself. He moved slowly downstream looking for food. Once he took after a rabbit, but the creature was too fast for him.

A warning came an hour later where a clear stream flowed into the glacier stream. A bear, not long from hibernation, was preparing to fish. Kerry's hair stood on end, but he made no sound other than a menacing growl, deep in his throat. The bear moved over to the clear water and stared a long time at the shallows.

The first salmon were coming upstream and suddenly the bear batted at a salmon and knocked it onto the grass. Kerry burst from a thicket and bounded for the prize. But the bear was nearer, and roared a challenge. Kerry stopped, then backed into the thicket. The bear ate the salmon and returned to the stream. Kerry slipped up and licked the grass. He had been two days on the glacier and his stomach was crying for food. Kerry slunk into a nearby thicket and waited. The bear caught and ate two more salmon.

As the bear knocked the fourth from the stream, Kerry caught it up inches ahead of the bear's paw and went downstream on the dead run.

For a long time he heard the bear crashing the brush behind him; then it grew quiet.

He stopped and ate ravenously, then slowly as his stomach took on a comfortable feeling. He trotted leisurely downstream, found a spot to his liking and went to sleep, all unaware of a drama taking place further downstream that would have an effect on his career in the wilderness.

Old Man Enders, a trapper, was not the North's noblest character. Among other shortcomings he took a sadistic delight in whipping his dogs when anything annoyed him. Today Molly, who hated him as all his sled dogs did, had raked his hand with her teeth when she seized a salmon before he tossed it to another dog. Enders had gone into a rage and proceeded to beat Molly with a handy hunk of firewood. Molly fought back as best she could while chained to a stake until the brutal trapper knocked her unconscious. But the beating proved fortunate for Molly. In her struggle she had loosened the stake to which she was chained and Old Man Enders in his blind anger did not notice it.

That night after dark Molly discovered the weakened stake. Merely by throwing her weight heavily against the chain several times, she pulled the spur out of the ground, and for the first time in her life she was free.

But freedom was over within an hour. As she made her way through some litter the stake, which acted as a clog, got caught and Molly was held fast again at the end of a broad trail that Old Man Enders would have little difficulty following next morning . . .

Kerry awakened with a start. A whimper had reached his ears and aroused responses that had come down through the ages. He jumped to his feet and looked around. Possibly he thought it a dream, because dogs do dream. Then it came again, and Kerry was off, shedding the weariness of the recent days with each step. Then he saw Molly, tugging at her chain. He barked a greeting.

Molly tried to respond, but the chain held her. She did her best, wagging her tail and whining. They rubbed noses, and Kerry sank his teeth into her leather collar and pulled. It choked Molly until her tongue hung out. Kerry relaxed and began chewing. His teeth shredded the collar and when Molly again pulled, she was free. She shook herself and they trotted away together.

After a while Kerry smelled smoke which meant mankind, and he thought McGee might be near. He made his way to a clearing, but Molly refused to follow. She had known too much unpleasantness to venture near the cabin now that she was free. Her life had been from dog harness to dog chain and back again.

Kerry was hungry, but wary. Old Man Enders came out of his cabin and climbed the ladder to his meat cache, a small structure on stilts well above reach of prowling animals. He dragged out a side of bacon and dropped it to the ground. Kerry bounded the intervening distance, caught up the bacon and was off.

Enders swore at all wolves, but in the midst of a sentence broke off with an amazed, "Sa-ay, that's no wolf. It had a collar on. By Jupiter, I'll trap me a sled dog."

A half mile from the cabin, Kerry and Molly ate the bacon. The homing instinct made itself felt again, and without conscious direction, Kerry headed for the military camp that lay over the range, and when he moved Molly followed. And thus Old Man Enders lost Molly and a chance to trap Kerry.

Kerry didn't know—couldn't know—that except by plane neither man nor beast could leave the big valley except in winter when the river froze over. Oh, there were other ways, but they involved exhausting descents into deep canyons, crossing icy streams, and climbing out again, only to repeat the performance a few hours later.

Kerry followed the creeks to the river, then trotted confidently over a game trail until a sheer wall stopped him. Looking down the canyon he could see mists rising from a series of rapids. The walls were wet, and delicate ferns and mosses grew densely. He paced uneasily back and forth searching for a way down the canyon. At times he was almost beside himself from frustration. Through it all Molly watched him, her head cocked to one side, as if trying to understand his restlessness.

Hunger turned Kerry toward a creek. He watched the water, as the bear had done, then pounced on an unwary salmon and carried it ashore. No human could have been prouder of his first catch. The two ate the salmon, then Kerry was off again, searching for a trail that might lead him from the valley. Once he even ventured onto a glacier, but the first crevasse turned him back. He wanted no more of that.

When Kerry had first entered the valley, the ice was still on the ponds and swamps at the higher elevations. Now it was gone and swamp grasses were growing. Great flocks of geese and ducks had come from the south and were nesting.

Private Kerry learned to raid nests for their eggs by watching a fox. He caught rabbits and occasionally an unwary ptarmigan or fool hen. He retained the physical toughness he had built under Private McGee's training. The homing instinct burned as steadily as ever, and though he might drift over the valley, with the devoted Molly at his heels, he invariably returned to the canyon which drained the great valley and watched the water boil among the boulders and the mists drift to moss and magically turn to glittering diamonds.

Molly found an empty wolf den on a steep slope. The slope was littered with the bones of animals brought by generations of devoted parents to their offspring. Kerry returned one day from a hunting trip to be met with snarls and, peering into the darkened den, he saw five pups. He dropped the rabbit he had caught and went back for another. Molly, famished with the demands of her family on her, made short work of the rabbit.

For Kerry it was the beginning of a hardworking father role of a wolf. He hunted constantly and, as the pups grew, he lost weight supplying their needs. His quests brought him to a goose's nest. He approached with the silence of drifting thistledown, and licked his chops. Goose for the pups, a nest full of eggs for himself. The gander, Kerry reasoned, would fly, and he made no attempt to attack it.

To his astonishment the gander hissed,

and stood his ground. A slash of fangs would have killed the gander, but the dog, caught unprepared, was batted across the eyes with the gander's wings. In a matter of seconds, he was surrounded by indignant ganders. He felt the nip of their bills which was of little importance, but the wing blows around his eyes blinded and confused the dog. He fled with the triumphant ganders in hot pursuit.

Kerry stopped at last and sat down, overwhelmed by a sense of shame. He looked around, as if wondering whether his disgrace had been witnessed. The trumpeting of geese spread until the marsh was in an uproar. Kerry settled for a rabbit, and Molly gave him the withering look of a wife who finds her husband's pay check short by too many dollars.

When the pups were of an age to leave to themselves for short periods, Kerry and Molly hunted together and sometimes separately. They would return to find the pups playing in the sunshine, but the instant either parent appeared, play stopped and they squatted down, ears erect, nostrils sniffing for food. When they were through, bones with baby teeth marks lay around.

One morning Kerry, hard on a scent, caught a new scent that filled him with fury and fear. He had never seen, nor scented, a wolverine, yet the heritage of many experiences, none of them pleasant, had come

down to him. The scent led toward his own den and the dog raced through the timber, broke into a clearing, then bounded up the bone-littered slide. The pups, instinctively sensing danger, had retreated to the den, helpless before the worst scourge of the Northland.

The wolverine had tremendous strength in its compact body. It was solitary and mysterious and possessed a vile temper. It would often run a trapper's line, killing the trapped creatures for no apparent reason and tearing their bodies into shreds. And an unguarded den of cubs or pups was easy prey.

As Kerry neared the den, he heard the pup's frightened cries and saw the wolverine's bushy tail disappearing into the darkness. Now the pups were snarling, calling on the courage inherited from Kerry.

Kerry's teeth sank into the wolverine's tail, and the dog almost choked on the thick fur. Then trouble broke loose with a vengeance as Kerry dragged the wolverine from the den. In the open, the wolverine's claws came into play. But the dog leaped clear, then got a throat hold. It cost him dear, but he knew it was paying off. Again and again the claws found marks, as the fighting animals rolled down the slope. And it was the rolling that saved the dog's life, because the wolverine's claws kept missing the vital parts. The two animals rolled to the bottom of the slope, and

the wolverine lay there dying while Kerry watched.

When the dog tried to stand, his left front leg refused to support him. It was not broken, but there were torn tendons where claws had gone deep. On three legs, Kerry slowly climbed the slope to the den. The pups peered timidly, then seeing Kerry, came into the open. They began licking his wounds as he lay in the sunlight. He was there when Molly returned with a fifteen-pound salmon she had caught in the shallows below a sand bar.

Kerry crawled into the den that night, but when the sun came out the next morning, he slowly got onto his stiff legs and made his way into the sunlight. All day he watched the pups play while Molly hunted. She made repeated trips, bringing rabbits or salmon.

Snow was flying when Kerry's wounds healed, but his leg was useless. It had been a long season, with warmth and food for wild life. Most of the ducks and game birds had brought off two broods; tens of thousands of tiny salmon had hatched out and were swimming in the creeks and more would hatch before the freeze-up came and the water-covered gravels became solid.

The bears still prowled the streams eating salmon and laying up a store of fat against winter's hibernation. There were several ponderous brown fellows and numbers of blacks. In her constant quest for food Molly found several fresh kills and she led her half-grown pups to the spot. Kerry limped along in the rear, while the active pups covered nearby areas, growing excited over scents and occasionally bringing down a small cub.

The waterfowl rafted up and vanished in the southern sky as the swamps began freezing over. It was oddly silent after the long days of bird-life. The ptarmigan were there —a white cover.

Then one night, with a cold moon looking on, the silence was broken by the uproar of conflict. Two bull moose had met head on in the center of a pasture lightly covered with snow. A cow moose, the cause of it all, stood nearby. Kerry, Molly and the pups sat on a nearby ridge and watched the struggle. The bulls charged and retreated, gathered momentum and charged again with bone-crushing impact. Pieces of antlers lay on the snow amid patches of blood. Luck was with the older moose. An antler stub caught the younger's throat and severed an artery. He ran several hundred yards before he dropped. The victor turned to the cow while Molly led the way to the vanquished.

Here was food for days to come. They remained on the spot, keeping other animals away. The pups were constantly exploring the nearby thickets—ranging several hundred yards from Kerry and Molly, then returning to rest. They were learning to care for themselves and Molly saw to it that they kept well away from Old Man Ender's traps.

When the nearby creek froze tight, Kerry moved over the ice to its junction with the river. Already ice was forming along the river's edge. Again the gorge was defeating him. He whimpered, then burrowed into the snow. Molly and the pups made themselves comfortable nearby—bushy tails over nostrils to take some of the frost from the air.

Two days later, the canyon, filled with the river's roar since the break-up, was as silent as the valley it drained. Ice extended from wall to wall, and beneath the ice the river ran extremely slowly.

Kerry tested the ice. He was heading for the only home he knew—the dog barracks where his kind was trained for cold weather duty. He tried to trot the first half mile, then settled down to slow, three-legged progress. Molly and the pups followed him a short distance; then she sat down. The pups sat beside her. Plumes of vapor burst from their nostrils as they breathed. Perhaps she wondered where her mate was going. Possibly, for all her bad treatment by the trappers, faint home ties held her here.

Since his fight with the wolverine, Kerry had trailed the others. Now he was leaving them. Twice he looked back, then he kept his nose pointed downstream. He was three days making it through the series of deep canyons.

The brief days held too few hours for his purpose, and he traveled well into each night before he curled up in some snow bank for rest. He left the river, though he had never been in the region before, and unerringly set a course for the camp. There were no guide posts, no familiar scents, no directing voice. Kerry *knew,* without realizing he knew. It was unquestioning obedience to an instinct that Private McGee had often questioned, but never found a satisfying answer unless it was "God must show 'em the way."

Kerry was lean and hungry when he caught sight of a sentry. The old training to avoid sentries gripped him. He slunk from thicket to thicket, and when the sentry's back was turned, slipped past. He began happy whimpers as he trotted down the familiar company street. He sniffed and, when he came to the right door, he stopped. His whimpers increased and became a howl.

The other dogs took it up, and the night was hideous for several minutes; then it died down, and somewhere a man demanded testily, "What set that off?"

Kerry scratched at the door, then began biting at it with his fangs.

"What goes on here?" McGee demanded. He was Sergeant McGee now, who had a way with good dogs, bad dogs, and sick dogs. He opened the door, and was almost knocked flat. At first he thought it was an attack; then in the gloom he recognized the best dog he had ever known—the legendary Kerry that had vanished in a chute.

In an instant, he was on his knees hugging Kerry, and tears ran down his cheeks.

"Crying over a dog," he gulped. "If anybody laughs I'll murder 'em. I'm crying after all this time, he's so doggoned glad to see me. Boy! Boy! What happened to you? All these scars. And that left leg—not much good. Let me feel, Kerry boy, I won't hurt you. Sa-ay I'll bet that did hurt. But give me time, and I'll have you fixed up. Scar tissue and tendons all messed up together. Hi, those claw marks! Only a wolverine could do that. And you're skin and bones!"

He put Kerry on his bunk, then got a fire going and heated a moose mulligan he had planned to eat tomorrow. He watched Kerry eat; then he telephoned the major.

"Private Kerry is back, sir. No, sir, I'm not crazy. He's here . . . in person, or I should say, in *dog."*

The major came over and Kerry, remembering his one-man-dog days, growled.

"It's okay, Kerry boy," McGee said.

The major examined the dog's leg and body scars.

"The most promising dog we ever had, McGee," he said. "Can we fit him for duty?"

"I think so, sir," McGee said. "There's the phone." He answered and said, "Are you nuts? Wait, I'll take that back, sentry. I was asked the same question. This seems to be one of those nights." He hung up.

"The sentry wants to know if some of the dogs got loose. Claims he saw a dog and five half-grown pups, but they were like ghosts."

"Watch Private Kerry," the major said.

For all his exhaustion Kerry was alert. He whimpered and there was a scratching on the door. McGee opened it slowly, and a pup turned a flip. He had had no previous experience with doors and never dreamed people were behind them.

McGee squatted down and called Molly. "Come here, girl," he said. "You're no wolf."

It was ten minutes before McGee's low, friendly voice won Molly's confidence. She was oddly drawn to the man, and yet afraid, but Kerry's presence helped. McGee put forth his hand very slowly to her head, rubbed the junction of throat and shoulders where a dog can't scratch itself; she stretched her neck, and a warm light filled her eyes.

The pups watched with interest, but wanted no part of any man. "We'll tie the mother in a pen," McGee said, "and when the pups come in, we'll close the door. They'll get used to us—finest bunch of recruits I've seen in a long time."

"Any recommendation on Private Kerry?" the major asked.

"He's got a wife and five kids, hasn't he?" McGee answered. "This man's army isn't sending men with six dependents to the front if it can help it. Make Kerry sergeant and keep him on recruiting duty."

The First Basketball Game

By RAYMOND P. KAIGHN as told to BOB BROOKS

The last survivor of the original basketball team tells how the game was invented

Mr. Kaighn entered Springfield YMCA Training School in 1891, taking the course for executive secretaries. Besides playing basketball, he was on the school's football team with famous coach Amos Alonzo Stagg and basketball originator Jim Naismith, both of whom were students learning to be YMCA physical directors. After completing his executive secretary training, Mr. Kaighn moved to St. Paul, Minnesota, where he introduced YMCA work to Rice County and basketball to Hamline University. In 1911, he joined the staff of the International Committee of the YMCA in New York City where after his retirement at the age of 70, he moved to Chapel Hill, North Carolina.

On a cold December day in 1891, our class trotted into the gym at the YMCA Training School in Springfield, Massachusetts, resigned to our daily workout in Swedish gymnastics. We wished these exercises had never slipped by U. S. Customs.

Several instructors had tried to get us interested in the tedious, one-two-three-four calisthenics and heavy apparatus work, but after a season of football these drills were mighty tame. That day we were all set for another dull dose—but we hadn't reckoned on Jim Naismith, a man as determined as he was imaginative.

First, Jim pointed out a peach basket at each end of the gym, fastened at the base of the balcony running track. Some of our class members groaned. We were going to play guinea pig, they feared, for another instructor's crazy ideas on winter indoor athletics.

But when Jim got through telling about his new game and reading the rules, we perked up. He showed us the soccer ball we'd use, and then chose eighteen men— nine for each side. I was one of them.

He threw the ball into play from the center, and we all scrambled for it. Equipment, dumbbells, and Indian clubs, stowed around the sides of the gym, tumbled everywhere as we chased the ball. The racket sounded like league night at a bowling alley.

At first every fellow tried madly to throw the ball into those peach baskets, regardless of where he was on the floor. I'm afraid that Jim's hopes of close teamwork didn't pan out in those first minutes of play. "Pass it! Pass it!" he yelled, blowing his whistle to stop the rough play.

But we were having fun—and for the first time—with winter indoor athletics.

As we kept playing the game each day, more teamwork crept into the scrimmages. No doubt it was mostly because of Jim's constant emphasis on passing the ball. "Pass it" became the slogan of the class.

What to Call It

With the game growing more popular every day, we wanted to give it a name. We thought of "gymnasium ball" and a punster even rhymed that into "Jim Naismith ball." But, since the baskets were there anyway, we just got in the habit of calling it basketball—and the name stuck.

The selection of baskets as the goals for this new game was actually an accident. Jim had wondered what to have the team do with the ball. He'd thought of a boxed-in net for a goal, such as you have in lacrosse. But that was no good, for we football-minded players would be tumbling all over the net. Then he considered a goalpost like the one used in football. But finally he decided to put the ball somewhere that it would stay—and the best idea, he reasoned, was to throw it into a raised box.

So he asked the gym's janitor to fasten up a couple of old boxes. But the janitor couldn't find any, and put up two half-bushel peach baskets instead. Jim settled for them, and, without realizing it, chose the principle of his game.

Jim developed thirteen basic rules for that first scrimmage—compared with two hundred fifty rules in present-day basketball. One of these original regulations was that when the ball went out of bounds, it belonged to the side which first got hold of it.

This always produced an uproar, with all eighteen men diving after the ball and scattering all over the floor those Indian clubs and other apparatus stacked under the running track. We'd usually have to take time out for gathering up equipment and players before we could continue the game.

Then, when the ball went into the balcony, we'd stampede up the narrow stairway or climb up over the railing by jumping on each other's shoulders to get at the ball.

But even with these complications, the out-of-bounds regulation wasn't changed until 1913.

Now Get It Out

Most basketball players worry about getting the ball *in* the basket. But Jim's biggest problem was getting it *out* of the basket. Since we used a basket with the bottom still in it, the ball—naturally—just sat inside until somebody lifted it out. At first we'd set a ladder against the balcony and have someone climb up each time we made a goal. Or else we'd hoist a teammate up on our shoulders to lift it out.

But this slowed up the game so much that we began getting the "muckers"—that's what we called the school kids jamming the balcony to watch us play—to reach over the railing and throw the ball back to us.

Finally somebody thought of taking the bottom out of the basket and poking the ball back up through the top with a gymnasium wand, the sticks we used in workouts. However, two years later, a man from Spalding Sporting Goods Company saw the game and devised a heavy cord net basket fastened around an iron hoop. He put a drawcord through a pulley and fastened it to the net. Then the referee just pulled the cord and bounced the ball back out through the top of the basket.

Several years afterwards, some nameless genius reasoned that it might be more practical for the ball to drop directly through the basket. So he left an opening in the bottom of the net.

Those muckers gave players another headache. They'd often help their favorite team by leaning over the gallery rail to knock a ball in or out of the basket.

We kept bawling them out for it, but they didn't stop. So one day Jim thwarted them by putting a large square of wooden planking behind the basket. This turned out to be a more important move than he realized at the moment, for it was the start of our present-day backboard.

Game Goes Everywhere

At Christmas vacation a few days after that first scrimmage, we all took the basketball idea home with us. Later on the YMCA began spreading it and has since helped carry the game all over the world. The Springfield gym floor was well below street level, and we'd always have a large crowd of spectators—teachers, sports enthusiasts, and just plain curious people—who'd look through the windows or come in on the running track to see us play below.

We'd been completely sold on basketball from that first day we'd learned it. We didn't grumble any more about gym period, and we didn't even mind doing a few of those Swedish gymnastics, just so we could get started on a game of basketball.

It Was Quite a Change

The men studying to be physical directors had promptly taken up the game after their classmate Jim Naismith had introduced it to our class of executive secretarial students. The faculty also made up a team. Before school closed that year, we put on our own tournament, and our secretarial team won—over both faculty and physical directors—much to our satisfaction.

Incidentally, the picture often published of the first basketball team shows these secretarial champs. They're dressed in the clothes worn for playing in those days—black, long-sleeved jerseys and long gray pants. However, this picture doesn't show me. Shortly after the start of basketball, an old football knee injury took me out of active play.

We soon found out just how popular this new game was when girls began playing it. Shortly after that first scrimmage, some teachers from the local Buckingham Grade School had watched us from the balcony. They took the game back with them to their school and introduced it to girls.

At first, the girls had more trouble with teamwork than we'd had. Every time one of them got the ball, she'd let out a squeal and try for a basket. It took a long time to persuade them that the game was played on a team basis, and to pass the ball from one to another.

In our first game, we had no boundaries except the walls of the gym. Our gym was quite solid all the way around because the people who'd backed the construction of the school hadn't been sure whether it would be a success. So they'd built it well. If it didn't succeed as a school, they figured they'd turn it into a soap factory. The foundation was deeply sunken and heavily constructed to support big soap vats—if necessary.

Odd-Shaped Courts

So our playing area looked almost like an enormous, rugged vault. The gym was about 65 feet long, and that was the length of the court. Not until 1894—three years later—was a definite boundary line set at three feet from whatever wall or fence there might be around the playing area. This gave some courts an irregular shape when stairways and other openings led off the straight line of the wall. Several years later, the court was finally put at today's 50 by 94 feet, and a center line was added.

The number of players was another up-and-down regulation. In 1894, when basketball was still played on all shapes of courts, the number varied with the size of the court. This got confusing when a team played on one court at home, then had to add or subtract men from its squad when it played on another court. But in 1897, the number was permanently set at five.

Teams and spectators both showed plenty of enthusiasm and spirit for basketball right from the first time they saw or played it. And this sometimes made a rather uncertain existence for the referees.

At first the game had two officials—a referee to control the ball and an umpire to control the men. Later the ball referee was also given the power of calling fouls on men.

Sometimes the crowd after a game gave an official more troubles than the players did during the game. One umpire named Fields once told Jim Naismith that whenever he worked a game, he was careful to see that a window in the room where he dressed was left unlatched. Then immediately after the game he could, if necessary, grab his clothes and leave unnoticed.

The fouls were simple. You couldn't shoulder, hold, push, trip or strike an opponent, you couldn't bat the ball with your fist (though you could with your hands), and you couldn't run with the ball. That was it.

The second foul against a man put him out of the game until the next goal was made—or, if the umpire thought he was trying to injure an opposing player, the man could be put out for the whole game, with no substitute allowed.

If either side made three consecutive fouls (that is, without the opposing side making a foul in the meantime), it counted as a goal for the other side.

Soon the rules were changed so the team fouled upon got a try for the basket from the line twenty feet from the goal. Another change sent a player with two personal fouls out of the game.

Dribble and Pivot Show Up

By the second year, the pivot was allowed so a man could turn in his position to pass or shoot the ball, provided he didn't advance.

Then came dribbling, which was first a defensive measure. When a player had the ball and was so closely guarded he couldn't pass it, he had to lose it deliberately, then recover it again. So he'd roll or bounce it. And that was the start of present-day dribbling. By 1896, the present dribble style had developed and soon became a basic part of basketball.

Another big development was speeding the game up to satisfy the public's desire for fast action. Probably the most noticeable part of this change was the way the ball was put into play after a goal. At first, the referee brought it back to the middle and tossed it up. But that was soon cut to the current practice of having the opposing team put it into play as soon as the goal is made.

What Naismith Was Like

Basketball inventor Jim Naismith was a Canadian, full of enthusiasm, imagination, and fiery disposition—yet a man of character and determination. He had a Scotch-Irish background and loved a good argument, especially at the training table. He sported a bristling mustache, and his voice squeaked a bit when he got excited in a word battle.

He'd started out to be a minister, but in college had gotten interested in athletics. Here's the way he put it himself.

"During a hotly contested football game,

the guard on my left encountered some difficulty, and losing his temper, made some remarks that, though forceful, are unprintable. When he'd cooled a little, he leaned over to me and whispered, 'I beg your pardon, Jim; I forget you were there.'

"This surprised me more than a little. The only reason I could give for his action was that I played the game with all my might and yet held myself under control. It was then I discovered that there might be other ways of doing good besides preaching."

At Springfield, Jim had joined the football team as soon as he arrived. Famous coach Amos Alonzo Stagg put him at center, which was a difficult position to play in those days. Said Stagg, "I play you at center because you do the meanest things in the most gentlemanly way."

Jim was in the YMCA physical directors' class at Springfield, which had a program much like our executive secretary class, except with much more physical education work. After Dr. Luther Gulick, head of the college physical education department, had so much trouble in interesting our class in those Swedish gymnastics, he'd appealed to Naismith's physical directors' group.

Jim took Dr. Gulick's request as a real challenge. He worked for days, trying to figure out a game with the excitement of football but without its danger of injury. Football, he figured, is dangerous for indoor play because you tackle the man when he's running with the ball.

Okay, say a man can't run, he decided. Then, instead of tackling the *man,* you tackle the *ball.*

With this simple basis, Jim started a game which today is classed as one of the world's most popular sports. The rules have been translated into more than thirty languages, and its original eighteen men have been joined by some twenty million who play the game each year and a hundred million more who watch.

Since Jim Naismith died in 1939, his game has grown to be America's favorite spectator and participant sport. He can be justly proud.

The Vireo's Song

By DEE DUNSING

The young scout thought the Seminoles were after his scalp when an arrow from ambush tore through his thigh

At the creek Tom paused and stepped off-trail into a bay thicket. In its concealing shade he stood quietly and listened. His alert senses probed down through layers of forest sound, seeking the elusive thing that made him afraid.

Beneath the incessant sigh of the Florida wind, forever being sucked from restless Atlantic to placid Gulf, were lesser noises: the faint groan of a live oak, the whirring flight of a ground dove, the drumming of a woodpecker against a bug-infested trunk; the far-off cry of a blue heron in flight. It was a lazy melange of sound, softened by the warm sunlight that dripped through the bay trees.

Nothing to alarm anyone, Tom decided. Not even a ribbon of smoke to stain the polished sky. For as this year of 1835 neared its close, fires were frequent. Many an isolated cabin lay charred in the sun, its owner dead among the ashes. And in a few days the Second Seminole War, long-smoldering, was to burst into bright consuming fury.

Tom repeated to himself the message he carried from General Thompson at Fort King to George Clay, recruiter of volunteer troops in the Suwannee settlements. It was a short and simple message—five or six words at most—but at intervals he said it over to himself as he had learned to do on his trips from fort to fort.

Although he was not officially attached to the army, he had been used several times by General Thompson as scout and messenger. His youth—he was fifteen and small for his age—had allowed him to travel unmolested in a territory swarming with Seminoles, some of whom were said to be collecting white scalps.

He lingered in the thicket for another ten minutes, listening for the click of palmetto fronds, or a light footfall against the earth. There was only the carefree chant of an ovenbird, ringing loudly through the woods. He wanted to imitate it, for he was proud of his skill at whistling bird calls, and they were useful as signals to other scouts. But now he did not dare.

At last he emerged from the thicket and waded into the stream, taking off his water-bag as he did so.

"Must be gettin' mighty scary," he murmured to himself. "Didn'a really hear nothin' noway."

He stooped to fill his bag but decided the water here was too brackish. When he had waded upstream a way the creek narrowed and the water was clear and swift-flowing. He scooped some into his hand and drank, then filled his container and started back.

Again some instinct made him halt in midstream. There was no sound he could isolate from the natural noise of the afternoon forest, yet this time he was positive he was not alone. Ears straining, he waited.

Nothing happened. A school of spotted

273

minnows flashed past his feet. The ovenbird, nearer now, burst into song, again tempting him to answer. And up the stream a way he saw the shy face of a deer peering through the lush growth along the water.

In spite of signs that no one was frightening the woods creatures, he stood there for a long time, watching the forest and listening. When he moved at last, it was to seek shelter beneath the thick leaves of a wild grape. For fully an hour he crouched there, rifle at ready.

Unable to verify his suspicions, he came into the open again and walked slowly down the middle of the stream. At the trail he paused again, listened and looked, but could find no alien presence. He turned toward the creek bank and gingerly put one foot into a clump of palmettos, watching carefully for snakes. Ordinarily he rattled the stiff leaves to scare reptiles out of his path. Today he moved softly.

As he set his foot on the ground, a sharp twang sounded from a grove of pines. His lower thigh jerked in agony. With horror, he saw the shaft of an arrow protruding from the flesh. Two inches from its entry, the bloody point emerged. Blood dripped from the wound in a thick bright stream. It fell on the palmettos, staining them red.

Tom turned sharply, splashed back across the stream and plunged into the forest. At first he ran unthinkingly, terror giving him strength. But before he had gone any distance his own body became unbearably heavy. It was like a tremendous burden that grew heavier and heavier until he could go no farther.

Half dead with fear and exhaustion, he crept into a welter of live oak saplings. When his heart had stopped pounding a little, he looked at the arrow. He wanted it out, yet he could not withdraw it without tearing flesh and tendons. Urged by a panicky desire to be rid of it, he grasped his hunting knife and cut the flint head from the shaft. When the head dropped to the ground, he tensed himself and withdrew the shaft.

A frightening gush of blood followed— more than he had expected. With his fingers he gouged into the flesh above the wound.

The flow of blood lessened. With all his remaining strength, he pressed the leg, praying silently for life and time to escape his attacker.

During these moments he thought he heard moccasined feet treading lightly through the brush, but he could not be sure. They went away and returned, then seemed to disappear altogether.

After a time he released the pressure of his fingers and found that the bleeding had stopped. Now that both hands were free, he tore a bandage from his homespun shirt and bound the wound loosely. Still he dared not leave his shelter.

Night was coming swiftly. He welcomed its concealing cloak, but not the chill air that made him shiver. When the stars were bright, he drew the bandage tight around his leg, resolved upon a desperate move. Not waiting for the moon to rise, he left his hiding place and moved through the woods—northeast this time instead of northwest. Traveling was difficult and slow, along deer trails that meandered endlessly.

When the moon came up, he made better time. The leg pained, and he was weak. But there was some strength left in him, and for that he was thankful. It was about eight miles to John Taber's cabin, he figured. If he could make it there, John would carry his message to George Clay, and Mrs. Taber would care for his wound.

These hopes sustained him through the night.

He was limping slowly through an oak hammock when morning came. At first it was only a gray light seeping down through the trees. Hungry birds whirred through the treetops, and a frightened rabbit bounded out of Tom's path. Ahead sounded the gurgle of the creek that ran across the Taber property.

Abruptly the forest ended. He was in a clearing. There was the creek, still lying in shadow, although the sun was rearing above the treetops. Beyond it should lie the Taber cabin, a friendly thread of smoke rising lazily from its chimney.

Tom halted. At first he could not believe what he saw. The cabin was gone. In its place there was only a stick-and-mud chimney rising starkly into the air. Around it lay a few tumbled logs—charred, all of them—and billows of gray ashes.

Suddenly so weak he could not stand, Tom walked to the debris of the cabin and dropped onto the blackened hearth. Head against the chimney, he lay there, trying to absorb the catastrophe.

This cabin had been such a busy, hospitable little spot when last he stopped here. John Taber trapped and farmed, and his wife wove her own cloth from cotton he grew. She had fed Tom a wonderful 'possum stew and sweet potato pie that last visit. The pewter on her table was clean and shining, and he had enjoyed eating from it. When he left, she had given him a piece of homemade soap, something he prized almost as much as food.

He wondered if the Tabers had escaped.

Although his grief for his friends was deep, he suffered even more from the thought that he could not deliver his message. The situation at Fort King was tense, and most of its fighting men had been ordered to Fort Drane, where General Clinch was gathering troops for a campaign against the Indians. If the Suwannee men could not reach the fort soon, lives might be lost.

Tom stirred and sat up to loosen the bandage around his leg. The pain was intense and the flesh around the wound had become discolored. Gently he rubbed it, taking care not to disturb the clotted blood.

When the pain had eased, he lay back again, wondering what he must do. There was no cabin within forty miles, and he could not walk another five on his wounded leg. The knowledge was like lead in his stomach.

Could he relay the message in any way? But he knew he could not.

His one hope lay in a quick recovery. If the leg would heal and his strength return in a matter of hours, he could go on—slowly perhaps—but fast enough to deliver his message in time.

Having decided that, he turned his attention to caring for himself. He tried to take off his leg bandage, but the blood had dried and the rag was glued tight. He retied it loosely. Next he drank from his water bag and ate some jerky that he carried in his pocket. The tough dried meat was hard to chew at first, but it brought him strength. When it was gone, he dozed, almost forgetting the pain in his thigh.

The sun was washing warmly over him when he woke, and his body was afire. He was nauseated and the leg was throbbing violently. One look showed that it was badly swollen. A red line led upward from the wound.

A cold fear gripped Tom. Blood poisoning! It was a dread complication, well-known along America's frontiers. Many strong men had died of it. In one panicky instant he realized that luck was all against him. He had no medication and already was weak from loss of blood. He could expect no help, for there were few white men traveling trails below the Suwannee. And if an Indian found him, he would get a ball in the heart or the swift stab of a hunting knife.

"I can die bravely," he said aloud, and the sound of his own voice helped him.

Because he was a dependable scout, he thought of his message as more important than his life. He prepared to write it out in hope that someone would find it if he did not live. There was charred wood aplenty, but nothing on which to pencil the words.

He looked around and found a half-burned piece of hickory wood that might have been the remains of a wooden mixing bowl. With a bit of charcoal he laboriously traced the words "Ft. King Needs Men." He tried to think if there was a stream down which he could send the stick, but the main rivers from this part of the country all ran southwest, toward the Gulf. And he knew of no nearby tributary to the Suwannee.

Best to leave the message here, he decided. The first white men to come this way would look through the ashes of the cabin for the body of John Taber and his wife—or for a message left by them. If his own body were still there, they would search for some word from him.

He laid the stick carefully beside him and leaned back, trying to isolate the pain in his body from his thoughts. Mind and body were separate, some people said, and he tried to ignore the agony that throbbed and spread in the infected leg.

Unreasonably, he listened for sounds of men riding through the forest. A terrible hope burned in him that someone would ride this way. Every stick that snapped in the woods meant the approach of a rescuer. Every tap was the far hoofbeat of a horse. Yet all the while he knew no one would come.

The sun rose higher and pressed over him with the full breathless heat of noon. In the woods he heard the brisk call of a white-eyed vireo. "What's the matter? What is it?" the bird seemed to say.

He stirred. Was it a real bird or the call of a scout? It had an honest birdlike sound, and it came from a thicket at the edge of the clearing. Yet a sixth sense told him it was not a bird.

He waited. Again the sound came. "What's the matter? What's the matter?" Then "Dick-a-dee-da."

Tom roused himself and took a sip of water to wet his parched mouth. Pursing his lips, he gave the vireo call as he had learned it in the woods. "Dick-a-dee-da. Who are you, hey?"

The bird was silent. Tom whistled again. "Who are you, hey? Who are you, hey?" with as much brisk impertinence as he could put into the note.

A gun muzzle pushed through the thicket. It was followed by a lean body clad in belted deerskin shirt and leggings. The face above the gun was reddish-brown with eyes as black as the dark waters of the Withlacoochee.

The figure halted. Lips puckered. Again came the vireo's call: "Who are you? What's the matter?"

Tom's whistle stuck in his throat. He shrank against the mud chimney. But it was too late to hide from the Seminole. Already he must have been seen. For some reason he himself could not fathom, he did not reach for his gun, but stayed as he was, half-sitting, half-lying, watching the boy move cautiously across the clearing.

It seemed a long time before the Indian reached the cabin and stood inside its charred wall, ashes drifting up over his moccasins. His gun muzzle was a black circle leveled at Tom. But he did not squeeze the trigger.

Instead, he pursed his lips and again gave the bird song, as if he asked for an answer. "Who are you? What's the matter? What's the matter? Who are you?"

A chill raced over Tom as he saw a white man's scalp dangling from the boy's belt. But with a great effort he gave the bird call, clear and sharp. "Who are you? What's the matter? Can't see you sir today."

The gun muzzle wavered. A smile flashed across the Seminole's face.

"It is good," he said softly. "I did think it was the gray bird."

Through the paralyzing fear of the moment Tom felt a tiny thrust of pride. His skill at bird calls had amazed more than one white man. But to draw admiration from an Indian was another matter. He puckered his lips and imitated the towhee's nasal chewink and its more musical song.

The Indian listened sharply and chuckled at its end. His rifle was lowered.

"More," he said.

Tom imitated the wild turkey and the sweet clear trill of the pine warbler. Then he paused, pointed to his leg. "I am sick," he said.

The Indian came forward, crouched beside the throbbing leg. He touched it lightly with his hand and uttered a word in Seminole. Tom looked at him, not understanding. The Indian spoke again. Tom shook his head.

To Tom's surprise, the boy stalked away into the woods, holding his rifle loosely under his arm. Could it be that he was going away? That Tom did not believe. His heart leaped as he thought perhaps the boy was going to bring a pony. Then he could ride into the Suwannee settlements. But even as the thought came, he discarded it. He could not

make such a ride now. He would fall from his saddle within a few miles.

The pain became intolerable. He tossed and moaned. His water was gone and his lips dry with thirst. After a time a welcome oblivion stole over him for moments at a time. In this semiconscious state, he saw the Indian come again. This time he was not frightened, nor eager. He was only dimly aware, and the knowledge meant nothing.

He knew, too, that the Indian put something on his wound. He saw a tiny flame and felt warmth around his leg.

Darkness came and with it the sudden cold of Florida nights in winter. Tom was not cold, for the fever continued. He saw the Indian crouching in the glow of a little fire, built inside the cabin area. He felt a remote stinging around the skin near the wound. None of it mattered. Life and the world were far away. Even the message lay forgotten beside him.

In the morning a shivering pale sun struck through the mists in the hollows. Tom stirred. The leg hurt. But he was awake and clear-headed. He lifted his head to see where he was.

The Indian was tumbled beside a dead fire, asleep. There were stones in the ashes, and other stones of the same sort banked around Tom's wounded leg. A mat of strange dark green leaves lay over the wound.

Tom felt a warm elation as he raised the leaves and looked at the skin beneath. The red mark was almost gone. The wound itself was ugly and wet, but its poison had localized. He was better.

His first thought was to get away. The Indian was sleeping and seemed exhausted. With luck the message still could be delivered.

Tom reached for his gun. But his hand had not touched the maple butt when the Seminole roused. The Indian's gun lay in the crook of his arm, and it was against his shoulder in an instant. Without a word, Tom drew back his arm. He grinned with embarrassment.

The other boy rose without lowering his rifle and kicked Tom's weapon out of reach.

Then he laid down his own—well out of Tom's reach also. He looked very serious.

"You sick," he said, pointing to the wound.

He found a spark deep in the fire, rekindled it and again heated the stones. When they were warm, he placed them around the injured leg. One stone he heated very hot and scooped into a pewter dish which had once been Mrs. Taber's. He poured water over the stone and put some of the strange leaves to soak. Next he removed the old dressing from Tom's wound and examined the discolored flesh around the puncture.

"Good," he said with satisfaction.

And it was good. The red streak had faded to nothing. The wound was draining freely. Yesterday Tom would not have believed it possible. He had watched his father treat farm horses and cattle with homemade remedies, but he had never seen a poultice which acted so quickly, nor had he ever thought of doctoring an infection this way.

"You sing now?" said the Indian hesitantly, when the new dressing was on.

Tom obediently whistled the vireo's song, and the kinglet's, and gave the loud note of the chuck-will's-widow. It was like a game. Sometimes the Indian whistled, too. Both boys were skilled imitators. Each laughed if the other struck a false note, or said "Good" if the performance was exceptionally fine.

He is a good Indian, Tom was thinking to himself. And as a look at the white man's scalp sickened him, he repeated the words stoutly to himself. He is a good Indian. Something has made him hate white men so that he has killed one and taken his scalp. And Tom could not avoid the question: What is it that would make a good man hate another so that he would kill and mutilate him?

Yet he knew the answer. It was the hatred nourished through the years, beginning more than ten autumns ago with the Treaty of Fort Moultrie. It was the white man pushing the Indian off his hunting grounds and out of his villages. It was the white man promising the Seminoles twenty years in the state, and then changing his mind almost before the echoes of his promise had died away in the pinelands. It was white men flogging the Indians, quarreling with them about their slaves—and holding the life of an Indian cheap.

It was the Indian, too, striking back. Burning cabins and killing whole families. Carrying white scalps at their belts as the Seminole boy was doing right now.

Tom imitated the ovenbird he had heard that morning, and the other boy listened quietly. He, too, tried the ovenbird call.

So engrossed were both the boys that they did not hear the faint tap-tap of horses' hoofs along the dirt trail. Only when three horses nosed into the clearing did the Indian look up. In an instant he was on his feet, gun at shoulder.

Tom raised a warning hand. "Don't shoot!"

It was too late. The lad's rifle roared. Almost at the same moment another gun sounded. A ball zinged across the clearing and the Seminole lurched backward, as if struck. He caught himself quickly, ducked low and ran across the open space to the forest, where he vanished.

Tom raised his hand hastily to halt the three white men in the clearing. They were John Taber, George Clay and a stranger. Clay alone reined his horse and turned toward Tom. The other two galloped past the charred cabin and plunged into the woods after the Seminole.

"Shot you, eh?" said Clay grimly.

"Not he," replied Tom. He pointed to the green leaves that lay wetly across the wound. "Saved me. Best poultice I ever did see. It took the red right out—and I was plumb bad, too."

Clay stared at him strangely. "You're a boy," he said. "That makes the difference in how they treat you, I guess. Though some of them have throwed their tomahawks right through the skulls of little children."

Tom started to say "Not he" again, but remembered the scalp. He was silent. Inside of himself he wished with all his heart that the boy would get away. He was a good Indian. Maybe he had a white man's scalp, but he had saved a white boy's life, too. If only he could get a start, he would throw them off the trail. Indians were smart that way. And he couldn't have been badly wounded or he wouldn't have been able to run—

A rifle shot rang out from the forest. Only one. Clay lifted his head. But no other shots followed.

"That'll be him," said Clay. "Taber's got three Seminole scalps now since his cabin burned." And at sight of Tom's face: "This is a war, boy, 'tween them and us. Ain't no time to feel sorry."

Tom was silent. His throat was too swollen and painful to speak. His lips were stiff with anguish. Then he thought of his message.

He could not say it, but he reached down, picked up the board with the charcoal words and handed it to the white man.

The Chastisement of Horsey

By KERRY WOOD

He was rich enough to buy out the Snob Creek Angling Club but a bullfrog and a monster trout played him for a sucker

"Brrrump!" said the bullfrog, climbing to the top of a large rock.

"Spllaash!" went the big fish, arching two feet out of the water but not quite catching the frog.

And up at the palatial clubhouse above the stream the pudgy little man called Horsey asked meekly, "Errrr . . . can I join?"

The president of the famous angling club known as the Four-Xers held up his hand and looked down his aristocratic snout and said, "No! You may *not!*"

Horsey G. G. Brown slunk away from the palatial clubhouse overlooking the harmless little river which, because of the people who fished it, was known all over the North Country as Snob Creek. Horsey didn't know about the big fish and the bullfrog. He didn't care, either, because he felt so bad about being denied membership in the club. He'd just made a million dollars out of oil, uranium, atoms, kitchen-sinks, and a $985,000 inheritance from a rich uncle, and he wanted to join all the best clubs and do what the best people did.

Horsey G. G. didn't know fried beans about fishing, but the Four-Xers were the most exclusive anglers in the country and Mr. Brown longed to be one of them.

"Brrruuummmp!" said the bullfrog again, making it sound almost exactly like a Brook-lyn Dodger fan's opinion of an unfriendly umpire.

"Whooooooosh!" went the fish, but again he was far short of the frog's exalted position.

It is unusual for a bullfrog to take up an exposed position right on top of a rock, but this frog was an individualist and didn't care a hoot about what he was supposed to do. He had three good reasons for choosing the lofty perch. First, it gave him a broad outlook on life which suited his philosophic frame of mind. Second, flies were more plentiful up in the air than down among the grass roots. And the third reason was the presence of the big fish.

It was truly a monster trout. It measured from this hand to that in length and weighed more than a plumber's bucket of lead. Such a large body required a lot of nourishment, and while the frog had been skulking in the grass, it had often heard the trout jumping to snatch from high a mouthful of dancing flies. So the frog was not unaware that it was poaching on someone else's territory when it climbed up and started grabbing off a few insects.

The fish resented this. He showed his resentment by changing the location of his lair. Once he had lived under a sunken log on the far side of the pool, but he moved over and took up his abode in the dark, deep water directly under the large rock and stared nastily up at the smirking frog.

The trout hoped the frog would fall in. And the bullfrog knew what would happen if it did tumble. One of the first lessons it had learned about living was to take its daily bath in shallow water out of reach of fishy creatures. So the frog moistened the gluey suction pads on his tootsies and hung firmly onto the smooth rock, while the fish waited hungrily underneath and hoped for the best.

Occasionally the trout rushed hither and yon after water beetles, sand leeches, or jumped skywards after June bugs, May flies, and moths, but no matter how stuffed it was with these and other foods, the fish always returned to the lair under the rock and gave the impression it had saved room for one large bullfrog.

The summer passed, and the frog did not fall in. Meanwhile, Horsey G. G. Brown had been busy, too. He'd made more money, thanks to the legacy of a rich aunt who'd liked his round, fat face. That following spring, he heard there was a new president of the snooty Four-Xers, and so he trundled right out in his Cadillac and asked if he could join.

"Certainly not!" said the Four-Xers.

Horsey slunk away, unaware that on that particular day the big frog climbed back onto the rock after finishing its winter sleep.

"Brrrrump!" said the frog, making it sound like "Brrrrack!"

"Per—lunk!" went the large trout but still couldn't reach the lofty frog.

The fish was just back from its wintering lake down at the estuary of Snob Creek. There was almost a pleased curve to the fish's jutting underjaw, so delighted was he to see that the frog had come safely through the winter and might yet tumble into the pool to provide a meal. The trout began to look on that frog as his own property and viciously chased away any other fish that ventured near the pool. He didn't want one of these lesser trout to be around at the strategic second when the frog fell. Day after day the frog sat on the rock, and the fish

rested in the deep waters nearby, staring at each other between moments of catching flies. So the second summer passed, and still the frog hadn't tumbled.

The third spring, there was a new leader of the Four-Xers. G. G. Brown had won a sweepstake fortune and was richer than ever, so he went out to the swanky clubhouse and took his hat off on the porch and cleaned his shoes thoroughly on the doormat and wore his best smile when he introduced himself to the new president and carefully shook and re-shook that gentleman's hand.

"Can I—I mean, may I join the club?"

"No!" said the president.

Again Horsey went sadly away, unaware that the frog had come brrrrumping from its winter quarters and that the big fish was swooshing hither and yon around its pool.

That summer passed, and the next one. Perhaps the years mellowed the bullfrog and that huge trout, because by this time each knew that the other fellow, in his own peculiar way, wasn't such a bad sort after all. The trout now admitted that the frog wasn't depriving him of any flies, because the insects the frog captured were high above the fish's leaping range. Similarly, the frog realized that the flies the trout nabbed were too low to come near his elevated position on the rock; hence he wasn't being robbed, either.

Occasionally, the splashing of the fish frightened a fly up to the frog's position and gave him an extra tidbit, while sometimes an insect that he missed catching dived downward to provide the trout with a little additional nourishment. So the fish and the frog began to view each other in friendly fashion.

This sentimental state of affairs had been reached when Horsey, having inherited more money from a well-to-do uncle of his wife's mother's other brother, came back to the Four-Xer Club during the balmy month of May and asked to see the president.

The president elevated his haughty chin and was about to tell G. G. Brown to go roll a hoop, when Mr. Brown said, "I have bought all the land on both sides of Snob Creek for miles around, and I'm half thinking of starting a pulp and paper mill upstream and emptying the poisonous waste products into the water. But of course, I wouldn't do that if I were a member of the Four-Xer Club and were allowed to fish here, ha-ha-ha!"

"Ha-ha-ha!" echoed the president, struggling to smile. "Ummmmm! By the way, Mr. Brown—would you care to join our little club? We'd be delighted to have you, y'know."

"Don't mind if I do," said G. G., delighted as could be. "By the way, why do you call yourselves the Four-Xers?"

Along with his membership card, Horsey Brown got a long lecture on the why and wherefore of fishing. Anglers use lengths of silkworm gut as the invisible link between the hook and the end of the fishing line. This transparent gut fools the fish into believing that there is no connection between the artificial fly and that grim-faced man standing thigh-deep in the rapids downstream and wildly waving a fancified buggy whip, called a rod.

Fishermen believe that the sportingest fishing is done with tiny tufts of feathers tied in imitation of live insects. Trout sometimes grab at these cleverly made artificial dry flies and find out about the nasty deception only when they feel the hook fastened to that transparent gut.

The better the angler, the finer he likes his gut. Four-X gut is about as thick as a silken strand from a blond teen-ager's head, and not much stronger, either. The general idea is that the smaller the dry fly hook, the finer the gut, and the lighter the rod, the more chance the fish has to escape.

"This is being sporty," said the president to Horsey.

"Well, look," protested the befuddled G. G., "isn't catching fish the main idea of fishing?"

"Ummmmm! Well, yes. But it must be done in the sportiest tradition, y'know."

He went on to explain that the Four-Xers were a group of superfishermen who believed in giving fish every possible chance to get away. Horsey was introduced to the gentlemen-anglers, who all proceeded to tell him the club rules. This included a long list of what he Must Not Do in the fair name of sport. Then the new member was turned loose on Snob Creek.

Horsey fished it steadily for two weeks, during which time he saw plenty of trout and even managed to hook a few. But the combination of flimsy tackle and his utter lack of angling skill resulted in the final netting of only one fish. Its length was four and an eighth inches, its weight about one and a half ounces, and in appearance it looked like an anemic goldfish. When he proudly displayed this specimen at the luxurious clubrooms, there was a shocked silence among the members. Then the president cleared his throat reprovingly.

"Ummmm! That trout isn't yet of legal size, Mr. Brown, and such small fish should be returned to the water unharmed as soon as hooked. It's the sporting thing to do, y'know."

"Oh," said Horsey Brown.

The incident put him in a bad light with the pompous Four-Xers, and Horsey longed to make amends and be slapped on the back in friendly fashion and admitted to the good fellowship of the august club. Thus he was in a receptive frame of mind when he came to the edge of a pool near a large rock and chanced to see the big trout leap out of the depths and snaffle a May fly.

"A whale!" gasped Horsey. "A positive bewhiskered lunker of a whale!"

The large fish hadn't reached that size without learning a thing or two about anglers and their wiles. The trout refused to be interested in Horsey's feathered lures.

Instead, the fish devoted itself exclusively to a May fly diet, frisking here and there to break water and at every jump snatching a hapless May fly from the ozone to be tucked away in the trout's digestive tract. All of which the bullfrog watched with goggle-eyed admiration, occasionally licking off a fly himself.

G. G. Brown quivered with eagerness to get his hooks into the huge fish. He imagined the sensation such a fish would create among the aloof Four-Xers. But it was soon apparent that his artificial flies were worthless, whereupon Horsey remembered that the use of natural insects was, on rare occasions, sanctioned by club rules.

The man fitted a tiny net over the tip of his rod. This item of equipment was permitted so that Four-Xers could catch and copy the pattern of any insect hatched upon the waters. Horsey attached the net, all the while having his ears tantalized by the heavy splashings of the big trout. But when he got the net all ready for action, G. G. was horrified to see that there was only one May fly left of the swarm that had hovered above the pool.

That fly had to be captured, if he expected to catch the large trout. So G. G. swooped after the fly, grimly determined not to fail. The fish watched the chase from the pool, while the bullfrog stared solemnly at the dancing fly Horsey was after. The man did not notice the frog—not until he chanced to chase the fly right over the rock. Then, suddenly, the frog jumped up into the air and his pink tongue flicked out.

The May fly disappeared. The frog swallowed contentedly. The trout and frog exchanged a fond glance, as though congratulating themselves that they had foiled this red-faced human called G. G. Brown. The trout was really grateful, appreciating the fact that its life might have been saved by the frog's kindly disposal of that strategic fly.

But Horsey was not a man to take defeat easily. He wanted that May fly, and the fact that it was now in a frog's stomach didn't matter a pie-bald whoop. He glanced up and down Snob Creek to make sure no other Four-Xers were near. Convinced of his privacy, Horsey reached into a secret pocket and pulled out a black-japanned hook of a size used by sea-fishermen. He yanked the gossamer off his line and attached the huge hook directly to the end of the enameled cord.

"Now I'm ready for that fish," said G. G., his eyes fastened upon the bullfrog.

The startled amphibian jumped off the rock when Horsey drew near, but the froggie was not prepared for the amazing burst of agility that G. G. suddenly uncorked. A hand crashed down through the grass, and the old frog had his snout jabbed firmly into the mud. Next second, Horsey had the bullfrog firmly between thumb and forefinger and was chuckling his satisfaction.

"I'll just wash the mud off you, so's the fish can see what you look like," said the man, with the black hook held murderously ready in his other hand.

Horsey did not know that the trout's lair was alongside that rock, else he would not have reached over there to rinse the struggling frog. But lean over he did, ducking the bullfrog into the water right above the broad snout of the fish. And at that climactic moment the pool churned in titanic upheaval and a set of toothy jaws yawned wide and snapped together with the speed of a steel trap.

"Wwwoooouuuuccccchhhh!" yelled Horsey.

Speculate all you like about the fish's behavior. You can say that the trout saw the frog kicking in the man's fingers and made a grab for that delicious mouthful it had been wanting for years. It may sound reasonable, but that's not what really happened. Remember, that big fish could leap two feet out of the pool and neatly pluck a tiny mosquito from the air, ten times out of ten. So why should the trout be so inaccurate this time, if it really intended to grab the frog? Why did it miss the frog completely and sink its molars into the fleshy ball of Horsey G. G.'s thumb?

That fish knew exactly what it was doing. He was returning a good deed with interest. And after the frog had swum safely ashore and waited until Horsey Brown crashed away to get medical attention, the amphibian climbed out of the grass onto the old rock while the big trout hovered in his lair beneath the frog's position. And the look of brotherly love they exchanged then was beautiful to behold.

As for Horsey, he gave up fishing. Pitching horseshoes was more in his line, anyway.

Fancy Footwork

By ARNOLD A. FENTON

Coaches know that without good kickers their finest strategy can fall apart

At fifteen Pete Lenotti's promising football career as a left halfback at Bellows High School, Mamaroneck, New York, seemed doomed. A serious operation had left him hopeful but handicapped. But Pete, a spirited competitor, refused to be sidelined. With full scale action out, why couldn't he go in to punt? He started to work.

Lenotti kicked a football by himself day after day. He patiently devoted a whole year to the mastery of this art. Long before the doctor okayed him for unlimited rugged contact, Lenotti was a kicking sensation whose brilliant punting upset rival teams. By the time he was a sophomore at Utah State, he was on the way to gridiron fame.

Pete had to learn how to punt from the beginning. Each movement of his body involved a special skill which he had to practice hard at before he could execute a good punt. You, too, can learn how to get off an accurate punt if you follow these suggestions for developing the basic skills of punting.

Stance: Half of good kicking is balance. Place your kicking foot slightly ahead of your balance foot, not too far apart or too close together. Experiment until you feel your weight is comfortably and evenly distributed. Can you bend forwards, or lean over sideways, and still hold your position? You may have to with a bad pass from center. See if you can kick chin high with your kicking foot while standing steady on your balance foot.

Holding: Hold the ball along the sides. Turn the front tip in about two inches toward the center of your body. (This gives the punt a bullet-like spiral.) Hold the ball hip high and perfectly level. Extend it out a comfortable arm's length directly in front of the kicking foot. As you do this, your weight will be thrown slightly forward on your kicking foot.

Stepping: Take a half step forward with your kicking foot and a full step on the balance foot, and kick. From the moment the ball lands on your kicking foot until you have finished your kick, be sure to keep your balance foot planted solidly on the ground. Otherwise, you will lose both control and distance.

Dropping: Release the ball by letting your hands fall away gently. Pulling them away deflects the ball. Practice dropping it so that it falls to the ground accurately.

Contact: Next to balance, this ranks second in importance. Dropped accurately, the ball should land snugly on the instep (the lower shoelaces) of your kicking foot as it comes up to meet the ball. You can develop accuracy by this exercise: Extend your kicking foot out, raise it off the ground to eight inches, and drop the ball so that it lands on the instep.

When you start kicking, make this further check: If you feel the ball on your ankle, you released it too close to your body. If you feel it on your toe, it was kicked too far

BALANCE   HOLD

out, on the inside or outside of your foot.

Eye on the ball: Slick golf pros like Gene Sarazen glue their eyes on the ball when teeing off. That goes equally for the slick kicker.

Follow-through: Dick Lackey of North Carolina recently led the nation's college punters by developing a good follow-through. He was able to move his average punt up from fifty-five to sixty-five yards because distance results automatically from concentration on the follow-through.

Remember to keep the toe of your kicking foot turned down when you follow through. This gives the ball a smooth getaway. Snap your leg out straight with the knees and ankle locked.

Details: Until you master all these fundamentals, kick short distances in slow motion. Kick slowly and easily at some close-up object. And try to kick into the hands of another player fifteen to twenty yards away. This helps perfect your balance, timing, and coordination—the three basic elements of superb punting—and lets you spot your errors.

Observe the position of your feet and body on completion of your punt. A good kicker ends up in practically the same stance with which he started. If your feet point in different directions, your body is pulled over to the side, and then your balance and coordination are bad. Toppling back also shows poor balance.

Listen to the sound of your kick. A loud smack means you have smashed at the ball. Perfect contact with a long, easy follow-through produces a soft thud.

The Quick Kick

Here's what you do to perfect your quick kicking. Take a regular punting stance five yards behind the line of scrimmage. However, instead of standing up straight, fake a running or passing play by crouching. You fade back—to get away from the line of scrimmage—by taking a step back with your kicking foot, followed by another on your balance foot. Since football rules allow one backfield man in motion, the ball won't be snapped to you until you step back. With the ball in your possession, you need no longer fake. Coming out of your crouching position, take the usual half step, then a full step, and punt.

Practice stepping until you are fast and sure-footed. Perfect your split second timing and coordination with the center before you start kicking.

The quick kick is a fairly low kick, twelve to fifteen feet high, and averages sixty yards or more. A long, fast roll is what counts and you won't get it with high kicks. You want the safety man to chase the ball; picking it up on the roll and bounce, he may fumble.

To kick it low, extend the ball out a trifle farther than usual and drop it lower, turning the front tip down slightly. A quick kick is pulled on early downs while the safety man is up close, but never try it against a

DROP   FOLLOW-THROUGH

stiff wind. (You will have to use a low kick, though, on a regular fourth down punt against a high wind.)

The Place Kick

You can become a dependable place kicker for your team with lots of practice. Here's the procedure:

Target: Stand on the ten-yard stripe. Place a small object (e.g., a coin, a bottletop) on the ground on a straight line with the dead center of the crossbar. A step and a half back, line up your kicking toe with the object so that all three—toe, object, and cross-bar center—are on a straight line. Take a last look at the target just before the ball is snapped back to the holder who will place it on the object. *Keep your eye on the ball as the holder puts it down.* An expert place kicker concentrates so completely on the ball that he never sees his kick in the air!

Stepping: You need the same well-balanced stance and steps as in punting: a half step forward with the kicking foot, a full step through on the balance foot, and the kick. Your balance foot must be placed on a line with the ball. Try to develop a measured stride, for too short or too long steps will throw your contact off. Your balance foot, as it comes forward, should point straight at the target to keep your body from turning.

Contact: For those short extra point kicks, to get height and avoid blocks, get your holder to tilt the ball back slightly. Lock your kicking ankle and knee. Make contact in the center of the ball about three inches from the bottom.

Follow-through: This should be an easy swing with pendulum action, never a smash or a quick, power stab. Work for relaxed, smooth rhythm in your place kicking. From start to finish, you should be able to time it to an even one, two, three count.

Added tips: Limit your daily practice in goal kicking to forty kicks in order to avoid muscle strain and staleness.

Here's a good exercise: Toss a shirt over the center of the crossbar. Step back twenty yards. When you can kick the ball directly over or near the shirt, begin moving over five yards at a time until you can kick over or near the target accurately and skillfully at the side line.

Get someone to call your shots while you look down at the spot from which you have kicked. This will help you concentrate and will help you from looking up as you kick.

Check your holder to see that he gives you a good setup. Otherwise, he will ruin your best kicking form.

Wear well-fitting shoes. Make sure that the cleats are not too long.

Coaches can spend weeks mapping out a powerful offense and defense for crucial games. They know, however, that without good kickers their finest strategy can fail.

If you can do some fancy footwork, you'll have no trouble making the team and getting in the game.

Spiked Switches

By CARL HENRY RATHJEN

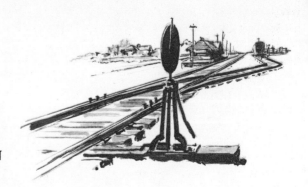

Frank Casey acted the part of a big hogger until the safety valve let go

I was eagerly looking for my name on the call board of the Hannibal & St. Joseph Railroad early that eventful day, April 3, 1860, when Frank Casey spoke over my shoulder.

"You're looking too high, Eddie. Only topnotch railroadmen are posted for the special that's taking the first mail to St. Joe for the Pony Express."

I set the brakes on my temper before I managed to turn around smiling.

"Guess you're right about topnotchers. But how is it your name isn't posted as engineer in place of your dad?"

Nearby a couple of grizzled railroadmen guffawed. I hadn't intended to be overheard even though it was about time that Frank, the youngest hogger on the line, was taken down a peg or two. His cinder-scarred face got as fiery red as an open firebox.

"Some day I will hold the throttle of a fast train," he retorted. "But you'll still be a third-rate brakie busting couplings on slow freights and fouling up the main line."

I winced. Frank and I were the same age. He'd had the advantage of his father's coaching to get ahead, but even so, other fellows who'd started as brakie with me were now tallowpots, apprentice telegraphers, signalmen, or dispatchers. I seemed firmly spiked to one job, head-end brakie on Number 23, local freight, Hannibal to Macon and return, Frank Casey, engineer.

As I turned and walked out, Frank called after me, "Guess Roadmaster Davis had you

in mind when he ordered the main line switches spiked for the special's fast run today."

Outside hostlers swarmed over his dad's fast woodburning engine, the Missouri, polishing her brass and scroll work about the headlight, the bell, and the big drivers, getting her ready for the part she'd play this afternoon in the history of this growing nation. She'd rush the mail from the east to St. Joseph where the first Pony Express was all set to start galloping to California.

Jim Casey, Frank's fearless father, would be at her throttle with all switches spiked to keep the line clear for him and orders from Roadmaster Davis to hang up a record that would stand for fifty years. It wasn't just to help the Pony get started, it was also to persuade the Government to grant contracts to the railroads for carrying mail.

The eyes of the nation would be on that special and Davis himself would be in charge of it. That's why I'd been hoping I'd be one of its brakies. If I was ever going to get anywhere with the Hannibal & St. Joe, I'd need a little favorable attention without Frank Casey around to spike my chances. But to be fair, the situation could be blamed on me.

The trouble had started several months back. Frank was always proudly talking about his famous dad as though he, Frank, was every inch as good a hogger. He was pretty good, but not that good, and I'd made the mistake once of saying that railroading

288

was teamwork, that no engineer, including his dad, was any better than his crew let him be. Frank decided that I was criticizing him, despite my assurances, and when I pulled a boner with brakes and it "looked" as though a broken coupling were his fault he was positive I'd done it deliberately.

From then on he'd done things to retaliate, making me look like an unreliable brakie that a good hogger like himself had to put up with. And even on this great day with everyone excited about the Pony Express special he still managed his usual tactics when he highballed Number 23 from the Hannibal yards through morning mist from the Mississippi.

I had to admit that he hooked her up neatly, getting our short but heavy freight drag wheeling without the drivers spinning away from him, with businesslike barks from the diamond stacks spewing smoke speckled with sparks and ashes. I sat on the cordwood back in the tender and morosely watched his tallowpot, lanky Hank Evans, toss wood with the deft twist that made them land crosswise in the roaring firebox. Unknown to anyone I'd been practicing that with a dummy firebox I'd built outside my folks' home in Hannibal, but the way things were going for me, or rather not going, I doubted if I'd ever be a tallowpot.

So I was off my feet, angrily slapping at sparks that tried to burn holes in the gray shirt I'd had my Ma specially starch and iron for this great day, when Frank's toot for brakes near Monroe City startled me. Scrambling, I ripped the shirt sleeve on a splintery cordwood. Frank laughed. I turned my temper on the tender's brake wheel, hurled myself onto the following car and screeched home the brakes on the forward trucks, raced along the swaying catwalk to

the rear brake wheel, leaped the gap to the next car, then another, and another. . . .

I could see Whitey Jones, our rear-end brakie, working forward from the crummy. I knew I was setting brakes tighter than he was because the momentum of his section was pushing up the slack among the un-braked cars between us. But suddenly above the rasp of brake shoes I heard the slack going out with a faint *bunk-bunk-kabunking,* pulling out from the head end.

Tugging at a stubborn wheel with my brake stick I glanced forward and spotted faint blasts of smoke and cinders shooting from the engine. Frank was quietly letting steam dribble into the cylinders so we *over-ran* the siding switch. He tooted impatiently for brakes to be released so he could back up the whole train to clear the switch.

Freeing the brakes I wondered what this was all about. Our genial conductor back in the crummy had told Frank to lay off this tactic. It didn't discredit me with the con-ductor anymore. I was releasing the tender's brakes when Frank glanced beyond me.

"Feeling weak again today, Eddie?" he asked loudly. The next instant Roadmaster Davis dropped into the tender and gave me a penetrating look. I wanted to wrap my brake stick around Frank's head. Davis popped open the cover of his watch.

"Keep this drag up to schedule. I want to be back in Hannibal before the special high-balls."

"Yes, sir," said Frank, glancing at me. "I'll do my best under the circumstances."

"I'll expect to see your best, not hear about it," Davis replied, snapping his watch closed. I remembered hearing rumors he was becom-ing fed up with Frank's cockiness even though Frank was the son of his crack engi-neer. He swung from the cab, pausing on the steps with his face on level with the deck.

"I'll be hiking the ties inspecting the re-ballasting for this afternoon's fast run. Watch for me and pick me up."

We set out two loaded cars and picked up three empties, coupled to the drag and started west again. Frank wheeled her fast, faster, until Tallowpot Evans reminded him about having to slow down for Davis. Frank nodded, and kept right on wheeling. I moved to a brake wheel and squinted uneasily ahead through stinging cinders.

Rounding a bend we spotted the figure of Davis down the tangent in the straight chan-nel of trees. He stepped to the shoulder and waited.

Frank tooted for brakes. I got grimly to work. I saw what was up now. We'd over-run again, forcing Davis to make a danger-ous flying leap for the grab irons because the head-end brakie, me, didn't have what it took to do his job right!

I pounded along swaying catwalks, poured everything I had into the brakes. Shoes screeched. Cars shuddered. Couplings jostled and rattled. And this time Frank *didn't* dribble steam. We shook to a halt a good hundred yards short of Davis. And just be-fore we stopped, Frank put on a show of feeding steam when our lack of momentum and the tightly set brakes made the engine's drivers spin futilely as the drag stalled. Davis strode along the ballast and climbed aboard, looking at his watch.

"Nice job of setting brakes," he said to me, *"if* it had been an emergency!" He turned to Frank. "Equally nice job of mak-ing it look like poor brake-setting back up the line!" He snapped down the cover of his watch. "But we're running a railroad! Our only feud is our continual one with the time schedule!"

We caught the warning and ignored each other, but we were twenty minutes late when we pulled into Macon, the end of our out-bound run, forty-odd miles out from Han-nibal. Davis spoke to our conductor loud enough for Frank and me to overhear.

"I don't intend to get aboard the special by flagging her down somewhere along the line. I'll arrange to skip a few return stops to regain time your head-end crew lost."

He stalked toward the Macon telegrapher's office. The conductor spat disgustedly toward us. Tallowpot Evans looked smug.

"My shoes feel good, how are yours?"

"The same as always," I replied. "They never were getting anywhere anyway."

Frank's grimy face tightened. He had plenty to lose.

"I can make up that time, *if* my crew can match up."

Still cocky. Going to show what a great hogger he was. Throwing my own words back at me. I listened as he explained how he was going to save time with me getting the brunt of it. We had three jobs in Macon before starting back to Hannibal. Four loaded cars to spot on two adjoining sidings and some empties to pick up a bit down the line.

Frank planned to do all three in one risky maneuver. I realized that if I protested it would look like a grudge interfering with operations again.

Telling myself I was a fool to help Frank Casey, I uncoupled the first of the cars and climbed up to the catwalk. The engine gave all four cars a shove, eased up a bit to let my car lead out, then rammed the other three after it and let them go. Double drilling, double switching, calling for split-second timing.

My car lurched off the high iron onto a siding, clattered over more frog-points and barely cleared them before Whitey Jones threw the switch just in time to shunt the three following cars onto the adjoining track. Whitey was supposed to swing aboard and brake them. He stumbled, sprawled, let them get away.

On my lone car I manhandled the brake wheel, racing against time while out on the main line a section foreman threw a switch so Frank could take the engine on down for the empties. When I saw my car would stop safely, the other three were rolling down the adjoining track. I gripped my stick and got set to jump across. One slip and I'd go down between . . . a good way to lose a leg or my life.

I didn't like the momentum Frank had given those cars and wondered if he had done it deliberately, if Whitey had feigned falling. But I didn't think they'd go that far. I jumped and got to work fast, anxiously watching the gap narrowing as we bore down on cars already on the siding.

I was still braking when . . . *blump!* The crash could have been heard back in Hannibal.

My hands tore loose from a brake wheel. I pitched headlong, clawing at the catwalk to save myself from rolling off. I lifted my head in time to see a lone car, at the far end of the string, move out because someone hadn't set its brakes. She sprung a switch and ambled toward the main line as the engine came along.

Frank spotted the wild car the instant I shouted. He slammed the engine in reverse and Tallowpot Evans, unaware of the situation, was flung forward. He instinctively put out his hands, flesh sizzling on the hot firebox. The engine slid to a stop. In front of its cowcatcher the boxcar derailed on the main line switch, already spiked for the afternoon, then went on, gouging ties and springing rails.

Roadmaster Davis highballed from the telegrapher's office to confront Frank and me. He had a full head of steam, sparks shooting from his eyes, and no brakes on his tongue. He sifted everything down finally to the cold fact that he'd had enough of our feud. We were through with the Hannibal & St. Joe, could draw our time as soon as we arrived in Hannibal.

"You can count on it this time," he glared at Frank. "It won't do any good for your father to go to bat for you, let you get by on his reputation. And as for you," Davis glowered at me, "I've wondered why you never got ahead. Now I know!" He whipped toward the section foreman. "Get a crew and clear that line!"

"Yes, sir. In jig time. Well before the special arrives."

"Never mind speed! Do it slow! Let's have one job done *right* today! That special will be three hours late anyway," Davis snapped, glancing toward the telegrapher's office. "Thanks to more bungling by so-called railroadmen who let the mail miss a train connection back in Detroit. A fine thing! The Pony all set to go and the Iron Horse stumbles!"

With a click of his watch cover he climbed aboard the engine and saw the conductor bandaging Tallowpot Evan's hands. Evans obviously couldn't heave a toothpick. Before Davis' pressure could climb dangerously again, I yanked open the firebox door, tossed in a length and spoke quietly to Frank.

"Get 'er wheeling, mister."

Davis grunted skeptically, but didn't try to stop me. I outdid myself, keeping up a full head of steam besides handling brakes. Frank never herded an engine with smoother feel. But Davis was too mad to change his mind about us. Nice! I'd practiced hard at home to prepare for a job like this, tallowpot, apprentice engineer. Now it was taking me out of a job.

All along the line we saw crowds gathering to see the history-making run of the Pony Express special. When we hauled into Hannibal, the mob looked like a sea of beaver hats, sombreros, sunbonnets and parasols. I saw people pointing at Frank and me, causing others to gape, making me want to crawl under the woodpile, wondering who'd sent the news of our disgrace ahead to Hannibal. Then, worst of all, I saw my folks, Dad's sad look, Ma's tears. Suddenly, Ma spotted me.

"He's alive!" she cried joyfully. "Not even scratched! Oh, thank Heavens!"

Even Davis, overhearing, was puzzled. Questions and reassurances flew back and forth but it was several minutes before I learned what had happened. A telegraphed report had routinely arrived from Macon about the derailment and the *near-crash*. It had leaked out to the crowd. Someone sprinkled it with a bit of colorful exaggeration, others poured on more, and by the time it had soaked through the mob and reached my folks it was a flood of catastrophe —a horrible wreck killing Frank and me.

My folks had rushed to the depot. Frank's mother had collapsed at home. A doctor couldn't be found with everyone somewhere out along the railroad line to see the run of the special.

Frank's father had borrowed a team and buckboard and dashed away to try to find a doctor. He hadn't come back yet. No one knew where he'd gone. His tallowpot was keeping up steam. Roadmaster Davis, clenching his watch, dispatched every available railroadman in every possible direction to find Jim Casey. The line would send its own doctor.

Jim Casey was to come back and stand by the throttle of the Missouri.

The sun doggedly maintained its schedule across the sky. Time kept pace, bringing two o'clock and the mail closer.

But no Jim Casey. Not even a word of his possible whereabouts.

The mail arrived about seven minutes after two. The big brass and guests of the Hannibal & St. Joe climbed into the cars of the special. The crowds waited. The Pony waited from St. Joe all the way to California.

The whole nation watched. Roadmaster Davis *had* to get that special wheeling, crack engineer or not. He spun Frank toward the Missouri's gleaming grab irons.

"All right, Mr. Casey. We've been hearing you're as good as your dad. Now show us!"

With set face Frank clambered up. With equally set face the boomer tallowpot jumped down.

"Not with me he don't," he declared, letting go a spurt of amber tobacco juice. "I worked on too many railroads, seen too many cocky punks to commit suicide on a *fast* run with this. . . ."

He was drowned out by Davis' roar and approving murmurs from other railroadmen. Frank gave me a tense nod, raggedly blasted the whistle and opened the throttle with a jerk.

I piled aboard and grabbed the bellcord setting up a clamor and starting cheers from the mob as Davis leaped for the grab irons. He was too mad and humiliated to prevent his engine being manned by two punks he'd fired. More important, his special *was moving* at long last toward St. Joe, 206 miles away and three hours late!

Davis stayed in the cab, his watch popping open, snapping shut. His eyes were stabbing and distrustful. He was probably praying that we two hooligans could do the job for him without messing it up.

We wheeled. The drivers pounded. The roaring stack belched smoke and sparks. The furious draft through the firebox consumed wood faster than I could heave it in. Staggering on the swaying deck, I blinked away sweat-blur and saw the steam gauge dropping!

"I might have known!" barked Davis. "Slow down at Hunnewell," he called to Frank. "I'll toss out an order for a relief fireman."

"All right, sir," Frank snapped back. "But just remember Eddie did a lot of tough braking this morning, then fired all the way back to Hannibal. All he needs is his second wind."

Was that Frank Casey speaking? Davis was as surprised as I was. Suddenly he snatched away the wood I was holding and heaved it into the inferno of the firebox.

"Feed 'em to me!"

I stacked wood on the deck beside him. Unmindful of his good clothes he pitched away. The steam gauge began a steady climb. She hit a hundred and twenty-five pounds and stayed there.

"Think you can hold it there now?" he demanded.

In answer I picked up a length from the tender and javelined it with all the skill I'd practiced at home. Davis jumped aside as it shot by into the box without brushing the frame. His grim expression didn't change as he popped open his watch.

"I'll look into this again when we arrive at Macon."

Then, his suit grimy and rumpled, his face sweating and smudged, he went back to join the brass in the lurching cars. I slammed wood home, daring that gauge to drop again.

"Thanks, Frank," I gasped and grinned.

Frank Casey just gave me a cold pale look, tightened his grip on the throttle and squinted ahead. What was this all about? He'd done me a real favor with Roadmaster Davis, now he acted as though the feud were still on.

Puzzled, I heaved wood.

I was still bewildered when we reached Macon where we'd have to refuel. Frank whistled for brakes. I handled the engine brake, part of the tallowpot's job, and with a full head of steam I anxiously wondered what Roadmaster Davis had decided about me as the Missouri panted proudly down a lane of cheering spectators with horses rearing and plunging behind them.

I looked ahead to the refueling station of L. S. Coleman who had orders to refuel us in record time. I prayed I wouldn't see a relief tallowpot waiting to jump aboard. All I could see was a gang of men crowded on a specially built platform, every man loaded with cordwood. They emptied their arms as the tender rolled by. We'd scarcely jolted to a stop when Coleman, with watch in hand, waved at Frank.

"Highball! Wheel 'er! Fifteen seconds! Not bad, huh?"

Frank whistled for brakes released. The stack snorted smoke. Sparks shot skyward. Ashes snowflaked the grinning gang. We wheeled out, and I hadn't been relieved! I piled wood on the deck and grinned at Frank again.

His grim tightlipped stare made me wonder if I'd imagined his attitude had changed.

We wheeled west. The draft roared. Wind thundered past the cab. The alligator legs clanked in mighty rhythm with the pounding drivers. Then, through all that sound, I heard the hissing blast as the safety valve let go. I waited, but Frank didn't open that throttle one notch to take advantage of the

pressure for more speed for the Pony Express special.

"We're running late, you know," I reminded him.

He ignored me. The throttle stayed where it was. The safety swirled wasted steam. I closed the firebox and moved across deck.

"Are you letting a personal grudge interfere with something more important than a couple of punks?" He didn't answer me. "Why didn't you want me booted off at Macon?" I demanded. "Was it because Davis might have sent you with me?"

Just a set squint at the track ahead.

I started to get mad. "If you're thinking of lying down on the job and telling Davis my second wind failed me. . . ."

I stared unbelievingly as we started down the steep grade to the Chariton River and Frank began to close the throttle.

"We're not going too fast," I shouted. He closed the throttle some more. "If you won't open it, I will," I snapped, reaching out. He pushed me away. I reached again. He half-swung at me.

"Cut it out!" he yelled. "You want to get us killed?"

Then I noticed his pallor under the grime, his wide eyes as he guarded that throttle with desperate fear.

"So that's it!" I gasped. "The great Frank Casey! Scared stiff!"

He didn't deny it. Just hunched there, miserably hanging onto that closed throttle as we picked up speed on the downgrade.

"Now I know why you always talked big," I accused him. "Always tried to make someone else look bad, mainly me, so no one would notice what a hoax you are as a hogger!"

His eyes looked sick. I wanted to get mad after all I'd taken from him, but I couldn't. It wasn't pretty, or even pitiful, to see a fellow going to pieces like that. Cringing, ashamed, but too frightened to do anything about it now that the truth was out.

I remembered seeing that look in his eyes that morning by the call board when my remark had been overheard. I wondered if his fear of the truth being known was greater than his fear of speed.

"Don't worry," I gibed above the wind buffeting about the cab. "I won't tell anyone, not a single soul." A puzzled, hopeful look flickered in his eyes. "Not a word from me. I'll let *you* tell."

I yanked open the firebox and began heaving wood. I made that safety valve scream for mercy.

"Davis and the big brass will hear that," I shouted. "They'll lean out a window and see it. They'll *know* you're holding back. That Jim Casey's son is a wash-out. And what about your dad? He'll be so ashamed he'll never be able to face a real railroadman again. His own son, a quivering, yel—"

"Shut up!"

Frank's face looked chalky under the black smudges. He gingerly eased the throttle open a bit. I heaved wood and kept on taunting him about his dad, making him think about someone beside himself, making him mad. The safety roared an accompaniment. Frank kept opening that throttle.

The Missouri rocketed down that Chariton grade. She lurched, careened. I could feel her drivers bouncing clear, slamming back on the rails. Behind us the cars weaved, rocked, and pitched.

Then we hit a soft spot in the roadbed. I staggered across the deck, dropping wood and reaching wildly for a handhold. I clung, waiting for the rolling plunge from the right of way.

"Who's scared now!" Frank challenged, and opened her wide.

I tossed my panic in the firebox. For every stick of wood that went in Frank opened her another notch. The safety hissed faintly, then held its breath while we Juggernauted downgrade as though we were dropping from the sky. Somehow we stayed on the rails. A silvery slit shot by. The river. Then we lunged up the opposite grade almost to the top before the exhaust began to slow and labor. A new Frank Casey grinned at me.

"When we're not stopping to refuel, I'll bet that you can't make the safety let go again between here and St. Joe."

"Here goes," I smiled, opening the roaring firebox.

No, we didn't make up the three hours that had been lost in Detroit. That was an impossibility. But we did set a record of four hours and 51 minutes for 206 miles on a roadbed that in a few years would be considered dangerous in its construction and ballasting. And our record down that Chariton grade stood for *more* than fifty years!

When the puffing Missouri clanged to a stop in front of the huge crowd of frontiersmen waiting at St. Joseph, Frank held out his grimy hand.

"Thanks, Eddie, for helping me become worthy of being called Jim Casey's son."

"Jim Casey's son nothing," declared Roadmaster Davis, climbing from the platform where the big brass, with a couple of crushed beaver hats among them, stood shaken·and green about the gills from their wild ride. "You're Frank Casey, engineer. And from now on live up to being yourself, not an imitation of someone else. Stand on your own feet like this former brakie who's going to be your tallowpot from now on."

Man, did it feel good to know that *my* switches were no longer spiked!

Roadmaster Davis studied us a moment, absently popping and snapping his watch cover.

"I wasn't going to mention this, but I've got to," he growled. "I was in the tender and saw the climax of your feud on the Chariton grade."

Frank looked worried. I stepped in front of Davis. "That's going to stay just among the three of us, sir."

He looked me up and down.

"Let me warn you," he retorted. "About that new feud you've started: Who's going to make the safety valve pop and who isn't. Lay off that kind of speed. . . ." His eyes twinkled. ". . . until we've got rails to the Pacific so you can really get wheeling."

Frank and I laughed with him, agreeing that that day wasn't too far off even though a cannonshot announced that the Pony was on its way with the mail we'd brought on the Iron Horse.

The Great Drop Game

By EARL CHAPIN

Pigtail pandemonium breaks out when Sissy Wyatt tries out her secret pitch on the North End Nuggets

Somebody said something the other day about "one of the greatest games of organized baseball." Well, whatever that game was like, it couldn't compare with what you can see in unorganized baseball.

Like the great drop game, which decided the junior (boys) championship of Montrose, and was pitched by a girl. What was a girl doing in a boys' league? Well, our baseball was not only unorganized, it was disorganized. And there was only one Sissy Wyatt.

That's right. The name is spelled with an "S," not a "C," and maybe that is what got her going. In the Wyatt family there were a lot of boys but only one girl, and as the last of the troupe, she was called "Sister." You know what happens to a name like that. Pretty soon everyone in the neighborhood called her "Sissy," and it seemed that when she grew to understand the name, she went out to prove she wasn't one. Which is all right, but she overdid it.

It got so that we kids of the South Side couldn't have a game of baseball or football or shinny, but that the first thing we knew, Sissy was right in the middle of it. At first her brother Jim, who is my age, used to pick her up and toss her off the field. But you know, after a few years, he couldn't do that.

Sissy grew up fast and tall, with knobby knees and sharp elbows. She had dark red hair which she parted down the middle, combed to the sides, and conquered with two pigtails that stuck out on either side of her freckled face. She looked formidable, and she was.

Sissy was sharp, too, and that made things all the more difficult. She got the local paper route, and had more money to spend than any of us. That's how she got on the ball team. She owned the catcher's mitt, the chest protector, and the baseballs.

In practice, we let Sissy play shortstop. We were short of players anyway. Besides, she was really good, and I admit it. We wouldn't let her play regular games, but she was always right with us, whooping and yelling, which was embarrassing enough. In fact, our opposition called us the Sissies! But when we tried to shush her up, she always threatened to take her catcher's mitt, chest protector, and baseballs, and go home.

To make matters worse, in time she fancied herself to be a pitcher. She bought a book on how to pitch and practiced on some poor dope, and it was weird. She had just one delivery, which she called a fork ball. Somehow her hand was just big enough so she could get her first and second fingers on either side of the ball. That was quite a pitch. The batter never knew where it was going. Neither did Sissy.

We never let her pitch to us, and to that I ascribed the fact that our South Side

297

Scrappers got through the season uninjured, and also unbeaten. We proudly announced that we were the Junior Champs of Montrose, and promptly received a challenge from a team we'd never heard about, the North End Nuggets. They said *they* were the champs, and challenged us to put up or shut up. A showdown was okay with us, just as long as they agreed on a couple of basic rules—nobody over fourteen should be on the team, and all members should come from the immediate neighborhood. The Nuggets crossed their hearts and hoped to die, and so we took them at their word.

Well, not exactly. We went over and scouted their practice, and they were a pretty seedy looking outfit. So we agreed to a seven-inning championship game on their field.

I'm sort of the manager of the Scrappers, and I saw too late that we had been suckered. I'd never seen half the Nuggets that were working out on the field when we arrived. And if some of their boys were only fourteen, they must have been eating an awful lot of Wheaties.

Well, what could we do? We had a good crowd which had paid admission, and we wanted our split of the gate mighty bad in order to buy a chest protector and get rid of Sissy. Besides, the Scrappers never walked out on anything.

I consoled myself that Fats Walker was the best pitcher this side of high school, and we just might pull the game out of the fire at that.

We went to bat and fanned out in order. The boy who was throwing for the Nuggets must have been a brother of Robin Roberts.

Fats rose to the occasion and retired the Nuggets without a score, but not nearly as handily.

That Nuggets' pitcher was mean, too. He dusted off Paul Jass so close he got rattled and struck at two balls and the shadow of a bird crossing the diamond, and our side was down again.

It was a hot day in August and Fats Walker was perspiring profusely as he fogged them in. He was good, too, but I could see he was outdoing himself.

The Nuggets got a scratch hit, executed a nice bunt, got a sacrifice and a single. At the end of the third inning, it was 2 to 0.

In the fourth, Fats began to come unraveled. I kept my eye on Bill Brady, our other pitcher, who was playing in left field. The Nuggets had two on when Fats put one across the corner that was hard to hit. But the batter was one of those overgrown fourteen-year-olds. He got the ball on the end of his bat and lofted it into the outfield. Bill Brady saw it coming, started to run back, changed his calculations on the arc of the ball, and plunged back again, his arms outstretched like an Indian invoking the great spirit. The ball sailed between his outstretched arms and hit Bill square on the noggin. While our outfielder-pitcher measured his length on the grass, the three Nuggets streaked for home. We helped Bill to the bench where he sat, holding his head.

You have no idea of the troubles of a manager. Fats dragged himself up, looking like a limp dishrag. "I'm woofed," he said. "I can hardly reach the plate."

"But we haven't any more pitchers!" I cried.

"Let me pitch!" I winced at that shrill voice. I'd been hearing it from the bench since the game started. "You," I snorted at Sissy. "You've only got one pitch and you can't hit the plate—" I stopped, suddenly thinking of the beanballs we had been suffering, and evil flowered in my heart. "It would serve 'em right," I muttered.

"I have, too," shrilled Sissy. "I've got two pitches. And I've got a secret one, too."

I looked at the boys. I think some of them had caught my idea. Anyway, we had no choice, and never would it be said that the Scrappers forfeited a game.

"All right," I said. "You pitch."

"Girls are against the rules," the Nuggets protested indignantly.

"What rules?" I demanded. I had them there.

They went into a huddle and conceded. Actually I could see they thought it was very funny. It was, and it wasn't.

Sissy started the last of the fifth, with the score 5 to 0 against us. We were going to get beat, anyway. Her first pitch got stuck in the screen about twelve feet above the plate, and I was ready to go home. But on the next one, the batter just topped the ball. It dribbled out to the plate. Sissy fielded it nicely and one was out.

The next batter was the Nuggets' tough pitcher. Sissy stuck out the tip of her tongue and I could tell by that she was going to throw her fork ball again. The ball floated up as big as a barn. You could count every stitch in it. The pitcher took a clout that would have knocked it right through the sound barrier. But just as he swung, the ball fell away. The bat met nothing but air.

The pitcher spun around like a top and went to the ground. When the Nuggets got him untangled, they claimed he had dislocated a vertebrae and fractured his collarbone. That was an exaggeration. But one thing was sure, the bean ball pitcher had sure removed himself from the game.

The Nuggets were so unnerved by this disaster that the third man up fanned ingloriously.

With that hotshot pitcher out of the way, the future looked a little less glum. We Scrappers and our rooters came to life, and we had two on before our next moundsman put one away. The next man—oops, girl—up, was Sissy. The Nuggets' pitcher might have taken a clue from what had happened already, but he had to show his contempt of girls. He tossed up a nice, fat patsy. Sissy teed off like Ben Hogan at his best. The ball was still rising when it disappeared over the fence.

That didn't end the inning, either. The score was tied by the time the Nuggets got three away.

I was feeling pretty complacent when Sissy took to the mound again, but you can never trust a girl. Sissy wound up, then stopped, and rearranged one of her pigtails.

"It's a balk!" yelled the Nuggets.

The umpire agreed. The batter took his base. Sissy threw another great drop. It struck the ground in front of the plate and before the catcher could get it, the runner had advanced to second. Sissy threw another floater. The batter missed it, and so did the catcher. The runner was on third.

"Holy cow!" I screamed at our catcher. "Tell her to try her other pitch!"

Sissy's pigtails were sticking straight out. She rared back and threw the ball up in the air. I thought I'd pass out. But the arc couldn't have been more perfect. The ball dropped down cleanly in the strike zone. The batter just stood there with his mouth open.

We opened the seventh and last inning by breaking the tie. With the score 5 to 6, all we had to do was hang on. But, oh, brother! I mean, oh, sister! The first man hit a looper that creased the second baseman's head.

Then, advancing to the plate, swinging three bats, came one of those overgrown "fourteen-year-olds." He had hit safely every time.

Sissy prepared her very best knuckle ball, but it slipped prematurely from her fingers. The batter grinned and lowered his head to let the overthrow pass. But as the ball neared the plate, it took a drop like the graph of a bad day in a subscription contest and struck with a sodden thump on the head of the guy in the batter's box.

The next man smacked a perfect bounce to third for a force-out, and the next one fanned.

Sissy's eyes brightened. She smiled a smile of triumph. But pride cometh before a fall. She tossed a blooper. Nick had to run out in front of the plate to catch it. She threw another. Nick jumped back to catch it. Sissy tried another but it was a ball. She had lost the range, and the man walked.

Two out, and the bases loaded! A great quiet settled over the diamond. Sissy was trying hard and her drop was breaking more crazily than ever. The batsman decided if

he just waited them out, the odds would be in his favor. He was right. He stood there until the count was three and two. Never since the Stover boys left Yale had the grand old game witnessed such a moment.

"Tell her to throw that dark one!" I yelled. I was instructing the catcher, but you could hear me all over the diamond. Sissy motioned for a conference. She stood with her hands on her waist, talking vehemently, her pigtails bobbing. I could see that Nick didn't believe her. But finally he shrugged resignedly and took his position.

"Please," I muttered, "let it be a double curve!"

Sissy went into an awesome windup, and let loose. It was a nothing ball, straight down the middle, and so fast I don't think Stan Musial could have hit it. Only after the ball whanged into the catcher's mitt did the batter show a slight twitch of reflex movement.

"Why didn't you throw that fast one before!" I chortled, slapping Sissy on the back.

"Oh," she said innocently, "I was saving that for an emergency."

That's the way it is with girls. But we could teach her.

"Next year you can be our starting pitcher," I promised, enthusiastically.

Sissy drew herself up, primly. "I have decided," she announced, "that it's unladylike to play baseball."

Maybe it was for the best. I don't know if we could have stood a whole year of Sissy's pitching. And I'm sure our opponents couldn't.

Tall Bram of Little Pigeon

By MANLY WADE WELLMAN

A rambunctious young man tangles with a stray bull, a local bully, and a mean old man

The boy and man were finishing their half-camp. Real pioneer axmen on the Indiana Trace in the 1820's might have smiled at it —three rickety walls of hogpenned logs, the south side open, the twig-thatched roof slanting and sway-backed. But it was the best the boy and man could do.

"Son," said Wilmore Cutler to fourteen-year-old Nevis, "this stamps us as green-horns in the woods. But you've done a man's work all day yesterday, and most of today." He peered through the trees to where water gleamed. "Rest now—ramble a little, but not far. We don't know our way even around this quarter-section of timber we're claiming on. I'll have some kind of supper at sun-down."

"Tomorrow we'll finish the roof, Pa," said Nevis Cutler. He was not tall for his age, but wiry and square-faced. His one pair of cow-hide brogans was scuffed and worn, even this early on the frontier. He smiled to cheer his father. "And we've got all the rest of autumn to clear land for spring planting."

Stooping above bundles that had been un-loaded from the wagon, he searched out a book he loved to reread. He strolled past the two patient horses tethered to a willow and headed for the creek. His father began to chink spaces between logs.

Nevis had heard the name of the creek—Little Pigeon. To him it looked almost as broad as a river, and it ran swift and deep here. Twenty-odd miles southwest, he re-membered, it ran into the broad Ohio. Near by was the start of a village called Gentry-ville. Through the woods were scattered other homesteads. Perhaps enough neighbors to help him and his father scare away wolves, bears or Indians. The new life might not be bad, if they learned to live it.

Sitting, he looked at the creek. It must have plenty of fish. The two Cutlers must consider every possible food supply to see them through the coming winter. He opened the book. Every time Nevis read it, he liked it better. Then, "Hey," grumbled somebody behind him.

He looked up. It was a boy a year older than himself, and probably twice as heavy. A scowling face, round and doughy as an un-cooked pudding, slanted above him. Close-set eyes gleamed. The fat boy was looking hard for trouble. "What you doin' here?" demanded the grumbling voice.

"My father and I are proving up this claim," said Nevis.

"Ain't got no right here." The scowl deep-ened. "What's your name?"

"Nevis Cutler. I do have a right here."

"You callin' me a liar?" A meaty hand clamped on Nevis' shoulder. The other hand grabbed his book. The fat boy snarled and tossed the volume toward some bushes.

Out of those bushes shot an arm longer and bonier than Nevis thought possible. Its big hand caught the book in mid-air. The owner of the arm strode into view, a towering

301

buckskin figure only a little shorter than the creek-side saplings.

"Turn him loose, Tady," said the tall one, and the fat hand dropped from Nevis' shoulder.

The newcomer was of an age with Nevis. Where the boy called Tady seemed grown all to gross flesh, this one seemed grown all to long tough bone and sinew. His legs in their fringed buckskin were mostly gigantic shins, and the feet in the worn moccasins were immense almost to a deformity. Big, too, was the hand that held the book; big was the protruding Adam's apple on the lean corded neck, and extra big the jutting nose below the black brows.

"What you botherin' around for, Bram?" blustered Tady.

"I don't like fights started by big fellers agin little 'uns," was the deep, quiet reply.

"You fight frequent yourself, Bram," sneered Tady.

" 'Cause fellers rile me up frequent. Remember when you sassed me too loud last July? I flung you down and rubbed your face in some stingin' nettles."

"Awwww!" Tady could find no more to say than that. He turned and trudged away, plainly afraid to look back. The tall boy in buckskin smiled down at Nevis. His smile relieved the ugliness of his face.

"This book," he said, gazing at its cover, *"Gulliver's Travels*. Never heard tell on it. Books ain't as frequent as wildcats here in Indiany. But," he went on with sudden earnestness, "readin's what I'd rather do than anything. My best friend's the feller who gits me a book I ain't read."

He opened the volume and stared at the page, his lips moving almost raptly. "Don't fret about Tady," he said after a moment. "Bad-talkin', but scared of anything more'n half his size. You named yourself to him. Nevis Cutler. Isn't your pa the new schoolmaster who allows to teach in Gentryville?"

"That's right," said Nevis. "We just came."

"From whar?" The tall boy dropped down and sat against a tree, his great knees cocking almost as high as his great nose.

"Pennsylvania. Pa was sick last year, lost his school. My mother died, so when we heard things made to settle fast hereabouts, we came and made our claim. Pa aims to talk about the school tomorrow in Gentryville. I heard Tady call your name—Bram, isn't it?"

Bram came unwillingly from his reading. "I'm glad about a school comin'. I'm too big to go—never had no more'n four months of school all told, but I allow to learn what I can by readin' and figgerin'. Nevis, I'm right sorry your ma died. Mine did, years back. I got a good stepma, though."

And again he was lost in the book, eyes bright and lips stirring. Nevis tried once more.

"You want to read *Gulliver,* Bram? It's a noble book—about a man traveling to foreign parts, with dwarfs one place and giants the next. Got pictures, too."

Bram turned a page with a big finger. "Ho!" he cried, loud as the crow of a rooster. "Look at that picture—big man showin' his watch to the least little feller possible, small 'nough to stand in his hand." He looked up and smiled, this time in apology. "Sorry, but when I get to readin' I fergit all besides." He offered the book, somewhat sadly. "Happen you'll lend me the book later, Nevis? I'll take right good care of it and give it back good as I got it. But now," and he rose, "this ain't what I come for. A pig of ours outstrayed. We fixed to butcher him for bacon, but a penrail got loose—hog got loose, too."

Nevis smiled and Bram smiled back. "Ain't much of a joke, maybe, but somebody might like it. Anyway, if the pig's lost—he was a lively little feller, prime for streaky bacon—my pa won't like it. I'm headin' down creek on his trail."

"I'll help you look," offered Nevis. "You can really see where the pig went?"

"There's his tracks." Bram was striding loose-jointedly away along the bank. To town-reared Nevis the trail was dim, but Bram seemed able to follow it as fast as his feet could lumber. "Look yonder, where he went to the edge of the creek. It shelves off right deep for a fair piece along here. And if he stops to eat acorns in that oak thicket yonder, maybe we kin— Whup!"

Bram had stopped so suddenly that Nevis, trotting behind, almost bumped his nose on the tall boy's sinewy back. "Somebody kind of told my pig howdy," he said, "and my pig never got the chance to say howdy back. Looky, see yonder."

Nevis followed Bram's huge pointing finger. "Blood," he said. "Lots of it."

"A knife in the pig's neck," Bram said. "Then the feller dragged him along. Mark the tracks."

"An—Indian?" ventured Nevis.

"No. White man—and I know who. Only one feller 'round Gentryville parts wears boots with nails like that. Old Rube Demmin. He likes to get sidemeat and such things on the spot. Maybe that's why he has so much of the little specie money hereabouts. Keeps from spendin' it. I fear I've got to say something right unpleasant to him."

Bram was away on the trail, plain even to Nevis for the tramping bootmarks and the dragged carcass. "In some quiet spot he'll hang him up for the blood to drain off. If I don't hurry, he'll have the butcherin' done, maybe half the eatin'."

If Bram had moved fast before, he fairly flew now. Nevis scampered his best, but his best could not keep him close to his new friend. Bram drew ahead, rounded a thicket, and for a moment was out of sight. When Nevis caught up again, Bram had stopped as before. He shot out an arm to stop Nevis beside him.

"Look," said Bram, and Nevis looked.

The two had come to a straggly line of bushes, against which lay a big fallen trunk. Beyond, the trees grew thinly, and from a jutting branch of maple hung the carcass of a pig, smallish and limp. In the tree just beyond was another body, human, alive and very much frightened. It was a middle-aged little man in rough homespun. Every bristle of unkempt hair and grizzled beard stood on end, and his eyes started from the pale face as they looked down to what had sent him climbing the tree.

"Overby's scrub bull," breathed Bram, as if he was trying not to laugh. "Overby's fence must have gone bad along the same time ours did."

Nevis, staring, trembled. What Bram had called a scrub bull seemed to him big and terrible.

"Easy to see what happened," said Bram, smiling quietly. "Rube hung up my pig to bleed off. Bull smelled the blood and came ransackin' over to git mad—bulls do that. Maybe he tried to hook at the pig where it hung. Rube was gone gump enough to yell or throw clods or whack at it—and it turned from the pig and ran him up a tree. He didn't have time to pick a good big 'un, even."

"But he's in danger," Nevis said. "That tree will break, or shake him out. Aren't we going to save him?"

"Certain sure. But I had to think a minute, and the minute's up." Turning, he bent his face toward Nevis, and the face was dead serious now. "Up a tree. That biggest 'un. I'll boost you."

A clutch, a heave, and Bram fairly hurled the smaller boy among the branches. So abrupt was Nevis' ascent that he dropped the *Gulliver* book. A moment later Bram had jumped over the big fallen log, slipped past the bushes, and was moving swiftly but watchfully toward the treed man and the shoving, pawing, raging bull.

By the time Nevis thought to wonder what Bram would do, Bram was doing it. He caught the bull's cocked-up tail in both his big hands, braced one boat-sized moccasin on the bull's hip and threw his tall young strength into a fierce, concerted tug. The bull roared the way Nevis thought lions must roar, and Bram actually laughed, happy and fearless. Then, letting go, Bram whirled and ran. For all the scarecrow legs and big feet Nevis had thought clumsy, Bram could run like a deer. Over his shoulder he whooped, "Hi, bull! Hi, bull!"

The big spotted bulk whirled itself around, broad hoofs splattering the loam and fallen leaves. Down went its murderous head. It bounced after Bram with a deadly intent. Nevis could see the gleam of its eye, and found the wit to ponder that he had always

heard how a bull charged with lids clamped shut. You couldn't believe everything you heard.

Bram had reached another tree. He shot his hands up to the lower branches and swung up as nimbly as a dog-hunted raccoon. A moment later the bull was raging, prodding and pawing beneath him as it had raged, prodded and pawed beneath Rube Demmin. But Bram laughed again, louder than the bull bellowed.

"I picked this tree to suit what I aim to do," he yelled across to Nevis. "This branch—"

The branch jutted straight out for many feet. Bram waited until the bull had paused beneath that very branch, shoving against the trunk as though it were a living enemy. Then Bram scrambled out along the branch until his weight forced its tip down, dropped lightly to the ground, and as before seized the bull's tail for a twist and a tug. Bram supplemented this with a mighty kick at the bull's flank, and the bull turned in that direction.

Again Bram ran, and this time the bull did not need to be taunted into pursuit. It charged after its new and maddening foe. Bram headed for the tree where Nevis perched. Would he climb up? Nevis would welcome company. A chill that was not from the fall atmosphere made him shiver a little.

Bram slid through the sparse bushes, then sprang high as a spry-hopping rabbit to clear the fallen log. Running on, he put himself behind a thick tree. The bull, blundering after him, drove into the log as Bram had foreseen and sprawled over it.

"Hi, bull, git up! Happen you barked your shins bad, old man Overby'll have to put bear's grease to 'em—now, wait! Here I am, over here! Leave that book be!"

Nevis had dropped the *Gulliver* book at the root of the tree into which Bram had boosted him. The bull, falling, had found its nose almost touching that strange little human-smelling object. Rising, the beast lowered its horns, poking and then tossing the book. Its pages fluttered as it flew through the air.

"Don't, Bram, don't!" screamed Nevis from the branches, but Bram had sprung from his shelter. He rushed in, suddenly as fierce and angry as the bull itself. He stooped, caught up the *Gulliver*. For one sickened moment Nevis thought the bull had Bram. Not even the swift long boy could slip aside from that rush.

Bram did not try to slip aside. He did the one thing in all the world he could and should do. Even as the heavy head dipped to whip upward at him, he planted one foot between the horns and hoisted himself like a man climbing stairs. The bull tossed and Bram, doubly impelled by the upheave of the toss and the lift of his own leg, sailed like a leaf in a storm above the bull's back, past its tail, down to earth. He struck on one knee, got up running. The bull was after him. They headed for the creek, lost themselves among the trees. Even as the gay remains of autumn leafage shut them from sight, Nevis stared wretchedly and thought the bull was upon his friend. Then he heard Bram's loud yell, and the splash of something heavy falling into the water.

Silence. Nevis sat in his tree, old Rube Demmin in his. A minute crawled past. Another. There was a rustle of branches. Something came slowly back into view. Bram had the *Gulliver* book open in his big hands. His feet moved heavily and half gropingly, because his eyes were fixed on the print, the pictures. He came to the tree where Nevis perched, set the big angle of an elbow against it. Lounging, he read on, grunting now and then in wonder and delight. Nevis climbed down and stood beside him, knees bobbing and swaying under him.

"Bram," he whispered.

"What's that?" Bram pried himself out of his wonderland of reading. "Well, Nevis, I got back your book. Couldn't let a scrub bull hook it to pieces."

"But the bull—"

"Him? He dogged me right to the bank of the Little Pigeon, where it was steepest and deepest. At the last moment I got time to jump sideways, and he kept goin' on. Did you hear him splash? That's how ten million bullfrogs must sound if they all hit the water at once. The current took him along, and it'll be a quarter-mile, near about, before he can find a low place to climb out. Let's go, because maybe he'll find his way back again."

He handed the book to Nevis, who wedged it into the waistband of his trousers. The two walked to where the bewhiskered Rube Demmin was lowering himself from his tree of refuge.

"Bram," the old man said shakily. "Bram, sakes alive! Ye saved my life, ye did."

"Oh, it wasn't nothin'," said Bram. " 'Scuse me, I didn't mean your life wasn't nothin'. I just mean I ain't had such fun since the Barker barn-raisin'. Next time a bull jumps you up, Mr. Demmin, you'll know how to handle him."

"Ye saved my life, boy," said Rube Demmin again. "To pay ye fer that, Bram, I'll give ye anythin'—anythin'—"

"A—well," said Bram slowly, "since you make that kind of fair offer, Mr. Demmin, will you give me the pig you stuck and hung up to butcher?"

"The pig?" said Rube Demmin, as if he had never heard of such a creature. Bram pointed helpfully, and Rube Demmin's whiskered face turned slowly, gazing to where the carcass dangled. "Oh. That. Why, boy—" He turned back, but he did not look at Bram. "Take it. You're welcome."

"Thank you kindly," said Bram. The old man's homespun-clad figure was walking away, somewhat as Tady had walked off earlier.

Bram chuckled.

"Ain't right to embarrass an old feller like that, Nevis. First off he seen the pig, he knew whose it was. But I'm saved the trouble of stickin' the pig—I don't like killin' things, even turkeys. Now to tote him home."

"The feet are tied together, fore and hind," pointed out Nevis, speaking steadily at last. "Let's get a pole and poke it between the feet. That way you carry one end, and I the other."

"You're right smart, and right kind," replied Bram. "I figger you Cutlers'll be prime neighbors."

The way back was not far. Just beyond the Cutler homestead they came to Bram's cabin. It was well built, its log-ends notched and fitted with canny skill, the cracks well chinked and plastered with clay. The roof was of hand-split shakes, and Nevis judged that there was a loft above—elegance in that land and year. From a little shed at the edge of the clearing beyond approached a sturdy man, who had a smile that was like Bram's smile.

"Yonder comes my pa," said Bram, lowering his end of the pig-laden pole. "I'll make you acquainted with him. He'll want to cut you off a hunk of the pig for helpin' me bring it back."

"That would be kind," replied Nevis. "And, Bram, I want to give you something, seeing how much you like it. You'd even fight a bull to save it, so you can have it."

From his waistband he drew the book about Gulliver and held it out.

"You mean that, Nevis?" Bram snatched the book as though he feared Nevis would change his mind. "Come up to the cabin right now. We've got ink in a jug—a little—and I'll cut us a quill pen. Then you can write in the front that it's my gift from you."

"That's right. From Nevis Cutler to his friend Bram—what's your full name, Bram?"

"Since we're goin' to be friends and neighbors," said the tall boy, "let's not have so much Bram. Folks that don't know me so well, nor like me too much—like Rube Demmin and Tady—shorten my name down to Bram, because I was christened Abraham Lincoln. I'm proud to have you for a friend, Nevis Cutler. Call me Abe, if you like."

"And," replied Nevis, "anybody'd be proud to have you for a friend, Abe Lincoln."

The boys shook hands.

Swimming for Speed

By ROBERT J. H. KIPHUTH

An ex-Olympic swimming team coach tells how to condition yourself out of water

It is a far cry from the primitive two-beat Australian crawl, which once revolutionized speed swimming, to the comparatively smooth six-beat crawl of today. Yet even today it is felt that the surface has only been scratched so far as future aquatic accomplishments are concerned. Each year new records are made in speed swimming.

Just when someone like Weismuller comes along to convince sports writers that the ultimate has been achieved, another star crops up out of nowhere to top the records before the ink dries in the record books.

One instance of this recently is the splashing assault on speed marks by the Japanese team headed by Furuhashi. Swimming fans were astonished by the marks he set in his first appearance in our country. Some calamity criers publicly stated that it marked the end of Western supremacy in the world's record books. And there is no question that Hironoshim Furuhashi is a terrific swimmer, whose exploits shook the swimming world.

Yet, within the same year, here at Yale, freshman John Marshall developed to the point where he beat Furuhashi's new 400-meter record. This showed anew that it is unwise to discount man's ability to improve on any performance of his rivals.

We are no longer living in the era when water athletes thought that the only preparation needed for competitive swimming was a lot of time spent churning up and down the pool. No serious swimmer today would think of omitting a certain amount of pre-water conditioning.

A physical conditioning program conducted out of the water, before the actual swimming begins, is extremely beneficial to swimmers. Exercises which strengthen swimming muscles and make joints more flexible will develop more of the muscular strength which is needed in swimming than can be obtained by an equal amount of time spent in the water. Such out-of-the-water exercises have the further advantage of providing conditioning work for those boys who do not have easy access to a pool. All of the exercises are easy to do and should be conscientiously done for 30 to 40 minutes of hard work at least once a day.

Getting in Shape on Land

I have scores of exercises, with and without equipment, which I give my swimmers. A complete listing of them would be beyond the scope of this article, but the following basic exercises will give you some idea of what a speed swimmer does to condition his muscles and acquire flexibility before the actual water season starts. Try to work the following series of exercises into your daily conditioning program. It will pay off well.

Exercise 1. Sit on the floor with trunk upright, legs spread, hands behind your neck. Bend your trunk forward and downward;

then raise to the original sitting position, keeping your back arched. Repeat 25 times. This is for flexibility, spreading the ribs, flexing the hips, and stretching the long muscles of the back and behind your thighs.

Exercise 2. Sit on the floor with ankles together and hands on the floor back of your hips. Push yourself up to a leaning back rest so that your body forms an incline, supported by your heels and hands. Lower yourself to the sitting position. Repeat this 25 times. This stretches your chest and abdominal muscles while strengthening the muscles of the lower back.

Exercise 3. Lie face down on the floor, with your hands on the back of your neck, and raise your head and chest as high as you can; then return to the starting position. Repeat 20 times to strengthen back muscles and stretch chest muscles.

Build a Strong Back

Exercise 4. Lie face down on the floor with your arms extended overhead, palms down. Lift both ends of your body off the ground simultaneously so that your arms, head, chest, and legs are as high off the floor as you can manage. Now, in smooth rhythmic action, spread your arms and legs out to the sides and bring them together for 30 to 50 counts. Keep your back well arched throughout the drill. This will strengthen the muscles of the entire back, as well as the thighs, arms, and shoulders.

Exercise 5. Sit on the floor with your legs spread and your arms straight out toward the sides of your body. Lifting your feet slightly off the floor, while maintaining your sitting position, swing your arms and legs in a scissoring action across the middle line of your body. Alternate by crossing the right leg and arm over the left, then vice versa. Keep your legs off the ground throughout the drill. This exercise strengthens chest muscles and the retractor muscles of the shoulder blades, the abdominals, and the hip joint flexors, as well as the abductors of the thighs.

Exercise 6. Sit in the familiar over-the-hurdles position with right leg extended.

Grasp the right ankle with your right hand, and the left ankle with your left hand. Now, bend your trunk forward and downward on the inside of the extended leg as far as you can and return to the starting position. Repeat 30 times, then do the same thing with your left leg extended in an over-the-hurdles position. This is a good workout for the hip and knee points as well as the long muscles of the back and thighs.

Exercise 7. Sitting on your heels with ankles flexed, bend your body backward until your head touches the floor, then return to the upright position.

Your arms should support your body in the back bend, with the knees remaining on the floor throughout the exercise. This is a muscle stretcher for the front trunk, hip joints, and ankle joints.

Exercise 8. The bridge exercise is also a good one for strengthening your back and thighs. Lie on your back with legs drawn up so that your heels are close to your buttocks and hands behind your head. Slowly lift your hips and shoulders off the floor as high as possible, creating an arc of the trunk from feet to hands, and return to the lying position. You should repeat this exercise about 30 times.

Exercise 9. Have a buddy hold your ankles as you lie face down with arms extended overhead. Raise your upper body as high as you can. Do it slowly and lower it without jerky movements. Repeat this exercise 20 times.

Now, have your friend hold your shoulders down as your head rests on your forearms. Lift your legs and lower torso as high as you can and lower slowly. Repeat 20 times.

Finally, lie on your side as he sits on your ankles and holds down the thigh of your lower leg. Lift your body up in a side arch as high as you can, repeating this 15 times on each side.

Into the Water

After two months of conditioning exercises on land, the athlete is ready for the pool. The first few days are usually con-

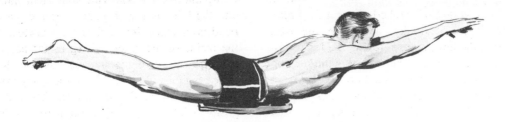

For strengthening the muscles of the entire back, spread the arms and legs apart and return 30 to 50 times.

To strengthen chest muscles and retractors of shoulder blades swing the arms and legs across the midline of the body.

To strengthen chest muscles, abdominals and hip-joint flexors, push up to a back leaning rest 25 times. Also raise legs as high as possible while in sitting position and touch toes 20 to 40 times.

cerned with testing the improvement in physical fitness. Each of the early swimming sessions is opened by a practice breathing drill.

As far as possible, all the air in your lungs should be expelled by forced exhalation through the nose and mouth. Bobbing up and down in the water is a good way to practice breathing. Take a deep breath above water and drop below the surface just enough to cover your head as you force the air out. Practice it until you can bob up and down 50 to 100 times in rhythmic breathing.

After you have mastered this, lie in the water with one hand grasping the gutter of the pool and the other against the wall of the pool, below the gutter, to help keep your body in a horizontal plane approximating that used in swimming. Practice the same breathing exercise, exhaling with face down, and twisting the neck to get your head in the side position for your breath of air. Free-style swimmers should add their up and down kicking action in the ratio of one breath to every six leg beats.

A Fast Racing Start

A good start is important in competitive swimming. When the starter puts you on the mark, get into a crouched position, arms hanging easily. Your feet should take a firm grip on the edge of the starting platform, with the toes curling over the edge. Be sure you have actually gathered yourself for the drive before the starter's gun sounds.

With the pistol shot, push off hard with your legs, swinging your arms forward vigorously to get out as far as possible. Your body should form a straight line from the finger tips to the toes. Anything which might create resistance to the water, such as bent elbows, dropped head, jack-knifed hips, or excessive arch, should be avoided.

Throwing your arms forward vigorously will utilize the advantage of your arm weight to gain momentum in your start.

A correct body position should be maintained until your body is well under water, at which time your legs should start the swimming beat. At the same time, a gradual raising of your head and arms will start your approach to the surface. Just before breaking the surface, your first arm stroke is started so that the pull is completed just as your body breaks the surface of the water.

The stroke should not be started too soon because your diving start saves energy. On the other hand, you should not sacrifice speed by staying under the surface too long. Swimming should start at that point where your speed on the surface equals the speed of your glide. Swim the first few strokes without breathing to help establish a smooth rhythm to your stroke.

The Free-Style Stroke

The body should lie in a perfectly flat position with the head and feet equally high. The water level should be just above the eyes, and the shoulders should be level with the surface of the water. Ideally, there should be no dipping of the shoulders or rolling of the body.

The action of the arm stroke is in four parts: catch, press, pull, and push. As the hand comes forward for the catch, it should be in line with the forearm and the elbow should be higher than the hand and the wrist. The catch is made in a line with the shoulder and as far forward as a high elbow and wrist will permit without exaggerating the lift of the elbow.

On catching, the hand starts a downward and backward press, pulling toward the middle line of the body. The broadest part of the hand and wrist should press, then pull, and at the end push the water at all times. The pull through of the arm from catch to finish should be fairly straight with only a slight inward tendency.

Free-Style Turns

On recovery, the elbow is flexed and the hand is moved outward and inward in a semicircular motion to a position close to the ear. From here it is extended forward to catch the water for the next press, pull, and push.

The leg stroke is an alternate, rhythmic, up-and-down drive of the legs, which pushes water back, resulting in the forward movement of your body. The tempo used by most swimmers today is the six-beat crawl, in which there are six up and down beats of the legs to a full cycle of the right and left arms.

According to the rules of competitive swimming, the swimmer must touch the end of the pool with either or both hands. A good swimmer should be able to turn on either side.

From the very beginning, you must learn to make the turn by whipping around with the head, shoulders, waist, and hips, rather than by pushing the body around off the wall as support. As the leading hand approaches the wall for the touch the head should be swung around, facing the far end of the pool. The shoulders should also swing into this movement, followed by a twist in the waist, throwing the hips toward the wall. During this whip, the knees should be drawn up to a close, tucked position to get your legs set for a drive off the wall with your hips as close to the wall as possible.

During this turning motion the arm, which has pulled through to the thigh while the leading arm has been making the touch, should be rotated outward and then inward with a semi-circular whip under the body. This helps to turn the body and to keep it close to the wall. Both arms are then pushed forward, fully extended overhead with hands together, arms close to the ears, and elbows straight. The legs are extended with all the power you are able to muster to drive your body off the wall in a vigorous push-off.

Keep your abdominal and buttocks muscles tight to help streamline the body during the glide after your push-off. Start your stroke in the same manner as after the racing dive.

Remember to speed up your stroke somewhat on approaching the turn. A great deal of time is lost by indecision in approaching the turn. In sprint swimming, no attempt is made to get a breath during the turn. In middle distance swimming, the swimmer takes a breath while making the turn, since the time element is not as crucial as in sprint swimming. The breath, when taken, is made by lifting the head a little as it turns, or by twisting the head so that the mouth comes to the surface for a breath.

Hints for Competitive Swimmers

1. A good start is a combination of the power in the swing of the arms, the drive of the legs, and the quickness with which the swimmer leaves the mark.

2. Faulty body position often results from distortions during efforts to get a breath. It may sometimes be corrected by swimming 40 to 50 feet without breathing.

3. If your arm stroke is weak, practice swimming with the arms alone, tying the legs with a strap or rubber band.

4. Breathing should be done with a neck twist rather than a shoulder dip. Wait until your forward arm is well into its pull before you inhale.

Og's Dogs

By IRVING CRUMP

In the stone age, a cave boy and two wolf cubs form a strange alliance

Og, son of Og, gave a final twist to the thick vines that bound the logs together and forced the loose ends down between them. Then he sat back on his haunches and looked at his handiwork with evident satisfaction. He had built a raft, something he had never done before.

He had reached far back in his memory for this idea. He remembered that his father Og, son of Fire, had built a raft when he had been a very young boy, before he had been stolen from the cave village by the great apes and kept captive for so many years.

Haunting recollections of his father and how he had built the raft of logs and twisted willow bark and vine had come to Og, dimly at first but stronger as he thought of them with almost painful effort.

Suddenly the cave boy became fired with ambition. He would build a raft so that he could cross this river.

It did not take him long to drag together as many logs as he had fingers of both hands. Standing on these or wading around them, he bound the logs firmly together with vines and tough bark.

It took him all of one day and the best part of another before he finished the craft. But when he made the last piece of vine secure, he was elated. He had made a raft not quite as big but just as sturdy as the one his father and the cave people had made. Young Og became eager to try it.

He found a long pushing pole and climbed on board. Then he shoved off, placing his spear in a handy position lest a crocodile, bolder than the rest, should try to climb on board. It was a slow, clumsy craft, but to young Og it was a source of pride. It gave him a tremendous feeling of accomplishment as he poled the crude craft out upon the muddy water until the current caught it.

Then the cave boy rested from his effort. Standing with the wind blowing back his long hair, he gazed off across the muddy water. The fact that he was master of his own craft —and one he had built himself—gave him a sense of power such as he had experienced only once before. That had been when he had made his first fire.

The river was swollen and dirty. The surface was cluttered with flotsam of all kinds. Young Og let his eyes rove over it as he looked toward the opposite shore. His attention was attracted by something moving on the trunk of a huge, floating tree. He looked closer, and his face wrinkled into a satisfied grin. The flood must have driven two animals to take refuge there. They could be easily captured, and they meant food to the cave boy. Picking up his long pole, he worked the raft across the current to intercept the objects on the floating tree.

At first the cave boy could see only that there were two animals crouched on the big tree trunk. But as he drew closer, he saw with satisfaction that they were half-grown wolves. Young Og could not know that the flood had washed out the den in which they and three other members of their litter had lived. These two had managed to struggle to the temporary safety of a floating log. The others had been drowned.

Young Og did not care where the young wolves came from or how they got on the log. To him they represented just one thing, food. Young wolves weren't as tasty as a big rabbit, but they were something to eat.

As the raft and the slowly floating log began to draw closer, Og picked up his weapon and waited until they were close enough so he could spear first one, then the other, on the flint-tipped shaft. Later he would eat them, either raw or scorched by fire when he got on shore and could kindle one.

But as raft and log approached each other, the watching cave boy noticed with interest that the young wolves did not glare at him and show their teeth in savage snarls as adult wolves would do. Instead, they looked at him eagerly and uttered soft, whining sounds. They were pleading to be rescued from the log they were on. Their tails wagged in friendly fashion, too, suggesting that they trusted the cave boy.

Because of some strange, incomprehensible impulse, Og lowered his weapon and, making a soft, clucking sound to them, held out his hand.

Instantly, the young wolves' ears cocked up, and they began to caper excitedly. The moment the raft was within leaping distance, they bounded aboard Og's craft and began to grovel at his feet, licking his hairy legs as they made friendly sounds.

Og watched them curiously, his brow puckered in thought. Slowly he remembered that his father had once told him that he too had once rescued two wolf cubs from death and that the animals had become his friends. They had lived with him, hunted with him, and fought for him. They had even attacked a hairy mammoth in his defense, and both had lost their lives trying to protect him. His father had called these creatures "dogs," which to a cave man meant that they were creatures who repaid friendship with loyalty.

These young wolves were thankful for their rescue. Their long, pink tongues licking his hands when he extended them told Og this. The soft, whining sounds must mean they were happy to be on the raft with him instead of on that log in peril of being

313

dragged off and devoured by a river monster.

Strangely enough, Og too felt happy that they were on the raft with him. He liked their company, and that was why he did not strangle them and tear them to pieces for food as he had intended when he had first seen them. In his slow way he reasoned he could always do that if he got very hungry.

Picking up the long pole, he began to work the raft toward the distant shore of the swollen river. But as he poled, his mind was working. Maybe he had better kill the young wolves before he reached the far bank, he reflected, because once they could leap from the raft to dry land, they would probably dash off into the forest and get away. Then his meal would be gone.

For a while Og watched them with puckered brow as he worked, guiding the raft with the long pole. Soon the heavy current of midriver gripped the raft and caused it to twist and turn crazily. Presently the cave boy found he had his hands full trying to guide the heavy craft toward shore. He struggled with all his strong body to battle the sullen flood while the young wolves sat watching him, pink tongues lolling, eyes warm with interest.

As they drew closer to the shore, the animals began to show a strange eagerness. They whined more loudly, sometimes yapping in their excitement, and constantly tested the air with uptilted nostrils. The cave boy watched them as he worked with the pushing pole, but he could not understand their actions. The way they tested the air suggested they were more interested in what they smelled than in the fact that they were drawing closer to shore.

Young Og, keen of smell-himself, began to test the soft breeze, too. Then he caught a welcome odor. It was the scent of fresh meat. It was a rich, pleasant smell, and it made him extremely hungry. Someone or something had killed a tapir, one of those four-toed, grass-eating animals. They furnished the most delicious meat to fall to the weapons of the cave men. Og forgot about the young wolves. The shore was close now.

It was very rocky, with cliffs rising in the background. Above the cliffs circled three big black birds. Their presence meant there was something dead in the vicinity.

While he watched them, one after another the vultures spiraled downward. Two came to rest on a boulder. But the third dropped down behind the big rock. Presently the others followed.

Then, as the raft drifted slowly downstream, Og and the young wolves could see that the boulder pinned down the black and white body of a tapir much larger than a three-toed horse. It was probably one of a band of these creatures that had passed that way and had been killed by the rock when it had come crashing down from the cliffs above.

Og grew excited. "Hi-yah!" he cried. "Here is big meat." With all his strength he began to pole his craft shoreward, forgetting the young wolves that jumped about the raft and yapped eagerly.

Before Og could get the raft close enough to have it ground itself and stay still, it drifted past the point where the tapir's body was pinned down by the boulder. But even as it scraped on the stony bottom, the young wolves leaped excitedly into the shallow water and scrambled up the rocky beach. Then they bolted as fast as they could run toward the fresh meat.

Young Og was not far behind them. As soon as the raft was firmly grounded, he grabbed his spear and leaped into the shallow water, too. He soon was running up the stony beach toward the feast that awaited him.

As the young wolves had scattered off the vultures, Og with clouts of his big hand drove the cubs away, too. Then, yanking his flint knife, he began to hack chunks off the carcass, which he ate with loud, smacking sounds.

When they saw that the cave boy was too busy to pay attention to them, the young wolves sneaked back and, out of Og's reach, began to tear at the tapir too. Meanwhile, the croaking vultures, joined by others, sat on the rocks and watched them hungrily, but did not dare venture down to join the feast.

For a time the cave boy and the young wolves ate voraciously. Soon, his appetite blunted, though not completely satisfied, Og sat back on his haunches and licked his dripping fingers. The meat had been good, but he could not help thinking that it would have been so much better if he had a fire to cook it over. He thought of making one. His eyes began to search the shore for handy driftwood.

He found himself looking in the direction of the young wolves. For a moment he watched them tearing at the tough rump of the tapir. With a grin he hacked off a piece of tender meat and tossed it to the nearer of the two. Pouncing on it, the wolf gobbled it down gluttonously. Og cut off another piece to toss to the other wolf. But his head jerked up quickly as a sinister, blood-chilling sound came down the wind. It was the horrible, laughing cry of a giant hyena.

The cave boy shot a quick glance at the two young wolves. They stopped eating. With ears cocked, they nosed upwind, as growls rumbled in their throats and their backs bristled. That hideous cry meant hunting hyenas were on the prowl—and close at hand, too. Og guessed that they scented the blood of the tapir also and were coming down the river shore expecting a feast.

Of all the animals the cave people feared, these were the most dreaded. They were savage, slinking creatures and arrant cowards. They rarely attacked in the open like a cave tiger, but they would slip into a cave at night to attack the sleeping people. But sometimes, if they were really hungry, they were known to hunt in the daytime.

Og gripped his spear and stood up while the young wolves came around the carcass of the tapir and, growling defiantly, stood beside the cave boy. They plainly showed they meant to fight by Og's side. That warmed his heart and gave him courage.

Suddenly they saw the hyenas, a pair of ugly, hunchbacked creatures, slinking among the boulders. Their appearance chilled Og's blood. For a moment he wanted to retreat, to break and run back to the river and the raft, his only refuge. But the young wolves displayed more courage than Og felt, for when they saw the repulsive animals, their backs bristled and their eyes glared as they made short, charging rushes toward the marauders. They bared their teeth and howled their anger, indicating plainly they meant to fight for the meat they had found.

Og was loath to show any lack of courage in the face of their bravery and, moving forward with the young wolves, he began to shout and brandish his spear. However, these hyenas were not as cowardly as most of their kind, and they were very hungry. Og's threatening attitude, his shouts, and the charges of the young wolves did not frighten them. They slowed up a little and became more cautious. But they came on. The cave boy knew that he and the young wolves might be in for a savage fight to the finish.

He shouted louder and, reaching down, grabbed a round throwing stone in his strong right hand. Then, as the hyenas seemed on the point of charging, he suddenly whipped the missile with telling accuracy at the female of the pair.

Too late she saw the whistling stone hurtling toward her. She tried to leap aside, but the round rock hit her solidly on the left foreleg. It knocked her down, and for a mo-

ment she struggled among the boulders, howling with pain. Slowly she staggered to her feet and went hobbling off, her leg dangling helplessly.

The howls of pain and the retreat of his mate caused the male hyena to stop in his tracks, uncertain for a moment whether to follow her. As he hesitated, the young wolves saw an opportunity and took advantage of it. Like two hairy thunderbolts, they rushed in and leaped for the hyena's throat.

Howling with pain, the hyena tried to shake them off. But so savage was the young wolves' attack that the bigger beast lost his footing and went down struggling among the rocks. As he tried to fight his way back to his feet again and get free of the savage young animals swarming over him, Og saw his opportunity and finished the battle with a blow of his stone axe.

The hyena's body collapsed and sprawled twitching among the rocks. For a few moments the young wolves continued to swarm over it, snapping and snarling savagely, but Og drove them back with shouts and hard cuffs. When they finally sat back and looked at him curiously, the cave boy grinned happily.

"Hi-yah! This is good," he gloated. "I have found two dogs, and together we have killed a great hyena. I have something to show my father and tell the cave people when I get back to my village. I have two new friends."

Flight of the Jungle Bird

By HUGH B. CAVE

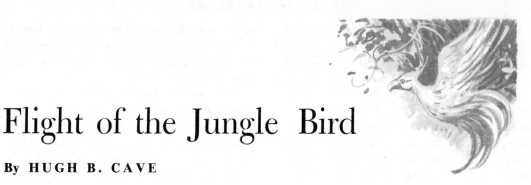

The bird couldn't fly, his buddy couldn't walk, but Johnny wasn't ready to throw in the towel

Johnny Bannon awoke at four in the morning with every nerve tingling. The house was quiet. The sound which had disturbed him, if any had, was not repeated. No breeze jostled the palms. The frogs weren't talking.

The frogs. They should be talking. In the islands of the West Indies, the frogs always talked unless something frightened them. Johnny slid from his bed and glided to the door, past the painting propped against the wall.

He had left the sitting-room windows open, for a breeze. Now a dark shape crouched on one of the sills, about to drop into the room. Johnny went for him in a silent rush.

The man leaped backward out of the aperture, his bare feet beating a frantic patter on the wooden veranda as he fled. Johnny shot the bolts on the heavy front door and raced after him.

It was no use. That house with its acre of overgrown garden was made to order for a thief. At the end of the garden path, Johnny gave up and turned back. He went straight to the telephone.

Armand Duval was evidently a light sleeper. His anxious voice responded almost at once.

"Mr. Duval," Johnny said, "I've just scared a thief out of my place. He was after the picture, I'm sure."

Seconds of silence were followed by a weary sigh. "Then our plan didn't work, Johnny. They know what we're up to."

"I guess they do. What now? Shall I try to reach Jacmel just the same?"

More silence. Then: "You will be followed if you leave the house alone. I will send someone. Meanwhile, remove the painting from the frame and discover some way to carry it under your clothing. And hide the frame, so they will not know what you have done if they search the house."

Johnny closed the shutters at the windows and removed the canvas from its heavy gilt frame. It was too large to be worn under his shirt. Breaking the handle off a kitchen broom, he rolled the painting around that and strapped it to his leg with adhesive tape. When he tugged his trousers on over it, he could not bend his knee, but he could walk.

He hid the frame and then sat down to wait, wondering what was going to happen.

Johnny had first seen the painting when he had arrived in Port-au-Prince, the capital of Haiti, two weeks before, and gone to the artist's home to pay his respects. It hung then in Duval's modest sitting-room. Duval, a frail, diminutive Frenchman wasted by illness, warmly gripped Johnny's hand. He was not old, but long sickness had turned his hair white.

"My son has written me about you, M'sieu Bannon."

317

Johnny had met Guy Duval at art school in Boston. It was because of Guy that he had chosen to study in Haiti when awarded a scholarship. Armand Duval was to be his tutor.

"My house is yours, Johnny," the white-haired man said simply. But it was a small house, and Johnny went to a hotel, feeling he'd be in the way. A week later he rented a small furnished place of his own.

He worked with Duval daily thereafter. Sometimes Pierre Duval, Guy's younger brother, would be there—an alert, dark-eyed boy of sixteen who respected his father's great talent but refused to touch a paint-brush himself.

"When I am through school," Pierre said, grinning, "I'm going to be a pilot. You will see. Jets!"

"Just remember that my car is not a plane," his father scolded, "and don't drive it so fast through the streets of Port-au-Prince!"

One day Armand Duval said matter-of-factly, "When Guy returns to Haiti, Johnny, there is something you must do for me. Has he ever told you of the fortune my father left when he fled from his political enemies here years ago?"

"He said you had a map."

"A map of the cave where the treasure is hidden. My father drew it in Cuba, just before he died. He dared not send it to me, of course. He sent it to a brother in France, and it came into my hands only a short while ago. When Guy returns, you and he must go into the mountains and find this treasure."

Johnny said he would do anything he could to help, and had heard no more of the map until the night before. About eleven o'clock Armand Duval had phoned him, begging him to come over at once.

A hurricane had swept Duval's sitting-room. "I have had visitors," the white-haired man said grimly. "Please sit down, Johnny."

Johnny sat.

"There was something I did not tell you when we discussed the map," Duval said. "When it was sent to me from France, I made one grave mistake. I told a friend about it. At least, I thought of André Mion as a friend, but a week ago he stood in this room and told me I must surrender the map for the good of Haiti."

"Surrender it!" Johnny gasped.

"In this country there are sometimes malcontents who would overthrow the government. Since I told André Mion about the map, he has become an enemy of the state and wants my father's treasure to finance a revolution. When I declared myself a supporter of our excellent president, he flew into a rage."

Johnny looked about the devastated room. "They tried to *steal* the map?"

"This evening, when I was out. But they were not successful. It is still here, behind you."

Johnny turned in his chair. The only thing behind him was Armand Duval's famous painting, *Jungle Bird,* hanging on the wall. It was a remarkable painting. To stand before it was to be drawn inexorably into the green depths of its mysterious jungle, then startled by the baleful red eye of the small white bird lurking there. But what did the painting have to do with the map?

"The original map was old and worn," Duval explained. "Soon after I received it, I copied it on the back of the *Jungle Bird,* for safekeeping, and destroyed the paper. They looked in all the wrong places. But the next time it'll be—"

"You think they'll try again?"

"I'm sure they will. And that is why I called you, Johnny. You must take the picture to my sister in Jacmel, a little town on the other side of the mountains. They will never suspect her of having it; she is very old. Will you do this for me? Will you go to Jacmel in the morning?"

"You know I will," Johnny replied.

Duval lifted the picture down from the wall. "Your car is outside? Be careful, Johnny. Believe me, André Mion and his friends are determined men. They will stop at nothing!"

About an hour after daybreak a car swung into Johnny's driveway and Johnny stepped out on the veranda. The car was one he had never seen before, but Pierre Duval, Armand Duval's dark-haired son, leaned from the wheel and waved.

"Hi!" he called. "I'm going up to Kenscoff for some mountain strawberries, Johnny! Come with me for the ride."

Johnny hesitated only a moment, then locked the door and limped down the steps.

"You have the painting?" Pierre whispered as he got into the car.

"This isn't a wooden leg."

"We have to be careful. They are watching us."

"Won't they follow us?"

"I think not. I am considered too young to know my father's business, and, besides, you obviously were not expecting me. The car belongs to a friend."

Cramped for space with his stiff leg extended, Johnny sat sideways and watched Pierre as he drove. The lad was an expert driver. On that rutted road, twisting through rank tropical growth, he proved it a moment later when his hands suddenly stiffened on the wheel.

Just ahead, where the ruts joined the paved highway, an army sedan was parked at the road's edge. A man in khaki stepped into the road and spread his arms.

"Hang on!" Pierre warned. The car leaped as though shot from a catapult.

The uniformed man reached for the revolver at his hip but had no time. His frantic leap barely carried him from the car's path. He fired twice, missed twice, as the car swung left on whining tires.

When they were straightened out again, Johnny let go his grip on the door and looked at Pierre. The boy's lips were flat against his teeth.

"Are you good at walking, Johnny?"

"I've done some in my day. Why?"

"Because as soon as that man can reach a telephone, every road will be blocked."

Five miles farther on, Pierre turned off the road into a field of sugar cane. The cane was taller than the car.

"You can't walk with that thing fastened to your leg," he said. "We'll have to carry it."

Johnny removed the painting. They fought their way through the cane to a river trail leading into the mountains.

It was easy at first. Country women gossiped along the stream. *Marchandes* trudged down to the capital with head-loads of produce for the city markets. The sun was warm, the scene so peaceful that any fear of pursuit seemed fantastic.

But soon the mountains towered black before them, and the trail became vertical. Rocks bit through Johnny's soft-soled shoes. The rolled-up painting on his shoulder seemed heavy as a rifle.

Pierre would not rest. Hour after hour he trudged on.

"They know these hills as well as I do, and they'll easily find the car," he said. "They won't stop until they have found us, Johnny."

When night fell they were deep in the mountains, on a path that climbed through a boulder-strewn cornfield. At sight of a light glowing among the trees, Pierre halted.

"It is all right. These are the family of Francine, our cook."

The house stood alone in a small clearing; a mud-and-wattle hut with a roof of thatch. Johnny was introduced to the man and woman who appeared in the lamplit doorway.

"This is Papa Alcinde, Johnny. And Mama." He shook hands and found himself inside, struggling in vain to make sense of the rapid-fire French in which Pierre and the two old people conversed.

At last Pierre turned to him. "I had hoped we could spend the night here, Johnny. We can't."

"Why not?"

"Francine was here just a short while ago. The word has spread quickly. Everyone knows we are being hunted."

Johnny frowned at him, unbelieving.

"In Haiti," Pierre explained, "the country people walk, walk, all the time. One tells another." He frowned. "But the people have not been told the real reason for our flight."

"What have they been told?"

"That you are a dangerous thief who has stolen a valuable art treasure. That you seized me when I tried to stop you. That you tried to kill Captain Massine when *he* tried to halt you."

Johnny knew his face was white as he sat down. "Is that all?"

"We must travel by night and hide by day."

Mama Alcinde brought rice and beans, and Johnny ate in silence, wondering what Guy Duval would think if he suddenly arrived in Haiti, as he might do at any moment. But of course Guy wouldn't believe the lies; his father would set him straight.

Scowling, Johnny watched Mama Alcinde fill a basket with cassava bread and mangoes. When Pierre and he stepped outside, the yard was black as pitch.

"God go with you," the old lady called softly from the doorway.

By midnight Johnny was certain they had walked a week, if it could be called walking. Most of the time they clawed their way through thornbush thickets and forests of wiry underbrush, or clambered over limestone crags that crumbled under them.

His hands bled. The sole of one shoe was gone. He ached all over and was so cold his teeth chattered. But they were making time, putting the miles behind. When the moon appeared, a black mass of mountains towered close on their right and Pierre, halting, said, "That is Morne Rouge. We are halfway there."

Ten minutes later, the dark-haired younger son of Armand Duval lay moaning in a mound of rubble, with Johnny on his knees beside him and the roar of a rockslide still loud in the night. Halfway up a difficult ascent, Pierre had trusted his weight on a ledge that looked solid but wasn't.

"Lift me up, Johnny."

Johnny lifted him as gently as possible, but at the first tentative step the boy moaned again and would have fallen. Seated on the ground, he looked up at Johnny and shook his head. "I've hurt my knee."

Johnny rolled up the denim pants leg and examined the injury. A razor-sharp stone had laid open the side of the leg, bone deep. The pain made Pierre wince.

"Will the peasants help us?" Johnny asked. "You've got to be carried back to the city!"

Pierre caught at his arm to stop him. "The peasants won't open their doors to a stranger at night. I can walk, Johnny. We'll find a place where I can rest a little. Look." Clinging to Johnny's hands, he drew himself up. "It doesn't hurt much."

His drawn face gave the lie to what he said, but Johnny picked up the painting and basket and got an arm around the boy's waist. Maybe Pierre was right. Perhaps he ought to rest until daylight, anyway. They walked a little way, and when the boy stumbled, Johnny lifted him in his arms. Half an hour later, after innumerable halts, Johnny found a hole in the side of the mountain and carried him in.

The cave was small, but it would do. He made a bed of leaves and laid Pierre on it, bandaged the leg as best he could with a clean handkerchief that had escaped his notice in his back pocket. When he bent to look again at the leg a little later, the boy was asleep.

They washed breakfast down with sips of water from a calabash Mama Alcinde had wisely placed in the basket. The hurt leg was good as new again, Pierre insisted. But he walked stiffly and stopped to rest often throughout the morning.

They were deep in the mountains now. Using a stick to scratch a rude map on the ground, Pierre showed Johnny exactly where. "With luck, we'll be in Jacmel tomorrow."

They were not lucky. The afternoon was only half gone when Johnny saw the first of the watchers. The man appeared on a high perch of rock for an instant, then abruptly halted.

Pierre, on ahead, anxiously halted. "What is it, Johnny?"

"A man in uniform, watching us."

"You must be mistaken. It was probably some peasant."

But Johnny knew better, and half an hour later he saw the man again. Or was it another man?

This time he didn't stop but plodded on to a stream.

A better place for ambush than the stream crossing would have been hard to find. Pierre struggled to keep his balance among the river-bed boulders. Johnny waded knee-deep in the swift flow on his downstream side, to catch him if he stumbled. The jungle suddenly parted. Two men appeared on each bank of the river.

Pierre halted. There was nothing they could do.

"Keep going," Johnny advised. "Don't let them know you're scared."

"The painting, m'sieu." Surprisingly the thin, youthful spokesman for the quartet spoke English. "Give it to me."

"I haven't got it," Johnny said.

Handing his rifle to a companion, the fellow stepped forward. Had there been a scrap of paper one tenth the size of the painting concealed under Johnny's clothing, his hands would have discovered it. He gave Pierre the same thorough treatment and folded his arms.

"You had it ten minutes ago. What have you done with it?"

"Go jump in the river."

Johnny expected at least a slapped face, but the other only shrugged. Two of his companions splashed across the stream and plunged into the bush.

"Come with me, please." The spokesman gestured with a graceful hand. "Captain Massine will wish to speak to you."

The camp was no temporary affair. An entire community of peasant huts in a mountain clearing had been commandeered for it. A score of men lounged about cook-fires in the compound.

Through a front room crowded with cots, Johnny and Pierre were pushed into the windowless rear bedroom of a central hut. The connecting door creaked shut. Pierre, white with exhaustion, sank onto the single rude bed.

"The map, Johnny. You had it before we reached the river."

"And I don't have it now. That's enough for you to know." Johnny scowled at the door. "Evidently Massine isn't here yet. Would they listen to a bribe?"

"I think not."

"Then it's the painting."

"To buy our freedom? No, Johnny. Massine would never keep his word. The alternative is too easy. Remember, we fled into the mountains—no one knows where. People disappear in these wild mountains."

"You'd better get some rest," Johnny said glumly.

Massine's men had taken his watch; he could only guess the time as the hours passed. Pierre moaned in his sleep. Johnny sat on the floor with his back against the mud wall. The hut was still dark when he heard hoofbeats in the clearing and a sudden flurry of voices in the outer room.

He lay back and closed his eyes. A moment later a muddy boot dug at his ribs. "Get up!"

With a glance at Pierre, Johnny obeyed. The commotion had aroused the boy on the bed. He lay propped on one elbow.

"We will not waste time." Massine's voice was like his face, heavy and coarse. "You know what I want. Where is it?"

"Take us back to Port-au-Prince and you can have it."

Massine's hand was huge, and his slap was like a mule-kick. Johnny staggered against the wall. Pierre's gasp was smothered by the big man's angry roar. *"Where is it?"*

"You and I should have met in some nice quiet place, with no one around," Johnny said grimly. Then he looked at Pierre. It had been a long night and he had done a lot of thinking. Once, leaning over the boy in the dark, he had anxiously laid a hand on the injured leg and felt the hard swelling under the bandage.

"I'll bargain with you, Massine. Take Pierre Duval to the hospital in Jacmel, bring back a note in his handwriting to prove he is there, and you'll get your picture."

Massine curled his lip. "I will get it without so much trouble."

"It will take much longer."

Stepping to the bed, Massine stared with sadistic satisfaction at the swollen leg. *"When* you have given me the map, you may escort the boy to the hospital yourself," he said. "Until then he stays here." With a shrug he turned away. The door closed behind him.

Groping to the bed, Johnny caught Pierre's hand. "What shall I do?"

"If you give him the map, Johnny, he will kill us both."

"But you can't be sure—"

"I know him. I am sure."

Johnny returned to the wall and sat down. Daylight came. He looked at Pierre again. The boy's eyes were shut, his hands clenched.

Johnny bent over him and laid a hand on his forehead, then opened the door and stood for a moment gazing at the men in the room beyond.

"All right. Take me to Massine."

Massine was hard to convince. "Beside the trail?" he retorted. "I think you lie! My men have searched that trail a dozen times!"

"They were looking for a roll of canvas," Johnny replied wearily. "I unrolled it and propped it upright in a bush. Armand Duval knew his jungle colors. His leaves and vines look like the real thing."

Massine sent two men to get the painting and Johnny sat to await the outcome of the gamble. The camp was awake now. A smell of food filled the clearing. But he was not hungry, only cold and scared. What would Massine do?

The two men returned with the picture. Massine drew his pistol. "Now, m'sieu, you may go."

"Go where?" Johnny said, rising.

"Why, anywhere. You run well, I trust. I like a moving target."

Johnny looked at the man's ugly leer and tried to think. His mind wouldn't work. Scared? He had never been more scared in his life. But he would not run. He would not give Massine that much satisfaction.

From the edge of the clearing came sounds of a sudden commotion, and Massine stepped back to look in that direction.

It was hard to know what had happened. Apparently a man had burst into camp from the jungle, and some of Massine's followers had leaped up from a cook-fire to intercept him. He flung them aside and stood revealed, a husky young fellow with his hair in his eyes, angry mouth spitting a string of French yells.

Johnny's own mouth came open. "Guy! Guy Duval!" he gasped.

"Where is he?" Guy bellowed. They could have halted him—his flailing hands were

empty—but the fury and audacity of his advance seemed to awe them. "Where is the man who kidnaped my brother? Let me get my hands on him!"

Massine, with a grin of enlightenment, stepped toward him. "This way, M'sieu Duval," he called. "He is waiting for you!"

Johnny had no time to defend himself. Guy Duval came at him in a rush, and the rush bore him backward. In vain he struggled to break loose as the assault carried him away from Massine and the watching men.

Suddenly through the barrage of angry French, Guy's normal voice got through to him in English. "Where is Pierre, Johnny? Quick! Tell me!"

"Behind me," Johnny gasped. "In the hut with the closed door."

With what appeared to be a murderous blow to the face but actually was only a thrusting arm against his chest, Guy sent him stumbling toward the hut and followed with another furious rush. With the door at his back, Johnny felt something hard pressing against his hand and heard Guy's voice saying sharply, "Take care of him!" Then a gun leaped into Guy's hand, too, and Guy dropped to one knee and began shooting.

It was a signal. While Massine's men were in a state of shock, the jungle on all sides erupted men and gunfire. Massine himself staggered but stayed on his feet. Johnny saw men pouring from the bush, leaping the cook-fires, shooting as they came. Behind him the door of the prison hut flew open.

Johnny lurched about. Two men, left to guard the prisoner, stood in the doorway. Johnny's sudden charge took them by surprise and bowled them over.

He burst between them into the hut and slammed the door shut, ran into the rear room and found Pierre seated on the bed, struggling to rise. Johnny eased him to the floor.

"Keep down!" he warned. "Guy is here with a rescue party." Then he ran out. Massine's men would not be interested in Pierre just then.

Almost at once he saw the thing he wanted. Massine had clung to it in spite of everything, and was trying to get away with it. Johnny sped toward him and brought him to earth with a flying tackle.

A shot rang out. Massine, with a groan, collapsed on top of the painting he had tried to escape with. It was the last shot fired.

As Johnny bent to pick up the roll of canvas, the clearing was quiet. With Guy Duval at his side, he turned back to the prison hut.

They stood, the two of them, on the balcony of the little Jacmel hotel, together again as they had been so often in America. Next day they were going into the mountains with the map. Pierre, now in the hospital, would be ready for discharge when they got back, and the three of them would return to Port-au-Prince together, with the treasure.

"When dad told me what had happened, I asked myself why the revolutionists suddenly needed money so desperately," Guy said. "There seemed to be only one answer. They were expecting arms and ammunition, probably by ship, and needed a large amount of cash for payment. So I went hunting with an army pilot and we found the ship hiding in Barradères Bay, and then we went straight to the palace with our information. We took them the next day."

Johnny glanced at him with a head-shake of admiration.

"At Barradères I learned where Massine was," Guy went on, "then flew to Jacmel with some loyal army men and headed for the mountain hideout, to make him tell me where you were. Peasants said you were prisoners in the camp. But we couldn't attack without knowing what hut you were in. Bullets are too impersonal."

"For a minute," Johnny said, "I thought you really had it in for me."

"Because of the lies Massine spread?" Guy's grin was enormous. "You think I would believe such lies even for a minute? As we say in America, *mon ami*—are you kidding?"

A Shamrock for O'Toole

By S. K. HINGLEY

The cranky little leprechaun traded Ted a valuable secret for a trip to the old sod in Kilkenny

His name is O'Toole; he is twenty-two inches from the bottom of his heel to the top of his bald head, and his disposition is cheerful until he is crossed, when it is likely to be as fiery as his whiskers. Some say he isn't real, but Mike Gallagher talked with him and Ted Carmichael saw him and talked to him.

It all goes back to a hot day last August, a day that had been filled with problems. Some of them concerned T. Carmichael, Sr., who sat on the shady farmhouse porch with his leg in a white cast. One of them concerned Ted junior, recently graduated from Honeybrook High School.

Ted, at the moment, was curled up in the crotch of a cherry tree in the back orchard trying to think out a solution to his troubles. White clouds drifted against the blue sky, drowsy birds chirped in the top limbs, honey bees droned between the hives and the meadow, and Shep's bark sounded clear over the barnyard chatter.

A fellow could not think with all this going on about him. Slipping down from his perch, Ted climbed the steep slope from the west meadow, up among the cedars on the shoulder of old Welsh Mountain. Parting the underbrush around the entrance, he entered a cool, quiet cave. It had once been a small mine where the colonial settlers had obtained some necessary lead ore.

Walking deep into the slope, guiding himself with a candle he had hidden at the entrance, he found a ledge where he placed the light and then settled himself on the floor of the cave with his back against the rock wall. There he sank deep into thought.

But not for long.

"Have ye seen a bit of shamrock about?" It was a tiny voice and seemed to come from the candle ledge.

Ted stretched his long legs and tilted his curly head back to observe the source of the interruption. A little man, no higher than Shep's back, sat on the ledge beside the candle, a peaked cap cocked jauntily over a rugged face.

"And who might you be?" Ted demanded.

"O'Toole!" the leprechaun snapped, "and don't be answerin' a question with a question."

"I beg your pardon, sir," Ted apologized. "I'm sorry, I have not seen any shamrock around here."

" 'Tis a shame but thank you, anyway," the little man said. "Now, then, me lad, you be keeping your eyes open, and fetch it to me if ye find one."

"But," Ted questioned, "why do you want a shamrock and what are you doing in my cave?"

"*Your* cave!" O'Toole snorted. "Your cave indeed! I'll have ye know I have lived here since your great, great, great grandfather settled this farm. This is my cave."

"But that was way back in Revolutionary days," Ted argued.

"Aye." O'Toole swung his tiny legs over the ledge. "So 'twas."

"Where did you come from before that?" Ted asked.

"Where I'll be going for a visit just as soon as I find me a shamrock to carry me there."

"And where might that be?" Ted asked.

"Ballyragger in Kilkenny."

"Never heard of it."

" 'Tis in Ireland, ye numbskull," O'Toole jeered. "The schoolin' ye have had is insufficient, inefficient and derogatory to the glory that is Erin's pride. Be still now and I'll be educating ye. There were Irish among them as fought with Washington and one av them was Patsy O'Brien from Kilkenny. I know, for I came across with him, tangled up in the roots of a bit of shamrock where I had settled for a nap when he tore it from the ground and stowed it in his knapsack to carry a bit o' the old soil to the new land. They buried him at Valley Forge. But we had worked together right in this mine."

"Are you a miner?" Ted asked, wondering at the same time why it did not seem a bit strange to be sitting in the cave conversing with an elf.

"That's me trade." O'Toole reached behind him and tossed a bit of rock down to Ted. "Do you know what that is?"

"Sure," said Ted, glancing at the specimen. "That is galena. I have some in my rock collection."

"Well, what d'ye know," O'Toole gibed. "The lad kens a bit of rock and now he is a collector. Ye know, sonny, we used to have tons of that stuff around here. It made a big stink when we roasted it in the ovens but it made silvery lead for the bullet mold."

The elf settled himself crosslegged on the ledge and peered thoughtfully at the lad.

"Now then, sonny," he said, "what has been troubling you since you came here? You have something on your mind."

"How do you know that?" Ted asked.

"By the rings," came the cryptic answer.

"The rings?" Ted was puzzled. "But I don't have any rings on."

"Not on your fingers, stupid," O'Toole snorted, whirling his thumbs rapidly around each pointed ear. "They come out of your head. Whenever you mortals work your brains overtime, there are colored rings all around your heads. Sometimes I can almost tell what you are thinking. I remember when I used to collect gold nuggets and hide them in the streams and wait for someone to find them. The rings were bright green until they got to fighting and then they were red."

"Gold nuggets!" Ted gasped. "Around here! How do you find them?"

"Green rings! Green rings!" O'Toole shouted, dancing about on the rocky shelf. "They are all around your head right now. You want gold!"

"Well," Ted admitted, "I suppose I would like to have some gold, but I don't want it just for myself! I want it for my father also. He had to borrow a lot of money when he broke his leg, and we have to pay that back and make some more before I can go to college."

my clothes every time I go down it. This one ends up on a ledge of cobalt. Here's a chunk for your collection."

He tossed the piece of mineral toward Ted who caught it and examined it with interest.

"Thank you," he said. "I don't have any of that."

"There are tons and tons of it down there," O'Toole explained. "Fellow named Stiegel from over Manheim way used to sort it out of our ore dump. They said he mixed it with glass to make blue pitchers. Haven't seen him in years."

Ted rose slowly to his feet, carefully placing the cobalt specimen in his pocket.

"I'm sorry. I must be getting back to the house. My mother will be serving dinner shortly, and she will worry if I am not there. Will you have dinner with us?"

O'Toole chuckled, then made a quaint, old-fashioned bow.

"Thank ye, kindly," he said. "But for one thing, I'd niver enjoy the things ye ate, me stomach bein' thot delicate, and for another, yer folks would niver be knowing I was there. 'Tis only the young who have the wisdom to see and believe. Away with ye now, and don't forget to be looking for me shamrock. I'd like to be taking a trip home to visit me auld mither."

Once out in the broad daylight, Ted began to doubt the evidence of his eyes and ears. If it had not been for the specimen of rock, he would not have been entirely sure that it had not been a dream. One thing however was certain in his mind. There would be no use trying to explain O'Toole to the folks outside.

Old Hans Saurman was seated at the table when Ted entered the farmhouse. He greeted the visitor with a nod and took his place at the table facing him. Hans was a neighbor over Morgantown way and owned a number of farms in the neighborhood. He was not a popular man in the community. Stout, flabby features, with piggish eyes gleaming above a scraggly black beard, he devoted the major portion of his time to the accumulation of wealth. There were those who said he was not too particular how he got it, but there

"Hmmm." O'Toole sat with his pointed chin in his hand and thought deeply. "There's no gold here. There isn't enough lead left to make a dozen bullets. There is plenty of iron, but it is over on the other side of the mountain."

"But, how do you know all that?" Ted asked. "How can you tell what is inside the mountain?"

"I live there, numbskull," O'Toole snapped. "Why shouldn't I know what's in me own house?"

Ted thought that one over carefully. He was a queer one, this O'Toole, but people just didn't live in the middle of the earth.

"Your rings are wiggling." O'Toole shook a finger at the lad accusingly. "You don't believe me. Watch, now!"

The little leprechaun rose to his feet, placed a slender hand in a crevice of the rock, and slithered out of sight. In a few moments his head emerged and he was standing on the ledge brushing off his coat.

"That vein of mica leaves specks all over

was no one who had actually pinned him down in a crooked deal.

It could not be said that either Theodore Carmichael or Annie, his wife, was fond of the wily gentleman, but all who passed their gate when the farm bell tolled were entitled to take the empty place which was always set at their table for an unexpected guest. Hans Saurman was no exception.

Hans dug into the food with gusto. After he had satisfied the first ravenous pangs of hunger, he ceased shoveling and attempted to converse with his mouth full.

"Nu then, Carmichael," he paused to shift the cud from left to right cheek, "you're in drouble right now, and I'm gonna help you out. The farm ain't vurt much, but I'll give you five thousand cash money. That will keep you going until the leg mends and give you a start."

"Thank you, Hans," Mr. Carmichael smiled gently. "We can discuss that later. We make it a practice here never to bring business to the table. Have some more chicken, sir."

The rebuke had no effect upon Hans. Throughout the meal he continued to press the sale of the farm. Ted excused himself after dessert and climbed into the limbs of the big maple by the side of the house. Curled into a crotch twenty feet in the air, he examined the situation.

"There is something about that man I don't like," he muttered.

O'Toole's head emerged slowly from a woodpecker's home in the trunk just above Ted's unruly thatch.

"He's a blackguarding thafe."

Ted squirmed about and looked up at the leprechaun.

"What are you doing here?" he demanded.

"Sticking me nose into other folks' business as usual," came the brassy reply as O'Toole swung himself to a perch opposite Ted, "and furthermore, there's red rings wit' the green."

"Red rings! Where?" Ted asked.

"Hans Saurman's head," O'Toole snapped. "Where did you think?"

"I don't understand," Ted replied.

"Sure. Then I'll explain." O'Toole cocked his head to one side and spelled it off on his fingers. "The green is gold. That ye know. But the red means stealing it. Ye understand that?"

"Yes," Ted said puzzled, "but how can he steal something my father doesn't have?"

O'Toole gave a double flip and landed feet first in the hole in the trunk.

"Thot I don't know," he answered, "but I'd be keeping me eyes open if I were you."

O'Toole then disappeared, leaving Ted in a worse muddle than before. Climbing slowly down from the tree, he slipped into the living room and settled down beside the fireplace to listen to the conversation. Hans was still dickering for the farm. He had raised his offer to six thousand by this time.

Ted squirmed restlessly as he listened. His father did not seem particularly interested in the deal, but that was not important either. There was that note at the bank. If Hans Saurman took that up and demanded payment, his father would be forced to sell the farm to meet it. Ted sat there toying with the bit of cobalt that O'Toole had given him. Suddenly the rock caught the man's eye.

"What you got there, boy?" Hans demanded.

"A piece of rock," Ted replied, handing it over reluctantly.

Hans scanned it swiftly, his crafty eyes shifting back to Ted's face.

"You know what it is?" he asked.

Ted was about to reply when he spied O'Toole sitting on the window sill shaking his head vigorously from side to side.

"Not exactly," he stammered, wondering why the others could not see the little elf.

"Vell, vell," Hans leaned back in his chair and tossed the bit of stone to Ted. "You yoost ask an old-timer like me when you want to know something. I plowed lots of that under in my time. Shale. Yoost plain shale. Common everywhere. Vort nodding. Couldn't even build a decent foundation with the stuff."

"Thank you, sir," Ted answered, stifling a grin as O'Toole threw out his chest and hooked his thumbs into his vest in imitation of Hans Saurman. Then the leprechaun slipped back over the sill, beckoned with his forefinger and disappeared. Ted excused himself and wandered into the side yard where he found O'Toole seated on the grass at the far side of the maple tree.

"They were black," he squeaked. "The rings were black."

"What does that mean?" Ted asked.

"Black's fer lying." O'Toole shook a fist toward the house. "And he's a big one, I tell you."

"Perhaps he made a mistake," Ted replied.

"Perhaps, me eye!" O'Toole stamped his foot three times and whirled around twice. "He knew that was cobalt. He has two pieces in his pocket right now, and I know where they came from."

"He does! He has! I mean, where did they come from?" Ted sputtered in amazement.

"They came from the gully just west of the cave. The vein outcrops there and dips back on the other side. Ye'd better look up someone who knows the stuff. Somebody must be willing to pay money for it, or that old scoundrel wouldn't be trying to stale it from ye."

Ted pondered that one for a moment.

"My science professor lives just over the rise at Churchtown," he said. "I could see him in the morning."

"Tomorrow," jeered O'Toole, "always tomorrow. Did yer great, great, great Uncle John Carmichael that preached salvation and rebellion over at Brandywine Manor wait till tomorrow to take supplies to Washington at Valley Forge?"

"Did he do that?" Ted asked.

"Aye, that and more," O'Toole shook a tiny forefinger under Ted's nose, "and niver a bit of a chance did King George's redcoats have o' catching him though they sent a whole company on his trail. Thim British were forever getting tomorrow where he had been today. A man of prompt action were he, and ye should be taking pattern after him. Over the hill wid ye, now! Not tomorrow."

With that parting thrust, O'Toole dived

under a toadstool and disappeared. Ted decided the advice was sound. Over the hill he trudged, arriving at Professor Gallagher's home just as the sun was disappearing behind Welsh Mountain. The professor, an active young man, was sorting rock specimens on the back porch. He beckoned Ted to join him there.

"Something on your mind?" he asked.

"This." Ted handed over the rock he had received from O'Toole. "I think it is cobalt, but does it have any value?"

"It is cobalt," Michael Gallagher fingered the specimen speculatively. "Smaltite to be exact. Its value would depend largely on the quantity and how easily you could get it. A good vein of this within fifty miles of here would be worth as much as if it were gold. There should be some around here. The early glassmaker Stiegel used it to get a beautiful blue in his glassware. However, I haven't been able to locate any, and I have been searching for the last two months in my spare time."

"You won't laugh at me if I tell you?" Ted asked hesitatingly.

"Laugh at you?" Gallagher was puzzled. "At jokes I laugh. Rocks are serious business with me. No laughs, I assure you."

"It came from the same place that Stiegel got his cobalt, the old mine on our farm, and there are tons and tons of it underground yet."

"How do you know this? Does it outcrop in the shaft? How large is the vein?" Professor Gallagher shot the questions rapidly as he envisioned success near after many weeks of fruitless search.

Ted painstakingly explained about O'Toole, including his need for a shamrock, while the professor leaned back in his old rocker contentedly puffing on his blackened briar, his feet resting on the specimen table.

"I know it sounds like a fairy tale," Ted concluded.

Mike Gallagher's field boots thumped to the porch floor.

"Tomorrow morning you will meet me at the mine and we shall look into this," he said. "In the meantime, say nothing to anyone about it."

"Then you believe O'Toole is real. That I didn't dream all this?" Ted exclaimed.

"Dream it?" Gallagher chuckled. "You have the rock for proof, haven't you? Furthermore, it would be rank heresy for a Gallagher to deny the existence of 'the little people.' I shall see you in the morning."

Immediately after breakfast the next day Ted hurried through the dew drenched grass to the mouth of the cave. O'Toole's legs dangled from the rock shelf just inside the entrance.

"Well!" snapped the leprechaun. "Did you see him?"

"Oh, yes," Ted replied. "He will be here this morning."

They did not have long to wait. In a few minutes Professor Gallagher entered the cavern.

"Good morning, Ted," he said. "Did our friend O'Toole show up this morning?"

Ted pointed up to the ledge where the elf sat.

"There he is, sir."

"Good morrow to you, O'Toole," Michael Gallagher bowed from his hips, a broad grin spread across his face. "I can't see you, but my friend Ted assures me you are there, so I bid you the top of the morning."

"Niver mind the blarney," O'Toole snapped. "Did ye fetch me a shamrock?"

"I did," answered Gallagher.

"Give it to me!" demanded O'Toole.

"Not until you show us where the vein of cobalt lies," the professor countered.

A series of shrill cries echoed through the gallery while O'Toole stamped his feet furiously on the ledge.

Ted turned to Gallagher with a question. "You really can hear him?"

"I hear him all right," Gallagher assured him. "What is more, he has been keeping bad company. There are a lot of Pennsylvania Dutch curses mixed in with his native Gaelic. Never mind. If he doesn't care to bargain, we shall proceed anyway. I brought my pick along so we shall start digging."

"Dig, ye spalpane, dig!" screeched

O'Toole. "Ye'll niver find it. I'll hide it from ye! It's mine."

Ted wriggled uncomfortably beside the older man.

"It really is his, Mr. Gallagher. He found it first."

"Sure now, you are right, after a fashion," Gallagher chuckled, "but what can he do with it? Nothing except sleep on it and it makes a hard bed. Not nearly so soft as the peat moss of Old Erin. So, we make a deal with the old scoundrel. He shows us where the ledge begins, and I produce a shamrock from the auld sod. He settles himself in the shamrock, and we mail him back to Killarney."

"It's Kilkenny," snapped O'Toole, "and let me be seein' the shamrock."

"Oh, no," Michael Gallagher shook his head. "You might be able to trick me somehow. Show me the cobalt vein first."

O'Toole hesitated.

"And how will I be knowing that ye'll do what ye say?" he asked.

"The word of one Irishman to another," Gallagher answered.

"I'll give you my word, too," Ted added earnestly.

"It's a bargain," said O'Toole.

"Where is the ledge?" Gallagher demanded.

O'Toole chuckled.

"Ye are leaning against it right now."

Gallagher turned and flashed his light against the wall. His pick dug deep into the rock, and he examined the result with an anxious eye. In a few minutes he had laid bare a wide strip and his grin was reassuring.

"That is it, all right," he exclaimed exultantly.

"The shamrock!" screamed O'Toole.

"Hold your temper," admonished Gallagher as he reached into his pocket and produced his lucky piece, a shamrock enclosed in plastic.

"He is inside already!" Ted shouted.

"Are you sure?" Michael Gallagher asked, grinning. "He wasn't taking any chances, was he?"

Reaching into his pocket, he produced a heavy envelope. After addressing it carefully to Ballyragger, Kilkenny, he inserted the shamrock and sealed it.

"We will drop this into the mailbox at the end of your lane, Ted. Then we shall go in and tell your folks and mind you, now, no word about O'Toole. I've a reputation to maintain as a geologist, and if it ever gets about that I made my finds with the aid of a leprechaun, I would be out of a job."

That is how the Carmichael Cobalt Mine came into existence. It is also how the ink stain came upon the post office desk in Ballyragger.

Paddy Regan opened the envelope addressed to the postmaster and decided to pilfer the lucky piece against the time he should buy a ticket in the Sweepstakes. For which audacity O'Toole kicked over his inkwell!

331

The Hunch

By MARVIN L. DE VRIES

Guessing, forbidden to all State Troopers, forces Dizzy and Storm into a show-down with hijackers

Patrol car Number 44 trailed the big red truck through the puddles and chuckholes of Tiplady Road for some time before closing in on it.

State Trooper Storm Allen was at the wheel. His partner, Lyle Dame, known as Dizzy to his friends, sat beside him, his long legs tucked away like broken sticks. He looked sound asleep.

"Wake up, Diz," Storm told him. "That's our dish."

"I'm awake," Diz answered, opening one eye. "Wide awake."

It was early spring, and the frost law setting load limits on specified roads was in force on Tiplady Road. The rain had stopped, but the patrol car radio sputtered with the promise of more to come. A vague far-off voice, Sergeant Drubb's, no doubt, was trying to get a word in edgewise between the static. It was downhill country, and here and there swollen streams wandered out of the shallow ditches and took to the road. Wide cracks in the blacktop seeped water, and whenever the big truck hit a weak spot, water spouted up, and pieces of broken blacktop slid into the ditch.

Temporary road signs along the way read, "Load Limit, 15,000 lbs."

"Those signs," Sergeant Drubb had told them before they left the post that morning for the day's work, "weren't put up for kids to shoot at. Now you get out there with that portable scale and grab anything that's overweight. Dump the overload on the spot. That's the law. Make use of it."

Storm Allen pursed his lips. "This is new to me, Sergeant," he remarked. "S'pose we grab a truck that's carrying perishables, like tomatoes or cabbages. What do we do about that?"

"Dump it."

"S'pose it's chickens or ducks or pigs, anything with legs. They'll run all over creation."

"Dump 'em."

"I got a hunch we're going to ruffle a lot of feathers," Dizzy put in.

"Do you mind?" Drubb asked, giving Dizzy a slant-eyed look.

"Oh, no."

"Speaking of hunches," Drubb stated with a severe frown, "we don't operate that way. You know that by this time, don't you?"

"I ought to," Dizzy said, rolling his tongue along his cheek.

"I don't like the word," Drubb went on. "I don't like the idea. Everybody going off half-cocked in all directions. That's what that amounts to."

"Sure," Dizzy agreed.

"All right, get going."

Load restrictions were supposed to be the private headache of the State Highway Department, but it was a bad season, and they had called for help. Drubb's answer was a borrowed portable scale and Troopers Allen and Dame to operate it.

"If you get in a jam, all you got to do is call in, you know. We got the answers."

"Sure," Storm agreed, and went out.

Tiplady Road ran parallel to the main road. There was a Highway Department weighing station on the main road, which some truckers tried to avoid when they had an overload by taking the longer route through the hills. Arrests and fines didn't stop the practice, because profit on the overload more than took care of the fines, but the frost law, requiring the overload to be dumped on the spot, was giving truckers more concern. Tiplady Road was already chewed to pieces, but the two troopers had a quiet day.

Truckers stuck to their trip sheets, and there was no occasion to dump anything until, on their way back to the post, the troopers caught up with the big red truck. It was in a hurry, and anyone could tell from the solid pounding it gave the blacktop that it carried a heavy load.

Storm swung around it through the splash and signaled it to a stop.

There were two men in the cab. The driver rolled down the window and eyed Storm with solid enmity.

Staring him down, Storm said crisply, "Your rig looks overloaded to me."

He saw a look of relief spread over the driver's face, as if he were getting good news instead of bad. "Yeah, guess she is a little heavy. Gimme the ticket," he said, holding out his hand.

Storm shook his head. "We got a scale. You've got to dump the overload. I'll give you a ticket, too."

The driver pushed back his cap, and his eyes flashed with sudden anger. "You gone crazy?" he demanded.

Dizzy opened the trunk, and they lifted out the scale. The driver and his companion, who was bundled to his nose in a red mackinaw, got down out of the cab. Dizzy wheeled the scale into position, and Storm started to write the complaint.

The driver said his name was Joe Kelly

and had a license to prove it. He said he had picked up his passenger along the way.

A tote road wandered off into the woods on the far side, and a boy on a horse came out of it into the open, and stood to watch.

"Hello, Mr. Scalen," he called out in a surprised voice.

The hitch-hiker mumbled an irritated answer.

The truck carried plumbing supplies. According to Dizzy, who read the gauge, at least half of it had to be dumped to bring the weight down to the allowed limit.

"If you hurry, you can probably get it done before dark," he suggested.

The driver growled angrily and kicked a piece of blacktop into the ditch. The boy on the horse came in closer.

"Maybe I ought to go on," the hitch-hiker said. It seemed like a question he was asking the driver, but he didn't get an answer and he didn't go.

A passenger car came down the hill and stopped. The boy on the horse told him the truck was overloaded. He got out of his car, as if he had some time to satisfy his curiosity, and took a look at the scale.

"Quite a thing," he remarked, finally. "You wouldn't think it could handle a big load like that."

"It does," Storm said.

"Very interesting," the man said. "It's time something was done to protect these roads."

"Maybe I'll leave the whole shebang standing right there," the truck driver spoke up. He glanced at the driver of the passenger car. "Would you give me a lift into the next town?"

The other man considered it. "Why, yes, I will. But, if I were you, I'd start unloading. You're hooked and you might as well make the best of it."

The truck driver didn't seem to like the advice. He glared a moment, then turned his back and went to work.

"Keep up the good work, boys," the other man said and started back for his car. At the last minute, he offered the hitch-hiker a ride.

"Me?" The offer took Scalen by surprise.

"Yes, you. You're a hitch-hiker, aren't you?"

Scalen got into the car. Storm noticed before it drove away that the radio was tuned in to the state police wave length, and what they were getting was mostly static, too, just like the one in the patrol car.

"That old fool might've given me a lift," the truck driver muttered.

"Leave it to old Tom Scalen to dig out when there's a job to do," the boy on the horse answered.

"You know him, eh?"

"Yes, he lives up the next road. We always have trouble with him. He's got an old truck and hauls firewood and fenceposts for a living. Half the time he helps himself to our firewood."

"What do you do, just look on?"

"No, but he's so sly we can't catch him."

In the end, everybody pitched in, and fixtures and fittings, brass castings, washbowls, medicine cabinets, crated bathtubs, and a lot of items Storm had no name for came off the truck. When it was finished, the driver thanked them and went on with half his load. Storm and Dizzy headed back for the post. It was already past dark.

Soon after they hit the main road, a man stepped into the glare of their headlights and flagged them down. The patrol car screeched to a stop, and the man sagged to his knees on the pavement in front of it. His face was bruised and cut, his clothing torn. He pulled himself up on the bumper, but before Storm and Dizzy could get to him, he fell again.

Dizzy went down the road looking for a wreck, but he couldn't find one. "Maybe a hit-and-run driver hit him," he muttered when he came back. "I can't find anything wrong down the road."

"He's a truck driver," Storm said. "I got that much out of him. He claims he was hijacked and dumped out. His name's Joe Kelly."

Dizzy's jaw dropped. "That's the name of the driver we stopped on Tiplady Road."

"Yeah. We better get him to a doctor."

They got him into the patrol car, and Storm turned around. "We'll take him to Doc Turner in Anchor. That's the closest."

"If he's Joe Kelly, who was the guy on the truck?"

"The hijacker, Diz."

"Oh, oh," Dizzy breathed. He tried to reach the post on the radio, but he couldn't get through the static. He tried again and again, but finally gave it up. "You'd think it would let up once in a while," he muttered. "We'll have to phone in from Charley's place in Anchor."

They swung onto Tiplady Road again, and in twenty minutes passed the dumped load of plumbing supplies. "You'd think a man ought to have a hunch about something like that, wouldn't you?" Storm growled.

"No hunches," Dizzy answered. "Drubb won't allow them."

Another twenty minutes brought them to Anchor. Doc Turner was just going to bed.

"From the looks of that bump on his head, he's lucky to be alive," Turner remarked. "What'd he do, jump out of a tree?"

"He's a truck driver. He was hijacked. You think he's going to be all right, Doc?"

"I don't know. I couldn't promise. You better leave him right here."

"Thanks, Doc. We'll be back in the morning. If he's got anything to say, phone the post, will you?"

Doctor Turner nodded, and they went out. Charley's Dixie Diner, with the new neon sign, stood out like a sore thumb on the dark street. Charley had one customer, the man who had picked up the stranded hitch-hiker on Tiplady Road. An empty plate stood in front of him. He glanced over his shoulder and nodded at the two troopers.

"Mr. Gates, here"—Charley pointed a thumb at his customer—"tells me you caught a whopper today, boys."

Storm nodded glumly. "I've got to use your phone, Charley, or do you want to, Dizzy?"

"Not me," Dizzy begged off. He sat down and ordered coffee and sinkers for two.

Storm got Drubb on the telephone and

told him what had happened. Dizzy at the counter winced and hunched his shoulders when Drubb's shouted answer vibrated out into the room. Storm had to go over it a second time, and Drubb had a second set of answers.

"If you're talking about that truck you stopped, Trooper," Gates spoke up, "I saw it go through town some time ago. It's headed south."

"Just a minute"—Storm put his hand over the mouthpiece, and had Gates repeat his information. Then he relayed it to Drubb, and Drubb blew his top.

"Don't stand there poundin' my ear, then," he roared. "Get going. You'll get instructions in a minute."

"We aren't getting anything on the radio, Sergeant."

"Keep your ears open and you'll get it," Drubb roared. Then he slammed the receiver, and Storm hung up.

"I'll get out there and listen," Dizzy said. "You drink your coffee."

"So that's it," Charley remarked, while Storm gulped his hot coffee. "Hijackers, eh?"

"That truck went south an hour ago," Gates repeated. "I saw it go past. It surprised me he didn't stop to telephone. That stuff's likely to get damaged out there on the road."

"I can't for the life of me see why anybody would want to steal a load of plumbing supplies," Charley remarked.

"I can see one good reason," Gates said. "That load's probably worth twenty to thirty thousand dollars."

Charley whistled. "Honestly?"

"I've been in the business," Gates said. "I know."

"It must've made the guy feel bad to dump half of it," Charley went on.

Gates shrugged. "He didn't look happy, but I'll bet he doesn't feel bad enough to come back and pick it up after the close shave he had." He turned to Storm. "You'll catch him on that south road, Trooper, if you step on it."

Storm nodded. "Thanks for the tip," he said, and went out.

But he only went south a block, then turned. "I think Gates is a phony, Diz. I think he gave us a bum steer. I got a hunch—"

"Whoa!" Dizzy stopped him. "There's that word again."

"Yes," Storm agreed, "there it is, and that's what we operate on, if it suits you."

"It suits me, if I don't need to explain it to Drubb. What do we do?"

"We go back to the dump heap. I've got a hunch Gates is the big shot in this deal, and I think he's going to make a try for the rest of that load. The only reason he said the truck went south was to get us out of his hair."

"All very nice," Dizzy agreed, "if it works. But Drubb said—"

"He said he would give us instructions, but I don't hear any."

"He's spouting a mile a minute, but I can't get it."

"Good."

Deep pools of mist lay in the dips and hollows along Tiplady Road. A drizzle hit the windshield, and the twin blades went after it like fighters sparring in a ring. Dizzy kept his hands off the radio, and nothing sensible came out of it. When they reached the spot where the plumbing supplies were piled up, Storm backed into the tote road on the other side, swung the car so the headlights would hit the pile of freight, and stopped the engine. He pushed the light knob, and darkness engulfed them.

"Turn off the radio, Diz," he told his partner. "We're going to wait it out."

It was a long, hard wait. Storm thought about his hunch, and tried to make it seem reasonable and sound. A hunch wasn't something a man could grab out of thin air and use as an alibi for a mistake. If it were, Sergeant Drubb had a right to object. But if it had a solid basis, a man had a right to act on it, not only a right, but a duty, and he had to risk whatever criticism might come his way.

Separately, the items he gathered together didn't make an imposing list. Every move of Gates could be called the move of an honest man. He had happened to be following the hijacked truck. He had stopped out of idle curiosity. He had happened to be listening to police business on the radio, even though reception was poor. People did. He had told the driver to start unloading when the driver acted balky, and what he had said could be called kindly advice to a hot-head. He had given Scalen a lift, pulling him out of what would have developed into serious trouble as soon as the real truck driver was discovered. His statement that the truck had gone south might be true.

All these things, item by item, could be straightforward and honest, but it was Gates, Gates, Gates, all the way through. The man had come into the picture often enough to make it seem more than sheer chance. Putting them all together, Storm had his hunch. He knew only success would save him from Drubb's hot fury, and still more serious consequences, but he had to take the risk.

He opened the car door so he could step out without making a noise, and Dizzy did the same. The sound of a motor came their way, and, a little later, headlights whipped over the hill. The freight was piled in plain sight, and the car slowed down when it came near. The car was the same make as the one Gates drove. It came to a full stop. A spotlight flicked on and hit the abandoned load.

"That could be him," Dizzy breathed.

"Did Gates have a spotlight?" Storm whispered.

"I—I dunno. Guess not."

The spotlight veered across the road and hit the patrol car. It held there a second, then whipped back to the road, and the car went on.

"Maybe it was him and we've scared him," Dizzy muttered, disgustedly.

Storm didn't answer. Anyone who happened to notice something unusual along the road was apt to do exactly what this driver had done. Like the other pieces of his hunch, it could be meaningless, or it could be sly treachery. He wouldn't call it one or the other until there was something to back it up. He still had a strong hunch that Gates would show up.

An animal made a rustling sound in the underbrush, but it was too dark to get a look at it. The cooling motor made a sharp clicking sound at regular intervals. Mist seeped over the blacktop and swirled around them. Storm began to wonder if the headlights would reach through it when, and if, the time came to use them.

"If we're right about this," he muttered, impatiently, "Scalen's in on this, too, and the truck is holed up at his place. But Gates is the man we're after, and this is the only way I can see to grab him."

His voice, louder than he intended, scared off their underbrush visitors, a herd of browsing deer, probably, from the sudden uproar they raised.

"Wow!" Dizzy breathed, sheepishly. "I thought they were coming right down my neck."

They heard another car, but no headlights showed up. The sound drifted down the hill, coming nearer and nearer. It came as far as the tote-road, then stopped. It was strange how in the misty darkness sounds might be either far away or close by. There was a feeling that these were not far off. Suddenly there came the distinct sound of a car door opening from across the road.

"There," Dizzy breathed.

Storm poked him with his elbow. A flashlight showed briefly. Someone on the far side of the road spoke in an undertone and got an answer. Wood scraped on wood, metal on metal. A box clattered, and someone spoke again.

Storm eased himself out of the patrol car, keeping one hand on the light switch. Dizzy got out on the other side. "Here goes," Storm whispered, and pulled the switch.

Light blazed across the road. It hit an old ramshackle truck, probably the one the boy on the horse had mentioned. Scalen, in his red mackinaw, was lifting a box into it when the light hit. He staggered back as if it were lead out of a gun. The driver who had claimed he was Joe Kelly let a box drop and spun around, lifting his arm to shield his eyes against the blinding light. A third man moved around behind the beaten old truck and went out of sight.

"Stand in your tracks," Storm warned, but he couldn't tell whether the man stopped or not.

"Everybody reach," Dizzy added, and walked in, skirting the fan of light.

Storm crossed through it to get on Dizzy's side, intending to circle the truck and block off the man behind it. But he made the mistake of glancing into the headlights, and by the time he got across he was thoroughly blinded. Dizzy went on, and spoke to the two men again. Their hands went higher.

Storm's sight came back. He started across the road, but before he got halfway, Gates' car leaped out from behind the truck and came at him. He sidestepped and the fenders scraped his legs and almost threw him down. Dizzy swung and fired a shot, risking the loss of his prisoners, but they didn't move.

Gates' car rolled faster. Storm grabbed for the door handle, and it came open under the pressure of his thumb. He started to fall, but he reached for the steering wheel and gave it a yank. Then he went rolling.

The car swerved and tires squealed. It hit the soft shoulder and sagged down. The door swung wide open. Gates reached out for it. Storm, flat on the pavement, fired a shot. Gates yelped. He killed the motor trying to back out of trouble, but he got it started again. Storm got his feet under him and made a rush. He grabbed Gates' dangling arm and pulled him out. The driverless car started down the road and crashed a little further on. Gates yelped again and went down with a splash. Gunflame leaped out of his hand. Storm kicked and sent the weapon flying.

Gates rolled and landed in deep water. Storm caught his leg and lifted it high. Another yelp from Gates turned to a strangled gurgle. "I'm drowning—I'm drown— I'm dr—"

Storm hung on until Gates' complaint was close to the truth. Then he pulled him back on the road. Dizzy had his two prisoners handcuffed to the truck, and came on the run. He thought Gates had gotten away, and started up the road toward the crashed car. Storm called him back. "He's on ice, Diz. Right here. All we need is another set of handcuffs."

A little later, Dizzy turned on the patrol car radio again. Drubb was still busy with his road block, but he was a faint futile cry in a wilderness of static. Dizzy lifted the mike off the hook and pushed the button. "This is Patrol Car 44," he reported. "You can call it all off, Sarge. Everything's under control."

He didn't get an answer. He didn't expect one on account of the static, but he switched to the car-to-car frequency, hoping to get things back to normal, and announced the capture of the hijackers. Then he swung back to the car-to-post frequency and started to talk again, his voice filled with soft mockery. "We did it on a hunch, Sarge. How d'you like that? You don't like it, eh? You're going to wring our necks, eh? Well, well, hear the man talk. . . ."

Storm laughed and glanced at the puzzled prisoners. Dizzy joined in.

"I got a hunch I will—" this came out of the radio, clear as crystal, and it was unmistakably Drubb's voice, mimicking Dizzy's soft mockery.

"Oh, oh," Dizzy breathed, and quietly placed the speaker back on the hook.

"Yeah," Drubb answered, and then the static began again.

Hunting with Bow and Arrow

By CORKY JOHNSON as told to ROY CIVILLE

A field-archery champ tells how an instinctive shooter shoots

When you've got a bow and arrow in your hands and a squirrel or deer ahead of you in the brush, you know the thrill that bowhunters have felt for thousands of years. Maybe that's why archery, one of man's oldest skills, has become today's fastest growing sport.

Thousands of boys who love the outdoors are learning the thrill of archery, on the plain target range and in the rough country of woods and field, where the archer shoots under simulated hunting conditions, or actually goes after wild game—birds, small animals, bear, deer, or even moose.

Most of today's field archers are "instinctive" shooters. They use no mechanical sights, no formal method of aiming. They seem to hit their target by "feel," as savage warriors and hunters have done for 50,000 years and more.

Because I'm an instinctive field archer myself, I'll show you how an instinctive "bare-bow" man works. If you prefer to shoot with mechanical sights or want to learn "point-of-aim" style, the same basic shooting fundamentals apply, with one or two exceptions.

Here are the fundamentals: stance, grip, bow-arm, draw, hold, release, follow-through. Each one is basic because each one affects your shot. Practice each one sep-arately, faithfully. Mastery of each detail makes the champion.

1. *Stance.* With shoulder to target, balance your weight evenly and spread feet twelve to eighteen inches. This will depend on your height and personal "feel." What you want is a solid, comfortable feeling. A line through your heels or shoulders should point to the target. Straighten your legs, but never lock the knees. Do not lean in any direction; do not twist your body. Only your head and arms move. Once your stance is set, try to hold it, for it is your shooting platform, the first fundamental of good shooting.

2. *Grip.* Hold the bow in your left hand (if you are right-handed) in a firm but not tight or rigid grip. Find the best spot on the handle for your particular hand; then stick to it. If you don't have an arrow-rest or overdraw on your bow, better mark the handle where the top of your hand circles the bow to make sure of a standard position for your grip. Keep the wrist straight or slightly bent inward, but not out. The bow handle should pull back against the fatty part of your thumb joint, not against the finger joints, not against the heel of your hand.

3. *Bow-arm.* Your bow-arm is held straight out, as if slightly pushing at the target. Keep your arm straight, but not rigid.

The anchor position is at full draw no matter what distance the archer expects to shoot.

Nocking the arrow, it is important that you draw the string, never pull back on the arrow.

4. *Drawing.* Before you draw, you need to notch, or *nock,* the arrow on the bowstring. There are three feathers, or *vanes,* on your arrow. One of them, called the *cockfeather,* is set at right angles to the nock in the end. When you nock the arrow in the bowstring, turn it so the cockfeather is away from the bow to prevent its being damaged when passing the bow. It's easier if you do all this with the bow held low and horizontal. Just lay the arrow on top of the bow, fit it to the string, and set the three finger joints of your drawing hand to the bowstring.

Now begin to draw, pulling the STRING, not the arrow. The arrow, lightly nipped between first and second fingers, will come back with the string. (Don't grip the arrow with these fingers. Just pull back on the string.) The bowstring itself, in forming an angle, pinches your fingers down on the arrow just enough to bring the arrow along.

Draw all the way back to the *anchor point* at your cheek—always—in one smooth motion, raising the bow arm as the drawing arm pulls back. (See illustrations.) The two movements start and end together, with about equal force of push on the bow and pull on the string. Your bow arm should reach shooting position just as the drawing hand reaches *anchor point* on the side of your face. (You'll want to be sure your arrows are properly fitted to your bow and

your arm length. Check this with your archery shop or an experienced archer.)

Most field archers use the index finger lightly touching the corner of the mouth as the anchor point. Once you settle on this location for your anchor point, stick to it, for the anchor point is the same thing as a rear sight on a rifle.

Always give a full draw to the anchor point, whether on nearby or distant targets. The angle of elevation, not the draw, determines the distance.

5. *Hold.* With the draw at anchor position and with both eyes open and fixed on the target, hold for the few moments it takes to get that "just right" feeling. You'll do a lot of shooting before you really get this feeling. Until you do, I'd suggest a pause of just two or three seconds before releasing the arrow.

6. *Release.* When you're "just right," release the arrow by opening the fingers smoothly, but very quickly. In this quick releasing movement, the hand will dart back along the face toward the ear in a recoil motion. Never allow the string or hand to creep forward of the anchor point before the instant of release, or you will lose some of your power, causing a low arrow. Just remember that the arrow should be released at the full draw position. You might spend hours and days practicing a smooth, ac-

The bow is not "gripped." It's pushed away, arm straight. Arrow lies on bow, not across thumb.

Arrow seems to split lips in this low-angle view, but is actually based on lower lip.

curate, quick-release, for serious errors here can mean targets missed.

7. *Follow-through.* After releasing the arrow, hold the bow, the release hand, the stance, and keep both eyes on the target until the arrow hits. Then and only then, lower the bow. You have learned the value of follow-through in golf, baseball, tennis, and many other sports. In archery, this follow-through is equally important.

You'll notice that these seven fundamentals say nothing about how to aim or where to point the arrow in order to hit the target. That's because this article deals with "instinctive" shooting. The instinctive archer, remember, shoots by feel, by instinct. He senses the distance or range in much the same way that a basketball, baseball, or football player does when he throws a ball.

A good forward passer can hit his moving target at ten, twenty, thirty, or even forty yards. Yet he probably never thinks about the actual number of yards. He simply spots his receiver, cocks his arm, and throws. This is instinctive shooting.

Just how does the average person learn to judge distance and become a fair shot in a short time? As I said, a true instinctive archer shoots by feel, not by actually sighting his bow and arrow. It takes lots of practice to acquire this feel, and there are some archers who never do. In my case it took about six months of constant practice and

many, many, missed targets, but after acquiring it, I developed into a good enough shot to win three California state field championships and keep meat on the table from the meager supply of wild game where I live.

There is very little flat trajectory to an arrow. The moment an arrow leaves the bow, it is under the influence of gravity and therefore on a downhill path. To make up for this downward pull, you must raise your bow slightly, even at the shorter distances. The first question is—just how much elevation is needed at the different distances? Actually, it's impossible to predetermine these elevations, as there are too many factors involved. For instance, there is the difference in the archer's height, the difference in the weight of arrows, the difference in the pulling power of various bows, and variations in the anchor point used.

However, let's assume that you are an average guy with a bow that has the correct pulling power for you and with arrows that are matched to the bow. You are using the anchor point described in this article—the index finger at the corner of your mouth. Now, starting at a very close range, say about ten or fifteen yards, pick a spot somewhere below the target. After coming to a full draw, place the point of the arrow on this spot. If you shoot high or low, just change your spot according to how far you

341

missed the target. Your alignment right or left is automatic, as there should be a straight line from your eye over the arrow tip to the target.

After becoming accurate at this range, move back a few yards and try again. You will see that the spot is now nearer the target. As you move back, the aiming spot will climb nearer and nearer and finally climb right up on the target itself. At the extreme long ranges, you actually have to hold the point of your arrow over your target in order to hit it. In all this preliminary practice, you're training your "built-in" range-finder, your two eyes, to feel this range, this distance.

Stay with each distance until your arrows are hitting with fair regularity. Remember— at each distance, pull back to full draw to the anchor point, with both eyes open.

You don't need an elaborate target for this practice. A piece of newspaper, a square of cardboard, an outline drawing of an animal or bird will do. Sometimes, when I feel the need of practice of any one of the fundamentals, I'll throw an empty milk carton on the ground, then stand off ten yards or so, and shoot it into shreds.

"You'll find that as you move back, you'll be adjusting the height of the bow-arm automatically, probably without thinking about it. Without knowing just how you do it, you'll gradually discover that you are hitting your targets, if you keep in mind the seven fundamentals outlined in this article.

I've heard it said that this natural target-hitting skill is built into modern humans through thousands of years of bare-bow shooting in the prehistoric past. Perhaps there is some truth in this. If there is, then your early practice in shooting the bow will "bring out" what instinctive ability you have. I couldn't say for sure. At any rate, most archers who go after wild game shoot in this instinctive style.

Summing it up, you'll become a first-class archer if you master the seven fundamentals. If you're meant to be an instinctive shooter, and if you really practice, hitting the target will come naturally.

Good luck and good shooting!

Oliver's Ox

By DAVID LAVENDER

Cattle rustlers learn a lesson: Don't underestimate the intelligence of an oversized steer

Young Joe Vickery did not hear the horse approach over the rain-softened ground. His ax thunked on another length of stove wood, the two halves plopped neatly on either side of the chopping block, and his nose wrinkled pleasurably at the aromatic smell.

Of all his chores on the Double Lightning ranch, hidden deep in the sandstone canyon lands of southeastern Utah, Joe liked the morning wood detail best. It drove the sunrise shivers from the April dawns. The rhythmic cleaving of the knotty wood made his own worries seem less knotty. As his blood sprang alive, he could forget the loneliness and anxiety that beset him each night in the empty bunkhouse.

Behind him a Texan voice drawled, "If I was a snake, I could of bit you."

Joe spun around. "Rafe!" he gasped.

It was Rafe Oliver's voice, all right. It was Rafe Oliver's wizened, weather-beaten face. But it certainly was not Rafe's normal outfit of batwing chaps, denim jumper, and shapeless gray hat. This apparition, sitting in Rafe's brush-scarred saddle, wore a round black derby, a green hand-me-down suit, and a striped bow tie askew on a stand-up collar. The appearance of neither the suit nor the high-button shoes had been improved by riding over the rocky trails leading to the ranch —riding which must have been mostly done in the dark.

"Great bulls of Bashan!" Joe Vickery gulped, borrowing Rafe's favorite expression. Then a grin of welcome lightened his bony face. "You sure got back from Texas sooner than I expected."

"Back?" Rafe's face bunched into a sour pucker. "I ain't gone yet."

"But—"

"Remember that cold I had when I left the timber camp? Well, it clabbered up into pneumonia. I've been hawg-tied in the horspital. They jobbed me with needles big as a woodpeckeh's bill, an' fed me pap an old-maid schoolma'am wouldn't eat at a sewin'-circle tea. I've even—" his hairy ears grew red—"I've even been warshed right while I was in bed. Too weak to fight back—just lie theah an' holler—you've no idee."

"You're looking fine now," Joe said.

Rafe chose to regard the words as a compliment to his haberdashery. "Travelin' togs." He slapped his suit so the dust flew. "If them lawyers that are tryin' to do Aunt Mandy out of her homestead haul me into court, they won't think they're dealin' with an igner int cowpoke. No, suh!"

Loneliness engulfed Joe Vickery again. A lawsuit in far-off Texas, dragging out—how long? Each night he had marked off another day on the calendar, dreaming of the time when Rafe and he could set up their own wild-cow camp on the shaggy piñon mesas above the Colorado River. Up there he'd be free to start learning the cattle business from a man who, as Joe's father said, "had more savvy in his little finger than most cowboys have in every bone in their heads."

But now the hoped-for day, instead of being nearer, was as distant as ever.

"I'm takin' a stage out of town fo' the railroad this aftehnoon," Rafe Oliver rattled on, not noticing the boy's dejection. "First, though, I wanted to see how you an' Robert E. Lee are makin' out. So I got up early this mawnin'— Say, wheah is Robbie?"

He put two fingers in his mouth for the shrill whistle of summons Joe had learned so well. But this time Robert E. Lee, Rafe Oliver's gigantic, dun-colored ox, would not be able to answer. Hastily Joe interrupted.

"Robbie is behind the barn. I'll show you."

"He can still walk, cain't he?"

Joe shot an uneasy glance toward the stone ranchhouse, where the owner, Al Worden, was stumping about on his game leg, preparing breakfast.

"Worden—he—well—he doesn't like the ox around the house."

Oliver's face crinkled into an insulted scowl. "Ain't he got no taste?"

"It's Robbie that's got too much taste. He raided the corncrib and broke into the oats Worden was saving for the saddle ponies."

"He's makin' up fo' the meals he postponed last winteh," Rafe said. "Oughtn't begrudge him that."

"Worden caught him chewing open the grain sacks and larruped him over the snout with his cane. Robbie chased him all the way up a derrick pole."

"Sma't ox."

"I took Robbie," Joe continued unhappily, "to one of the line camps to get him out of the way. Yesterday he came back."

"Naturally. He's been trained always to come home."

"When he got here, he broke into Worden's prize cornfield. Al found him gorging on the new shoots, with a big hunk of the new barbed wire fence draped over his horns. It riled the boss considerable. He—well—he—"

Rafe glowered suspiciously. "If that mizzuble man dared tech a haih on Robbie's head . . ."

His heels thumped his pony's ribs. Startled out of its doze, the horse leaped around the corner of the barn. Hollow-stomached, Joe pursued.

On the other side of the pinelog building was a horse-breaking corral. Bound by a ponderous log chain to the snubbing-post in the center of the enclosure was the disgruntled Robert E. Lee.

"Robbie!" Rafe Oliver choked. "What they done to you? Speak to me, Robbie!"

He flung himself from the saddle and crawled between the bars of the gate. The enormous ox recognized his voice and gave a bawl of greeting.

As Joe followed, he could not help reflecting on this strange partnership between the undersized man and the oversized steer. Rafe's business was rounding up cattle which had escaped from their owners and had gone wild. Often the only way to handle the fighting beasts was to rope them and, at the risk of being gored, drag them one by one into camp.

To spare himself and his saddle horse the bone-racking ordeal, Rafe had hit on the idea of training, as helper, a yearling he had rescued a couple of years before from a quicksand bog and had made into a pet. By now the steer, grandiloquently named Robert E. Lee, had grown prodigious in size. His curved horns spread six feet from tip to tip, and his boiler-plate hide sheathed a ton and a half of solid muscle.

Rafe's pampering had made him gentle as a dog. It was no trick to halter-break him so that he could be led out into the wilderness, and then teach him to return to camp, where his insatiable appetite was tickled, each time he came back, with strange, choice foods. Thereafter, when Rafe roped a rebellious cow, he neck-yoked the creature to Robbie with a short piece of rope, and the ox did the rest.

All this Joe had learned after a furious blizzard last winter, when Rafe and Robbie had stumbled into the timber camp operated by Joe's father. Straightway Joe and the wizened Texan had become friends. While Robbie recovered by foraging with the outfit's draft horses, Oliver earned their keep by choring around the camp. He spun Joe countless yarns and discovered the boy's longing to learn the cattle business.

The upshot was that Rafe offered to take Joe into the breaks with him as soon as winter relaxed its iron grip.

Just before they were to leave, however, one of Rafe's relatives in Texas had written for help. It put the newly formed partnership into a precarious situation. The timber camp was closing for the season. There was no place to provide for Oliver's ox, and much of the money they had saved for equipment would be swallowed by Rafe's trip. The only solution was for Joe to find temporary employment on some ranch where Robbie would be acceptable.

This was easier said than done. The severe winter had wrought havoc among the cattle herds of southeastern Utah. Most outfits were firing rather than hiring men. The best Joe could land was a menial job with fiery Al Worden, who had recently broken his leg and needed someone to help him hobble around the place.

Unfortunately, Robbie's voracious appetite had soon dumped them into one predicament after another. Worse, the ox had taken as violent a dislike to Worden as the rancher had to him. Now Robbie was chained to the snubbing-post to keep him out of further mischief while Worden decided what to do with the creature.

It was a horrible time for Rafe to have appeared.

Angrily, the Texan's gnarled fist closed over the iron links.

"Chained!" he rumbled. "Like a common criminal!"

Robbie butted him up against the post. There was a lump in Rafe's coat pocket. The ox probed it with his wet black muzzle, an operation that did not improve the coat's already bedraggled condition. Finally Rafe produced a turnip.

"Yo' favorite fruit. I brung it special," he chortled as Robbie devoured the morsel. Then his face turned purple again. "Chained!

I'm goin' up to that house an' give Worden a piece of my mind!"

Joe shuddered. If those two cantankerous individuals locked horns, the resultant explosion would blow the ticklish situation into shreds.

"Cool off, Rafe," he pleaded desperately, "and give Worden a chance to cool off. He's worried sick. He took big losses this winter. To save his shirt, he borrowed enough money to buy a herd of yearlings that he got at a bargain over beyond the river. But it's going to be a snaky job bringing them through the desert, with the Rimrockers ready to—"

"Rimrockers?"

"Some half-outlaws that live in the breaks west of the Colorado canyon. Cattle that stray into those mesas and gullies never stray out again, I understand. The Rimrockers would be right happy to stampede the yearlings and grab up the loose edges of the herd. Besides, there's the river—cold swimming now that thaws are melting the snow in the mountains. And for the first time in his life, Worden can't be out with his men, because of his broken leg."

"Serves him right," Rafe grumbled. "Anyone who'd—carnsarn you, Robbie; leave my shirttail be!"

Using his rough tongue, the ox was trying to work the garment out of Oliver's trouser band.

"That's another thing," Joe said morosely. "Robbie ate two of Worden's fresh-laundered shirts off the clothesline."

"Enjoys the starch," Rafe said, as though that justified everything. To save his shirt, he gave Robert E. Lee his pocket handkerchief. While the ox munched happily, Rafe started to unfasten the chain. Joe's throat turned dry with alarm as he watched him.

"Let me handle this, Rafe," he begged, "or you'll get me and Robbie run off the place. Then where'll we go?"

He saw Rafe begin to weaken and redoubled his earnestness. "As soon as the yearlings are here, Robbie can run with them. He won't be getting into trouble around the ranch buildings. He'll help the new cattle locate on the range. Worden will appreciate him more. Everything will be O.K. until you're back."

Gradually, Joe won him over. After a series of rumblings, Rafe squinted at the sun, opined that its paleness forecast rain, and decided he'd better start back to town. Off he jogged.

"Vickery!" Worden's impatient shout recalled Joe to his duties. "Get that kindling in!"

The rancher had not seen Rafe, for he asked no questions about the visitor. Relieved, Joe dumped his armload of wood in the box by the kitchen stove and slid into a seat at the long, oilcloth-covered table. Normally the meal would have been enlivened by the banter of the Double Lightning's half dozen hands. Now, however, a glum silence held the eaters. Red-faced, with his pale blue eyes as hard as marbles above a bristle of sandy mustache, Worden sat humped over a cup of bitter black coffee, lost in his worries. When he spoke, it was like a gun firing buckshot.

"Take these binoculars to the top of Haystack Butte. Try to spot the herd. They ought to have been at the crossing two days ago. Unless something has happened— *What's that?*"

From the root cellar underneath the house came a muffled crash of glass. It was followed by contented grunts. Worden let out a strangled roar, seized his cane, and disappeared through the door. Joe trailed behind, afraid to let himself think what had occurred.

Sure enough, it was Robert E. Lee. Before leaving the corral, Rafe must have loosened the chain around the ox's neck and left the gate unfastened.

His appetite for turnips aroused by the morning's nibble, Robbie had sniffed around the ranch yard until he had discovered the double doors of the cellar carelessly left open. Down the half dozen stone steps he had gone. In the dark, cramped hole his great horns had swept the last jars of Worden's choice plum preserves from the shelves.

Now he was standing hoof-deep in the syrupy mess, gorging himself at the vegetable bins. Through the entryway, his bushy tail

could be seen swaying in gentle self-satisfaction.

Enraged beyond caution, Worden attacked him from the rear with his cane. With a huff of annoyance, Robbie backed ponderously up the steps and turned, dried turnip leaves hanging from his mouth. At sight of his favorite enemy, he lowered his horns for a charge. Worden gave a yelp of fright. Dropping his cane, he took off in ungainly flight toward a ladder leaning against a nearby hencoop. Up it to the roof he scrambled, with no more than inches to spare.

Calmly, Robbie hooked the ladder aside and glared up, chewing his interrupted mouthful with majestic defiance.

Worden's face grew redder than the sandstone canyon walls. "How did that walking hunk of misery get loose?" he howled.

Joe's jaw worked, but no sounds came forth.

"I chained him myself," Worden fumed. "He couldn't have got away, unless— So! You did it! You—"

"Honest, Mr. Worden. I—"

But suddenly the rancher was not listening. His pale blue eyes were staring over Joe's head as if he had seen a ghost.

"Lafoon!" he croaked hoarsely.

Joe turned. Riding toward them on a jaded pinto pony was Bill Lafoon, the ranch foreman. Under a grimy stubble of whiskers, his long-nosed face looked gaunt. His eyes were red-rimmed with weariness. Damp mud stained his clothing.

"What's the matter?" Worden called, his fury forgotten in a sharper dread. "Where's the herd?"

Bill Lafoon waved a tired hand in the direction of the Colorado. "T'other side of the river." He glanced from Worden's perch on the henhouse roof to Robert E. Lee. A faint grin relaxed his haggard lips. "Huntin' aiggs?" he asked dryly.

"You aren't funny!" Worden bawled. But he was too worried to nurse his resentment. "What are you doing here alone? Did the Rimrockers raid you?"

"Naw," Lafoon said. "We kept tight-bunched comin' acrost the desert. We saw tracks where they scouted us, hopin' to manufacture a stampede. But they haven't had a chance to cut it—yet."

"What do you mean, 'yet'?"

"Those yearlings are wall-eyed scared and bewildered, plumb off their home range with no old she-stock along to steady 'em. And the river is in flood, more water—wilder water—than the pore little critters knowed there was in the world. They won't take it. Four times we've driven 'em into it. Each time they've gone into a mill and broke back to shore. By now they're so spooked we can hardly handle 'em."

Joe said reasonably, "Can't you let them stay put until they quiet down and the river drops?"

Lafoon shook his head. "They've et up what little feed was in the cove. They're powerful hungry and restless. Once they start edgin' into the side gullies, the Rimrockers will snap 'em up sure. Now there's a storm makin'." His hand gestured toward the pearl-gray mist that was curdling the sky to the north.

"Our horses are played out. They were tuckered from the drive, and those mills in the river finished 'em. I swum over at dawn to fetch fresh mounts. With good horses maybe we can hold through the night and take the ford again at dawn, afore the storm hits. If we don't make it then, we're liable never to make it."

Worden jumped as if he'd been stung. "What are you standing around for, Vickery! Round up the horses in the east pasture. Hurry up—no, wait! Get the buggy mares, too. They're in the west pasture. I'm going with Bill."

"You can't cross that river in no buggy," Lafoon protested.

"Joe can row me in that boat the boys use when they're after catfish. Move, will you? Hold on!"

Joe set the ladder against the roof. Worden started down. Then Robbie gave a menacing bawl and shook his horns. The rancher scrambled back.

"That finishes it!" he bayed. "Vickery, bring me my rifle!"

Joe's knees turned limp. "Think what you're doing, Mr. Worden! That steer is the way Rafe Oliver makes his living. It—"

"You heard me!"

Joe's fists clenched at his sides. He was about to blurt that he would leave the ranch then and there, taking Robbie with him, rather than obey such an order. Leave for where? Do what? He reluctantly shook the thought aside.

"I—"

Then he saw the solemn wink that Bill Lafoon gave him. With his face held exaggeratedly straight, the foreman drew a .45 from the holster at his hip and tossed it up.

"That's as good as a rifle," he said in his slow, dry way.

Joe sensed what Lafoon meant. As Worden's pale eyes squinted over the sights, the boy put his hand on Robbie's neck.

"It'd be like shooting a man in cold blood," he said. "I don't reckon you can do it."

Worden fumed and swore. But like most ranchers he was basically fond of animals. Slowly the gun muzzle lowered.

Then, embarrassed by his show of softness and infuriated by Lafoon's grin, he sputtered, "Think you're mighty smart, don't you? Well, there's something I can do. We'll take that ox with us across the river. We'll run him back into the breaks. Then maybe we'll be rid of him!"

Robert E. Lee had no liking for what he saw of the Colorado River. Chocolate-colored, it stretched a thaw-swollen quarter of a mile in front of his wrinkled nose, full of angry waves and giving forth ominous sounds. Obstinately he refused to be driven into it with the more obedient saddle horses. Nor could he be roped and dragged. Lafoon tried, but his horse was in swimming water, unable to pull, before Robbie's feet were off the bottom.

All the while precious minutes were slipping by. There had been trouble rounding up the horses and trouble with the buggy on the drive to the river. Now darkness was threatening to catch them away from the herd.

"This ain't gettin' us nowhere," Lafoon exploded, and Joe glanced hopefully at Worden. Perhaps the rancher would abandon the attempt.

The stubborn Worden, however, had hit on another idea. One end of a lariat was tied around the base of Robbie's horns; the other was secured to a ring bolt in the stern of the rowboat. Worden picked up one oar, told Joe to take the other. Lafoon was ordered to cut a long willow switch.

Bracing his good leg against a thwart, the rancher threw his weight onto the oar. Joe had no choice but to follow suit. Meanwhile, whooping like a Ute, Lafoon belabored the ox.

Unendurably harassed, Robbie gave a groan and launched himself. Once in the water he swam so strongly that the rowers had difficulty keeping ahead. They had reached midstream, when Joe glimpsed from the corner of his eye an uprooted cottonwood, still spiked with branches, bearing down on them. He called a warning.

Worden reversed, caught a crab, and fell flat on his back.

The tree hit the bow a glancing blow. The craft shuddered backward. There was another dismal bang from behind. The rear end of the flimsy boat shot upward.

"We're on top the ox!" Worden shrieked.

With a hollow splat the boat dropped back. A careening branch sent it into a spin. Worden struggled onto his knees. At the same moment Robbie's dripping horns appeared above the gunwales. Robbie gave a bubbly moo, and it looked as if he meant to climb aboard. Quickly, Joe made both ends of a rope fast to the boat and looped it over the horns.

"My gun!" Worden choked and clawed at the holster he had buckled about his waist before leaving the ranch. Joe seized his arm. The boat bobbed sickeningly, and Robbie disappeared.

"He's drowned!" Joe groaned. Then the craft gave a lurch and they were being towed, stern first. Ahead of them Robbie's horns rose and fell with the current.

Up to the shore he dragged them, across a sandbar, and into the sagebrush. There he stopped, flanks heaving.

"Great bulls of Bashan!" Joe murmured weakly. As for Worden, he hadn't breath enough left to speak.

A couple of cowboys who had seen the crossing galloped up. Gritting his teeth against the pain of his leg, Worden crawled up behind one of them for the short ride upriver to the herd. The other he ordered to drive Robbie back into a side canyon off the gorge. Joe was left to walk to the cattle camp.

Northward, purple clouds were climbing the evening sky. Far off, lightning flickered. The storm was gathering faster than Lafoon had predicted. If it hit in the middle of the night, the yearlings would indeed be hard to hold.

The cowboy who had driven Robbie off loped by on his way to the camp. With a shiver Joe looked at the shadowed cove. All along its western edge were hillocks grisly with alkali, and stony gulches leading into the shaggy breaks. A hundred hiding places. Rimrockers. . . .

Putting his fingers between his teeth, he whistled shrilly. It was high time to call Robbie back. Under cover of darkness he could slip the ox into the herd. In the confusion of the crossing tomorrow morning, perhaps Robbie could reach the home shore unnoticed. Then he might hang up with the yearlings away from the ranch buildings and keep out of trouble until Rafe returned.

Nothing happened. Perhaps Robbie hadn't heard the whistle above the roar of the river. Joe moved through the dusk along the ox's track, and was about to whistle again when a drift of wood smoke reached his nostrils. He paused, guessing what it meant. And Robbie's tracks continued straight on, although the horseman had turned back.

Cautiously Joe edged around a bend. Ahead of him, beyond a shoulder of rock, he saw a dim flicker of firelight. Closer by, on his own side of the rock, was the humped shadow of the ox under a piñon tree.

Tied! Joe grinned to himself. That was easily remedied. He inched ahead, swallowed his heart when Robbie gave a rumble of greeting, and loosened the knot. Then the fitful wind died away. As its drone faded, he caught a snatch of conversation from beyond the rock.

". . . gentlest steer I ever seen. Why that hombre drove him almost into our camp and then turned around I'll never know."

"What difference does it make? We kin use him. When the storm comes up an' we stampede the herd, them yearlings will scatter like fluff. But that steer won't spook, I'll warrant. We'll use him for a lead ox. . . ."

The wind boomed again. Joe gave the rope around Robbie's neck a tug. Fortunately the ground was sandy for a ways, and he emerged into the cove undetected. There his eyes fell on the boat, and an idea came to him.

"For Pete's sake, Robbie, cooperate!"

Swiftly he knotted a hackamore out of the rope and placed it on the ox's head. Next he picked up the end of the lariat that was still fastened to the rowboat, drew a shaky breath, and boosted himself onto Robbie's back.

The ox gave his tail an indignant swish. But the past days had convinced him that humans sometimes acted strangely. After a moment of dreadful hesitation, he decided not to buck. It took the remaining twilight, however, to persuade him to drag the boat to the river. There Joe yanked his horn to the left and so turned him upstream, splashing through the shallow water at the edge of the sandbars and towing the boat behind.

Generally speaking, cowboys do not ride their cattle. Joe's appearance astride the huge beast drew forth facetious shouts that changed to alarm as he told his story. Worden shot an anguished glance at the piling thunderheads, and then at the black wall of the cliffs across the river. A glow edged their tops. Soon the moon would be rising. Perhaps, before its eerie light was drowned by the clouds, they could force part of the herd over the ford.

"They'll mill for sure," Lafoon protested. "In the dark we—"

"They'll stampede the minute a Rimrocker fires a gun," Worden retorted. "Our only chance is to rush 'em into the water."

Joe tried to get in a word. "If Robbie—"

"Get that ox out of my sight!" Worden roared and began crackling orders. "Bunch the herd! Cut pitch pine torches! Swing the leaders over—"

Realizing the rancher was too excited to heed him, Joe climbed aboard an extra horse

tethered to the chuck wagon, lassoed a yearling, tied its feet, and managed to neck-yoke
it to Robbie, who was placidly eating hay
reserved for the saddle horses. Then he
roped another beast to tie to the ox's other
side.

This time Worden saw what he was doing.
He charged over. Bruised and winded by his
exertions, Joe lost his temper.

"You hardheaded old windbag, suppose
you listen to someone else for a change!"

Worden blinked in amazement. While he
was off-balance, Joe explained his plan. Since
it was a plan, and not just a mad melee to
escape, the rancher agreed to try it.

The yearlings' feet were unbound.
Promptly they tried to bolt. Mildly annoyed,
Robbie planted his legs and brought them
up short. They ran out their tongues and
bawled. Robbie gave his shoulders a twitch
like a man shrugging off flies and lumbered
on. The yearlings had to follow. Led by
Lafoon, the cowboys crowded the restless
herd behind them.

"Now for the boat!" Joe shouted. Armed
with a burning pine torch, Worden took position in the bow. The camp cook, impressed
into service as oarsman, followed gingerly.

As Robbie hit the water, Joe shoved the
boat into the current on the downstream side
of the ox. He leaped into the stern of the
boat, checked the pistol he had borrowed
from Lafoon, and reached out to light his
torch from Worden's.

"Row!" he yelled at the gape-mouthed
cook.

Under the rising moon the river ran like
agitated oil, flecked with silver fire. Robbie's
great head was a black silhouette. On either
side of it bobbed his reluctant tows. The sight
gave confidence to the animals behind. Urged
on by the men, they plunged into the water.
Too late the lurking Rimrockers grasped
what was happening. With a frenzied blast
of sixshooters they came squalling out of the
hills, but the commotion served only to stampede the remainder of the herd into the
water.

Worden shook his torch in fierce exulta-
tion. "We made it! We—"

A terrific crash of thunder drowned the
words. The reaching cloud fingers choked
the moon. In the ruddy light of the torches
Joe saw Robbie falter. Behind him the steady
motion of the yearlings began to waver. In
another instant the mill would start.

Lashing at the terrified beasts with their torches, screaming their lungs out, banging away with their guns, the crew in the boat tried to fight the line straight. Joe caught himself yelling insanely, "Turnips, Robbie! Turnips ahead!"

The words made no sense to the ox, of course. But training did. Cattle were yoked to him; he was supposed to take them home. Downing his hesitation, he forged on, and the long line behind swung into pattern.

A lash of rain caught them as they reached the shore. Their torches sputtered out. There was no possibility of regrouping the frightened animals.

"It doesn't matter," Worden gasped as he felt his way toward the buggy. "They're on our side of the river. We can go home—the horses will take us—and catch some rest. In the morning we'll round 'em up. . . ."

At sunup, a familiar roar of rage roused Joe from a sound sleep. He jerked up, rubbing his eyes.

"Vickery!"

He peered through the bunkhouse window. From that angle all he could see was a tree at the edge of the cornfield. Perched in its lower branches was Al Worden, frantically brandishing his cane.

"Robbie," Joe groaned and reached for his trousers.

In the doorway, he stopped short, while the other cowboys peered over his shoulder. Robbie and his two neck-yoked prisoners were not alone in the field. Several hundred other yearlings had followed the ox from the river and through the gap he had made in the fence.

"Vickery!" Worden bawled again. "Get that ox—"

"Get him a turnip?" Joe interrupted. "Is that what you mean?"

"Turnip!" Worden bleated. Then he saw his men grinning from ear to ear, and the humiliation of his position began to dawn on him. "A social introduction to this gristle factory, huh? Well, if he's going to stay around and help locate the yearlings on their new range, I suppose I'd better learn to like him."

Anxiously he glanced down at the ponderous horns. "But do you reckon he'll learn to like me?"

"Sure. Just you feed him turnips," Joe said and turned toward the root cellar.

351

The Rainmakers

By JAMES W. ENGLISH

A cloudburst is ordered, brewed, and hatched at a meeting of the Tailbone Patrol

Maybe the cloudburst in Phoenix didn't make headlines in your hometown newspaper, but it sure did in ours. Why, rain is unheard of in Arizona. Besides, the Chamber of Commerce doesn't permit it. So, when the wet stuff accidentally strays out over the desert, that is news.

The local newspapers, however, really botched up this story. They quoted the Phoenix weather bureau as saying the storm had moved in quite unexpectedly. But we knew better. That storm was brewed, hatched, and ordered right in a meeting of the Tailbone Patrol.

The rain was to be a gag, our way of kidding Ronnie Price, a First Class Scout who had just transferred to Troop Ten. Ronnie, who of course was a Tailboner, had moved to Phoenix from the rain-soaked Pacific Northwest, so he didn't know that it never rains in Arizona. And we sure had a hard time convincing him.

We got off on the subject of rain when Billy Spears, the Patrol Quartermaster, read the equipment list for our next hike. When we Arizona guys okayed the list, Ronnie protested.

"How about tents?" he demanded. "And ground cloths, and ponchos? What do you do if it rains?"

"Rain!" exclaimed Toby, our owl-eyed Assistant Patrol Leader. "Never heard of the stuff. What is it?"

"It's fog with the water left in. You find it in California," explained Tommy Thompson. "That's the state just west of us," he added.

"In Arizona your chance of being caught in a rain is one in ten thousand," stated Johnny Karsten, our statistic-soaked Scribe.

Billy Spears, anxious to have his list approved, turned to me. "Even the Troop doesn't have tents or rain gear, do they, Mike?"

I'm Mike Peterson, Patrol Leader of this wacky outfit, and I agreed with Billy.

"You see, Ronnie," I said, trying to give him a sensible answer, "we only get a couple inches of rain a year. And that's usually dumped all at once, so by staying indoors that day we have 364 days a year when we don't need tents."

Ronnie wasn't convinced. "Think I'll bring my Lite-pac tent along, just to be safe," he said.

Ronnie had to leave Patrol Meeting early that night and he was hardly out the door before Toby spoke up.

"You know," he said, "I like Ronnie. He's a swell Scout, only . . ."

"Only what?" I demanded. When my overstuffed assistant melts with brotherly love, he's usually plotting trouble for someone.

Toby gave me a hurt look. "You're so suspicious, Mike. I was only going to say that Ronnie can't get it into his head that it never rains in Arizona."

"Looks like we might have to give the guy a rain to keep him happy," Tommy Thompson said.

"Exactly!" stated Toby.

"Make it rain Pennies from Heaven," put in Johnny Karsten. "The Patrol treasury is kinda low."

"You're a piker, Johnny," I said. "Make it nickels. Toby can do anything."

My assistant gave me a dirty look and a bit of fast talk. "Thank you! And now—before these practical minds interrupted me—I was about to point out the merits of a Hopi Indian Snake Dance. The snake dance is a colorful ritual for the rain gods."

"Hey!" I interrupted, realizing where this sinister plot was leading, "count me out. You rain-in-the-face Indians can kid Ronnie if you want, but not me. At Troop Green Bar Meeting the Patrol Leaders decided to can the horseplay. So I don't even want to hear about your plans." I grabbed my *Patrol Leader's Handbook* and started for the door.

"Wait for me!" cried Billy Spears. "That guy Ronnie probably has a trunk full of rain gear. One little shower and you'd all want the stuff. It's all I can do to keep track of the equipment we have now. So count me out."

The day of the hike arrived without a cloud in the sky. In fact, I had forgotten about the snake dance scheme until Billy Spears and I got to the post office, where we were to catch the mail stage to Cave Creek.

This hike was to be a three-day cross-country affair, so I was giving Billy Spears a hand with the Patrol equipment. Burdened with this extra gear, we were the last Tailboners to arrive. Immediately we had cause to regret having come at all, for the parking lot overflowed with a standing-room-only crowd.

"I didn't think Toby and the others would go through with it," Billy muttered.

"We'd better see what it is they're going through with." I elbowed my way into the crowd.

Billy and I finally squirmed up to the orchestra pit, which was the front fenders of the Cave Creek stage. Toby and Pete Sweeney, their sweet potato and harmonica, were the orchestra. This duet was making rapid and futile passes at a little tune called "Singing in the Rain." At that, they were closer to the tune than the chorus of Tailboners, whose vocal efforts sounded like an alley full of wet cats.

But the hideous sound effects were nothing compared to the sight that met the eye. Not since Noah's Ark had anyone been so well prepared for rain. Toby was wearing hip-length fishing waders and was waving a big black umbrella overhead. The only visible portion of Pete Sweeney was his head and hands, sticking through holes in a table-sized piece of old yellow oilcloth.

Out in front of the orchestra was the chorus. It was out of line, out of step, and out of tune. Apparently none of this mattered for it was definitely not out of costume.

It was next to impossible to see Tommy Thompson. He was almost hidden from view by a huge army poncho. At times this tent-like shape appeared to be doing kick-steps with the rest of the chorus. Beans Roberts wore a sandwich sign that read "Slippery When Wet." And Johnny Karsten was a scientific marvel of this atomic age. Hanging from his belt were a rain gauge, a collapsible water bucket, a trenching shovel, a wind-sock, and a weather vane.

And, of course, everyone had turkey feathers stuck in his hair and streaks of bright red paint on his face.

Then I saw Ronnie Price sitting alone by the packs. He was grinning and taking his ribbing in stride. I felt somewhat better.

"Can the racket!" I yelled. "What goes on here?"

"We're being prepared, Mike," Toby explained.

"If Ronnie wants rain, we'll give him some," shouted Tommy Thompson. "Anything for a Tailboner."

"Or a laugh!" I added.

Just then the driver of the mail stage called us, so we tossed our gear in the truck and climbed in.

"Hey, Mac," Toby called to the driver. "You ever see it rain out here?"

"Wal, let's see," replied the good-natured driver. "It was thirty years ago, no, forty."

"You see!" yelled a triumphant Toby. "Only forty years ago! It could happen again. We've got to be prepared when it does."

He slipped an arm around Ronnie's shoulder. "If only we'd had time to rehearse our rain dance," he said sadly.

"Hey, Chief Foggy Frog," he called, "what's the weather prediction?"

Johnny Karsten squinted up at the bright sun and cloudless sky. "Rain! Heap big rain!"

Everyone cheered wildly.

"You brought your tent, didn't you?" Toby demanded.

Ronnie nodded, laughing.

That night we made camp by a tiny water seepage several miles from the highway. Of course, there was no quiet until Ronnie had pitched his tent. Golly, it was a beauty.

"Almost wish it'd rain so we could see how it works," I said.

Toby sprang to his feet as though his anatomy had just been parked on a cactus thorn.

"Hey, rainmakers!" he yelled. "Command performance for Mike. Hup, hup, rainmakers!"

With Ronnie, Billy Spears and myself for an audience, the Indian element of the Tailboners climbed into their rainmaking costumes again. Then, with dime store toy snakes held between their teeth, they staged a snake dance that would have made a real snake's vertebrae shiver with fright. And, truthfully speaking, even the real Indians couldn't ask for better results from a snake dance.

Next morning the sky was overcast, with dark clouds moving in fast over the White Tank Mountains to the southwest.

As usual, I had to dump Toby out of the sack to get him up. "See what your darn rainmaking did," I said, pointing to the clouds.

He sat up, startled. "Golly!" he exclaimed. "We're actually scientific marvels. Maybe we dood it!"

"Look, genius," I replied, "you're the cook this morning. Start getting scientific about chow, will you?"

When we started hiking, I noticed that our rainmakers were lugging along their special gear, although I knew they had intended to cache it until the return trip. But even with this precaution, I don't think we seriously thought it would rain. Everyone was too busy kidding about the rain to be worried about it.

"I'm going to write my Congressman," Tommy Thompson complained. "Those Californians are dumping fog over here again."

"I thought your dance was a plea for rain," Ronnie said.

Toby grinned. "Yeah, but we didn't know we were so scientifically in tune with the stuff. We never expected . . ."

He didn't finish. We had been hiking along one of those twisting desert trails that no sensible person drives a car over. And no one had heard this car come up behind us until a loud blast on the horn sent us jumping.

We turned to find some girls laughing at us. There were four of them, riding in a fancy station wagon driven by an older woman.

"It's a desert mirage," exclaimed Toby, our ever hopeful Romeo. "I'm stranded in the desert with beautiful damsels."

"Young man, this is the art class from Miss Flattery's Girls' School," the driver of the car informed Toby. "We're going to make some sketches of the desert, over there," she added, pointing to some low hills a good distance down the road.

Up to then I had denied to myself that it was going to rain, but now I felt duty bound to do my good turn.

"I wouldn't cross that big wash, up ahead," I said. "If it rains, these desert washes can flood in one heck of a hurry."

"That dry ditch have water in it!" laughed one of the girls.

"Well, it didn't get washed that deep with root beer," Toby grinned. "But Mike's right. It looks like rain, and it would be better to stay on this side of the wash."

"Thank you!" the instructor said, "but dry ditches don't frighten us."

The girls laughed, the station wagon sped off, and we staggered out of a cloud of dust.

"They must be from California," growled Billy Spears, wiping the dust from his face.

"Not bad to look at, though," observed Toby.

"Look, Romeo," I said, "if it's going to rain—"

"Mike, it can't rain," Toby said ruefully.

"Of course not," grinned Ronnie. "Why, this is Arizona!"

"Nuts!" I stated, squinting at the sky. "You characters get wet if you want to, but I'm looking for a cave where I can sit out this climatic error."

Without waiting for a reply, I set off. A short distance above the road the big wash we'd warned the girls about cut through some ridges, and I expected to find a wind cave hollowed out in the soft sandstone.

I found my wind cave, dropped my pack, and started rustling firewood. Up to the northwest, toward Bloody Basin—where the big wash started—the sky looked as if some California fog was being squeezed dry.

One by one, as the other Tailboners topped the hill and glanced up Bloody Basin way, they got the lead out. Everyone rustled firewood except Johnny Karsten, who started digging holes in the damp sand of the wash to get seepage water.

Johnny was still busy filling our canteens when the rain came. There was a roar of wind, and then a beating, driving rain. We were drenched through before we could get to cover.

The rain brought Toby over the hill on the run. "Hey, Karsten!" he shouted through megaphoned hands. "Vamoose out of that wash. Pronto!"

Johnny grabbed his canteens and sprinted for high ground. And then we heard it too. A low rumble that swelled into an angry roar as a three-foot crest of water raced down the wash.

The wind was making our shelter rather damp, so we built a frame of saguaro cacti ribs and strung up Ronnie's tent as a windbreak.

"Boy," grinned Toby, admiring our handiwork, "as snug as a bug in a rug."

"That's the trouble," muttered Ronnie, pointing to the rock ceiling. It was alive with spiders, ants, and other things that crawl. They were attracted by the warmth of the fire by which we were drying our clothes.

We immediately put on our shirts, although they were still wet.

"I feel kinda itchy," admitted Billy Spears.

"Leave the poor bugs alone and they'll—"

Toby never finished his noble defense of insects. First there was a surprised, alarmed look on his face. This gave way to a look of desperation, then action, as with a cry of anguish he sprang to his feet. He wrapped one arm around his shoulder and slapped his back frantically. And all the while he was dancing up and down like a drum major with a hot foot.

"Hey! No more snake dances," complained Beans Roberts. "We've got a cloudburst now."

I turned my flashlight on my assistant and spotted his trouble. Always a slave to his stomach, Toby had several candy bars in his shirt pocket. And those pockets were as alive with ants as a picnic luncheon cloth.

"Always doing a Good Turn," I commented. "Now it's free lunches for the starving ants."

"Mike!" exploded Toby. "Don't make fun of my predicament!"

"Hey!" Ronnie exclaimed. "What sort of predicament are Toby's gal friends in?"

We quieted down. Of an accord we pulled back our windbreak and looked out, It was raining harder than ever and was now quite dark.

"That wash has risen another foot, at least," observed Johnny Karsten. "You couldn't get a truck across that flood now."

"They wouldn't be crazy enough to try to drive across that wash," Billy Spears said.

"They didn't act very smart when they went over there," observed Tommy Thompson.

"Well, if young Lochinvar wants to put

on his pants, I'll hike down to the crossing and see if there's any sign the damsels in distress made it across," I said.

"I'll be deloused, or de-anted, in a minute," Toby stated.

"I'm better outfitted for this sort of Arizona sunshine than you guys," pointed out Ronnie.

I nodded. Ronnie had on high-laced, water-resisting boots, and was wearing a plastic poncho that drew up tight around his neck and over his forehead.

"Billy," I said to our quartermaster, "give me our climbing rope. And Johnny, I'll take your trenching shovel. And Tommy Thompson, I'll try out your apartment-sized poncho."

Suddenly I stopped in speechless amazement. Toby had on a pair of swim trunks, was wearing Pete's oilcloth, and was pulling on the waders. The black umbrella was already open.

The three of us ducked our heads and plowed into the storm. It was tough going. Toby and I got wetter each step. Tommy Thompson's oversized poncho leaked, and Toby's umbrella just slowed down the force of the wind-driven rain. But there was Ronnie, hiking along as dry and unconcerned as you please.

"When we get back," Toby ruefully said to Ronnie, "tell me more about camping in the Northwest, will you. We seem to be having a climatic change down here on the desert."

We hit the road, or what was left of it, above where it crossed the wash.

"If the gals came along here, the tracks are probably washed into the Gulf of California by now," observed Toby.

"Listen!" Ronnie exclaimed.

Between lulls in the wind there was unmistakably the sound of a feminine voice. We set off on a run for the wash, which was

roaring along like a fast freight running free and easy down a grade.

Then we spotted the car. It was still upright, but had washed downstream from the crossing and was lodged against a tree.

Ronnie pulled out his waterproof flashlight. Its yellow beam swept over the empty car and up into the palo verde tree. There were the four girls and their instructor, perched on some limbs which seemed about to break.

"At least they're on this side of the wash," Ronnie observed. "We'd never make it out in the main channel. Look at that water doing roller coaster nip-ups."

Taking the end of the climbing rope, Toby started fastening a bowline around himself.

"Mike, you and Ronnie take a hitch on one of those mesquite trees," he said as he handed us the other end of the rope.

"What do you think you're going to do?" I demanded.

"Well, I doubt if Miss Flattery's Girls' School teaches tree sitting," Toby observed, hauling off his waders. "In a couple more hours these girls are going to get a dunking. And Mike, they don't have their beach outfits. How can they go swimming?"

"Look, make jokes some other time," I snapped. "Do you think you can make it?"

"If I lose my footing, you guys haul me back," he answered. "Don't let the rope get fouled."

He handed me his umbrella. "Better keep it, Mike. Never know when you'll need a little rain." Then he turned and walked upstream as far as the rope would allow.

Keeping the rope as taut as he could, Toby edged out into the water. In a wide arc he moved out toward the station wagon, trying not to let the force of the water sweep him downstream.

With about ten feet yet to go the bottom commenced to shelve away, and Toby stepped into a hole and nearly disappeared beneath the swirling waters. Ronnie and I tightened our grips on the rope, ready to pull him in.

Somehow, he got back on his feet and inched out a little farther. The water swept Toby the last few feet, as it rushed around the nearly submerged station wagon. He hung onto the top of the car and slowly pulled himself up on the hood. Then he made the rope fast to the steering wheel.

Ronnie and I tied ourselves to the climbing rope with short lengths of rope and commenced edging ourselves out into the water. Toby would help one of the girls out of the tree to the hood of the car; then out into the water until Ronnie and I could get hold of her. With one of us on each side, we would help her to where the water was shallow enough for her to make it.

By the time the four girls and their instructor were safe on shore, we were really bushed. But the girls were so cold and exhausted we had to start back to camp right away.

We hadn't gone far before we met Billy Spears, Pete Sweeney, and Tommy Thompson, who had come to see what was taking us so long. Together we got the girls up to the cave.

Johnny Karsten grinned as we came in. "Took so long I figured we'd have company for dinner," he said, handing each of us a cup of hot chocolate as we entered.

We all wrapped up in blankets and crowded around the fire, while Johnny Karsten served us dinner. And was it good! He was named cook-of-the-year.

The food made us all feel better. Soon everyone was talking.

"Toby," one of the girls asked, "how did you happen to have that umbrella along on a hike?"

"Sh!" Toby said. "Speak with respect. That's my magic rain-making outfit."

"If that umbrella caused this rain," one of the girls said, "I'd put it under lock and key."

Know something! That's just where it is today. Under lock and key in our Tailbone Patrol museum. And it's a fact, not a drop of rain has fallen in Phoenix since that umbrella was locked up. Even Ronnie is talking about leaving his tent at home on the next hike.

Man for Bait

By DAVID LAVENDER

The hills of California were full of hold-up men during the Gold Rush

As Andy Haldane lifted a bucket of water onto the iron hook dangling above his supper campfire, he heard small stones rattle on the opposite slope of the gulch. His head swiveled hungrily toward the sound. Perhaps a deer was coming through the waning twilight to water. And for ten days he'd been living on beans and sowbelly! Reaching inside the brush-roofed lean-to, he picked up the old smoothbore rifle his father had given him last Christmas Day, 1848, when finally Andy had won permission to sail with his cousin, Jim Haldane, and two neighborhood friends ten thousand miles around Cape Horn to the glittering promise of the California goldfields.

Softly he ran to the edge of the long wooden sluice box which he and the others had so laboriously built before Jim and the two Booths had abandoned everything to chase down rumors of a new strike over on the Stanislaus. Out in the darkness gravel slithered. The rifle jerked to his shoulder. Then a voice called, "Hold it!" and the shadow of a man moved against the grayer background of a huge boulder.

Andy Haldane lowered the gun, feeling deliberately tricked. What was the fellow trying to do? Anyone could see that an easy trail off the ridge lay only a quarter of a mile upstream, where the gulch widened enough to hold the huddled tents and log huts which constituted the settlement of Muleshoe Bar. But this wanderer had floundered down the steepest part of the brushy hill.

"The next time you slide on top a man's camp," Andy grumbled, "sing out. I had you tagged for venison."

"I've hurt my leg," the other said, as though it explained everything. "If you could lend a hand—"

Andy leaned the rifle against the sluice box. He was in the middle of the stream, with cold water swirling to his knees, before he wondered whether he should have brought the gun along. Lately there had been reports in Muleshoe Bar about a band of highwaymen preying on lone prospectors. But no bandit, the boy reflected wryly, was apt to be interested in the inseparable mixture of black sand and powder-fine gold dust which Andy kept in an iron pot in the rear of his lean-to. Shrugging off his hesitation, he sloshed on.

The man was leaning against the boulder, favoring his left leg. At Andy's approach he straightened. Either his injury or the weight of the small pack on his back made him sway. He was as tall as Andy Haldane, but thinner. A short ruff of beard shadowed his jaw and upper lip. Beyond this, his features were indistinguishable in the darkness.

"Thanks for coming over," he said. "My horse fell on me back in the brush. Before I could catch him, he'd run off with my blankets, gun, everything. And that's a rough hill for a gimpy ankle."

"You'd have had easy going on the trail."

"Too far to hop." His eyes searched Andy Haldane's face. "If I'm bothering you—"

Andy flushed. "Sorry," he said and tried to hide his confusion with a joke. "Since you didn't turn out to be a deer, I guess we'll have to eat beans. Climb aboard."

He crouched so that the stranger could swing up pickaback. The weight surprised him. Just straightening under it made him grunt, and twice he almost lost his footing in the stream.

"You look skinny," he grumbled, "but you sure don't feel that way."

"It's hard to walk in water," the other replied. He seemed oddly flustered. As soon as they emerged on the bank, he slid quickly to the ground, hobbled without support around the circle of firelight, and hauled up, sweating with pain, under the projecting roof-branches of the lean-to. As he lowered himself to a seat on a log end, he darted a glance toward the hilltop he had just left, as if to make sure the ragged eaves protected him from observation.

He's trying to keep out of sight, Andy thought. *That's why he didn't go down the trail into town. And where does that leave me?*

He poked fresh sticks onto the fire. As the blaze flared, he studied the newcomer's face. It was homely, even for California's motley population of Forty-Niners. Yet, to Andy's relief, it was also reassuring. Though the blue eyes were dulled now with pain and weariness, they were well-set under an intelligent forehead. His jaw looked belligerent, but the wide mouth appeared ready to grin under almost any circumstances. In spite of his whiskers, he seemed to be only a few years older than Andy himself.

The silence grew awkward. To break it the stranger began fumbling at his bootlaces. "I don't think the bone is broken, but I made a mistake in lacing the boot so tight for support. Now my ankle's swollen like a poisoned pup."

His pack interfered with his movements. Repressing a groan, he squirmed his shoulders out of the straps. Perhaps weariness betrayed him. Anyhow, as he lowered the burden toward the ground, it slipped from his grasp and struck with a far more solid thump than any load of mere personal possessions could account for.

Andy stared at it. No wonder the fellow had seemed heavy! Then he heard the stranger say, almost desperately, "I suppose we'd better introduce ourselves. My name's Sheridan—Mel Sheridan. I came in from Ohio across Panama last spring. Most of the summer I've been back on the North Fork."

Andy got the point. He had been in the goldfields long enough to know that wanderers were under no obligation to state their names and business. By doing so Mel Sheridan was clearly implying there was nothing dishonest about him.

"I'm Andy Haldane," the boy responded. Downing his questions, he pointed a thumb at one of the soot-blackened buckets above the fire. "That water ought to be warm by now, and I'll get some cold from the creek." He smiled reminiscently. "Alternate hot and cold—that's how Ma treated sprains back on the farm in Connecticut."

As he headed toward the stream, speculation rioted through his mind. Suppose that pack were full of gold! What else could account for so much weight in so little volume? Envy twisted him. It could be done, then, if a fellow was lucky. With clean dust bringing from sixteen to eighteen dollars an ounce in Sacramento and that weighing—how many pounds? He raised his head, scowling at the hill beyond the creek. Enough pounds so that someone would follow Sheridan to take the load from him?

When he returned from the creek, he carried, in addition to the water bucket, the rifle which he had left by the sluice box. Casually he leaned the weapon against the log within reach of Sheridan's hand. The man looked at it, startled. Then a warm smile relaxed his lips.

"Thanks, Andy," he said softly. "You didn't need to do that."

Andy glanced again toward the dark bulk of the hill. "I don't know what's needed. All I'm trying to say is that I prospect for my own gold, not for somebody else's."

He lifted the bucket of hot water from its hook and set it on the ground. Sheridan eased in one foot and then sat staring at the tiny ripples which circled the puffed flesh. At last he said, "I'm in a shape where I've got to trust somebody. And it looks now as if I picked even better than I dared hope."

Andy grinned. "You don't know how fast I can run."

Sheridan winced. "*I* ran." Memory darkened his eyes. "My partner, Phil Jocknick, and I had just wound up our claim on the North Fork and were headed out, when the gang came down on us. We split. I don't know whether Phil got clear or not. It seemed as if the whole bunch took after me. But my horse was a good one and I was pulling away until a shot got him in the flank. Luckily he didn't drop right away. I swung down the slope into a chinquapin thicket. Then he fell. My gun flew off somewhere in the brush, and I didn't dare take time to look for it. I was panicked. I scuttled off through the brush, ducked down into a ravine, and followed it to the top of the hill yonder."

"You never saw the bunch after that?"

"No. But they must have found the horse and learned I was afoot—easy pickings once they could catch up with me."

"You might have rustled up a posse in Muleshoe."

"I doubt it. No one has time to chase off through the hills. It's root, hog, or die these days, with the rainy season just around the corner and everybody digging like mad to make a stake so he can live through the winter." Sheridan's voice turned bitter. "That's the trouble. In the whole Territory of California there's no law to help a person who needs it. No sheriffs, no jails, nothing but the respect one man has for another's property. That is not enough any longer. These hills are filling up with desperate men, and they figure there's nothing to stop them."

"What about the Federal troops?"

"The nearest company's miles away. Even if I could reach them with this leg, the gang would be gone before we were back." His head sank on his chest. "I wish I knew how Phil is."

Andy hunkered on his heels, eying Sheridan's pack. Well enough he sensed what its contents might represent: the grueling trip across the Isthmus; the grinding labor of standing in icy water while sun sledge-hammered from above; shoveling gravel into a cradle or sluice from dawn to dark, week after relentless week. Yes, he knew it all, the poor food, the agues, the joints that stiffened until one could hardly crawl out of bed in the morning. The hopes, the dreams. The despairs.

Quietly he said, "I've a horse picketed up the canyon that you can borrow."

Sheridan's eyes flashed up. Then slowly he shook his head. "There's only one trail out of this gulch. Surely they're watching it."

"You can hole up here until the coast is clear."

"You're inviting trouble."

"The gang might not find out you're here. Anyhow, we're close to Muleshoe. Three shots fired in quick succession would bring me on the run. I reckon your friends will think twice before they get rough."

For a time Sheridan sat wrapped in thought. Then he reached for the rifle. "Under those conditions I accept. But we'd better not both go to sleep at the same time. As you've got to work tomorrow, I'll take the night trick."

Late the next afternoon a long-bearded rider jogged down the gulch on a sorry bay horse, halted beside the wet, shallow pit in which Andy was digging, and watched the boy dump a shovel-load of dirt into the hopper at the head of his sluice box. A perforated iron screen in the bottom of the hopper held back small pebbles. The rest of the material washed down the long wooden trough, the roily water that carried it rising in miniature waves over the transverse riffle poles. In theory, those riffles created eddies where the gold, being heavier than the dirt, settled to the bottom. In practice, however, the Muleshoe metal was so flour-fine and the accompanying sand so heavy that the two settled together in an inseparable mixture which had caused most of the camp's baffled prospectors, including Andy's erstwhile partners, to give up in despair.

Idly the black-bearded rider began conversing about placer mining. But Andy noticed that his eyes swept every corner of the claim as he talked, and suspicion tightened the boy's chest. Even after the stranger reined away, Andy kept stolidly on with his work. There was no telling who else might be watching from the ridgetop. Besides, it was time to clean his sluice.

Shutting off the water, he scooped out the tiny drifts of black sand that had col-

lected about each riffle. At sunset he carried the sand to his camp and placed it on a scoured shovel blade so that it could dry over the fire. As it began to steam he commenced preparations for supper.

Sheridan said from inside the lean-to, "I see you had a visitor."

"An inquisitive one," Andy said. "Mel, I'm afraid those birds suspect where you are. Worse, they've probably asked questions around Muleshoe and found out all they want to know about me. Then Long-Nose rode down to get the lay of the land."

"What do you think they'll do next?"

"Hang around, probably, until they figure out some way of moving in on us without rousing the whole gulch."

"So?" Sheridan muttered and sat hunched in thought until he saw Andy stir the drying sand with a stick. Then, rousing from his abstraction, the man asked, "Is that your day's clean-up?"

"A week's clean-up," Andy corrected with a sour smile. "When my partners and I first built the sluice, we cleaned up every day. Then we dropped to alternate days, and after the others stampeded to the Stanislaus, I slacked off to once a week. It's not very exciting when you can hardly see your gold with a magnifying glass." Glumly he added the pile on the shovel to the accumulation in the iron pot in the lean-to. "It beats me. If I speed up the current in the sluice, the gold washes through. If I slow the current, the sand settles thicker than ever. I've tried drying the mixture and blowing off the dust with my breath. I've dry-washed it the way the Mexicans do. Nothing works."

Sheridan started to say something, then seemed to change his mind. Silence trickled by. Andy began dishing up their supper of beans and saleratus biscuits, moving so that no one watching the fire would see that he was serving two people. In the back of his mind he was faintly astonished to realize that such care had already become second nature, that for twenty-four hours now he had gone through even routine motions with nerves stretched tight.

As Sheridan took his plate, he asked, "Why not quit this claim and come to Sacramento with me while I tend to some business? Then we'll take a flying trip to the North Fork before the rains. I know where there's some good gravel."

Andy's pulse jumped. A partner again. A fresh start after a summer too full of fresh starts. He shook his head.

"Thanks, Mel, but I'm staying."

"Why, if that sand is so ornery?"

"It goes a long way back." Andy squatted on his heels, forehead puckered with memory. "One thing my dad used to drill into me was always to make the best of what I had. I forgot that when Jim and the Booths and I landed in California. We thought we were going to make a million dollars overnight, and if a claim didn't quite suit us, we'd ride on after a new will-o'-the-wisp. Of course, nothing was ever perfect—too many boulders one place, not enough water another. After the summer was over and we had nothing but blisters for our chasing around, I decided Dad knew what he was talking about. That's why I stayed here instead of rushing off to the Stanislaus."

"How are you going to live through the winter on this stuff?"

"When the rains start, I'll pack the sand to a cabin somewhere. With a pin I can pick out the biggest grains of gold. Maybe I can squeak by until I learn how to separate the rest." He grimaced wryly. "It isn't what I dreamed of when we left home. But that's the way it turned out."

"Nothing will change your mind?"

"No."

"Your choice," Sheridan said. He sounded disappointed, but an odd notion struck Andy that the tone was a lie, that secretly the man was pleased by the decision.

And then Sheridan said, "If it's still all right with you, I'd like to take you up on the loan of your horse."

The finger of loneliness touched the boy. "When?"

"Tonight."

Andy frowned. "If they were watching the trail yesterday, they'll probably still be watching it."

"I won't use the trail at first. This hill isn't as steep as the one across the creek. I can work up it and cut around."

"The country up above is rough," Andy demurred. "You'll need daylight to get through."

"I'll sneak out by dark and wait on top until dawn."

"How about your ankle."

"I'll be riding."

"It's a long chance."

"So is sitting here," Sheridan said.

"I suppose," Andy agreed, though it had been just as long a chance yesterday, when Mel had decided that sitting tight was the wiser plan. Why had he changed?

Mel grinned at his long face. "I'll be back."

"Sure," Andy said, and tried to believe it.

The next morning passed with no sound of anything unusual on the hilltop. At first Andy was relieved. Then the old loneliness closed in, and he worked right through lunch hour rather than face his empty lean-to. He was still at it when another rider, this one with a red mustache and a black slouch hat, jogged up to the sluice box, introduced himself as Jay Grattan, and announced that he had a message from Jim Haldane on the Stanislaus. Jim and the Booths, Grattan said, had made a good strike and wanted Andy to join them immediately.

Temptation, fortified by lonesomeness, rippled through Andy and he asked eagerly for directions. Then he caught himself. Jim had been excited about prospects before, only to give up when obstacles rose in his way.

"I'll think about it," he told Grattan.

He was still wrestling with himself the following morning when a loose-jointed Muleshoe hanger-on named Hank Corwig wandered by carrying a rifle. Corwig said he had spotted a deer on the canyon rim and needed help hunting it down. Andy's mouth watered. Even his supply of beans was running low. But he remembered the mist which had clouded the sky at dawn.

"I've too much to do," he said and was mildly surprised when Corwig stamped off grumbling as if he had received a personal insult.

The day dragged on. Late that afternoon two walkers appeared from the direction of Muleshoe. Andy stiffened. One of them was the black-bearded long-nosed spy who had first scouted out the claim. The other was red-mustached Jay Grattan.

"So that's it!" Andy thought. First Grattan, who had probably learned about Jim Haldane in Muleshoe, and then Hank Corwig had tried to lure him away from the claim with lies, so they could move in on Sheridan without fuss. That having failed, they evidently were planning a more direct method. Well, they were due for a surprise when they found the place empty.

The pair stopped at the edge of the pit in which Andy stood. Silently Grattan pulled a hunting knife from the sheath on his belt, tested it with his thumb, and suddenly hurled it. The blade spun with a bright glitter, struck a nearby stump, and hung there quivering. Smiling, Grattan walked over and pulled it free.

Behind him Long-Nose said, "Red don't never miss. An' a knife don't make any noise."

Two more men came down the creek, Hank Corwig and a loose-wristed fellow Andy had never before seen, both of them carrying rifles. A third armed man appeared among the yellow pines on the slope above the lean-to. *Clever,* Andy thought, *not coming in a body that might attract attention.* Uneasily he looked toward Muleshoe, so near he could see men moving about their cabins, yet too far to signal for help.

Grattan hacked down some willows, seated himself on the stump, and pretended to be whittling riffle poles. "Jack," he said to Long-Nose, "you and Corwig search the lean-to. Spike, you and Nick scout the brush. Leave your guns here agin the sluice where they won't be in your way or look funny if someone wanders by. I'll watch our young friend."

The others moved away. Andy was baffled. Though the searchers soon realized Sheridan had disappeared, they showed no concern. He heard them paw through his pack boxes and panniers, and rattle his cooking pots. They searched through the roof-branches of the lean-to, dug into the ashes of the fireplace. The long-nosed man called Jack dumped Andy's pot of black sand and scattered the dust with his boot. Andy jerked forward and then paused, trembling, when Grattan growled, "Whoa!" *Sheridan's pack,* he thought. That's what they were after. But why, when Sheridan was gone?

His breath caught. Fats Walther, the Muleshoe storekeeper, was ambling down the creek with a fishing pole. If Andy could somehow warn—

"Keep digging!" Grattan's soft voice said. "One peep out of you an' the fat boy'll get the knife."

The storekeeper waddled up, nodding genially. "Hi, there, Mr. Grattan. I see you're still around."

"Yup," Grattan drawled, whittling away on a willow. "Jim Haldane wanted us to be sure the kid's all right. We're helpin' fix the place up."

Walther grinned idiotically. "That's what I admire about Californy—everybody so friendly. Ain't it right, Andy? Well, I'll be seein' you."

As he ambled away, Jack left the other searchers, who had pretended, for Walther's benefit, to be cutting fresh roof-branches for the lean-to. Hurrying to the sluicebox, he leaned across it and spoke furiously.

"Not a sign anywhere, Grattan."

"There's got to be," Grattan snarled. "Somebody watched this place every minute from the hill, an' he never left the lean-to."

"Maybe in the night—"

"An' him hardly able to walk? I reckon he didn't go far before he got the fresh horse. An' he wouldn't risk leavin' it along the trail. In the dark he couldn't locate a good cache he'd be sure of findin' agin."

Jack's angry eyes turned toward Andy. "The kid might of hid it for him."

Andy forced a shaky laugh. "If you're talking about Sheridan's pack, he left here with it two nights ago."

"That bluff won't wash," Jack growled. "There wasn't nothin' in the pack but a rock."

Andy's hands clenched on the shovel. "You caught him?"

"Like pickin' daisies. It was plain that if he tried a sneak, one of the ways might be that hill. Spike was waitin'."

"W-where is Mel now?"

Grattan spit out an oath. "Spike's a fool. Sheridan spun him a yarn about carrying the pack just to pull us away from his partner back on the North Fork, an' Spike was so hornswoggled to find only a rock that he let him go. But I aim to make sure." He ran a finger along the knife blade. "An' I've a hunch you can help us."

Andy wiped his nervous hands up and down the shovel handle. "I never looked inside the pack. I don't know—"

And then back by the lean-to, one of the searchers yelled shrilly, "Grattan! Up on the hill!"

They all whirled, and Andy saw a hunched figure duck behind a pine trunk. The uniformed figure of a Federal trooper!

Grattan jumped for the rifle leaning against the sluice. At the same instant Andy threw his shovel. The handle speared between Grattan's legs. He fell heavily, the knife clattering from his hands. The sound of it was still ringing on the rocks as Andy scrambled from the pit. Dodging Grattan's clutching fist, he scooped up one of the guns just as Jack vaulted over the sluice. The man froze, glaring. Then a pistol cracked at the edge of the brush, followed by the boom of a carbine. There was a confusion of shouted orders, and half a dozen soldiers deployed onto the flat, herding Grattan's crew. Behind them, riding Andy's horse and grinning from ear to ear, was Mel Sheridan.

Later, as they sat around the campfire, Sheridan apologized. "It was a dirty trick, Andy, using you for bait. But it was your idea."

"Mine!"

"Sure. You said the gang would probably stay quiet until they figured some way of moving in without rousing all Muleshoe. I knew then I might have time to ride for the troops, providing Grattan thought my pack was still here and providing you stuck tight to the claim. That's why I asked you to go with me to the North Fork—to see if you really meant to stay."

"Grattan and Corwig almost tricked me," Andy admitted. Then he frowned. "Why didn't you tell me your plan?"

"I was afraid I mightn't get back in time, and what you didn't know you couldn't give away."

"You mean, where you hid the gold?"

"Yes." Sheridan's eyes twinkled. "Only it wasn't gold, as you and Grattan assumed. It was a stone flask of quicksilver. Handy stuff. It absorbs even the finest gold into an amalgam which is easily scraped from a pan or riffle. Heated in a retort, the mercury passes off as vapor. It can be condensed and used over. Meanwhile the gold stays in the crucible. We can clean up this sand the raiders dumped and amalgamate the gold from it."

"Quicksilver!" Andy muttered. Still rare in the goldfields, it was almost priceless. "So your partner really was carrying the gold when Grattan first struck."

Sheridan's mouth hardened. "Yes, and Grattan got the gold. A couple of fellows brought Phil into the fort just before we left. They'd found him riding along the trail, delirious, shot twice. But the doc says he'll pull through, and Grattan will cough back the dust, believe me!"

"But how did you hide the mercury? They hunted everywhere."

Sheridan chuckled. "That was easy. I knew you had just cleaned your sluice and wouldn't be examining it closely again. So I hobbled down at night and smeared mercury around each riffle. It's been there ever since, picking up gold. Fortunately, you were stubborn enough to stay with it. And I'd like to stay too. A partnership deal—Phil's and my mercury and your claim. What do you say?"

"Great codfish!" was what Andy said. But Sheridan's grin indicated that it was enough.

Start Fishing

By GEORGE FICHTER

Panfishing is fun for beginner or expert, and it's good for the fish, too

Pick a pond or the quiet bay of a large lake. Or a pool in a stream where the water drifts by lazily. Find water where there are fish, and chances are that a large percentage will be some species of panfish.

Find out for yourself. Just dangle a worm down close to the bottom, or use an artificial fly, a spinning lure, or a miniature plug. In more cases than not, you'll soon be in big business with a lot of bulgy little scrappers.

And thrill?

Try banking a bluegill that was big enough to suck in your bait and a saucer full of surface all at the same time. Use the kind of tackle that gives these smaller fish a chance and you'll find out just how furiously panfish can fight. If you take size into consideration, they have no equals.

Fishermen who turn up their noses at panfish miss a lot of fine fishing. Bullheads, perch, sunfish, crappies—they're all there and lots of them, too. Best of all, there's seldom a time when they aren't willing.

Trouble is, there are too many panfish. Surveys made by biologists show that ten percent of the fishermen catch ninety percent of the fish. More fishermen need to learn how to catch fish—and more panfish should be caught.

A panfish spawns several times in a season, producing great numbers of young. As they become more and more numerous, there is less food available for each fish. Their growth is stunted. Before long, too, they become so plentiful that they crowd out the game fish living in the same water.

For this reason, a number of states no longer have size, season, or bag restrictions on panfish. You can catch as many as you want as often as you can because the more you catch, the better you make the fishing.

Catching panfish, in fact, is good fish conservation. Even if those you catch are too small to take home, *don't put them back into the water.* They are probably not young fish at all. Chances are they are old fish which have not had enough to eat. Every panfish which you take out of the water means that more food is available for those that remain —and they will grow bigger.

Panfish overpopulation is most easily recognized on farm fish ponds. There are nearly 2,000,000 of these one-quarter to one acre ponds in the country, and the great majority of them are *under*fished. They are generally stocked at the outset with predator fish—such as largemouth bass—and panfish —such as bluegills. A variety of stocking ratios and fish species are used, but the results are by and large the same: After a few seasons, the pond will teem with panfish.

Figure it out. Even if you start with lots of game fish and just a few panfish, once the panfish start to spawn thousands of young every few weeks it won't take them long to outnumber the game fish.

And here's the important point—most pond owners know that they don't help the fishing in their pond by being miserly with their fish. Most pond owners nowadays are glad to let you have the fun of catching panfish from their ponds—provided, of course, that you respect their property and do not abuse the privilege which is granted.

If you happen to find a pond owner who doesn't understand how panfish can soon take over his pond, explain it to him. Or let him talk to other pond owners in the area. He'll soon find out that the more panfish you take from a farm pond, the better the fishing becomes—that you are doing him a favor every time you catch a panfish.

You don't have to wait for an open season, either, to fish for panfish. In most states they are legal catches the year 'round. You don't have to wait for vacation time to go fishing (and then have the weather foul those few fishing days that you have). You can go fishing for panfish almost anytime the mood strikes you—especially if there are farm ponds near where you live or streams and lakes where panfish are plentiful. You'll have fun summer and winter, and you'll also fill your stringer with some of the finest eating fish.

But the pleasure you get from catching a panfish depends to a large degree on the type of tackle you use. For the most fun, use light tackle.

Bait Casting

Soon after you started fishing, other fishermen no doubt told you not to "horse in"

your catches—meaning, of course, not to haul them in as fast as you could crank the reel handle. It's more fun—and in the long run you'll take more fish, too—if you "play" the fish. Let him fight the bend of your rod. Let him take line—and tire himself out before you take him out of the water.

Bait casting was developed in this country specifically for bass fishing. The bait-casting reel permitted casting a bait or a lure greater distances more accurately and more easily. A bait-casting reel's spool turns four times for every turn of the reel handle. Any good bait-casting reel will work well for panfish. A drag adjustment, which prevents line breakage when a big fish is hooked, is not necessary—but it might come in handy in case your lure does appeal to a bigger fish than you're after.

Just make certain that your reel is not "cheap"—and "cheap" here refers to quality of materials and workmanship rather than to price. This principle applies to all tackle. You can't afford to fish with inferior equipment.

For panfish, you'll want a light-action rod. The standard length for a bait-casting rod is five or five-and-a-half feet. This will probably suit your needs, although a six-foot rod is better for casting light lures. The greater the taper toward the tip, the lighter the action—which is what you want for the midget-sized panfish.

The bait-casting lure for panfish should weigh about five-eighths of an ounce, and

you can use a five-pound test line—or heavier if you are fishing where there is a great chance of snagging on rocks or logs. A leader is not necessary, but this is an extra precaution which many fishermen prefer. It helps to keep the fish from detecting the connection of the line to the lure or bait.

You can also use a bait-casting outfit for still-fishing with natural baits.

Fly Casting

Fly fishing is no doubt the most ancient of the rod-and-reel sport fishing arts. Fly patterns used by the Greeks are still used successfully today, and techniques of fly fishing have varied only slightly down through the years.

And you don't have to fish for just trout and bass to use a fly rod. Fact is, throughout much of the country, fly rods are most used for panfish—for bluegills in farm ponds, for bullheads in mud-bottomed creeks and sloughs, for perch and rock bass in lakes and streams.

Fly rods vary in length from seven to nine feet, and since you will probably use your fly rod for both casting and still-fishing, an eight-foot length is a good compromise. With this length, you can cast in fairly close quarters, yet the rod is long enough to provide plenty of action. It should weigh three to four ounces.

In fishing for panfish, an automatic reel is generally best suited for your needs. It doesn't hold as much line as a single-action reel, but you won't be casting long distances for panfish—and they aren't the sort of fish which make long runs. The convenience of the automatic re-wind is hard to beat.

The most important part of the fly fishing outfit is the fly line, since it is the weight of the fly line which actually casts the fly. You can use a *level* line, which has the same diameter throughout its length, or you can use a *tapered* line, which is greater in diameter in the middle or at the end of the line. Your choice depends to a great extent upon what you become accustomed to using and the length of the casts you expect to make. Level lines, which are least expensive, will

suffice for most panfishing needs. A leader, as in bait casting, is not absolutely necessary, but it is preferred by many.

Flies are either *wet,* which sink below the surface and are supposedly imitations of drowned insects or of immature insects or other aquatic creatures, or are *dry,* which float on the surface and resemble a surface-swimming insect or one which has dropped to the surface from overhanging branches.

There are thousands of patterns from which to choose. You should find out which are the most productive in the area where you plan to fish, and you can also do your own experimenting. There are also miniature plugs, spinners, and spoons which can be used on a fly rod. You can still-fish with a fly rod, too.

Spinning

Spinning is the newest form of fishing in America. It originated in Europe and has become popular in this country since World War II. Spinning suits panfishing perfectly, since a spinning outfit can be used to cast light lures and natural baits. You need little working space to cast with a spinning rod, yet the rod itself is almost as limber as a fly rod.

The spool of the spinning reel does not revolve on the cast. Instead, the weight of the lure—which is less than five-eighths of an ounce—pulls the line from the end of the spool. The line is straightened as it passes through a series of successively smaller guides along the rod, the smallest one of which is at the tip.

Distance casting of light lures is possible because there are no revolving parts to offer resistance. If more weight is needed to make a cast, a bit of lead can be added to the line, or a plastic bubble, filled with water to give the desired weight, can be tied to the line. The bubble can also be used as a float. On the retrieve, the reel spool rotates so that the line is wound on in place.

The average spinning rod is seven feet in length and weighs four to five ounces.

Cane poles, or their glassrod equivalents, offer a lot of panfishing sport, too. This sort of tackle cuts your cost to a minimum, since all you need is a pole, a hunk of line, a hook, and maybe a bobber. But unless you're careful, you won't have much fun fishing, either. Make sure you get a long, limber pole so you can appreciate every move the fish makes.

Here are some final tackle items. If you use natural baits, you'll need a supply of hooks. Get small ones—size 4 to 6. They are easier to hide in a bait and also easier for small fish to bite on. And make certain you keep them sharp, too. It's a good idea to check the hooks on your artificials regularly, too. There's no easier way to lose a fish than with a dull hook.

Split-shot sinkers should be included with your tackle, too, or perhaps some wrap-around soft lead sinkers. Unless you are fishing on the bottom in a swift current, you won't need heavier weights to keep your bait down where you want it.

You should also have a stringer of some sort or a fish bag. You can buy these, or you can make them yourself—a web onion sack, for example, makes a good-enough fish bag, and you can make a stringer of strong cotton cord. Make certain you have a few swivels for attaching your lure to your line. They will keep you from having annoying line twists which might also disturb the action of your lure. You'll also want a small bobber or two for use in keeping your bait

off the bottom and to signal when a fish is biting.

You can add to these items a variety of accessories and near-essentials, such as a tackle box, bait bucket, knife, pliers, hook disgorger, ruler, and many others. But beyond the basic rod, reel, line, and hook, it's largely a matter of personal choice.

Natural Bait

Natural baits take a big toll of panfish. They are food with which a fish is familiar. Your chore, then, is simply to hide the hook in the bait and then to maneuver it in a manner which brings on a bite.

Earthworms, of course, rank near the top. Worm fishermen are sometimes laughed at by certain other fishermen, but you should keep in mind that it's not the fish who are laughing. They like worms.

You can generally get all the worms you'll want by digging them from rich, loose, moist soil—in a garden or from near a compost heap. You can prepare such ground especially to attract worms to have them when you need them. You can also find worms beneath rocks and logs, or if you live near a place where fishing is a recreational business, you can buy the worms, plus many other natural baits. In addition to earthworms, you can use small red wigglers or big night crawlers. Sometimes it may take more than

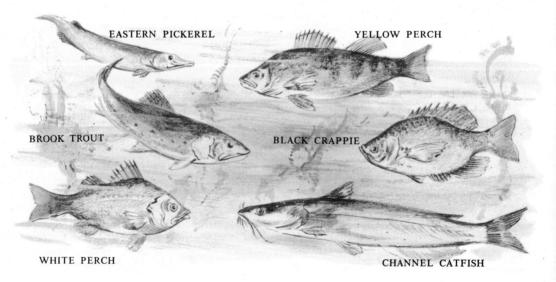

EASTERN PICKEREL   YELLOW PERCH

BROOK TROUT   BLACK CRAPPIE

WHITE PERCH   CHANNEL CATFISH

one wiggler to make a tempting bait, or a night crawler must be cut into pieces. But an earthworm is just about the right size. You can thread the worm on the hook and leave one end dangling to entice a fish, or for bullheads and other bottom feeders, you can lace the worm on tightly.

There are many other excellent natural baits. Minnows, for example, are especially good for crappies. They can be used either live or dead, and dead ones are particularly excellent catfish bait. Next in rank, perhaps, are crayfish. Softshelled crayfish can be fished whole. The tails alone can be used from hardshells. Either the firm, white meat can be pinched out or the shell can be cracked just enough so that the fish can get at the bait but so that the bait is still held firmly on the hook. You can also use grasshoppers, crickets, grubs, small toads, or frogs—there's no end to the variety of natural baits.

Panfish is a generalized term. It applies to those fish which will fit easily into a frying pan—and as a general rule, two or three may fit nicely. Most of them are spread open and then fried whole. A great variety of fish fit into the panfish category, and here is a list of a few of them.

Bullheads Are Everywhere

Bullheads, which undoubtedly gobble more bait than any other fresh-water fish in the country, make their mistake by downing the whole bait in one gulp. You'll seldom hook a bullhead lightly; instead, you'll pull your hook from deep in its throat or belly. Chances are good, in fact, that you'll have to cut your line, tie on a new hook, and retrieve the lost hook when you clean your catch.

Bullheads are found in all forty-eight states and are most abundant in sluggish, mud-bottomed streams and weedy ponds. Even isolated potholes may turn up with a sizable population of bullheads, the eggs having been carried there on the feet of wading birds.

Like other members of the catfish family, bullheads are most active at night or on dull, cloudy days. Or they can be caught in roiled and murky water. They find their food mainly by smell, and they are well equipped to detect the presence of food wherever it is since there are taste buds over their entire bodies, with an extra dosage around the chin and on the long, drooping chin whiskers. You can fish for them with "stink" baits of all sorts. Just make certain you get your bait on the bottom or close to it.

Most bullhead fishing is done with a bobber, and the bait is dropped around stumps or close to rooty banks. Bullheads don't come out into the open water to feed during the daytime.

You can use all types of tackle for bull-

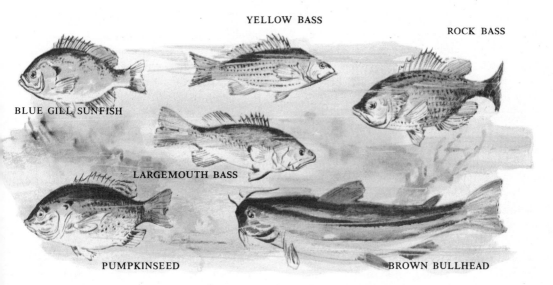

YELLOW BASS

ROCK BASS

BLUE GILL SUNFISH

LARGEMOUTH BASS

PUMPKINSEED

BROWN BULLHEAD

heads. They don't put up a spectacular fight or provide action on the surface. But they do give a determined battle.

Channel catfish, also members of the catfish family, are much larger than bullheads. When fullgrown, they may weigh as much as ten pounds—but the majority caught on hook and line weigh less than a pound.

Channel catfish like swift-flowing, clear water, and this choice of a more invigorating habitat reflects, too, in the sort of fight which they offer when hooked. They're fast—and they'll sometimes even roll on the surface.

Their tails are deeply forked, and their bellies are pure white. These characteristics distinguish them readily from the blunt-tailed black or muddy-yellow bullheads. Young channel catfish are called fiddlers and are spotted.

White and *yellow bass* are both closely related to the big saltwater striped bass. Neither, however, grows very big. The greatest sport in white bass fishing comes in the spring of the year when the white bass are on their spawning runs up streams which empty into the larger bodies of water where they spend most of the year. Fishermen crowd these streams elbow to elbow to catch some of the thick, surging droves of fish as they move in the fast water. White bass will take both artificials and naturals when they are on these runs. The remainder of the year they travel mostly in schools in larger lakes and streams and are generally caught by trolling.

White bass are silvery white and have eight to ten black stripes down each side. Yellow bass, common in southern waters, look very much like white bass but are a coppery yellow in color. Neither fish often exceeds a pound in weight. Both furnish a lot of fast fishing and frequent catches.

Good Eating

Yellow perch provide the best eating of all the panfish. Fishermen often disagree on the ways and wheres of fishing, but you'll seldom get an argument when it comes to talking about the eating qualities of the yellow perch. They are common in lakes, ponds, and many streams throughout the country east of Kansas and north of Kentucky. In these waters they often become too numerous, and stunted perch are common.

Perch travel in schools. So after a school is located, you can stay in business for a long time. Live minnows make excellent bait, but dead minnows, worms, and crayfish are also good. When there's an insect hatch, artificial flies are popular. One peculiarity: Perch sleep at night. Their schools disperse, and you seldom catch any perch after dark. The best time to fish for perch, in fact, is at midday. Since this is the time of day when many fish are off their feed, it makes the perch an even more popular fish. They also feed through the winter and make up a significant part of an ice fisherman's catch.

Yellow perch are easily identified by their yellow over-all color which is set off by five or more dark bands encircling the body. These dark bands have resulted in the descriptive common names of raccoon perch and ring perch. Most yellow perch caught by fishermen weigh a half pound or less. The record catch, though, weighed more than four pounds.

Sunfish is a broad term for a big family of fish. Black bass belong to the sunfish family, for example. But so do crappies, bluegills, and many other smaller "true" sunfish.

Crappies may be classed as panfish, but they are nevertheless often sizable—if they live in water where they can get plenty of food. In the South, it is not uncommon to catch a crappie that weighs three or four pounds. Most crappies caught on hook and line weigh less than half a pound.

Crappies can be caught at all seasons of the year, although fishing for them is best in the spring when they collect in the bays and streams to spawn. Like the yellow perch, they're schooling fish. If you catch one, you should be able to catch more. Some fishermen tie a balloon to the dorsal fin of the first one they catch and then put it back in the water. Then all they have to do is follow the balloon to stay with the school.

A crappie's mouth is paper thin. If you set your hook too hard or try to jerk the fish out of the water, you may tear the hook out of the fish's mouth and lose your catch. Most crappies are caught by still-fishing, but some fisherman prefer to troll for them. Minnows are excellent bait, either live or dead, but a variety of other natural and artificial baits work well, too.

Between them, black and white crappies share a total of more than seventy common names, such as strawberry bass, calico bass, newlights, and many others. As the name implies, the white crappie is silvery-white in color. But along its side there are seven to ten dark bars. Black crappies have a general darker, greener color, and there are black blotches rather than bars.

Pan-sized Bass

Rock bass are also popular sunfish. They have large and seemingly popped eyes with red rims and are called goggle-eyes by many fishermen. Since they are more common in streams than in lakes, they are companions of the smallmouth bass rather than the largemouth bass—and on their first furious strike, you may actually think you've hooked into a sizable bass. But, like other sunfish, their fight doesn't last long. They feed at all times of the night and day and will rush rambunctiously toward anything which is made to move in a lifelike manner. You can use your whole array of natural and artificial baits on rock bass.

Bluegills are no doubt the most common of the panfish platter fillers. They are the favorites of the farm ponds which are scattered across the country. As explained before, the bluegills present a serious problem in farm ponds because they breed rapidly and soon overpopulate them. This means, though, that there is no limit to the number of bluegills which you can catch if you find a farm pond nearby. Occasionally a bluegill grows to a pound in size, but the great ma-

jority usually weigh less than half a pound.

Fishermen generally agree, too, that if bluegills grew to be as big as bass, they would demand and deserve the regal position now claimed by the bass. Their fight is fast. The very moment the hook sinks in, they give forth with a burst of energy which is hard to match. Their runs are not long. They fight it out on the spot. All types of baits and lures can be used—just so the offering is panfish-sized.

Bluegills can be distinguished from other sunfish by the dark spot at the rear portion of each ear flap, and this dark spot is not set off by color as it is on other sunfish. Often their throats are orange and their gill covers are a brilliant blue—and there are many variations in color according to race and the type of water lived in.

Pumpkinseeds, red-ear sunfish, green sunfish, warmouths—these are among the many other sunfish which furnish sport in various sections of the country. None grow big, but all you have to do to have fun with them is to get their size tackle.

Some fishermen will object to this, no doubt, but it is nevertheless true that brook trout can also be classed as panfish. Most brook trout caught nowadays weigh less than half a pound. Brook trout are cold-water fish and are generally classed among the elite game fish. But in size, the bulk of them are panfish.

Pickerel are generally panfish-sized, as are sauger, suckers, and many other fish. Panfish, remember, is simply a term applied to fish which will fit in a pan. It refers to their size.

But the sport which these smaller fish offer depends on you and the sort of tackle you use. Make it light tackle, and you'll soon be enjoying fishing as an entirely new sport.

Scared Scatback

By COLIN LOCHLONS

A false All-State reputation he never claimed put Del of Riverville on the spot

He looked wistfully at the candidates for the Riverville High football team working out on the practice field. Del Smith wanted to be with them, running and passing and kicking footballs. But Del was sure that he would not go out for the squad.

No use in a fellow like me going out for football, he thought morosely. Remembering the season he had tried to make the team at Central City High, he shriveled up inside. You can't play football when you feel like you're—

"Okay, Buff, let's see you cover this one."

The shout from a husky boy cut through Del's thoughts. The shouter swung his foot mightily against a football. A tall, lithe boy with a shock of buff-colored hair shot erect from a linesman's crouch and raced downfield under the kick.

The husky kicker reminded Del of his cousin, Hal Smith. Del's fingers trailed across the front of the pullover sweater he wore. The sweater showed the outline where a letter C had been removed. Hal had given Del the sweater a month before when he left for the State U. football camp. It had been Hal who earned the letter-sweater, starring at halfback for Central City High.

Blame it, Del thought, why couldn't I have been husky and tough like Hal? Why couldn't I have been built more like . . .?

"Hey, watch it! Heads up!"

Del jerked a startled gaze toward the shouter. The husky boy gestured at the foot-

ball he had just kicked. The ball had sliced from his foot. The punt was spiraling toward Del on the sideline. Del made a deft catch of the twisting ball.

In the same instant, he was aware of the tall boy bearing down on him. Del feinted one direction, swerved sharply to the opposite. He tucked the ball beneath the arm away from the charging boy. Del jabbed out his free hand and used the stiff-arm to pivot neatly away, then abruptly he realized that he was interfering with practice. He stopped, tossed the ball to the other boy.

"Didn't mean to butt-in," Del said. "Sorry."

"You're sorry!" The taller boy snorted. "A guy makes me look like a clumsy monkey who never heard of a ballcarrier feinting— and he's sorry!"

He eyed Del. His gaze flicked across the brighter outline on Del's sweater where the C had been.

"I'm Buff Emery," he said. "Haven't I seen you around in the halls?"

Del nodded. "Del Smith," he said. "My folks just moved to Riverville. I enrolled just the day before yesterday."

"Smith, huh?" Buff Emery eyed the C-mark on the sweater again. "Just moved to Riverville, huh? From Central City?"

Again Del nodded. He was a little surprised. The look he gave Del held something close to respectful awe.

"And can we ever use Smith from Central

City!" Buff cried. "Jeeps, why haven't you reported out for the team?"

He did not wait for Del to answer. Buff yelled at the boy who had made the punt.

"Hey, Fred, c'm'ere!" Buff went on talking to Del as though he had not interrupted himself. "Happens the guys elected me captain for this year and two things have been worrying me. One is that I wasn't so hot at covering punts last year—looks from the way you foxed me a minute ago as though I still need plenty of work on it. But I guess being slickered by you shouldn't make a fellow feel too bad. The other thing that made it look as though we might have a rough season was because our star ballcarrier graduated. But with Smith of Central City playing halfback for us, we'll—"

The football captain broke off. He turned toward the husky boy who had come up.

"Meet Del Smith," Buff said. "Fred Lenter, Del. Jeeps, Fred, this is *the Central City High Smith!* And he enrolled at Riverville a couple of days ago!"

The thing hit Del with full force. Suddenly he felt limp and empty inside. This was just dandy. Buff Emery was taking him to be Hal. It was understandable that Buff would have read in sports sheets about Hal's gridiron feats for Central City High. That blamed letter-sweater he had slipped on after school!

"Jeeps!" Buff chortled. "Will we ever go to town with Smith in the tailback spot! Wouldn't surprise me if we kept that old County Championship and—"

"Hold up a sec," Del cut in. "You're going too fast. Maybe you'd better slow down."

"Listen to the guy!" Buff slapped Del on the shoulder. "It's okay to be modest. But after all!"

"Well, look. I'm not even out for the team. I don't intend to come out for the—"

"But you've got to! Jeeps, let's get this thing on the beam. You're Del Smith. Right?"

"Sure. But I—"

"And you're from Central City. Right? It's swell with us that you didn't swagger out here with a Central City letter blazing,

but a guy can see where it was before you ripped it off. Okay. Smith, plus moved here from Central City, plus—well, it adds up to a swell break for Riverville High.

"You've *got* to play football for us! We won't take any answer but yes. How about it? We look for you out here in practice gear tomorrow?"

Del hesitated. An aching longing for a place of his own in the football sun struggled with the knowledge that he would be riding on a ticket that Riverville thought was being handed to Hal Smith. Blame it, he hadn't *said* he was the Smith who had been a Central River star. He stifled the shriveled feeling inside. He shrugged, nodded.

"You're in for a big letdown. *I* wasn't the big shot at Central City," he said. "But if that's the way you want it, I'll report for practice tomorrow."

"That's sure the way we want it!"

Buff Emery ran off across the field, bent on telling the other boys. Fred Lenter stood regarding Del.

"Smith, of Central City fame," Fred said. His tone was flat. He eyed Del. There seemed to Del to be a doubt in Fred's expression.

"Let's have it straight, Smith," Fred said. "I'm trying for the left halfback spot. Whether you're a big-city-high hotshot or not, I'm still trying for the left halfback spot!"

He trotted off across the field.

Del stood in his position awaiting the opening kickoff for Riverville's first game. It was still hard to believe. Less than two weeks before, he had been just a new student at Riverville High. Now he was Riverville's regular left halfback. Little things that had happened flashed through his mind.

"Jeeps, Del, you fake a tackler out of his shoes! Where the heck did you learn to dodge like that?"

Del had pondered Buff Emery's question. Where *had* he learned to squirm and fake and swivel his hips? Sure, after watching Hal run away from tacklers in Central City games, Del Smith had pretended he was Hal in fancy maneuvers in his own back yard.

He had made many a make-believe touchdown run there. Wriggling and dodging tacklers. But they were only imaginary tacklers.

To his pleased amazement, he had discovered that he could run away from real tacklers. His confidence increased as practice went on. The boys accepted him. He was no flash in the pan. Fred Lenter had been shifted to blocking back. Del frowned as another scene came to his mind.

It happened one day in the dressing room. Fred Lenter regarded Del thoughtfully. He spoke in a low tone so that only Del heard him.

"You know, Smith," Fred said, "it's a funny thing. I saw a newsreel shot of the game last year when Central City won the State Championship. Anybody would think from the movie shots that Central City's Smith was a husky fellow. At least as big as I am. Did Central City provide players with over-stuffed padding? You don't weigh within twenty pounds of me."

Del had not answered Fred directly.

"As a matter of fact," he said, "I really put on weight during the summer. I weigh one-sixty-six."

"And I would have said the fellow I saw in the newsreel weighed better than one-eighty-five," Fred said. "Funny thing—if it was the same fellow!"

That was the first hint that Fred Lenter was suspicious.

There had been another time in practice scrimmage when a second-team player intercepted a pass Del aimed at Buff. The second-team boy eluded tacklers until only Del was between him and a touchdown. Del shivered now at recollection of the wincing fear that had welled in him. He had remembered vividly the broken collarbone and the searing pain when he had tackled a bigger boy that time he went out for football at Central City High.

He was physically unable to drive himself for an all-out tackle. He just crowded the second-team boy until he ran out of bounds. As they lined up for the next play, Fred Lenter sidled close beside Del.

"Smith, of Central City," Fred murmured. "Doesn't seem as though the big-city flash would lack the guts to make a tackle!"

Del moved a couple of restless steps now at the memory. Blame it, three or four times he had tried to work the talk around to where

he could let it out that he was only plain Del Smith. He would be just as good a player. He had found himself. The fellows would not hold it against him because—

Phre-e-e-e-e-et!

The blast of the referee's whistle cut through Del's thoughts. The other team's kicker booted a high kickoff. The ball arched toward Del. He fielded it in full stride and flashed a quick glance at the pattern of blocking. A clear lane opened down the right sideline.

Del angled across. A tackler partially slipped a block, lunged at him. Del swerved his hips and the tackler's hands slipped from his pants. Del sped past a tackler trying to cut in from the side. It looked as though he was away for a touchdown.

But the safety man of the other team raced over. He gave ground to lessen the angle. Del saw that he was not going to be able to beat the tackler. Del feinted left, cut

back quickly. The tackler was not fooled by the fake. He drove at Del. Just before he would have been hit, Del angled sharply out of bounds.

He railed at himself inwardly. He knew that he might have broken the tackler's effort, surely would have made a few more yards by driving straight.

"The way to go!" Buff Emery slapped Del on the back. The captain clapped his hands, yelled pepper talk. "Del's given us the start, gang. Let's show these guys who's boss right now!"

Going into the huddle, Del knew that Fred Lenter was eying him. A kind of disdain was in Fred's eyes.

"Should have had five or six more yards," Fred said flatly. Definite challenge was in his tone as he added, "Gutless fellows have no business playing football!"

On the second play from scrimmage, Del took the ball in the tailback position. He faked beautifully as though he was swinging wide on an end run and drew the defense over. Then he shot a hard pass diagonally across to the opposite side. Buff Emery grabbed the ball. The captain sped down the sideline into the end zone without a tackler getting closer than five yards. Fred Lenter kicked the point and it was 7-0.

Just before the end of the half, the rival team scored. They missed the conversion try, but Del was not happy. That touchdown was largely his fault. He had missed a tackle and a ballcarrier ran forty yards to the Riverville two-yard line before Lenter spilled him from behind.

So I missed a tackle, Del told himself fiercely. So what? Anybody can miss a tackle. But he knew that he had hesitated a second's fraction before he threw himself at the man. He just could not make himself go all out. Everytime there was that shriveling fear inside.

Between halves Fred Lenter jabbed with the needle again. "It's too bad they stopped the two platoon system," Fred said. "Maybe we could have a *defensive* half in the game as well as a flashy ballcarrier!"

Del flushed. Grimly he vowed that he would make Fred eat his words.

Fred Lenter did double duty all right. In the middle of the third quarter Fred demonstrated that he could block as well as tackle.

Del carried the ball on an off-tackle slant. It was Fred who threw the key block on a line backer to shake Del into the clear. Then, unbelievably, it was Fred who cut in front of Del and threw a crisp block that washed the safety man out of any chance for a tackle. Del carried the ball across the goal line. But he knew it was Fred's touchdown. He trotted near Fred as they went upfield after Fred kicked the conversion try to make the score 14-6 for Riverville.

"Eight of those points are yours, really," Del said. "Two points after and the TD they gave me credit for."

Fred glanced at Del. It was the closest thing to a friendly look Del had ever had from him. But then he merely grunted, giving no reply.

The rival team did not fold up. They received the kickoff and ground away with a line attack. Most of the plays were aimed at the side of the line backed up by Del. They scored a touchdown with two minutes of the fourth quarter gone. They kicked the point to make it 14-13 on the scoreboard.

Darn it, Del thought. They've spotted that I'm a rotten tackler. I've got to slam into them.

He just could not do it. Every time there was an opportunity to smash into a ballcarrier, he funked it.

In the last minute of play Fred saved the game after Del shirked a tackle. Buff was slickered on covering a punt. The ballcarrier roared downfield. He squeezed past as Del tried to crowd him out of bounds. Fred's desperation tackle from behind knocked him off his feet on the six-yard line. In the dressing room, Buff slapped Del on the back.

"Jeeps, am I glad we had you in there!" Buff cried. "That long run put the old game on ice!"

"Yea, man! . . . You left 'em like they stood still! . . . Sure did carry the mail! . . . Two TD's and both of them engineered by Smith!"

Other boys joined Buff in praising Del. Not Fred Lenter. He stood silently, scowling. When the room quieted, Fred faced Del.

"We were lucky to hold them to two touchdowns," Fred said clearly. "There *should* be *four* fellows in the secondary defense!"

Buff Emery broke the silence which followed. He glared at Fred.

"Never figured you for a sorehead," Buff said. "Jealous of Del because he beat you out for the tailback job! What are you talking about, anyhow?"

"I'm talking about the way Smith chickens out every time there's a tough tackle." Fred eyed Del steadily. "Smith won't deny it—he knows it's true!"

Other boys looked at Del. An air of expectancy held the dressing room. Del flicked a glance at Fred Lenter, then dropped his gaze to the floor.

"It's a free country," Del muttered.

"Everybody is entitled to his own opinion."

That dressing room scene was the beginning of friction that threatened to ruin Riverville High's football season. If there had been a coach, he might have worked things out. But Riverville was too small to afford a regular coach. The faculty member who handled the team knew little football. Buff Emery was the real coach. Buff was no fool. He saw things after the first game—and Fred Lenter—lifted the scales of adulation from his eyes. But he did not see them the way Fred did.

"Look, Del," the captain said after the second game, "you scored the winning touchdown this afternoon and we squeaked through. I'm grateful. But—well, the thing is, you aren't so hot on defense. Fred and Blacky have to make tackles on your side of the line. Didn't the coaches at Central City High teach you guys tackling?"

Del shuddered inwardly. He was remembering an assistant coach at the big high school yelling caustic criticism in tackling drill. He remembered hurling himself at a much heavier first team ballcarrier and the collision against hard-driving knees. Oh yes, Central City taught tackling! But there was nothing he could say.

"Guys are beginning to gripe about it," Buff went on. "Ever since Fred shot off his bazoo. It's no help that you take his needling without handing it back, either."

Del knew deep in his heart that there had to come a clash with Fred. He dreaded it. He tried to rationalize, tell himself that Fred was a bully, a sorehead because he had been beaten out of the tailback job. But it was no go. It bothered Del to realize that he was getting by under a false reputation. And he was more and more sure that Fred knew he was not the Smith who had starred at Central City.

Things were bound to come to a head— but the old shriveling fear ate inside him. He cringed at the thought of physical combat.

The fight came in the dressing room following the third game of the season.

The game had ended in a 7-7 tie. Del scored the Riverville touchdown—but he funked the tackle that would have kept the other team from making the tying touchdown late in the game. Fred Lenter called a spade a spade in the dressing room after the boys had dressed.

"I'm fed up," the husky blocking back said. "A fellow knocks himself out blocking for a mug who can run with the ball and that's all. He makes tackles that the mug ought to make. Comes one that the mug misses and nobody can make and—aw! Why don't you give the fellows the real story and stop masquerading as a hero, Smith!"

The room quieted. Del stood up slowly. He said, "What do you mean?"

"You never played football at Central

City! You've been riding high down here, playing us for a bunch of backwoods hicks! You're a four-flusher, Smith—and I can prove it!"

Fred reached in his locker. He pulled out a folded paper. In it there was a picture of a ballcarrier side-stepping a tackler.

"This is a copy of the *State University News,*" Fred said. "I wrote and asked a few questions. This picture in the *News*—and the story with it—answers all of them. Listen."

He read from the paper.

"Hal Smith, Freshman sensation who ran wild in his first varsity game, carries on the type of play that made him an All State selection as a Senior last year at Central City High. State is fortunate that relaxed eligibility rules makes it possible for Smith to play varsity ball as a Freshman . . ."

Fred's lips curled.

"Masquerading as a hot shot," he bit out. "A gutless fourflusher! Probably your cousin is the same breed and it will come out when the big boys begin really banging him!"

Del clenched his fist. That was hitting below the belt.

"Hal's more football player than a dozen like you," Del said.

He faced the other boys.

"Okay," he said. "I went to Central City High. I went out for the team in my sophomore year and—well, never mind. I never claimed to be Hal. I'm the same guy I was the day Buff talked me into coming out for the team. 'Course I know I should have knocked that idea out of your heads and I apologize for that, but—" He turned back to Fred Lenter. He said, "I think you'd better take back that crack about Hal."

Fred scowled. Something flickered across the back of his eyes. He said gruffly, "Nuts! I don't take back anything I said!"

Afterwards, Del was appalled at what he did then. He leaped at Fred. He swung a round-house right and his fist crashed full against Fred's mouth. The blow staggered the bigger boy. He looked incredulous, as though he could not believe what he saw. Then he said, "You asked for it, Gutless!"

It really was no fight. Fred Lenter outweighed Del twenty pounds. He knew something of boxing and Del knew nothing. Fred's first blow connected with Del's jaw and sent him sprawling. He crashed into a row of lockers. But he was up instantly. He rushed at Fred, thrashing both fists wildly. Fred shook off the blows. He knocked Del down again.

Del got up. He rushed at the bigger boy. Fred Lenter scowled. "Get some sense, fellow," Fred panted. "You couldn't punch your way out of a paper bag!"

Del landed two ineffective blows to Fred's head. Fred crashed a solid fist to Del's jaw. Again Del slammed into the lockers. He was groggy, practically out on his feet. But he struggled up. He stumbled forward toward Fred. Buff Emery caught him, held him with both arms.

" 'S enough," the captain said. He eyed Fred Lenter. "And you called the guy gutless!"

Fred Lenter wore a peculiar expression. He ran his tongue across his lips.

"Smith," he said, "I apologize for the crack I made about your cousin. Maybe I owe you an apology for other things I've thought but—oh, nuts!"

Fred turned and left the dressing room.

Del was thinking about the fight as he waited for the start of the Rock City game. Today he was going to lick the shriveling fear. He was going to show Fred Lenter that he wouldn't chicken out anymore!

But it was not so easy.

A Rock City halfback broke through the line and barreled downfield on Del's side. Del had every intention of meeting him head on—but he funked it. At the last second instead of hurling himself at the ballcarrier, he tried to edge the rival man out of bounds. He failed. The play went for a touchdown and although the try-for-point was missed, Riverville was behind.

Tears of frustration stung Del's eyes. He gritted his teeth. What was the matter with him?

You've got to lick this thing, he told himself furiously. You didn't dodge contact when

Fred Lenter knocked you sprawling. You got up from the floor and came back for more. Forget that tackle you tried when you were only a skinny sophomore!

The game went on. The first half was almost at an end when the same rival ballcarrier broke through tackle and roared down at Del. A blocker was in front. It was impossible to edge the ballcarrier out of bounds.

Del gritted his teeth. He found himself giving ground, desperately hoping a teammate would come up to help. But there were no teammates near enough. It was up to Del Smith to stop the play or give the opponents another touchdown.

He did not know that he made a decision. He only knew that abruptly he hurled his body desperately into the air as the blocker threw his block. Del sailed over the block. It was not really a tackle. He simply collided with the ballcarrier. But they both sprawled to the ground.

Del lay there, half unbelieving that he had done it. Buff ran up, pulled him to his feet.

"The way to go!" the captain shouted. "You slickered that blocker like you slicker tacklers. I knew you could do it!"

Del grinned. He felt wonderful. So he hadn't made a clean tackle, he had stopped the guy, hadn't he? Why, there was no more to it than getting up after Fred Lenter had battered him to the floor! He looked around for Fred. The husky blocking back was staring at him. Fred wore an odd look.

It was still 6-0 when the half ended. Scoreboard figures had not changed at the end of the third quarter. Del grew more and more grim. That one miserable missed tackle just couldn't cost his team the game!

"Let's go," he cried suddenly. "We've got to score!"

Fred Lenter eyed him. The husky boy said, "Lead the way, we'll follow—Smith!"

He had never called Del anything but the cold, formal Smith. The biting mockery in Fred's tone made Del more determined.

The signal for Del to carry on the off tackle slant was given in the huddle. He eyed Fred challengingly. "Give me a block," he said. "And I'll lead the way!"

Fred gave him the block. He cut down the Rock City line backer. Del raced downfield. But three men were cutting across to pin him against the sideline.

He had to score the touchdown. He had to wipe out the touchdown he had given Rock City. If only there was a blocker to take one of the tacklers.

"Cut over!" A panting voice gasped behind Del. "Give me a chance to block those fellows!"

Del knew it was Fred. But he also knew if he slowed or cut, one of the Rock City men would smear him. Suddenly he knew what he could do. The old, crawling shrivel curled inside him at the thought. It would be murder to throw himself at those big guys! He drove harder. He wasn't going to make it. He half-turned, yelled, "Take it! I'll give you a block!" He tossed the ball toward Fred.

He threw his body blindly at the two front tacklers. He felt the shock and jar of the collision and then he was tangled with arms and legs and bodies. The jam pile forced the third potential tackler to swerve. The instant he lost gave Fred his vital chance. He cut inside and the grasping fingers of the tackler were brushed aside by Fred's stiff arm. Fred raced on into the end zone.

Fred kicked the point after touchdown. Scoreboard figures changed to Riverville 7; Rock City 6. Buff and other teammates pounded Del's shoulders as they trotted upfield for the kickoff.

"You don't need to put out rave notices for me," Del said. "As a matter of fact, flipping that lateral was a reflex action. I had a closeup of those three Rock City bruisers and I didn't want any part of being tackled by them! So I threw the ball any old where. I was scared!"

"Yeah," Fred said. He was looking at Del. There was something about Fred's expression that told Del things were different.

"Yeah," Fred repeated. "You were scared. Scared scatback is what you are—Del!"

Del grinned. He had a comfortable feeling that Fred and other teammates fully accepted Del Smith—as Del Smith.

Tied

By MERRITT P. ALLEN

Rivalry between Hi and Sam was traditional among Rogers' Rangers

"Push it up another inch." The tall boy in buckskin breeches made an upward motion with one hand. He was stripped to the waist and his shoulders glistened with sweat in the warm April sunshine.

"That'll make it six-foot-one, Sam." The Ranger with the measuring stick waited.

"Push it up," the boy repeated.

"There she is." The man raised the cross-bar a peg on each of the two uprights and stepped back.

Sam dug in his toes and made the short run in quick, powerful strides. At a certain point his right foot stopped and his body went up and on as though hurled by a mighty spring. With arms wide and short queue straight out behind, he pulled his legs under him and to one side, throwing his shoulders the other way to aid the lift. For a split-second he seemed to hang over the bar, struggling to get his right heel up, then it touched the stick, knocking it to the ground behind him as he landed on his feet.

"Good try!"

"Missed by a flea's eyelash!"

"Bully venture, m' lad!"

The crowd of Rangers and British regulars yelled until the stone walls of Fort Amherst threw their jumbled words back to the Adirondacks.

"Come on, Hi, it's your turn." The referee picked up the crossbar. "Six foot?"

"Yeh." Hiram Brown grinned. He was shorter than Sam and older, perhaps twenty-five, but wiry and active as a red squirrel. He had been the best jumper of all Rogers' Rangers until Captain John Stark brought Sam Greene over from New Hampshire the year before. Hi and Sam had become bosom friends in spite of the fact that no matter what they did in work or play it was nip and tuck between them.

Now Hi spat on his hands, dug in his moccasined toes and shot away toward the take-off. He could run! And jump! As he went up his mouth opened wide and his face twisted with supreme effort. He tucked his feet under him and reached for the sky with his rigid fingers. The hundredth part of an inch would have taken him over—but he lacked that much. The sole of his left moccasin brushed the bar and brought it down.

"A dead tie!" the referee shouted above the yells of the crowd.

Hi walked over to Sam, grinning again, and asked, "Whatsay, bub, if we settle it though it takes all night?"

"Sure," the boy agreed. "I'll trim you next—" He stopped short.

"Rangers!" The major appeared from nowhere and the crowd fell silent, for when Robert Rogers spoke you listened, whether or not he was your commander. "Rangers! I want two volunteers for an important mission. Who will go?"

"I will, sir," Hi answered instantly.

"I will, sir," Sam echoed, just ahead of a hundred others.

"Done." Rogers nodded at the two. "Come to my headquarters for instructions."

"Still tied." Hi poked Sam in the ribs as they walked away. "Mebbe this'll show who's best man."

"You'll win if we have to run away from the enemy," Sam jibed. "Connecticut men are good at that."

"Huh!" Hi snorted. "Fer's I've noticed, New Hampshire men don't git nigh 'nough the enemy to run away from 'em."

"Tied again, even when it comes to sass," Sam laughed.

Rogers' Rangers took pride in the fact that they were ready for anything at any time. This was no exception and that night, when it was safely dark, Hi and the boy Sam were in a canoe paddling north along the east shore of Lake Champlain.

Their mission sounded simple enough: merely carry dispatches from General Amherst to General Murray, who was in command of a British and Colonial force that was marching on Montreal from Quebec and should be in the vicinity of Sorell within ten days.

Easy? Not when you understood it was five hundred miles from Crown Point through a wilderness where Indians and French settlers hated their southern neighbors with all their hearts. Furthermore, it was early April, a time when that country of streams and bogs would be congenial only to muskrats and frogs.

Hi knew the way, for he had been there the year before with Rogers when they wiped out the St. Francis Indian village. That was an awful trip, not the fighting but the struggle to get home again through swamps and forests that for some strange reason were destitute of game. Rangers died by the dozen from starvation and fatigue and only a few finally reached the settlements on the Connecticut River. But Hi was not afraid of anything that lived nor any set of conditions that might arise.

General Amherst, who wanted those messages delivered, was a good fellow, far better than the average Britisher in Ranger opinion, so Hi put the letters in an oilcloth bag, tied it firmly around his neck, crooked a finger at Sam, and they were off.

Before dawn they went ashore near the mouth of the Winooski River. The stream was a highway for Indians so they landed on rocks and carried the canoe into a cedar coppice. They dared not make a fire, so ate their meat cold and lay down on the moss.

"Maybe we should have fetched blankets," the boy suggested.

"Be you a Ranger or jest a soldier?" Hi gave him a look.

"I feel like a waterwheel, the way we paddled all night."

"That's the way to git there."

"I've heard the French voyagers stop every hour for ten minutes."

"Yeh, and what does that git 'em! They're losin' the war and America. It's them ten minuteses that tell the story."

"Cat's foot!" the boy said wearily. "I suppose the British never waste any time—though I haven't noticed it."

"Sure they do, bub, that's jest the p'int I'm aimin' at. That'll cost 'em this hull country some day." The man's tone was very earnest.

"Who'll they lose it to if, as you say, they lick the French?"

"To us Americans. You know, same's I do, we oughta be able to run our own country. Some day whilst they're lollygaggin' round drinkin' tea, we'll step in and muckle onto things."

"Shucks!" Sam commented drowsily.

"You oughter hear Cap'n John Stark talk. He'd make even a squirt your age understand things."

"I don't want to hear anybody talk right now. Go to sleep, Hi."

"Uh huh." But Hi stood watch for four hours, then called Sam to take over.

Early in the forenoon they saw four Indians go up the river in a canoe. In the afternoon they returned, a heap of fish showing above the sides of the canoe, and struck out north into the lake.

"They're camped on the islands," Hi said. "If they was up the bay, they'd fish the rivers nearer home."

After a while he laid his rifle over a log and went down to the lake for a drink. As he dropped over the bank, Sam, who was keeping an eye on the river, heard a frightened squall. The next moment a panther shot from the limb of a pine and gathered itself for a leap toward the water.

The boy's rifle cracked and the cat went into the air and disappeared. Woodsman that he was, he reloaded before he stirred out of his tracks, then ran to the top of the bank. Below, the panther was kicking its last at the edge of the waves and a few feet away a kitten and a snapping turtle appeared to be dancing together. Hi's knife flicked out, severing the turtle's neck, and the kitten vanished in the bushes.

"Git for cover," Hi whispered hoarsely, as he came up the bank. "The Injuns heard that shot."

"I can't help it," Sam said, falling back to the cedars. "That old cat would have made mincemeat of you."

"She was sort of unfriendly," the older scout admitted.

"What happened?"

"One of them fool things. The kitten must've been pokin' 'long the shore and made a swipe at the turtle's nose. Snap! 'Come quick, Ma, I'm in a trap!' the kit squalled. And Ma was comin', thinkin' I was the trap. Much obleeged, bub. The tie's busted 'n now—you're one ahead of me." Hi rubbed his stubbly chin and grinned.

"You'll catch up," Sam said. "Think the Indians'll be back?"

"Not with that load of fish, they won't. But they'll have their eyes peeled for us 'n from now on. We'll have to look wise."

Because of the added precautions, they made slower progress that night. There were islands to be skirted and sandbars to be felt out if they didn't want the bottom ripped out of the canoe. Toward morning they came to the big bar that, according to Hi's memory, reached from the mainland to one of the large islands and was so long it would have to be crossed on foot. They carried the canoe over and waited until daylight to brush out the trail in the sand. After that

they paddled into the marsh and along a stagnant channel to a pothole that was screened by the first spring leaves of high-bush blueberries.

They had lost mileage but gained security that paid off about noon when four canoe loads of warriors fanned out from the south and went back and forth on the bar.

"St. Francis pups," Hi whispered, peering through the bushes. "Hope I live to see the day a man can travel his own lake without dodgin' them varmints."

"They think it's their lake," the boy said. "They were here first."

"If you was old 'nough to understand the Bible, you'd know them critters 're Canaanites and we're the Chosen People."

"Then General Amherst is Moses or Joshua, as you look at it?"

"Condum it, bub, how many times I got to tell you Amherst is only a Britisher?"

"They're going!" Sam whispered.

"The Britishers? Oh, the Injuns. By grab, they be pullin' out!" Hi drew a long breath. "You take a nap now, bub, I'll watch."

"Don't you ever sleep, Hi?"

"I can, but I don't like to." The scout eyed the disappearing Indians and stretched his arms for the first time in hours.

They stayed in the canoe all day, for there was no dry land near the pothole. Their legs were cramped, but that was part of the job. When you were a Ranger, you took things as you found them. Ducks and geese were everywhere, but they dared not shoot one so they ate sparingly of their rations and dozed and watched. Twice during the day it rained in true April fashion and when they set out at night the wind was in the northeast, the "cold corner," which might mean sour weather for ten days. At that time of year you never could tell whether it was winter or spring.

The next five days seemed as many weeks to young Sam. Frontier life and Ranger training had toughened him to hardship, but that endless rain, sometimes mixed with snow, nearly got him down. They were never dry day or night. In that land of bogs northeast of Missisquoi Bay everything was wet; trees,

sky and earth dripped water and when darkness came it was hard to find enough solid ground to lie on.

"Are you sure you know where you're going?" the boy finally asked.

"I've told you forty times I was through here with Rogers last year," Hi answered tartly. "We'll hit the St. Francis river 'fore long."

"If we hit anything it's sure to be more water," Sam grumbled. "If *this* is Canada, why do we want to take it away from the French?"

"We don't," Hi said. "The Britishers want it. They an' the French are still tryin' to decide which one o' them got there first."

They came to the river early the next morning, at a place above a long stretch of rapids. One glance showed them it was too high to be forded. They lay in concealment for a while and saw no sign of human life, so while one stood guard the other gathered driftwood for a raft, tying it together with buckskin strings brought for that purpose.

Patiently, time after time, they tested the current until they found a place from where a log was carried diagonally to the opposite bank. The most hazardous step of the journey had come, but neither mentioned it.

As they launched the raft, snow began to fall from the treacherous April sky. Hanging on with one hand and holding their rifles and powder horns high with the other, they staked their fortunes on the whim of the river. The water was kind at first and the logs moved smoothly to midstream, beyond it and in toward shore.

Then, as Indians would have explained it, the Water Manitou turned his face away. And he turned it fast, too. With a suddenness that nearly pitched its crew overboard, the raft made a half circle and plunged downstream.

"We're in the rapids!" Sam yelled.

"Strip!" Hi roared. "It's our best chance when we have to swim for it."

"We'll lose everything!"

"Strip, you fool!"

They tore off their heavy clothes and threw themselves face down as the raft hit the plunging water. After that they had no clear idea of what happened.

Sometimes the raft was deep under water and the only reason they were able to hang on was that they were going with the current. Again they shot into the air and came down with a slap that all but knocked the wind out of them. Whirlpools spun them, crosscurrents buffeted them sideways, pieces of driftwood went by with the force of cannon balls. They could see and hear nothing but water and the whole world seemed a churning mass of fluid with not a single spot on which to rest and breathe again.

It could not last long. It didn't. With a shock that tore the logs apart, the raft hit a rock head-on and the men were hurled, sprawling like frogs, into a great pool under the bank.

When the boy came to, he was on land and gradually he understood that Hi was squeezing water out of his lungs.

"Are we dead, Hi?" he whispered, when he found the necessary breath.

"Mebbe you be, but I ain't," Hi answered stolidly.

Sam suddenly said in a queer voice, "I can hear bells. Where am I?"

"In the woods." Hi sat back on his heels and looked at him. "I lugged you back from the river in case somebody come along."

"You fished me out?"

"Yeh. Your long hair was handy."

"Then we're still tied." Sam smiled faintly. "The panther for me, now this for you." He came up on his elbow with a jerk. "There! Hear that bell? I tell you we are dead."

"Talk sense," Hi snapped. "We jest crossed the St. Francis, not the Jordan. That's a churchbell in a French settlement. I scouted the place last year. We'll go to town, if you can walk."

"Go to town!" The boy stared at him. "Man alive! Except for that bag of letters around your neck, we haven't a stitch on us."

"So I've noticed." Hi grinned. "But we'll git some. Most everybody'll be in church for the next hour. Come on, bub, spring to!"

Shivering in the snow that melted as it fell, they crept through the woods until they saw a log house on the outskirts of a small settlement.

"Look there!" Sam caught his partner's arm and pointed through a screen of bushes. "Look at that clothes-line back of the house."

"Yeh." Hi nodded. "Nice folks live there. It wouldn't be polite to walk right by and not stop."

"But look at the clothes on the line," the boy insisted. "Seven pairs of pants, five shirts and a lot of dresses."

"Must be mebbe ten children to home, all 'bout growed up," Hi estimated. "We'll jest walk up and git dressed."

"But the people in the house might— might see us, Hi."

"I told you, bub, they're all to church. Can't you remember nothin'? This is Sunday, that's why them clothes 're out on the line. The Frenchmen believe that if they hang their winter clothes out and let the Sunday air blow through 'em before they put 'em away for summer, it'll keep the moths out of 'em. Come along now and git dressed." He led the way out of the bushes.

Young Sam, at least, felt a lot more like facing the world when he was safely inside a pair of woolen trousers. They and the shirt he chose to go with them fitted none too well, but that didn't matter. He tore a strip from a red dress and tied it around his middle for a belt.

"How do I look?" he asked.

"Not so bad," Hi admitted, putting the final touches to his own new spring outfit. "Except that your feet stick out. There must be some extry shoes in the house. Let's look."

The cabin was empty of people, but the Rangers found a dozen pairs of cowhide shoes, which they didn't like, and two pairs of moccasins that fitted nicely. As a further act of friendship, to show they felt at home there, they took three long twisted loaves of bread and a quarter of smoked beef. They looked for weapons and had to be content with a hatchet and butcher knife.

The sun was shining when they came out, showing a fringe of wild spring flowers at the edge of the forest. An hour before they had been in desperate straits, but now they walked away well clothed and happy without, as Hi said, anyone having offered the slightest objection to what they had done.

So far as they knew, the villagers made no attempt to follow them. They spent the night in a cedar swamp and in the morning climbed a high hill.

"There she is!" Hi whooped.

And there she was, the broad and beautiful St. Lawrence.

"Look, man!" Sam pointed to the right. "There's an army camp. British. See the red coats?"

"Talk about luck!" Hi threw back his head and laughed.

They stood there for a few moments, looking and talking, as completely off guard as if they had been greenhorns from the settlements. They knew Indian scouts would be following the army along the high ground, but they forgot until a musket roared behind them. Hi half turned and fell on his back.

Sam spun around and faced a charging Indian who, believing one white man was out and the other unarmed, was coming in for the kill. The boy's only weapon was the butcher knife, but thanks to the rigid training of Major Roberts he knew how to use it.

Had the warrior seen the knife earlier, he would have taken the safer course of reloading and trying another shot, but he had now gone too far for that. He whipped out his own knife, started to circle, then turned like a wolf and lunged. At such a moment, if you wanted to live, you concentrated not on your weapon but on the hand that held your enemy's. Each man grabbed for the other's wrist and both made it, locking in a grip that could only be broken by brute force.

For a moment they stood that way, glaring into each other's eyes, then they began to struggle. It was a question of muscle and sure foot work. An instant's weakness or a slip would be the end. Their toes dug into the soft ground as they strained and heaved, each trying to throw the other off balance. The tension was terrific even on seasoned muscles.

Sam felt his arm and shoulders burning under the fearful pressure that was striving to bend them. If they did bend!

He glanced at the Indian's knife and saw it was nearer his face. He put everything he had into an effort to push it back, but it would not go. Nor could he force his own knife nearer the mark. He tried to think of a way to kick or trip the warrior, but dared not try to stand on one foot for even an instant. He shot another look at the knife and thought it was closer. His arm was not bend-

ing so it must be that his back was beginning to buckle.

If he failed now, with Hi gone, it could be said that Rogers' Rangers were too soft to carry out the routine job of delivering letters.

Sam watched the Indian's face for a clue to his thoughts and saw a look of wild joy creep into the beady eyes. The warrior knew he was winning. And then, in a flash, the eyes stared wide and the man collapsed in a heap. Sam fell over him, leaped up and saw that the blade of Hi's hatchet had severed the Indian's spinal cord close above the shoulders.

"Hi! You're not dead!" The boy was beside him in two steps and found him lying in a pool of blood.

"Guess I'm goin', bub," Hi mumbled. "My thigh. Bleedin' like a stuck pig."

"I'll stop it somehow."

"Too far up for a twister. Take the letters through to the Britishers."

Sam ripped Hi's trousers away from the wound and stared helplessly at the outpouring blood. Then a scene flashed through his brain: Lake George—deep snow—a Ranger bleeding to death—Rogers cutting off his own queue and plugging the hole. It worked then; it would work now. He slashed off his hair, pushed it into the wound and bound it tightly with strips of his shirt.

"Take the letters, bub. Take the letters," Hi whispered.

"I will," the boy said. He took his friend in his arms and went down the hill toward the British camp.

A few days later Sam went into the tent where Hi was convalescing under a surgeon's care.

"Much obleeged for fetchin' me in," Hi said simply.

"If you didn't know how to throw a hatchet, I wouldn't have been there to fetch you in," Sam answered.

"Well, I'll be hanged!" Hi slapped his sound leg.

"What now?"

"We're still tied, bub."

Welly's Orphan Animals

By HUGH ROBINSON

Wellington's mother opened the way for trouble when she ruled against adopting stray dogs and cats

We were straggling up the ranger's trail near the pass, about nine on a Saturday morning, when we jumped a jackrabbit. There was me, and Scrub McInnis, and Wellington James McInnis, who is six years old and about three-eighths as long as his name.

These Southern California mountains aren't spectacular, just rough country five or six thousand feet up, but they're mountains, covered with live oak and brush rather than evergreens. The air was sharp, the sun was warm and the shade cool. There was already even a little snow in some north hillside patches; swell day for a hike, even if Scrub did have to bring along a kid brother.

Wellington was ahead, casting back and forth like a setter, when this jackrabbit spooked and loped off, jumping high every few hops and swerving into a big curve that meant it would be back soon as we left.

Welly let out a screech.

"A baby one!" he yelled. "Lookit, lookit!"

He dived down in the weeds and picked up a little brown ball of fuzz. Scrub heaved a sort of sigh of relief.

"There's your show pet," he says. "A baby jackrabbit. Nobody'll have one like that. Now we can dig in and really do some hiking."

"Just what have we been doing since daybreak?" I asked him, emptying half a pint of sand and burrs out of each shoe. "Here I been fighting brush and leap-frogging cactus

for two daggone hours on this dried-up old mountain and you say it's not a hike yet."

"Well, Al," Scrub says, "we had something on our minds, me and Welly." He pointed at the rabbit. "How's about it, Welly boy?"

Wellington stood holding it, and it just lay there all limp in his hands and looked back at him.

"Aw," says Wellington. "The pore little thing."

Scrub glared at him.

"I'll bet that was his mamma ran away," says Wellington.

Scrub sort of wilted. "I knew it," he said. "Its mamma wants it back, I spose."

"Yeah," says Wellington. "Gee!" He set it down and it hopped back in the weeds, and Welly went wandering off up the trail.

"I guess I better explain," Scrub says to me. "Told you I had to bring him or I couldn't come, but there's more to it. I got to find him a pet."

So out it comes. Next Saturday there's to be a kid's pet show. Once when Scrub was a kid, he won a ribbon on an old pooch they used to have. Naturally, Welly has to do as well as big brother. Only dogs are out.

"Old Sandy ate so much, and had so many vet bills, and the fleas, why, every so often we'd have to move out and fumigate," Scrub says. "Mom says, 'Never again!' But Welly wore her down this much, she says okay, get him a pet if he has to have it, long as it's just

389

for the show; but no cats, and no dogs. Then last night you come over, so I thought maybe you wouldn't mind, and all that."

Me, I'm just long-suffering old Al. Dad was going over the mountains on business and I'd invited Scrub to spend the day up there, and Dad would pick us up in the evening. I hadn't minded when Scrub rang in his kid brother on the deal, but he'd held out on the pet angle until now.

"I could have got a tame rabbit or something," Scrub says, "only I figured we'd try to be original, see? I didn't count on this mushy streak he gets. He'll torture flies and kick cats and throw rocks at robins, but all of a sudden, when there's no sense to it, he goes soft-hearted. We couldn't even kill Sandy's fleas when Welly was around—had to take them outdoors where their mammas could find 'em."

Wellington had wandered back and overheard us. "Well," he began, "how'd *you* like to be a flea and have some big old—"

"Skip it!" Scrub says, disgusted.

Welly stood still, looking at me kind of funny. You could almost hear it perk in his head—idea!

"I'm cold," he says suddenly, and makes a great to-do about shivering.

"Where's your sweater?" says Scrub.

"In the front seat," Welly says, "with yours."

The front seat of Dad's car then being eighty or a hundred miles away and still going, I'm elected. I took off Dad's old hunting coat and draped it over Welly, and it fit like Grandpa's socks on the banty rooster. But Welly seemed happy enough. Pretty soon I saw why.

We started off again. Wellington began beating the brush, kicking at stumps and pushing his fingers into holes, and filling the jacket pockets with round rocks and square rocks and acorns and beetles—it still smells like a sowbug hotel. The little squirt wasn't really cold; all he wanted was the big pockets. He was a sight. The sleeves kept sliding over his hands, the tails tripped him up, the pockets sagged until they bumped along the ground behind him. He didn't care.

A couple of fellows about our age came down the road. They had a .22 and they kept snapping it off in all directions; we could hear the bullets whine till it gave us the willies.

"Hi," Scrub said when they came up to us. "Bag anything?"

One of them held up a couple of blood-and-hair things. "Worth two dollars and a half," he said proudly. "Took a pop at somebody's old yaller cat but it got away."

They walked on, banging away. Wellington watched them bug-eyed.

"They shoot people's kitties!" he says, shocked. "What were they carrying?"

"Some poor critter's ears," I said. "Punks like that'll shoot at anything. Glad they're going the other way."

Welly'd already lost interest. He was stooping over an old bucket half buried in the sand. "I hear something," he says.

We lifted the bucket and there was a little nest in it; and sitting there motionless with fright was a kangaroo mouse.

I'd never seen one close up before. They're yellowish, mouse-size, with hind legs as long as their body. In the nest was a pile of six tiny baby mice.

"Ah-ha!" I told Wellington. "There's mamma and the babies all together. Want a whole pet family for the show?"

"What about their daddy?" he says, doubtful.

"Welly," says Scrub, very fatherly, "kangaroo mice don't have daddies. Or, anyway, their daddies go away to hunt a job and never come back. They find a new kangaroolet and have a bunch more kangarooligans."

"That's another big ole fat whoopy-dolliper," Wellington says positively. "I can tell."

Of course it was, and Scrub sighed. "I give up," he says, putting the bucket back in its hole. "I dunno what to do with you. Welly, how'd you like to have a white bunny rabbit?"

"Aw," says Wellington, "everybody has white rabbits."

"Or a canary or something?"

"Canaries!" says Wellington.

"Hey," I said, "I know a guy raises hamsters—you know, cute little tame—"

"Aw, cute!" says Wellington, scornful. "Tame!"

"Awww . . . nuts!" says Scrub, getting mad.

"Look, you guys," I said, trying to keep peace in the family, "if this has to be an orphan hunt, there's a good lead to follow: let's backtrack those trigger-happy yaps we just met. If they're not orphan-makers, it's only because they can't shoot straight enough."

The road petered out and we began to get into real back country. Suddenly Wellington took off down a gully.

"Puppy, puppy!" he howled. He scrambled headlong down the bank, and came up with a snub-nosed scraggly yellowish specimen of canine that looked distinctly mangy.

"Darned if it isn't a pup!" I said, before I thought.

"Gee, a puppy!" says Wellington, sort of awed and hushed. "Kin I keep him?"

I really felt sorry for the kid in a no-dogs-allowed household. That look on his face would melt down a snowman.

Scrub shook his head. "No puppy could find his way alone clear up in this back country," he says. "Its mamma isn't far away—maybe with those kids we met."

I didn't give with any ideas on the subject. In fact, I didn't even think much about it then. Wellington, looking very wistful, let the pup go, and it sat down and scratched itself nonchalantly.

"Besides," Scrub says, "remember what Mom said about dogs, Welly."

Next thing Welly turned up—leaving out five pounds of rocks and seven bugs and a stick shaped like a Hoppy-gun—was a blob of blood in the dirt.

Welly's eyes got big again. "They killed something," he said.

We looked closer. There were claw-marks in the dust.

"Probably the cat they talked about," I said.

Scrub flew mad. "Blast these guys that shoot up the country with a .22 and leave the things to die!" he says. "Let's run it down and fix it up, or put it out of its misery."

It was mean tracking, a fleck of blood every few feet, over brushy ground and gullies and finally up a crooked little canyon. The cat sure hadn't headed for any farmhouse; the trail abruptly left the canyon bed and took off up a wall.

"Cat's gone clear wild," Scrub said. "Got a den up there."

We went topside, and I crawled out over a big rock at the edge of the canyon to look down. Ten feet below was a wide ledge and some sign to show the den was probably back under the rock I lay on.

"If we had a rope . . ." I said.

But we hadn't. It was warm on the rock and we had a couple of sandwiches to dispose of, so we ate and thought.

"Maybe over there where it slopes down . . ." Scrub says. I held his heels while he slid down and peered over.

"There's the cat down below," he said. "It's dead. Probably never got home."

"Can you drop?"

Scrub couldn't figure how to get back if he did drop, so finally I held Scrub again while he lowered Wellington onto the ledge.

"He's half squirrel, he won't fall off," Scrub insisted.

When Scrub sat up again, he looked at me kind of owly.

"What's the matter?" I said.

"Just the cat," he says. "Big one. About so long."

"Golly! What color?"

"It was pretty dusty," he says, not really answering. "You could see how they'd call it a 'yaller' cat."

"You think Wellington is all right down there?"

"Sure—papa cats don't hang around. But if there's kittens, they won't have a mamma, see?—it's worth a chance."

Well, it was *his* kid brother. Then we heard him yell: "Hey! I see a kitty!"

"How big is it?" I called, still worried.

"It ain't big," says Wellington's voice, muffled. "Here, kitty, kitty, kitty—ouch!—here, kitty."

The voice got fainter, then I heard him scrabbling back out. "Aw, poor kitty," he says, still out of sight. "Gee, it's purty. Something bit its tail off."

"What?" I yelled.

"Ouch!" says Wellington, again.

"What color is it?"

"Stripy. Nice kitty. . . ."

I whirled on Scrub. "It's a bobcat, sure as shootin'!"

"I know it," he says, looking sheepish. "I saw the old one. Go swell in a pet show, huh?"

The guy ain't got a lick of sense!

"But your Mom—she said—"

"I figured that out," he says. "This ain't, strictly, a cat, see? It's a lynx. You look it up—that's what bobcats are."

I gave up. "Hey, Welly," I shouted. "Come on back up here!"

"I'm coming," he says, his voice way back under again. "There ain't any more. Gee, it smells terrible in here."

We hauled him up. He had the kitten in

the big hunting-coat pocket; about the size of half a Persian, the head a little wider. No question, the kid had a way with him. The thing spit at us like a tom with a bellyache, but when Wellington hauled it around by the scruff of the neck and patted it, it ducked and arched its back for all the world like any half-grown tabby.

"Okay, Welly, you satisfied now?"

"Uh huh," says Wellington; then, "Wish I had the puppy too."

"Here we go again!" says Scrub. "You heard Mom, no dogs, and that's that."

So here up comes old Al with another of his shattering notions. "If you're gonna be technical," I said, *"was* it a dog? Didn't you say the bounty on bobcats is fifteen dollars?"

"Sure."

"That fellow said he had only two-and-a-half's worth of ears. Since you're hunting orphans . . ."

"Oh," says Scrub, getting it. "Say, reckon we could find that pup?"

I was getting my second thoughts now. "We better leave it alone," I said.

"Oh," says Scrub, "might's well be hung for a sheep as a lamb."

We went back down the trail, and where the pup had been we scattered out. Wellington found it; I could have stepped on it without ever seeing that sand-colored bundle of fur. These kids don't miss a thing.

"Aw, puppy," says Wellington, practically drooling on it, and it snapped at his finger like a coyote.

Naturally.

Coyote bounty is two dollars and a half. That's what the .22 boys had shot. This pup *was* a coyote—a poor, motherless, hungry little coyote, with wicked yellow eyes and a disposition mean as the saying goes. Wow, but it was mean!

We took it easy back down to the top of the pass where we would meet Dad. Wellington shagged along behind, the tails of the hunting coat dragging the ground. At the highway, Scrub looked Welly over. "Why don't you put the pup in the other pocket?" he says. "They couldn't reach each other then."

"Aw, it's too full of rocks, and things," says Wellington.

The pocket was buttoned. I saw it wiggle. I was on him in two shakes. "What things?" I said, unbuttoning the pocket, and I reached in and pulled out the baby jackrabbit. "Now where did this come from?"

"Right where it was before," says Wellington. "Its mamma hadn't come back."

"Those guys did do a lot of shooting," Scrub says. "Probably *is* an orphan now."

What's the harm in a rabbit? Dad came along in the car, and I dropped bunny back in the pocket. The kid now had a real menagerie, I figured. How right I was!

When I went over Saturday afternoon to see how Welly was making out in the pet show, I really stepped into something.

Ever been to a kids' pet show? Brrr!—of all the yapping, snarling, hysterical messes—kids, hundreds of 'em, pooches and ducks and goats and Shetlands, I never saw the like.

There seemed to be two shows, a main one and a smaller one off to one side. I found Scrub at the main show. He was talking to a big man, both standing beside a pen that held a pair of big red hunting dogs with a litter of puppies.

"Hi, Al," Scrub says. He looked almost haggard. "This is Mr. Corum. He wants to buy Welly out, only the little son-of-a-gun won't sell."

"Where is Welly?"

"Over yonder." Scrub pointed at what I thought was a sideshow. "For Pete's sake, Al, go over there quick and help keep that zoo boxed up. Oh-oh . . ."

All of a sudden the yapping had got louder, and the whole family of hunting dogs stood up and howled.

"Wind's changed again," says the big man, grabbing one of the dog's collars. "That wild smell drives 'em all nuts. Hey, hang onto that male or you'll lose coyote, cat and mice in one bite. Oh, golly!" He began to laugh, and when you looked at him close, you could see tear-streaks down his face like a kid's. "I haven't laughed so much in twenty years."

"Did you say mice?" I asked.

Scrub hooked a hand in the dog's collar. "You know what that little stinker had in that pocket?" he said, beginning to hang on for dear life. "Remember the mouse family?"

"The nest of 'em?"

"I mean, Al, right in the middle of that pocketful of rocks—hey, Al, get over there, the big kids keep dumping the box over. Welly's already been kicked out of the show—"

The big dog gave a lunge and spilled Scrub flat. I took one step toward Welly. It was too late. I saw the orange crate go over, and two yellow forms took off in opposite directions, and practically every dog in the place shed his leash and took out after them.

I saw Welly dive for the coyote and miss. A great big gray goose on a rope flew up in the air, and the coyote dodged and snapped at it. It looked like a standoff.

I looked for the cat: he was just a striped streak, the fanciest open-field runner I ever

hope to see. Every way he turned, a hound was barking in his face. The kitten would haul off and swipe with one paw as he went by, and the dog would howl. All of a sudden the cat made one wild flying zigzag and on the zag he was right beside us in the middle of everything.

This guy Corum was laughing so hard his hand let go the female dog's collar. I ran to grab her; in three big jumps she had the coyote by the scruff of the neck. He must have smelled young, she couldn't seem to figure what to do with it.

And then I saw why: the coyote had the goose by the leg, and that goose was whaling the daylights out of them with both wings, and they both stood there, eyes shut, and mouths full of feathers; and then the big old red hunter roared out a howl that like to drowned out the whole shebang.

The striped kitten had zigged again and landed on the dog's back with all four feet and nineteen claws, and that hunting dog was the most surprised animal, and the most helpless, and the maddest! And this guy Corum all but passed out.

I hope I never see a guy laugh like that again. The tears poured down. His face was purple. He sat down on a box and roared until his voice came out just a squeak.

The poor pooch came tearing by and I snaffled the cat off her back, with a handful of hair in each paw, and got her to loose the coyote pup. I don't know what happened to the goose; maybe the pup swallowed it, I wouldn't put it past him.

"Take 'em away!" Scrub was bawling at me. "Doggone it, Al, take those varmints away!"

I got them to Welly without much damage, barring thirty or forty scratches and two coyote nips. When I got back to Corum, he had come to enough to whistle his dog back and things settled down into a steady din that was almost peaceful.

"Oh gosh, oh golly!" Corum was saying, wiping his face with a big handkerchief. "I'll never miss a pet show again!"

Scrub looked at him as if he'd lost his mind.

"Maybe it's funny," he admitted, "only to my Mom and Dad it ain't funny. 'Take 'em

to the show,' Dad says, 'maybe he'll get an E for effort, but you better not come back with anything *but* a prize, and that's final.' "

"Oh, he'll win a prize," Corum said, wiping his eyes. "I'm on the committee, and we agreed any kid steals the show from a pet parade deserves something. Now let's get back to our deal."

"Mr. Corum runs a sporting goods store," Scrub explained. "He wants this collection of Welly's in his window for a week and then he'll give 'em to the zoo. He's offered Welly everything from skates to a junior bike—no sale. All Welly wants is to win a prize—and keep his pets. Aw, a kid oughta have a pet—a kid like him anyway."

Mr. Corum looked up quick. "Tell me that again," he said. "About your dad. He said not to bring home anything but a prize?"

Scrub nodded glumly.

Then we heard Welly screech, and they both dived for the dog collars again. But Welly was running at us, waving his hands. "Charlie got a prize! Charlie got a prize!" he screamed.

"Charlie?" I said.

"Prize for what?" says Scrub.

"Best b-behaved pet," Welly stuttered, out of breath.

Mr. Corum choked, but he managed not to laugh. When he got his voice going again, he solemnly shook Welly's hand.

"Now, sir, that's fine, boy," he said. "That Charlie is undoubtedly the best-behaved of his breed I ever saw—and I've seen a lot of the breed, too. Son, you know what the prize is for best-behaved pet?"

Welly shook his head.

"It's a griffon!"

Welly's mouth fell open. "A pet one?" he asked.

Mr. Corum nodded.

Scrub looked sick. "Ain't that a—a kind of dragon?" he asked.

Corum was turning purple around the gills again, trying not to laugh, but he shook his head.

"Near as I remember," I said, "it's half unicorn and half something else, only there isn't any such thing. Like on coats of arms."

Mr. Corum reached down and picked up a pup. He dropped it smack into Welly's arms. "This is a griffon, sonny," he said. "Don't let 'em kid you—it's just a breed of dog."

Welly looked down at the pup, and it licked him in the face, and Welly began to bawl.

"They won't let me," he wailed.

"Didn't your daddy say you could bring home a prize?" Corum demanded. "That's the prize. He can't go back on his word."

Scrub looked very doubtful. "How much do they eat?" he asked.

"Oh, just a couple, three cans of dog food," Corum says, "for breakfast. Maybe a little more, if you're not hunting with him. Now, Buster, can I have this zoo of yours?"

"Uh huh," says Welly, not paying attention to anything but the pup.

"It ain't Dad so much," Scrub says, still stewing. "It's Mom."

"Look, boy," Corum said, "I don't know your mom, but I know mammas. I had one. You let him take that pup home, in his arms, just like that—leave those tearstains on his face—and there's no woman alive can hold out."

We looked at Wellington, sitting on the ground with the pup, and he *was* the most pathetic sight imaginable.

"I think he's right," I said.

"Well, she *did* like Sandy," Scrub admitted. "I guess so."

"By the way," I said, "which one's Charlie?"

Scrub looked at me kind of queer. "The one with the perfect behavior. Come on, take a look."

That I had to see.

The coyote and bobcat were in the two sides of the orange crate. The pup was snarling and snapping at sticks the kids kept poking at him, and the kitten was curled up in a corner, yellow-eyed. Maybe it was good behavior, but it looked to me more like he was biding his time.

The rabbit and kangaroo mouse family were in another box. There were only five baby mice now. They already had a little fur and their eyes were open.

"*I* know," I said. "Charlie's the sixth mouse."

"Well," says Scrub, "yes and no. This is Charlie."

I stuck my head down to look in the box he pointed at, and I snapped back so quick I nearly broke my own neck. Charlie was a snake; a foot long, mottled steely blue, with a blunt tail.

The tail was blunt because, at the end, there was an unmistakable button.

"That hump in his middle," Scrub says, "is the sixth mouse. So it *is* Charlie, in a way. Charlie got hungry on the way in."

I began to give away at the knees. "W . . . where—hey, did . . . ?"

"He did," Scrub said. "Mom saw the coyote and the bobcat and she hit the ceiling; and she saw the rabbit and mice and she says, 'You and that Al!' And then we dumped the rocks and tumblebugs out of the pocket and there was Charlie, and Mom hasn't come back to earth yet."

"Is he—really . . . a rattlesnake?"

"That's what the snake man at the zoo says." Scrub licked his lips, still nervous thinking about it. "Welly said he rolled over a rock looking for kittens around the ledge, and there was a whole pile of snakes, all sizes. Dormant, see? Already snowed, they were hibernating, only Charlie was too young to get organized and he could still wiggle.

"We wrapped him up with a lump of ice and he passed out cold—excuse the pun, but that's what got the prize, I guess; perfect way for a rattlesnake to behave, they must have figured. Don't wake him up—they're poisonous the day they're born, the snake guy says.

"So I guess maybe Mom may let him keep the dog, long as we got his affections weaned away from Charlie."

Scrub suddenly shivered all over.

"You know what that Welly said when we found Charlie?" he demanded. " 'Pore little guy,' he says, 'his mamma was dead . . . She musta been,' he says, 'she didn't jump when I pinched her!' "

Inside Baseball

By STANLEY PASHKO

Every fan in the grandstand has an opportunity to understand the game if he watches the players as well as the ball

Charley Dressen is respected as one of the smartest strategists in baseball. In his last World Series, as manager of the Dodgers, he had Hodges on second and Pafko on third. The Brooklyn pitcher was at bat with instructions to squeeze the runner in from third with a bunt.

The Yankees suspected it but were helpless because they had to know the exact pitch on which the squeeze would be tried. Suddenly, Dressen gave the sign, touching his throat, but he forgot that Billy Martin of the Yankees used to play for him in the minors. Martin caught the sign and signaled Berra, who called for a pitchout which trapped Pafko halfway between home and third for an easy rundown out.

The tables were turned on Dressen that time. But he is so quick at intercepting enemy signs that he once claimed to have "stolen" a dozen games for his team that season. Those dozen games were more than the Dodgers' margin of victory and, in effect, Dressen was saying that his sign stealing won the pennant.

He could well have been right. Signs and signals play a tremendous role in the outcome of a baseball game. A major league game can be a battle of strategy so subtle that even expert fans will miss the secret war raging behind the plays. To the fans, a batter stepping away from the plate several times in succession appears to have a great deal of trouble in getting all the dirt out of his spikes. But that may only be a ruse.

Actually, he may just be worried that he has missed a sign from the third base coach. By stepping out, he is asking to have the sign repeated. Another reason batters may step out is that they hear a voice signal ordering them to back away from the plate to look for a new sign from the coach.

A sudden burst of loud enthusiasm from the visitors' bench is rarely "that old fighting spirit." When it happens in the course of a major league game, it often means the coach suspects that the home team is trying to pass some signs by voice code. He orders the demonstration as a defensive move aimed at "jamming" the enemy's communications.

No Code Is Perfect

Since there is no code that cannot be broken, it may happen that the experts of Team A will crack the code of Team B. One or two disastrous plays later, Team B realizes this. For such a situation there is an emergency sign which warns every player to switch to a different code. The emergency sign may be some special code phrase yelled by a coach or the manager; it may be a conference between the manager and his battery; or it may be simply some finger sign by the catcher to the pitcher. Once a successful counterspy forced a big league team to change signs three times in one game.

Most of the signs are flashed by the catcher to the pitcher or by the third base coach to the batter and runners. The more important decisions are made by the manager on the bench and relayed to the third base coach by a separate system of special signs. Frequently, the third base coach has a great deal of leeway in making his own decisions. This is especially true when he is an outstanding sign snatcher such as Frankie Crosetti, who stands on the third base coaching lines for the New York Yankees.

Many managers consider the third base coaching position so important that they take it over themselves. Charley Grimm, Lou Boudreau, Bill Rigney, Mayo Smith, Bobby Bragan, Walter Alston, Charley Dressen, and Paul Richards are just a few of the long list of big league managers who spent time on the third base coaching line.

The Hit-and-Run

One of the important signs flashed by the third base coach calls for the hit-and-run. As baseball fans know, on this maneuver the runner on first breaks for second with the pitch. The batter's job is to hit the pitch—safely, if possible, but at any rate to get a "piece of it" and try to hit the ball on the ground. Since either the shortstop or second baseman must break for second to take a throw from the catcher on what looks like an attempt to steal, there is a big gap open in the infield defense. Players like Al Dark,

Peewee Reese, Red Schoendienst, Enos Slaughter, and Richie Ashburn are experts at banging the ball through such an opening.

Meanwhile, the runner is practically at second when the ball is hit, so he usually winds up on third if the batter gets a single. Even if the batter grounds out, the result is as good as a sacrifice because the baserunner advances to second, eliminating the possibility of a routine double play.

A sign from either the batter or the third base coach will start the hit-and-run. This sign may be given in almost any kind of signal you can imagine. Usually, though, it is a very ordinary looking gesture.

Some Coach's Signs

Some samples from an actual set of big league coaching signs are:

Hands on hips—hit-and-run.

Hands to mouth—bunt.

Hands on knees—steal.

Touch elbows—take the pitch.

Naturally, the coach doesn't just stand there making the one gesture that is the signal. He goes through a whole series of fake movements which make him look as if itching powder had been dumped inside his shirt, and mixed in with all the "throw-offs" is the genuine sign. The batter protects the sign by continuing to look at the coach for a little while after the real sign has been flashed.

Manager Casey Stengel, of the champion

398

Yankees, now leaves the third base coaching to Frankie Crosetti, but when he coached at third for the Dodgers in the old days, he put on a one-man show which was often better than the ball game. Opposing third basemen were often his best audience. Once his act was so funny that the Cardinals' third baseman let a simple grounder go through because he was laughing so hard.

Naturally, the Cards' manager dashed out to protest to the umpires but Casey drew himself up with dignity and explained, "I was just using strategy."

Signs can be further camouflaged by being good only if the coach is standing in a certain position, has one foot on the line of his coaching box, has his mouth open, or is making some other combination gesture at the same time.

To complicate things still more, the hit-and-run sign can also be flashed a pitch ahead of time, generally when there are two balls and no strikes on the hitter. This special sign is often something like "flesh-to-flesh" (touching the face, hands, neck, wiping the forehead with a bare forearm, or any flesh-to-flesh contact). The batter who gets that signal takes the next pitch and executes the hit-and-run on the following one.

If the count on this hitter should then go to three and nothing, the coach will usually take off the hit-and-run by yelling some special take-off signal such as "he's wild," or "get hold of one."

Signs Can Boomerang

One of the real disasters to a batting rally comes when the defensive team catches the sign for the hit-and-run. The player who intercepted the sign flashes his own warning, the catcher calls for a pitch-out, and the runner going down to second is a dead duck.

All managers know that there is no such thing as a sure way to prevent slip-ups on signals. Even when the enemy doesn't steal his signs, the big league manager is often faced with the problem of getting through to the slower thinkers on his squad. When signs are missed at crucial moments, the game is lost, so sometimes the manager will not trust a sign. He will give his instructions in person.

But even this can backfire. For example, Leo Durocher tells of the time he walked out to the mound to call a conference. He wanted to make sure that the catcher did not try for the man on first if there was an attempted steal of second, but would fire right back to the pitcher and try to nail the runner who was perched on third. He might make a break for the plate if the catcher's hard throw to the pitcher fooled him into thinking it was a throw to second.

This was very important, manager Durocher emphasized, because the score was tied in the last of the ninth and the runner on first meant nothing—the important run was on third; if that scored, the game was over.

On the next pitch the runner broke, the catcher fired hard, as instructed, but the pitcher forgot that the throw was meant for him. He ducked, thinking it was a try to nail the runner at second. The ball went through into centerfield, since the infielders didn't expect a throw either, and the game was lost.

Signaling Base Runners

In addition to his secret signs, a third base coach has many wide-open signs. These are the ones he uses to tell a base runner whether to slide, hold up, round the base, try for the plate, etc. These signals are pretty standard and all ball players should know them:

Hands spread palms down with a beating motion toward the ground tells the runner to hit the dirt because the play will be close.

The left hand waving in a sweeping side motion means just what it looks like—keep coming, try for the plate. When the coach gives this sign from well down the third base line, he may be sizing up the situation in the field, ready to flash the stop sign for a hasty retreat to third, or continue waving the runner on if there is a good chance to score.

The palms of both hands thrust out toward the runner means stop at the base, but don't slow down. When the palms are lifted high, it means the runner need not slide.

Since a runner may also advance after a fly ball is caught, the third base coach also has the responsibility of sending the runner on his way at the exact split second the ball touches the fielder's glove. Because there is a tiny delay between the shouted "go," which the coach yells into the crouched runner's ear and the runner's reaction, big league coaches yell "go" just before the ball touches the fielder's glove. The extra split second it takes the runner to get moving makes the play legal.

Even with this simple sign, coaches have been known to have trouble. One American League player always froze to the bag when the coach yelled "go" and couldn't make himself run. Another player was all set to sprint in from third after a tremendous fly. He took off as the coach yelled but stopped short after four steps and turned back. The coach was hopping mad.

"You heard me holler 'go,'" yelled the coach. "What did you come back for?"

"Go? I thought you said 'whoa,'" explained the runner.

The Busiest Signaler

Probably most of the signs flashed in a ball game come from the catcher. When you consider that over two hundred and fifty pitches are thrown in the average game and each pitch requires its own sign, you can quickly see why this is so. In addition, the catcher may also signal for a pick-off try against a base runner.

The catcher's signs to the pitcher are not very complicated. The important thing for him to do is cover his finger signs so well that they can't be seen by the batter, the base line coaches, or any runners on base. The catcher usually gives signs to the pitcher by flashing a given number of fingers. For instance, he may flash 3-1-2. The pitcher knows which sign was the real one—it might have been any of the three. Or the sign may be the first number flashed after a three-finger sign or some other agreed-upon code.

When the catcher suspects that the opponents have picked up his code, he flashes a special sign by touching his glove to the ground, adjusting his mask a certain way, or making some other signal. Then if the batter is unlucky enough to believe his coach's signal that a curve is coming, he may get the shock of his life—not to mention some bruised ribs—when the curve doesn't break but turns out to be a fast ball inside.

Since signs are so important, naturally a great premium is placed on breaking the code. In the old days, and sportswriters claim one club did it recently, some teams had spies hidden in the outfield scoreboard with binoculars to steal the catcher's signs and pass them on to the batters.

Modern teams complain to the baseball commissioner's office against any such unethical tactics. When the old-time Detroit Tigers ran into such a situation long ago, they took matters into their own hands by burning down the enemy scoreboard.

Nowadays, sign stealing is usually the result of close study. Batters, catchers, and coaches are watched for clues. Expert sign snatchers go about their job efficiently. Sometimes they will work in pairs; say Frankie Crosetti watches the other team's third base coach while Billy Martin eyes the batter. Every move is reported simultaneously as they try to synchronize everything done on the field.

Their conversation might run something like this as they talk quietly to each other, sometimes both talking at the same time:

Crosetti: *He's got one foot on the line, he's touching his chest, grabbing his ear, rubbing hand on letters, he put his hand to his mouth, he hollered 'atta boy.'*

Martin: *He touched his cap, NOW HE'S LOOKING AT THIRD, LOOKING AT THIRD, looking down at the ground, picking up dirt, LOOKING AT THIRD and wiping hands, LOOKING AT THIRD and touching uniform, stepping into box.*

They especially watch to see what gestures are made by the coach when the hitter is looking at him. Later, with photographic memory, they analyze every movement that preceded a hit-and-run play or some other situation to try to reconstruct the vital clues. Eventually, they crack the code.

Abner's Gold Mine

By WILLIAM B. McMORRIS

Hardrock was a ghost town with its pay dirt gone until a trick burro named Agnes arrived

I went down to the corral on the highway this morning to watch Agnes stop cars again. It's not easy to stop cars here in Hardrock, Arizona. We're right out in the middle of the desert.

Tourists want to get through this part of the country in a hurry. They come down the road at seventy miles per hour and don't even plan to slow down. If you're running a roadside filling station and restaurant like my folks are, this can be bad for business.

That's where Agnes and Abner come in. They're our public relations unit. We don't really call them that, because Abner is more of a prospector than a public relations man and Agnes is more of a jackass than anything else. But they're a good combination. Their methods are a little unusual, but so is the problem of getting people to stop.

This morning Abner was currying Agnes and tying a big red bow around her neck, getting ready for the day's work. Agnes looked good. She's shiny, sleek, and black. You don't see many burros that color, but then, you don't see many burros like Agnes, no matter what their color is. About the time Abner had her looking like an Arabian show horse, Agnes flicked her big ears forward and stopped nuzzling my pockets looking for candy. She listened.

A few seconds later, Abner and I heard it too. It was the high-pitched whine of tires and an engine. The day's first tourist was coming down the road. The sound of the car got louder, and then we could see it coming around the big curve down the highway.

Abner led Agnes over to the side of the corral that fronted on the road. She sat down there on her haunches like a big dog and waited. The shiny Buick was one hundred yards away when Abner said, "Okay, Agnes."

Agnes went, "aahn-hee Aaahhn-Eee AA-AAHHHN-Eee AAAAHHHNN-EEEEE!"

I could tell you it sounded like a bagpipe played through a tuba or a diesel horn with a wheeze, but you still wouldn't know what it sounded like. It just sounded like a jackass braying, that's all.

The effect on the people in the car was interesting. The lady in the front seat glared at the kids in the back seat. The kids jumped over to press their faces against a side window and laugh at Agnes. The man who was driving automatically slowed down and stared at us. About the time the lady got her bearings and turned in the right direction, Agnes lifted a forefoot and waved.

That did it. The tail lights on the car glowed suddenly as the brakes took hold. The man wheeled the car off the road at the most convenient spot beyond the corral. This happened to be our filling station, and not by accident. Abner and Agnes practiced a long time along the highway before Abner decided to build the corral where it stands today.

Anyway, the car stopped beside the gas pumps. I saw the tall lean figure of my father go out to meet it. The kids piled out the door as soon as the wheels stopped turning. They headed for the corral, and Agnes brayed a greeting. The kids' mother was chasing along behind them, and their father said something to my dad and followed along, too.

Dad lifted the hose off one of the pumps and began putting gas in the car. Abner and Agnes had made another sale.

Now, on the surface, this just looks like a scheme to sell gasoline. It is, but there's more to it than that. The kids came up to pet Agnes and when the parents arrived, Abner doffed his sombrero to the lady and said, "Howdy folks. Welcome to Hardrock." The public relating began in earnest.

While Abner and the people talked, Agnes entertained the kids by opening the corral gate with her teeth and giving the kids a ride around to join the conversation. Then we got lucky. Agnes didn't have to flag down any more cars. Two groups of people, who weren't in any hurry, stopped to see what was going on. The crowd grew, and it attracted more people. I had to leave and go up to the station to help.

Later, between chores, I glanced toward the corral and saw Abner standing in the center of a group of maybe fifteen people. He was doing all the talking now, and they were all listening.

I knew pretty well what he was saying. I've heard the stories before, and when Abner tells them, they stay the same. He's no windy old character selling phony treasure maps to greenhorns. He's a real prospector.

His face is hidden in whiskers; he's small and wiry and mighty spry for a man almost seventy years old. He usually wears jeans, brogans, a blue poplin shirt, and an old leather vest. The yarns he tells are good ones. He was a boy in Hardrock when it was the richest mining town in the state. The things he talks about are the things he saw. And the way he tells a story, it's like the old

ghost town has come to life again. In fact, if the people want him to, he'll take them down the rutted, dusty road that leads to the old town of Hardrock. It's just a cluster of deserted wooden shacks now, but, like I say, the place comes to life when Abner talks about it.

Well, between watching Agnes and listening to Abner and going for a walk to Old Hardrock, it gets to be noon before anybody notices. Abner squints up at the sun and says to the crowd, "If you folks will 'scuse me, I'll be gettin' up to George Bowman's for a bite to eat."

Abner talks about my father's restaurant like it's the best restaurant in Hardrock. Of course it is, but it's also the only one.

Most of the folks follow Abner up to our place for lunch, where Abner introduces my mom to the crowd as the "best cook in Arizony," which, of course, she is. After lunch, there's no argument about that.

Better still, when they leave, these people are our friends. Some of them come back, and lots of them write to us and to Abner. It's this part that always surprises me, because Abner wasn't always so interested in people.

In fact, when we first came to Hardrock two years ago for Mom's health, when I was fourteen, we hardly knew Abner was around. He lived in one of the ghost-town houses off the highway by himself.

But we had our own problems then and didn't think much about Abner. We had sold our house in Illinois and sunk most of the money into the filling station and the restaurant by the highway. Dad worked hard putting a new roof on the restaurant and painting the whole place up to attract tourists. I helped clean up and rake the gravel drive. In between times I put water in radiators and wiped windshields. Motorists in those days were just people who inquired about distances from one town to another and sped off down the road.

I used to envy the people going away in their new cars. I missed the green, rolling hills of Illinois.

The desert, where everything had thorns

or fangs or stingers, scared me a little. One night I found a scorpion in my bed. It was really a silverfish, but a scorpion couldn't have scared me any more. I got so I wouldn't sleep until I had torn the bed-clothes off a couple of times and peered under the bed with a flashlight. Even then, I used to leap up when I thought I felt something crawling around my feet.

I was pretty unhappy with the desert, but mom was feeling better every day. One afternoon dad and I heard a clattering noise coming from the restaurant. Up to then, the place had been closed. Dad peered through the door and saw Mom moving dusty pots and pans off a shelf. She had a bandana wrapped around her brown hair, and she was scouring the whole place, kitchen, counter, tables and all, with hot soapy water.

Dad's jaw went slack for a minute and then he said, "Emma, you shouldn't . . ."

"George, I've decided to get up." Her chin was kind of stuck out, and her voice was firm, like the day she caught me throwing rocks at the cactus wren that nests in the spiny cholla near the station. Dad didn't say anything. He backed out of the place, shaking his head and grinning. The rest of the day he touched up the paint on the restaurant, and he whistled a lot while he did it.

Two or three days later we drove into Wickenburg for the supplies Mom said we needed for the restaurant. The next morning dad stuck a sign that said "Grand Opening" in the restaurant window.

I guess we had forgotten that people didn't stop very often. All day the bell on the restaurant door didn't jingle. By evening Mom looked a little discouraged, sitting in the kitchen looking out at the empty counter. About dusk she called me inside.

"Peter," she said, "we're going to have at least one guest in this place today. Go get that old prospector that lives down the road. Tell him his neighbors want him up for supper."

I hesitated, but I figured it wouldn't hurt to try. I didn't think the old man would come, because he hadn't been around to see us in the six months we lived there. He scarcely nodded when he crossed the highway by our place and headed into the desert. But I walked the quarter of a mile down the road to the shack where he lived. He was sitting outside on the rickety front steps of the place, staring at the ruins of a livery stable across the main street.

I walked right up beside him, but he didn't turn. I shuffled my feet and cleared my throat. He didn't move, just stared at the livery stable.

"Say, mister," I said, "how'd you like to eat at our place tonight?"

He turned and looked at me for what seemed like a long time.

"What fer?" he muttered.

I didn't know what else to do, so I said, "I'm Peter Bowman, and Mom told me to ask you up to supper tonight."

He turned and looked at me suspiciously. "I'm Abner J. Cobb, I got no money." He looked away as if that settled everything.

"But we just wanted to have you up for supper," I spluttered.

The old man swung around and looked at me as if he thought I was lying. I was getting nervous so I just said, "C'mon," and started walking back toward our place. I hadn't gone far when I heard him coming along behind me.

We walked in silence for a while until he said out from under his whiskers, "Thank yuh."

That was the whole conversation until we reached the restaurant where Mom had a table set with places for four of us. The old man shook hands with Dad and made a kind of jerky little bow toward Mom when they were introduced.

"You sit right over there, Mr. Cobb," she directed. He started toward the place she in-

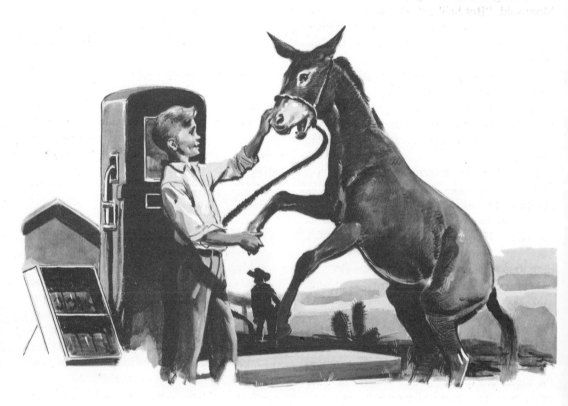

dicated, then halted. He turned to us with what was just a small crinkle of a grin on his face.

"Name's Abner," he said and sat down.

He didn't talk much during the meal, but you could see he was sizing us up. I guess he liked what he saw, because he paused and looked at me just before he left.

"Pete," he said, "whaddayuh think of the desert?"

"Well, it's not what I'm used to," I said, not wanting to say right out in front of Mom and Dad that I hated it.

"You come by tomorrow. Mebbeso I can show you some things."

We watched him go back down the road. The moonlight showed between his bow-legs when he walked. His head was down, and his eyes searched out every rock and out-crop, even in the moonlight.

"Well, I guess the Bowmans are accepted into the community. He practically made a speech to you, Pete," my father laughed.

"The poor man hasn't had any company for so long that he's forgotten how to talk," Mom said. "But he'll get used to us."

"Peter, this is the first time your mother ever adopted a stray prospector," Dad grinned, tipping me a big wink.

"All right, George Bowman, you just go out and lock up your gas pumps and let me worry about feeding strays." Mom tried to make her chin stick out like she does when she's angry and didn't succeed in getting it just right.

Dad went out laughing, and I took my flashlight and headed for bed. I wanted to get up early and talk to Abner.

I found him the next morning sitting on the steps. He nodded and grinned when I came up. We talked for a while and I told him about how I felt living in the desert.

"Mebbe you've never seen the desert, Pete."

"I've been here six months," I told him.

"Yep, that's right, but you gotta get spe-cial eyes to see it." He saw my puzzled ex-pression and continued, "Things growin' on the desert are special. Water's scarce and the sun's hot. The cactus figgered out how to store water and grew thorns fer pertection. The ground squirrel figgered out how to eat the cactus to get the water. Seeds lay in the ground four, mebbe five years without sproutin'. Come a good wet year and the seeds come out. Everthin' that lives here has just learned to make the best of it. Yuh gotta see that to see what goes on in the desert."

Then we went for a walk and I found out what he meant. A big leafy tree doesn't stand a chance in the desert. It gives off too much water. The mesquite trees had tiny leaves, and the cactus had no leaves at all. Thorns don't give off precious water like leaves do, so the cactus grew thorns and used them to protect the big pulpy stalks that store water for the plant. When I looked at it like that, it wasn't such a hostile-looking country. The plants just grew the best way they could. I suppose that's when I started developing "special eyes" for the desert. People have to change a little, too, to see the beauty in the desert.

Abner had supper with us again that night, and I asked him if he'd ever found any gold in his prospecting.

"Some," he answered. "There's more over yonder." His finger pointed toward the blue outlines of the Bighorn Mountain.

"Why don't we go over there sometime?"

"We'd need us a burro to pack water and food. Have to stay out a long time. I been in there plenty times, but I got no burro now."

He didn't seem very enthusiastic about the trip, so I didn't say anything more right then. Abner had supper with us every night that week, and gradually we got the whole story of the gold in the Bighorns.

Abner figured other prospectors in the Bighorns had quit looking too soon. He was sure a strike as big as the one at Old Hard-rock lay somewhere in those mountains.

His problem now was getting a burro. The burro he had used before we came to Hard-rock had died. It got too old and tired to go on. Abner hinted that maybe he was like the burro. Abner was sitting on the porch of the restaurant, watching the shadows on the mountains, when he said this.

"Look, Abner," my dad said, "there's a

horse auction in Wickenburg this week. Could you get a burro there?"

"Mebbe, but I'm broke."

"That's easy. I'll advance you whatever it takes."

"Don't take money from friends," Abner answered.

"I didn't say I'd give you the money," Dad explained. "I'll stake you now. When you make a strike, you can pay me back." Dad seemed to overlook the fact that Abner had never found any gold in the Bighorns, and neither had anyone else. Abner seemed to forget about this, too.

The two of them argued a little more, but the deal ended with Abner's hauling his pack saddle and harness up to our place. He planned to drive to Wickenburg with us the next morning when we went to buy supplies.

Abner went back home, and Mom looked at Dad and grinned, "Now who's adopting strays?"

Dad looked everywhere except at Mother, and remembered some painting that had to be done. The thing that made it funny was that it was almost too dark to see.

It was a sixty-mile drive to Wickenburg and a little farther to the red auction barn and the heavy timbered stock pens alongside it. People were already gathering in front of the auctioneer's platform when we arrived. The auctioneer in a wide-brimmed hat and jeans was rattling off bids on a pinto cow-pony that was up for sale. Nearby, Brahma and Hereford bulls rattled their horns against the corral poles. Horses snorted and pawed impatiently. Mules stood quietly as if they were asleep. We walked around to all the pens, but we didn't see a burro anywhere. Abner looked so dejected that dad suggested a horse or mule might do.

Abner just shook his head. "Horse 'er mule'd starve where a burro gets fat."

Dad and I left him looking and went down the street to buy the supplies. I picked up a little camera and some books on the desert. I was planning a special project for my high school correspondence course in biology. My grades could stand a little help.

We located Abner right away when we got back to the auction barn. He was holding the lead rope of a short-haired, black burro. Abner's grin beamed through the beard. He waved a five-dollar bill and then the lead rope at us.

"Nervous sorta feller give me this," he waved the bill, "fer takin' this." He shook the lead rope. "Smart as a whip too. Look here. Shake hands now, Agnes."

He bent down and held out his hand, and the burro promptly lifted a forefoot for him to shake. Abner laughed. "Feller said he had to get rid of her. His kids taught it tricks and made a pet of her. She tore up pea-patches, ate flowers, and kicked his landlord. Had to get rid of her or wind up in court."

"Will she be any good for work, Abner?" Dad asked.

"Burros is burros," Abner crowed. "They was all meant to work."

We left him there scratching Agnes' ears and laughing about the deal he had made. Dad and I couldn't figure out why somebody in Wickenburg hadn't bought her if she was such a good worker.

"Oh, well," Dad said, "Abner knows burros. Agnes will be a good worker."

Abner said it would take him four or five days to get back to Hardrock from Wickenburg. It took him seven days to get back and prove just how wrong Dad's prophecy was.

He was gone so long we thought maybe he'd found gold on the way. But one look at his face when he plodded into the station dragging Agnes behind him told us different. We could see he hadn't found anything at all unless it was something that would make a man almost seventy look almost eighty. He tied the burro to a gas pump and flopped down on the porch. His blue jeans were white with dust, and he carried a pack on his back. The kayak boxes and pack saddle were missing from the burro.

He said a lot of unpleasant things about burros and Agnes in particular. "Thet no-good donkey . . ." he began again, but ran out of words.

"What happened, Abner?" Dad asked, his face worried. "What happened?"

Abner groaned. Then he said, "I've know'd lotsa burros, but never any like thet jackass there. She shakes hands, she plays dead, she waltzes, she brays at cars, but she won't carry-no-pack-saddle. *Won't. Won't!*"

All of a sudden his voice rose louder than I had ever heard it before. Then he said in a quiet tone that sounded even worse than his shout, "Played games for sixty mile. One of them big oil trucks came past and backfired. Agnes played dead. Wrecked the kayak boxes, and I had to leave 'em. Then she started to waltz. Ever try to lead a waltzin' burro? Kept me awake all night braying at cars on the road. I dunno."

"You can always take her back," I said.

"Nope. Made a bargain. I'm stuck with her."

A big supper seemed to help Abner a little. He and my folks sat on the porch afterwards while I shook hands with Agnes and led her around. He even grinned a little at her antics, and Mom and Dad laughed out loud.

We hardly noticed the car that drove up until a man said, "Hey, son, that's a fine burro." I turned around to look at the traveler who leaned out the window. He had a big car and it was full of kids. One or two about my age and nine more that ranged down in age to the little baby the lady in the front seat held in her arms.

The man opened his door and that was a signal. The kids piled out of the car until it looked like one of the acts you see in a circus. You know, the one where fifteen clowns get out of a little auto that looks too small to hold more than one or two grown people. Anyway this flock of people gathered around Agnes, and I put her through her paces all over again.

Everybody laughed this time, even Abner.

Maybe it was one of the best evenings we ever had in Hardrock. Agnes topped it all off by braying a long mournful farewell to the people when they left.

That night, after Abner had gone home, I went to bed, but I couldn't sleep. There were a lot of thoughts going around in my head. It was all about Abner and Agnes and the way desert plants made the best of the desert, and then I remembered all those people who stood around and watched Agnes. They stopped just to see Agnes. Then it all began to add up. Agnes was a drawing card we needed. Once people stopped, they would stay to eat or to get their cars gassed up. I was pretty excited.

Before dawn I ran down to Abner's shack, busted in the door and yelled, "Abner, you're a cactus!"

It took a little while to explain it to Abner, but he got the idea. Just the other day, after Agnes had lured a batch of people into the restaurant, Abner told me, "Y'know, Pete, it's funny how I know'd so much about the desert and never figured people might be the same as desert plants. Agnes had changed to live with people. Me, I was a bigger jackass. It took me longer to change. I was too blamed stubborn to admit there was no more gold in the Bighorns.

"Why, shucks, the thing I was looking for was right here all the time. There's gold here too," he grinned, as Dad rang up another sale on the cash register and smiled our way.

That's the way it worked out. Abner gives me credit for the idea, but I think the idea belongs to somebody else. I hear her braying now, and that means I'll have to get outside and start wiping windshields.

407

Sea Scout Style!

By CAPTAIN BURR LEYSON

When life hung in the balance, Sea Scout training proved its worth to Bill Heeney

The fury of a full gale rocked the giant flying boat, tore at her broad expanse of wing, tossed her thirty-odd thousand pounds of weight. Almost solid sheets of rain, falling from a blanket of cold, leaden clouds that stretched from horizon to horizon, beat down on her structure and streaked in smoky wisps from the trailing edges. Barely two hundred feet below the broad vee of her keel, the seas, flattened by the wind, raced in an endless succession of mountainous combers.

Probationary co-pilot Bill Heeney sat in the right-hand pilot's seat, his eyes flickering from gauge to gauge as he watched the performance of the twin fifteen-hundred-horsepower engines set one to either side in the long monoplane wing. The left-hand motor was running warm, almost hot. The needle of the temperature gauge rose steadily. He turned and tapped Stan Taylor's shoulder.

The chief pilot turned his head, raised his eyebrows in question.

"Left motor running hot. All cowl air vents wide open. Temperature still mounting," Bill reported tersely.

Taylor frowned, shot a quick glance at the engine instruments which were grouped on Bill's side of the large cockpit. The chief pilot was about to make some comment but his words were never spoken.

There was a clatter from the left engine, the mad clang of metal on metal and the whole structure of the flying boat was shaken by vibration. Then there was a rending crash, the ship rocked wildly, yawed, and an instant later something struck the side of the cockpit with explosive force. Bits of metal flew like shrapnel, shatterproof glass whitened by a terrific impact shot in fragments across the cockpit. Bill's hand darted for the ignition switch controlling the left engine. His fingers were bruised on the metal as he snapped it off.

In almost the same move he looked up at Taylor. The pilot was slumped in his seat, arms limp and dangling at his sides!

Bill stiffened in his seat. For a fraction of a second he visualized the situation. Here he was, newly arrived at Seaboard Air Lines, a mere probationary co-pilot. He was on test until he made good!

"Not sufficient training and lacking sea experience," Pop Foster, the gruff head of the line, had said. He recalled how the old man had smiled when he had read of Bill's years with the Sea Scouts under the heading of Sea Training and Experience.

"Huh!" Foster had snorted. "Sea Scouts!"

Now here he was in a forced landing at sea in a storm, bringing down a crippled air liner with an unconscious chief pilot slumped over the controls! He was thankful that they were just ferrying a ship from one base to another and that there were no passengers aboard.

He grasped the controls, his feet found the rudder pedals and he strained against the wheel to pull the huge craft out of its wild plunge. For an instant he thought that they were crashing into the sea. Then he gained partial control.

The moment he had the flying boat level again he dropped one hand from the wheel and opened the remaining engine to its fullest. Then he looked out past Taylor's shoulder. There was nothing but a ragged hole where the window had been. And out on the wing there was no engine! Only a gaping hole showed where it had been. The engine with a part of its streamlined nacelle was hanging below the wing, held there by a twisted steel tube that had been a part of the engine mounting.

Bill looked at Taylor. An ominous dark strain was rapidly dyeing his uniform. Bill looked ahead and below while his mind raced trying to figure out a means of helping Taylor and still keeping the crippled plane in the air.

The sea was close, too close. And getting closer in spite of the fact that Bill was trying to climb the flying boat. They were losing height! The drag of that dangling motor and nacelle was too much for the remaining engine. Without that drag it would fly the boat with a full load but now, in spite of its being wide open, they were coming down. Bill braced himself for a crash.

Landing in those seas, even with as huge a boat as this, required little less than a miracle of skill and luck. Forgetting all else, Bill concentrated on the landing.

The great ship was driving through the air at ninety miles an hour; but the wind was roaring across the sea at nearly fifty. The flying boat was now headed dead into its force. Still, although the wind would lessen the landing speed, drop it by fifty miles, it was a desperate chance, for the huge craft would meet the oncoming waves at fully forty miles an hour. Crashing into a wave at that speed with the sea running so high meant the total destruction of the plane.

His one chance lay in dropping the boat down on the exact crest of a wave, letting it settle into the trough between the waves and hoping that it would lose speed suffi-

ciently to lessen the force of the impact against the next wave.

He scanned the seas, seeking that mythical great comber that is supposed to follow every so many waves. He caught sight of a wave that rose above the others. On that wave he would set down the mammoth boat, try to break its forward speed and hope for the best.

Bill braced himself against the rudder pedals, sat erect. His right hand gripped the wheel with a force that whitened his knuckles; his left rested firmly on the throttle of the remaining engine. Now the wave was upon him. Back came the throttle, up came the nose and he stalled her down for the crest. It was all or nothing and he tensed himself for the crash.

For an instant it seemed as though he had utterly failed. A gust of wind held the ship off the water, poised over the crest of the wave. Then the blast passed and the ship settled on the crest in a smother of foam and spray. With sickening speed it dropped into the trough of the wave, plowing into the succeeding one. Deeper and deeper the nose bored into the rushing water. The wave seemed about to engulf the flying boat when the sharp flaring bow began to tear free from the grip of the water—too late it seemed.

Higher and higher mounted the wave, carrying the partly submerged boat with it. Then the stout hull reached the crest of the wave and broke through. Down into the trough again and again a smother of spray but this time Bill knew that he was down. The hull shook off the grip of the sea, fought clear and settled to a stop.

Now the waves began to crash against the bow and batter the dangling motor and nacelle. Down went the left wing. A wave swept over it and Bill could hear the metal strain above the booming of the seas. No wing could long stand such a battering. And if the wing went, it meant that the hull would follow. Somehow that dragging motor had to be freed if they were to survive.

Bill turned to Taylor, still slumped in his seat. Quickly he loosened the safety belt and dragged the inert form from its place back into the empty cabin. Snatching cushions from the passenger seats, he made a rude couch for the injured man on the floor of the aisle. Then he darted back for the medicine cabinet, falling flat as a wave crashed on the crippled wing and hurled him headlong.

Splints and bandages in hand, he fought back to Taylor's side. Quickly he cut away the pilot's uniform and laid bare his arm. The bone was not broken but a fragment of metal had cut the flesh deeply. Blood flowed from the wound. A tourniquet stopped the flow, and bandages around the arm and the arm bound close to the chest, held it so that it would receive no further damage from movement until a doctor could look at it— if they survived to get to one! A shudder ran through the hull as Bill completed his task, bracing Taylor with additional pillows against the wild heaving of the crippled ship. Then Bill fought his way back to the pilot compartment.

It was high time that he did something but what he could do he did not know. Water shot through the gaping hole beside the chief pilot's seat where the window had been. There was a threatening grinding of metal out on the wing where the motor hung and he could hear the shrill noise of twisting steel where the wing was anchored to the hull. It was apt to let go at any minute and that would be the end of everything.

Bill's thoughts flashed to the emergency kit. There were wrecking tools there! Somehow he had to clear the wreck of the motor. He staggered into the narrow passage and quickly selected a short-handled ax and a hacksaw. Without pausing even to close the case, he went back into the pilot compartment and, clinging to the ragged edge of the window opening, looked out at the wing. Twisted tubes that had been the support for the motor held the dangling power plant to the wing.

If those tubes were cut—but thirty feet of bare slippery metal covering on the wing stretched between him and that tube. And along its entire length there was not the least place to secure a grip! He stepped over to the emergency hatch set in the ceiling of the compartment and threw it open. Then he climbed through into the fury of the storm.

The wind all but carried him away. Hooking a knee through the hatchway, he examined the surface of the wing. Then carefully he lay flat and reached out along the wing with his right hand holding the axe. A quick blow sent the blade through the thin dualuminum sheathing. Another blow made the hole into a long slit.

Firmly gripping the handle of the axe, he thrust the blade back through the hole, tugged to make sure it was solidly set, and then drew his body along the wing to where the axe was anchored.

The fingers of his left hand gripped the edge of the slit and took hold. Out came the axe and again it went crashing through the surface of the wing. Again he slithered forward, gaining another few feet. But the farther he went the harder his progress became. Now the wind and the sea seemed determined to thwart his efforts. The gale tore at his body and the sea tossed the crippled ship with renewed fury. It seemed as though the wing would go at any moment. And if it went now while he was clinging to it he was lost. Somehow it held. Why he did not know, since the sea was wrenching at it with giant hands of destruction.

Fighting grimly, he reached the last few feet and could see the ragged hole left by the nacelle when it was torn away with the motor. Sliding the axe under his body, he drew himself forward until he was in a position where he could hang head and shoulders over the edge. Then his hands found a twisted metal tube that had been an engine bearer; one of the many such tubes that took the strain of the powerful engine and held it in place.

Now he could feel the tubes twist and grind as the waves struck the dangling engine and its nacelle. Once it was free the ship would ride like a cork. Only the drag of that engine and nacelle gave the waves a grip. Shaking the stinging salt spray from his eyes he sought the tubes that were holding the engine still in place.

There was but one! Others, in a tangled mass, were wrapped around it. Yet near the base of the tube, where it was welded to the structure of the wing, the tube was clear. He drew out the hacksaw from under his shirt and carefully setting the edge against the tube began to saw.

He dared not risk breaking the blade. He knew only too well how easily it would snap. The hard steel would cut through nearly anything but the high temper made the blades brittle.

Clinging with one arm, grimly fighting the assault of the waves and the bucking of the ship, he sawed with the other while the fate of the ship and his companion hung in the balance.

Bill's arm, cramped in an awkward position, began to ache. The muscles seemed to be tied in knots. Now the blade was halfway through the tube; he wondered if his strength would last. Then, as the tube was weakened, the edges of the saw cut began to bind against the blade when the engine swung below the wing. His heart beat furiously. His eyes never left that cut. He watched every move it made, sawed frantically every time it opened, stopped every time it closed so he would not strain that fragile blade. Less than half an inch of the tube now held the engine. Then with a sharp snap it parted. There was a ripping of metal as the rest of the sheathing tore away and the engine and its mounting dropped into the sea.

The wing, freed of its drag, rose sharply, almost shaking Bill off. Now the seas rushed past underneath. The hull no longer quartered them but met them head on and breasted them far more easily. The return journey to the hull, made by clinging to the holes he had cut, was a comparatively simple matter. Taylor was still unconscious. Bill returned to the pilot compartment, and thought for the first time of his own situation.

The ship, although she pitched and pounded on the seas, seemed safe for the time being. But—what of that high rocky coast hidden by rain and low clouds? They had paralleled that coast on the trip. Now it lay downwind. The ship would drift onto it.

If they were driven ashore there, pounded on the reefs in the breakers that fringed the shore, the hull would not last a moment. Bill knew only too well what would happen. He reached for charts and looked at the last position which he had marked down as a part of his duties when the engine began to fail.

They had been about eight miles offshore, cutting along the coast to evade a wide headland that projected far out to sea. Estimating that they had been down on the sea about thirty minutes, Bill began to figure the drift of the ship. How far had the wind and the waves taken them?

As closely as he could calculate, they were now almost directly off the point of the headland and not over two miles from shore. At the rate the wind and sea drifted them they were due to crash into the breakers in less than half an hour! Suddenly Bill's eyes staring at the chart centered on an estuary marked just beyond the tip of the headland. The map showed it to be some five miles away if his estimate of their position was correct. But to get there the stricken flying boat would have to make a course of nearly forty-five degrees down the drift of the wind and waves.

One engine remained. Aloft, had the other not partially torn from its mount, that one engine would have kept them flying at reduced speed. Now, in this sea, there was no chance at all of being able to take-off on it alone. Nor would that crippled wing stand the strain. It would be suicidal even to try it. There was no hope either of using that one engine to turn the ship and taxi. The huge fin and rudder as well as the long reach of the hull would act as a weathervane and prevent the holding of the ship on a downwind course with but one motor. It was difficult enough to do so in a strong wind with both motors unless the ship taxied at high speed. Again, he doubted that he could turn the ship in these seas without a wave beating down a wing tip and swamping it. How, then, to sail a course at forty-five degrees to the drift downwind?

Suddenly a picture flashed into his mind.

Again he was studying courses. Simple navigation, with his Sea Scout Ship. The problem was to set a series of courses that would permit tacking against a wind and arrival at a set point. Beating back and forth, quartering the wind until one reached a certain point permitted the final "reach" for the destination. Somewhere in that picture was the solution to his present plight. But where? Then he saw it.

Why not reverse the procedure? Here, as closely as he could calculate, he was drifting astern at some twelve miles an hour. Well, why not start the engine, use it to help hold the head of the flying boat in a quartering position into the wind and then, by running the engine just fast enough, he could maneuver so that the ship would drift downwind on a forty-five degree course for that estuary where there was shelter and safety.

His hand reached for the starter switch and after a moment the engine sprang into life. He let it idle to warm up, then gently opened the throttle. By juggling the controls he worked the nose of the flying boat quartering into the wind. More engine held it there. He smiled, happy, confident he could hold the course. Only one thing was against him now and that was whether he had judged the position correctly. What if he were farther away than he thought from that headland? Or closer? If he were closer he would only drive ashore unless he could manage to claw clear with one engine.

Minutes that seemed hours passed. He sat at the controls, one hand on the wheel and one on the engine throttle, fighting and juggling them, eyes on the compass, holding a steady course—backwards! Now the land should loom close. He left the controls, stood erect and poked his head through the hatch. Rain beat down on him, blurred his vision, closed the horizon to less than half a mile. Only the tossing seas were all around him.

He returned to the controls, straightened the ship back on its angular course and decided to wait five more minutes. Then he cut the engine and again peered through the hatch.

Vaguely, through the whistling of the wind and the pounding of the flying boat on the waves, he seemed to hear a deeper sound. Was it the dull rumble of the breakers? And from what point did it come? It seemed to be from all sides. It might be a mile away and then it might be far less. The wind swept the sound back. Bill decided to chance a short wait. The ship rode easier now although it was necessary to cling to something to remain erect. In the waiting time he could take another look at Taylor.

The chief pilot lay white, breathing deeply. Two spots of color showed on his cheeks. His bandaged arm was still firmly held to his chest where Bill had lashed it. He looked all right. Bill dashed back to the hatchway.

The sound of the breakers, if it had been that, was louder now. It seemed to center to one side. Bill strained to pick up its direct bearing. Surf would be crashing on one side of that headland and the lee would be calm. If he were only right in his calculation of their position when he started!

Now the sound of the surf was clearer still and the seas were flattening. There was little doubt where the surf was. It was off to his left. He had rounded the headland and the crippled flying boat was slowly edging in for sheltered land.

The seas dropped still more although the rain still beat down. Now the wind dropped somewhat for he was well in the lee of the high headland. He returned to the seat and opened the motor. The rudder brought the nose around and held it with difficulty. Now he was tearing along, smashing through the tops of waves that were too small to bother the huge hull. His confidence returned.

Then, through the rain, he saw the loom of land less than a mile away. A buoy passed close to one side. Another followed—channel markers. Following them, in minutes he was drawing up to a low dock where startled men were standing ready to receive this unexpected aerial giant. He eased the ship near the dock, brought a wing tip pontoon into position so they could grasp it and draw the flying boat in to them. Then, when he saw they had him docked, he cut the motor and scurried aft to open the door.

It was an hour later that he spoke to crusty Pop Foster on the telephone. Briefly he reported a forced landing, the ship crippled, now in port, Taylor injured and under a doctor's care. He gave no details nor did Foster ask for them, for he was too much the man of action. Weather was clearing; Foster would have another ship fly him to where Bill had come ashore.

"Stand by!" was his terse order.

He arrived at dusk and no sooner was on the dock than he began a series of crisp questions.

"Huh," he finally snorted. "So you landed the ship, patched up Taylor's arm, cut away that wrecked engine, then, half-sailing and half-taxiing, you brought the ship to a safe harbor."

Suddenly his expression softened. A twinkle came into his eyes. He thrust out his hand:

"Nice work, young man, nice work! From now on you are a pilot for Seaboard Air Lines. You showed a stout heart and a level head. You brought in your ship in regular style!"

"Sea Scout style!" grinned Bill in reply.

Boy on a Uranium Hunt

By B. and J. GORSUCH

Life is tough for boy and beast on the Colorado Plateau, but it's a prospector's paradise

There you are, crawling up the face of a cliff in a million-acre wilderness, wondering if your next step will be your last. The sun blasts down like a blowtorch, but you keep looking up even when your eyes swell with scorching, because up there is the rim—your goal. You're "walking the rims" hunting uranium.

I spent the summer hunting uranium on the Colorado Plateau in Utah. I was twelve years old, which ought to prove that hunting uranium is for anyone healthy who wants to try it.

Dad and I went to the heart of the red rock country, a hundred miles out of Grand Junction, Colorado. All around cliffs rose like giant tables. Every canyon between was a starting point for prospecting. Uranium might lie anywhere up the face of any mesa.

We set up base camp by a stream coming from a strong spring, a good campsite. There were no people, but right away we met plenty of other living creatures. We had to share camp with some of them. I slept on the ground in my bedroll. Dad slept on a cot next to me. In the night a big spider would crawl over Dad, he'd half wake up, grab it, toss it, and it would land on me. I had to use T-shirts to sleep in, hot as it was, because the spiders kept crawling over my chest, waking me up.

The beetles were worse. They flew dive bomber style. They ranged from half-inch to hummingbird size. At night they'd dive at the tent, then crawl over it with a noise like Martians scratching their way in. They, too, kept me awake.

We had our black cocker, Shadow, with us—strictly a city dog. She wore me out first thing. She was crazy to go with us and she hated steep places. Practically every place we went was steep. We had to haul her up with a rope around her belly. Coming down, I'd think surely she'd try it alone, but she'd jump around on the rim whimpering, until I had to climb back up, tie the rope, and lower her into Dad's arms. That way I did twice as much climbing as Dad. Naturally I was twice as tired.

But Shadow and I soon toughened. When we set up camp, she was as fat as a barrel and just as hard to keep moving. In a few weeks she had slimmed into her original girlish figure and was slipping up and down cliffs like a cat. And she turned out to be good at one thing. The first time a rattler came into camp, Dad was inside the tent with his back touching the canvas side. The snake rattled and struck the canvas. Dad ran outside to kill it, but Shadow had the rattler, shaking it like a piece of rubber hose. She killed it.

She ran everywhere, crazy over the scent of deer, mountain lions, and bears. What would have happened if she'd ever faced one of these at close range? Once, running ahead of us and out of sight, she must have run into a lion, because she came skidding down the mountain with her tail tucked so far under her you couldn't see it. She crouched behind us and would not go back up the mountain.

Lions were more plentiful than bears. We saw tracks of them even in camp. One morning just after sunrise we came around a bend and nearly stumbled over a deer so freshly killed that the blood was still pumping from it. It had been brought down by a whopping big cougar, judging from the bite of meat torn from the deer's shoulder. We stopped and searched rocks and brush for the cat. We knew it was there, watching. But it kept out of sight.

In the evening when we came back, most of the meat was gone, and in a day or so when we dropped by, there was nothing but bones.

Most cougar tracks led to and from the roughest high cliffs where the mother lion could cache her cub safely while she roamed the lower canyons for food. Once in a blue moon a mother would have the bad luck to have her baby in low country and she'd have to leave it unprotected while she hunted for food. Every day I dreamed of coming across one of these cubs. I wanted to make a pet of it.

But in our three months at camp, we only caught a glimpse of one cat. They were too wary. We met a government trapper who told us he'd killed around eighty-one in two seasons. He turned in their ears for bounty and destroyed the carcasses.

This trapper was a husky six-footer whose tough body showed his lifetime out-of-doors. He was camped in a deserted cabin. He was the only human we met the whole summer.

"The thing I hate," he told us, "is the little foxes who come snooping around the traps and get caught. They look at you as if you're the meanest critter in the world. Of course you have to kill 'em. They're too mangled to survive in the wilds."

The trapper was never too interested in our hunt for uranium. Maybe it was because he was interested only in wildlife and nature.

Every morning Dad and I rolled out in the first gray light and ate a breakfast of nearly raw eggs mixed with chunks of toast—a dish I never liked before, but which I have come to think is nearly as good as steak.

After breakfast we'd fill two water canteens, fix some sandwiches, and tuck oranges and cans of juice in our pack. Dad would fasten the Geiger counter to his belt, and we'd start up one of the cliffs.

One day in particular, I thought the country had us, for sure. The whole day went wrong. First I lost my canteen falling down a cliff. Dad marked out too much area to survey and the day was sizzling hot. We kept sweating water out of our bodies in flood streams. We didn't dare drink much of our water at a time—it had to last the whole day. We were on top of a bare desert rim, the jeep far below.

By afternoon our water was gone and still the sweat poured. A big thundercloud

416

gathered in the sky and I thought, "This will help. We'll get a little rain." The dust and dirt scratched sticky skin and my tongue felt like a dry tennis ball. The thundercloud grew, drifted toward the sun. Just as we expected its shadow to cast a minute of shade, the sun's heat scattered the cloud.

I don't remember going down the cliff. But I'll never forget the ride back to camp. I kept imagining ice cold watermelon, ice cubes clinking in a frosty glass, gallons of frozen orange juice.

Plenty of Uranium

Not a single week went by that we didn't find a show of uranium somewhere on the face of the canyon walls. The first month we located over thirty claims.

One of the richest claims was one I found myself, without the Geiger counter. It happened because I never could keep my mind on uranium hidden somewhere underground; I was always looking for things I could *see*.

Dad found this little piece of uranium ore and he was pretty excited, thinking it must have fallen from a big deposit somewhere above him. We started up the cliff and I got above him because he stopped to chip samples. My foot knocked loose a rock that went bounding down. It struck him.

He yelled, "Why don't you quit messing around? Get over to the other side of this cliff and find some uranium of your own!"

So I worked my way around the cliffside. Ahead of me were several holes, some black, some yellow. I'd seen enough uranium ore to know that black or yellow rock is a good sign. I scrambled up to the holes, knocked out a good-sized chunk of yellow ore with my pick, and hurried back to the counter.

Dad had parked the counter yards below him. He was still picking away up there. I put my rock near the counter and the needle went wild. "Hey!" I yelled. "Come down here! I've got something better than anything you're chipping up there!"

At first he didn't pay attention. I was getting so excited I could hardly wait for him.

Finally he slid down, took a look. One glance at the needle and he grabbed the rock, set the machine to register higher, and still the needle flew to the end of the dial.

We knew then it was unusually high grade ore. "Bob, you've got it," he said. "This is the best ore I've ever seen." He turned it over and over under the Geiger snout. "Now the question is, how much of it have we got?" He picked up the counter. "Show me where you found it." I took him up and we started staking.

A Close One for Shadow

A couple of months later he went back to shoot some of the ore with dynamite, to learn how big the ore vein might be. I didn't go— he said shooting dynamite was too dangerous. But he took Shadow.

He set the dynamite and was scrambling over the ledge to get out of explosion range. The ledge crumbled, and he went falling over the cliff. A cedar tree caught him, breaking his glasses and his watch, and cutting his face, neck, and shoulders. He was not able to move, to get out of the tree. The blast went off and the force of it threw him outward, again down the cliff. He landed on another ledge. When he came to and started to get up, he found his knee was out of joint. He painfully shoved it back into place and crawled back to the jeep.

He whistled for Shadow, but she didn't come. He waited. But he felt too bad to wait and went back to camp, thinking she'd follow.

She didn't return. Dad wasn't able to drive back to look for her. We figured she got caught in the blast—nothing else would have kept her from camp.

Two days later he went back to find her body, to bury it from wild animals.

Exactly at the spot where he went over the ledge, Dad saw something black. He saw something move. It was Shadow, trying to wag her tail. She was waiting. Two days without food or water, but she had refused to leave the spot where she thought Dad was.

We still don't know how big the vein of uranium is, but a sample assayed at nearly forty percent. That's high—plenty!

It took us all summer, but we finally prospected every stretch of canyon around camp. One morning Dad said, "Let's look at the high country." He meant the mountain ranges towering behind the mesas. These were out of desert country.

We pulled camp, loaded the jeep. There were no real roads. We followed animal paths. Sometimes we wandered from canyon to canyon, hunting an opening upward.

Once on top, I knew what the pioneers felt when they reached a peak and looked down on their Promised Land. There were oak and cedar, fir and pine. Everywhere were green brush and berry bushes.

"This is ranch land," Dad said. He stopped the jeep. Sage hens strutted through the brush. Deer grazed peacefully in the meadows, their fur gleaming reddish-orange in the sun. They lifted velvet-covered horns proudly, unafraid.

Dad was right when he said this was ranch land. As soon as we started on, we came upon cattle grazing. We heard a happy stream gurgling. We camped under a big tree. It was heavenly cool, and I slept undisturbed. The first thing in the morning I saw sage hens scratching near me. Quietly I reached for my gun. We had fried sage hen for breakfast.

I chewed a piece of crisp chicken and leaned back, contented. Suddenly I knew what I wanted. Not to be a millionaire with uranium claims all over the Colorado Plateau. I was like the trapper. I wanted live things—live things to see, live things to live with. I wanted a ranch. A lonely ranch where few people came, but plenty of things lived, unfrightened and undisturbed.

If our uranium claims were any good, I could buy that ranch some day. I looked at Dad, cleaning chicken from the pan.

"Thanks," I said. "Thanks for bringing me out here this summer."

He looked surprised, then grinned. "You like this life, huh? Even when it's tough?"

"I sure do," I said. "I'm coming back."

Anybody Can Ski

By B. J. CHUTE

Only a genius or a nitwit could tie himself into as many knots as Dubby, who was just learning to ski

Tommy Anderson raised his nose from his stamp album. "Anybody can be taught anything," he said firmly.

"That's ridiculous." Joe Keene, who had been lying with two sofa pillows under his head and his feet in the fireplace, sat up in outrage. "You're blithering."

"Not at all," said Tommy. "I taught myself stamp-collecting, bee-keeping and photography, all out of books. Even allowing for my natural genius— Did you grunt?"

"I did."

"Well, don't do it again. Even allowing for my natural genius, I still say that anybody can be taught anything."

"Some people, maybe," said Joe. "Anybody, no."

"Anybody," said Tommy, now completely sold on his theory. He paused to anchor Switzerland to the page, and then added, "Of course, a person has to *want* to learn."

Joe shook his head. "Wanting's no help. If it was, Dubby Wells would be the world's greatest athlete."

"Nothing's wrong with Dubby that a little applied intellect wouldn't cure."

Joe stifled a sob. "Thomas, how can you say such things? Why, the only time in his life Dubby got into a basketball game, he shot for the wrong basket and scored for the other side."

"He did?" Tommy, having stuck Nicaragua on the end of his nose where he could find it when needed, gave Joe an interested and slightly cross-eyed look. "How come he got into the game in the first place?"

"The whole team came down with colds, and Dubby went in as a substitute for a substitute for a substitute. The coach figured he couldn't do much harm, and the coach was wrong."

"Ah, well-a-day," said Tommy sympathetically. "Still a thing like that could happen to anybody."

"But it always happens to Dubby," Joe pointed out. "He means well and he tries hard, but he's just a natural-born calamity. He's probably the only guy in history who not only managed to knock himself out cold in a hurdle race but knocked out the guy next to him. It took genius."

Tommy looked properly respectful. "A man like that should go far."

"And now," said Joe, "the poor deluded nut wants to join the Skiing Club."

"No soap?"

"None whatever. There's a feeling abroad that a member should be able to go down at least one hill, standing up. I know it's a very revolutionary idea, but that's the way we feel." Joe's sigh mounted from his shoelaces. "I like Dubby and I want him to be happy, but I'd rather have a kangaroo in the Skiing Club."

"You should teach him to ski the right way."

"Athletically speaking, there *is* no right way for Dubby."

"Anybody can be . . ."

". . . taught anything," Joe finished for him. "This is where I came in, and it just ain't so."

"It is too," said Tommy stubbornly, "and to prove it, *I'll* teach him."

"To ski?" Joe burst into a merry peal of laughter. "You can't even ski yourself, you poor fish, much less teach Dubby."

"I can read a book," said Tommy coldly, "and that's all that's necessary." He rose and removed Nicaragua formally from his nose. "Good-by."

"Where you going?"

"To the library. To get a book on skiing so I can teach Dubby."

Joe laid himself down tenderly, folded his hands and closed his eyes. "Now I've heard everything," he said. "Farewell."

"Farewell," said Tommy. He turned back for a moment to place Nicaragua on Joe's brow, and departed.

Tommy surveyed the snowy landscape thoughtfully and then transferred his scholarly attention to Dubby Wells.

Dubby, tall and thin and sprouting red earmuffs, reminded his teacher of a carelessly built but eager afghan, an illusion greatly enhanced when Dubby moved forward on his skis, making progress in a sort of fluttering lope.

"Like that?" said Dubby, peering back over his shoulder.

Tommy looked into his "How to Ski" book, borrowed from the public library and snugly wrapped in a kitchen towel to protect it from drafts and snow. He read three pages, scowling, and shook his head.

"Try it again. It says here it should be an easy, rhythmical motion."

Dubby tried it again. It was rhythmical, in the way that a rather dreamy camel is rhythmical. Tommy told himself that the camel was a noble animal and said "Okay" without much conviction.

"Now," he went on, "you're supposed to learn to turn around before you learn to go downhill. Can you turn around?"

"Sure," said Dubby, and began to inch one ski sideways and then follow it up with the other. The rate of progress was very stately and rather like a minuet.

"All wrong," Tommy informed him briskly. "You're supposed to kick one ski up front, pivot with it, lay it down, and bring the other ski around. Here, look in the book."

Dubby looked, and a happy smile wreathed his ears. "Why, that's wonderful. It turns you right around."

"You learn to do that," Tommy promised, "and the Skiing Club will be begging you to join." He gave himself a mental pat on the back. All this poor guy needed was a sensible, scholarly approach.

"Now," he said instructively, "when I say One, put your right pole forward and your left pole back. When I say Two, kick your left ski out and up. And when I say Three, pivot it and lay it flat in the snow. Got it?"

"One, poles," Dubby repeated. "Two, left ski up. Three, swing around. I've got it."

"Ready, set . . . ONE!" Tommy gazed upon his pupil with pride, one pole forward and one pole back. There may have been a slight unsteadiness east and west, but north and south he looked perfectly lovely. "Two," he said, "left ski up . . . GADZOOKS!"

He wouldn't have thought it was possible. Dubby's ski, rising alertly from the snow, had contrived to sock its owner square on the nose. This splendid achievement had apparently exhausted him, and he immediately lay down full length in the snow and made exotic noises. "How on earth did you manage to do that?" Tommy demanded.

Dubby said that his legs were too long. He said they always got in his way.

"Extraordinary," said Tommy with a kind of reluctant admiration, and scooped Dubby out of the snow. "Now, this time, take it slower."

"Yes," said Dubby meekly.

"Are your poles right? Okay, now, bring your ski up—I'll hold you. Steady to port, old man, steady— Ahhhhh." He peered over Dubby's shoulder approvingly; the position arrived at was definitely the number two position in the book. "Do you feel safe?"

"Sort of," said Dubby uncertainly.

"Good. Because I'm leaving you." He backed off cautiously, Dubby stayed upright, and Tommy returned to his book. "All right. You now swing the upright ski around and lay it parallel to the right ski, with its point going in the opposite direction. Swing!"

Dubby swung. He swung magnificently; in fact, he swung too far. The left ski landed directly on top of the right ski, effectively nailing its owner to the ground.

"Go back!" said Tommy.

"I can't."

"Go forward?" said Tommy in a small voice. It was, he realized, a foolish question. Dubby had gone all the forward that was possible. "How do you *do* these things?" he asked vainly.

"I don't know. They just happen." There was a pause. "What do I do now, Tommy?" he asked plaintively.

It was a time for frankness. "I can't imagine," said Tommy. "I could take you home and put you in the garden and we could grow vines up you, I suppose." He looked into his book again, but there was nothing in it about first aid to trellises. The next page, however, dealt with something called a herring-bone, a method for skiing uphill. After all, skiing was a downhill sport and, to go downhill, one must learn to go up. Also, it seemed to be a project in which long legs might come in useful.

"I think the thing for you to do is to fall down," he decided. "Later on in the book, there's a whole page about falling down, and you might as well get the experience early . . . Oh, very nice! You fall beautifully, Dubby."

Dubby removed his face from the snow and requested politely that Tommy take his right ski out of his left ear. This was not easy, as Dubby seemed to have more legs than a centipede, but nothing was too much trouble for an old friend.

"There, there," said Tommy soothingly, propping him upright once more. "Now, look, Dubby, we're going to abandon the kick turn for the moment and come back to it later. I want to teach you to herring-bone uphill. You'll like that."

"No kick turn?"

"Not just now," said Tommy. "I'm not as young as I was ten minutes ago." He referred in a businesslike manner to his book. "The herring-bone is really very simple. All you do is stick your left ski out, shift your weight, stick your right ski out, shift your weight again, and so onward and upward with the arts."

Dubby humped himself around obediently until he was facing the slope. He swung his left ski out and stamped on it, and then turned his attention to the right ski. Steam coming out of his ears, he stamped his way up five steps more and then came to a sudden stop.

"Go on," said Tommy, "you're doing fine."

"I can't go on."

"Why on earth not?"

"Something's standing on my tail," said Dubby plaintively. "I can't move."

Tommy lumbered uphill through the snow to investigate. It was quite true; Dubby's right ski was firmly anchored by his left one, a variation on the theme of his kick turn.

"Lift the left ski," said Tommy.

"Can't."

"Slide the right one out, then."

"Can't."

It seemed to Tommy that what some people lacked was initiative. "Well, hold on, and I'll hoist the left ski up for you. When I hoist, you get the right ski loose and go on from there."

On paper, it would have been a splendid idea. Unfortunately, when Tommy yanked up the left ski, the right one—over-stimulated by its sudden freedom—galloped backwards, with Dubby still on board. Tommy, caught off-balance, went flat on his face in the snow. Dubby, encountering obstacles, went backwards, his arms flailing wildly. He landed with his feet going uphill and his head downhill, squarely on top of Tommy who was traveling in the opposite direction. Together, they presented a pretty, if confusing, pattern in the snow.

time he got to the summit, some of his enthusiasm had revived and he was back at his "This is really very simple" philosophy.

"All you have to do, Dubby, is assume the correct posture and let nature take its course. Bend the waist, flex the knees and balance on the balls of the feet. Your knees do flex, don't they? Splendid. Yes, that's right. You look just like the picture." He admired him for a moment, and then said blithely, "Now give yourself a brisk push forward with your poles . . ."

Tommy was the first to speak. His voice had a bitter, snowy and subterranean sound. "Get offa me," he said.

"How?" asked Dubby, rather in the manner of an upper berth speaking to a lower berth.

"Never mind how," said Tommy, flapping about restlessly below. "Just get off before I smother. Roll sideways, you idiot. Do something!"

Dubby rolled, and after a brief and vigorous quarrel with the hillside Tommy managed to stagger erect. He gazed upon Dubby glumly. "I don't understand it," he said. "Does this kind of thing always happen to you?"

Dubby nodded. "Generally."

"Well, it's remarkable. Look, we'll try going downhill. After all, that's really what the Skiing Club seems to want." He then added thoughtfully, "Once you get in, it's their worry if you knock all the members out."

"Huh?" said Dubby.

"Nothing," said Tommy hastily. He took a look at the hill. "This isn't too steep. We'll go to the top and you try coming down."

"Shall I herring-bone up?"

"Uh, no. Go sideways or something. It takes longer, but I'm not insured."

Together, they surged upwards at the rate of about one surge a minute, Tommy filling in the pauses by studying his book. By the

Dubby pushed, shot forward and went approximately ten feet downhill, arms, legs, poles and ears waving discordantly. At this point, as Tommy had promised, nature took its course. Dubby's bent waist joined his flexed knees, his knees sank to the balls of his feet and, rolled up like some impassioned hedgehog, Dubby went the next several yards in a state of violent disintegration.

"It's incredible," said Tommy to himself, and went to join him. Dubby rose from the snow in a localized blizzard and gave himself a shake. Tommy went on talking in a mystified manner. "I don't understand it. In the book, it looks perfectly simple."

"It's different on skis," Dubby assured him.

"Yes, I suppose it is, but, even so, there's something about the way *you* do it . . .

Dubby, get out of those skis for a minute and let me try them, huh?" He frowned. "Maybe my theory's wrong. Maybe a person can't be taught skiing out of books, although I must say this one seems perfectly straightforward."

He took the skis from Dubby, strapped them on and glanced rapidly into his book again. Then he nodded, gripped the poles, edged himself around and started off.

For a moment, life seemed terribly perilous, until he remembered the instructions about bending forward and balancing on the balls of his feet, and, shouting a proud song in praise of himself, he succeeded in maintaining a perpendicular attitude to the bottom of the hill.

"Ha! Quite simple," said Tommy, and took a look at the hill behind him. Truly, it wasn't much of a hill, but still it was his first and he felt he had acquitted himself in a highly scientific manner.

He waited while Dubby galloped through the snow to his side. "You didn't fall down," said Dubby, obviously incredulous.

"I followed instructions."

"*I* followed instructions, Tommy. My feet get in the way."

"They do, don't they?" Tommy scratched his ear. "You know what, Dubby? I think the trouble with you is that you don't have a scholarly mind. I think you need to have everything translated to you in dynamic action."

"Dynamic action?" said Dubby wanly.

Tommy nodded with great wisdom. "Exactly. You need to *see* a thing done, instead of being told about it."

"I don't get it."

Tommy sighed, although this proved his point. "Listen," he said patiently, "*I* learn from the book, you learn from me. I'll borrow some skis somewhere, and tomorrow afternoon we'll come out again. I'll try it on skis first, and then I'll teach you."

"Well . . . it might work."

"It's going to work," said Tommy determinedly. "I'm going to teach you to ski if it's the last thing I ever do."

By the end of the week, Tommy had developed a passionate dislike for everything to do with snow, especially the way it sparkled softly in the sunshine and then turned to solid rock when a person landed on it.

On the other hand, Dubby seemed to be acquiring a slight mastery over his feet, and in fact had arrived upright at the bottom of the hill several times, although on each occasion he had collapsed at his destination, presumably from shock.

Tommy's efforts to teach him the rudiments of a snowplow, intended to slow the skier up in time of crisis, finally had to be abandoned.

"After all," Tommy decided, "once we get you into the Skiing Club, your fellow-members can teach you all the fancy bits." He suppressed a moment's pity for Dubby's fellow-members and concentrated instead on

Joe Keene's astonishment when he should observe the success of Tommy's theories on learning how to ski.

In spite of progress, however, there still seemed to be no visible limit to the ways in which Dubby could get into trouble. If he started with his skis together, they separated and he fell between them. If he started with them safely apart, they crossed and he finished the tour on his nose. If there was a bush or tree within ten miles, some strange internal radar caused Dubby to head for it like a homing pigeon and plunge himself into branches up to the ears.

Because of this, Tommy was obliged to inaugurate a system. The system consisted of his going downhill ahead of Dubby to make a track for his earnest student to follow. This restricted Dubby's rather unusual creative talents somewhat, and the tenth time that Dubby landed upright at the bottom of a hill, in Tommy's tracks, Tommy decided he was ready for a tryout with the Skiing Club.

"Or as ready as you'll ever be," he added. "If we wait much longer, it'll be summer."

Dubby sighed. "You'll come with me, won't you, Tommy?"

"To the tryout? I wouldn't miss it for the world."

Neither, it turned out, would the Skiing Club. Joe Keene had been busy notifying all concerned, and a fascinated audience assembled to observe the fruits of Tommy's intellectual approach to what was considered an insoluble athletic problem.

Joe, as president, welcomed Dubby gravely and presented him with the hill which he was expected to navigate. It was a rather fine hill, steeper than the ones they had been practicing on, but absolutely clear of any kind of foreign entanglements. Not a bush marred its pure expanse. It was impossible to see how Dubby could get into any kind of trouble, if he would only remember what he had learned.

Tommy accompanied him to the top and helped him strap on his skis. "Lean-forward-relax-bend-your-knees-and-balance-on-the-balls-of-your-feet," he said rapidly.

"There's no track to follow," said Dubby.

"Of course there's no track, you idiot. It's a lovely clear hill."

"It's much easier with a track. I don't get mixed up in things."

"Dubby! There's nothing to get mixed up in here." He took a look around and changed his mind. The onlookers had infiltrated and were lining the hill. Tommy was not the man to be caught off guard. "There's your track right there," he said cheerily. "Just stay between the people."

"I don't think . . ."

"You aren't supposed to think. Just ski."

"You know how I feel?" said Dubby. "I feel just the way I did when I tried out for the swimming team."

"What happened?"

"I sank."

"Dubby, old man," said Tommy earnestly, "will you please kindly stop brooding on your past glories and pay attention to what you're doing? After all, my honor is just as much at stake as yours. Relax. All you have to do is go downhill."

"Standing up," Dubby amended.

"Well, yes, that would help." He gave Dubby's shoulder a bracing pat. "Stick your poles in, and just shove off."

Dubby pushed his chin out about six inches, adopted the look of a Roman gladiator and jammed his poles into the snow.

"Okay, here I go," he said, and pushed. Unfortunately, he had jammed his poles in not wisely but too well. His feet went, and the rest of him stayed behind with the poles. Dubby lay down in the snow.

A cheer arose from the spectators. Tommy wailed. "Dubby! You never did that before!"

Dubby sat up, and Tommy hauled him to his feet and gave him a shake. "You know better than that," he said crossly. "Now, this time do it right."

Dubby gulped audibly, nodded and pushed off again. He achieved a promising start and then, inscrutably, managed to shift his weight over his right ski. Considering that Tommy had wasted several days trying to teach Dubby to stem-turn by exactly this method, it seemed hard that the talent should

·blossom forth within him so suddenly and at such a moment. Dubby veered to the right, and spectators scattered. Only one moved too late. That was the one that Dubby hit.

Tommy gave a moan and buried his face in his hands. Someone touched his shoulders, and he turned to find Joe Keene looking at him sympathetically.

"Look, Tommy," Joe said kindly, "don't you think you and Dubby better go home and take up some quiet sport like tatting? I hear there's nothing quite so exhilarating as tatting down the home stretch."

"You shuddup," said Tommy. "Anyone can have a couple of spills, and anyhow it's not Dubby's fault that the hill's all cluttered up with people." He stalked off to rescue his unhappy friend.

"Dubby," he said earnestly, "pay close attention to me. Do you think you could get down that hill in one piece if I go ahead of you and make a track?" Dubby nodded. "Well, then, that's what I'm going to do. There's no law against it, and anyway this is a very unusual situation." He turned toward the skier who had been the victim of Dubby's gallant charge. "Can I borrow your skis?"

"Oh, sure," said the victim, who was still taking snowballs out of his collar. He sounded rather huffy. "Don't mind me."

"Thank you kindly. Now, look, Dubby, give me time to get out of the way, and then you follow my tracks. Don't look at the audience, don't think about the Skiing Club. *Just follow my tracks.*"

"Just follow your tracks," said Dubby wisely.

"That's right." Tommy fastened his skis on, picked up the poles and led the way.

Joe greeted him inquisitively. "Where you going?"

"I'm making a track for Dubby."

"You?"

"Me." With an air of calm conviction, intended to mobilize Dubby's nervous system, Tommy took his place at the top of the hill with Dubby behind him. "I'm going to make it nice and wide so you can't miss," he said sternly. "If you *do* miss, I'm going to come

back and make you into mincemeat pie. Okay?"

"Okay," said Dubby.

Tommy gave himself a gentle push forward, gradually forcing the tails of his skis out and bringing the points together. He had studied the snowplow enough to realize that this would assure a conservative progress through the snow, leaving a boulevard for his student to follow.

It worked splendidly. An elephant could have followed the track he was preparing, even a dignified elephant with a poor sense of balance. Unfortunately, Tommy was not dealing with an elephant; he was dealing with Dubby.

Halfway down the hill, stately and controlled, Tommy heard a sudden shout. He looked back over his shoulder.

Dubby had shoved off. With the uncanny sense of timing of a cuckoo clock gone berserk, lured by the splendid trail he had to follow, as confident now as he had been unnerved before, Dubby flew in Tommy's wake.

Tommy screeched, stopped snowplowing and gave a frantic push with his poles, trying to race his doom to the finish line. It was hopeless. Dubby overtook him in a matter of seconds, there was a spectacular instant of collision, and then the two skiers, intricately tangled together, rolled, bounced, thumped and battered their way to the bottom.

Dubby was the first to rise. After a moment, Tommy sat up stiffly, not speaking. He undid his skis and pushed them aside. He reached over, still in a state of terrible calm, and undid Dubby's. He then staggered to his feet and took Dubby by the hand. "Come," said Tommy.

"Where?"

"Away," said Tommy in hollow tones.

"Away where?"

"Anywhere," said Tommy, "so long as it's away from skis."

"I'm awfully sorry," said Dubby. "I started too soon."

"Well, you're finished now," said Tommy. "In a year or two, my bones may knit them-

selves together, but I very much doubt it."
Limping, he led the way off the field of battle.

Dubby started to speak, thought better of it and followed him. The Skiing Club watched them go.

Several hours later, Joe Keene found them. They were in the living room of Tommy's home, Dubby sitting cross-legged on the floor with Tommy's stamps spread around him, Tommy lying on the sofa with eight cushions located at his more tender points.

They both looked up as Joe walked in, and Tommy said two words. He said, "Go away."

Dubby said, "Where does an Australian stamp go?"

"Under Australia. . . . Joe, go away. I don't like you."

"That's gratitude," Joe said. "I only dropped by to . . ." He broke off, suddenly aware of what was going on. "Dubby! What on earth are you doing?"

Dubby looked up, beaming proudly. "Fixing Tommy's stamps."

"Fixing his stamps? He wouldn't let the Postmaster-General himself do that."

"He's letting *me*," said Dubby happily. "You see, Joe, Tommy's been talking to me, and he's convinced me that I'm not really suited to athletics. He says my type of brains needs a more satisfying outlet, so he's teaching me philately."

Joe said thinly, "He's teaching you what?"

"Philately. Stamp-collecting." Dubby looked at Joe with beatific calm. "You see, you have an athlete's mind—you don't even know what philately means." He got to his feet with tremendous dignity. "I'll be over tomorrow, Tommy, and put some more stamps in for you, and you can explain about perforations." He handed the album graciously to its owner, nodded to Joe with the gravely superior air of one who has come to realize that brains are mightier than brawn, and made a thoroughly well-adjusted exit.

Joe watched him go. "Well, I'll be darned," he said softly. "Philately." He looked at Tommy, but Tommy was sitting bolt upright, peering into his stamp album

and making loud moaning noises. "Oh, no," said Tommy. "Oh, no!"

"Oh, no, what?"

Tommy hit himself distractedly on the brow. "Joe! He's stuck at least half those stamps in upside down."

Joe regarded him with a certain sympathy. "I don't see what else you could expect, you chump. What possessed you to let him loose in your precious stamps?"

Tommy drew a deep breath, calming himself somewhat. "Because the alternative was absolutely unthinkable," he said sternly. "Joe, do you realize that lunatic actually wanted me to go on teaching him to ski? After what happened this afternoon! Me without a single muscle I can call my own. No!" He gave his stamp album a remorseful pat. "This is a terrible sacrifice, Joe, but it's worth it. I never want to see a snowflake again as long as I live."

There was a short but profound silence. Then Joe said, "Tommy, old man, I have some news for you. After you and Dubby left, we had a meeting of the Skiing Club and elected a new member."

"As if I cared," said Tommy callously. "Give me his name and I'll send flowers. I . . ." He broke off. There was something about Joe's expression that caused him to turn pale. "Joe! You don't mean . . ."

"Yes, old man," said Joe. "We elected *you*. Unanimously." He gave his friend a hearty pat on the shoulder. "And I must say, Tommy, that I think you deserved it. With a little coaching, you'll make a very fine skier."

There was a sound of groaning. Tommy collapsed against his pillows, and the stamp album fell from his nerveless fingers. He closed his eyes.

Joe looked at him thoughtfully. If there had been a lily nearby, he would have put it into Tommy's hand. Instead, he carefully removed his Skiing Club badge from the front of his own jacket, pinned it to Tommy's shirt, just under his chin, and then tiptoed softly out of the room.

Tommy opened one eye. "This," said Tommy, "is . . . the end."

Secret and Urgent

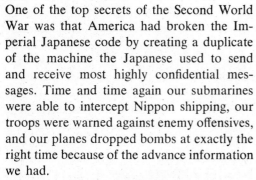

By STANLEY PASHKO

The experts are still looking for a code that can't be cracked

One of the top secrets of the Second World War was that America had broken the Imperial Japanese code by creating a duplicate of the machine the Japanese used to send and receive most highly confidential messages. Time and time again our submarines were able to intercept Nippon shipping, our troops were warned against enemy offensives, and our planes dropped bombs at exactly the right time because of the advance information we had.

So proud was the Japanese High Command of its code that it was used confidently until we intercepted and shot down General Yamamoto's plane in the South Pacific. Only then did they get wise and decide to use a new codebook.

However, their message announcing the change was intercepted together with the information that a copy of the new codebook was on its way to the Bougainville theater of operations aboard the ship Tami Maru. We sank that ship, then had our divers go down to recover the new codebooks, so that we were reading their messages right up to the end of the war.

This story furnishes one of the clearest proofs that no cipher system is permanently break-proof — although experts have been dreaming of a foolproof system almost since the dawn of communications.

There are only a few basic methods of trying to mask messages from the enemy. The code system is one of these methods. In code each word or phrase has a predetermined meaning. For instance, "owl" may mean "dynamite," "coin" may mean "submarine," "drop the hat" may mean "get all our nationals out of Europe," and so on. Messages sent in code can only be read when you have a codebook, but since the codebooks are as large and bulky as a dictionary, it is not a practical method for secret agents or for commanders in the field. Systems depending on memory will have to continue because, obviously, a spy cannot carry codebooks or cryptomachines with him where their discovery would mean certain death.

This brings us to another method of sending secret messages—the cipher system. With a cipher system you may substitute different letters or symbols for the actual letters in your message, or you may scramble the letters in your message in some prearranged manner known only to you and the person to whom you send the message.

A sample of the substitution system would be the Morse code. No one who is ignorant of the Morse code can read a message sent in it. Still, there are quite a few people who do know it, so suppose we substitute the consonant letters from B to M for dashes and the consonant letters from N through Z for dots. We can use the vowels to indicate end of a character or end of a word. Thus, even someone who knows Morse could be mystified by the message DNZRA TOESC FVUPG TAWET LBQOX HIRFN AZUDT

WIOIU. But, you should have no trouble reading it as "Be Prepared." Most code messages are sent in blocks of five letters to avoid furnishing clues by the size of the words.

Of course, the simplest sort of substitution system is just changing the letters of the alphabet, for example, A to D, B to E, C to F, and so on at random. But this sort of code is much too simple to decipher.

Many codes were born back in the Middle Ages when alchemists devised ways to keep their formulas from being stolen and philosophers used symbols to keep their thoughts and experiments from being exposed to Inquisitors.

Most of these old codes have been deciphered by modern experts, although there is one notable exception in a long work by Roger Bacon. This has stubbornly resisted all efforts to crack it. Some exasperated cryptographers insist that it is not a code at all, that it is a grisly practical joke without any meaning. Other authorities say that it is really a code and will eventually be broken, as have all codes since the beginning of communication.

Substitutional code systems are usually easy to memorize, but can be made quite hard to "crack." There are many variations. One invented by the Romans will be perfectly clear if you look at the example illustrated as "Code A." It is a criss-cross system in which the numbers locate the position of the letters. As you can see, "B" may be written as 26 or as 62, because it is in the "2" column going down and in the "6" column going across.

CODE "A"

	6	7	8	9	0
1	A	F	K	P	U
2	B	G	L	Q	V
3	C	H	M	R	W
4	D	I	N	S	X
5	E	J	O	T	YZ

A system like this is used by convicts to tap out messages on the prison plumbing system. As you may have noticed, a bang on the radiator in one end of your home can be heard in all the rooms. It travels along the pipes from room to room. Prisoners have used this to send information all over a jail. Thus, bang-bang is "A" because it is the letter in the first column across and down; "bang-bang-bang bang-bang" is "h" because it is the letter in the third column down and second column across. After you have memorized the position of the letters, it is as easy to read as Morse code.

Of course, you can use letters instead of numbers in making up such a criss-cross system.

There are scores of ways to create substitutional code systems, far too many ways to try to list all of them here, but an easy one to remember, and one which is fairly hard to decipher is the "plus and minus" type of code. In this system you select a number, something like "minus 235" or "plus 14," or "plus 31 minus 2." This becomes the key for reading and writing the message. It simply means that you add or subtract the number of letters in the key from the actual letters of the message in writing your cipher. With a key of minus 21, for example, the message, "meet me at noon," becomes KDCLK DVSLN MMXPQ.

Use a Newspaper

Another form of this is to have two copies of the same newspaper. Tear off the same page from each paper, for instance, the first page. Keep one copy and give the other copy of the paper to your friend. When you want to send a secret message, simply place a large blank piece of paper under your copy of the newspaper and make four pin points at the corners, so that your friend will be able to place his newspaper into the exact same position by using the same pin points to line up his paper.

Then read through the words or letters on your copy of the newspaper and stick a pin through those which will form your message. It will be easy for your friend to reverse the procedure to read what you have sent on the sheet of blank paper.

Another mechanical system involves owning the same dictionary or word book as your friend. You send him the page number and word number of each word in your message. For example, if you wanted to say "meet me at noon," you look up the word "meet." Suppose it is on page 213 and is the 23rd word down from the top. Your code number for "meet" will then be 213-23. Your friend can read it by looking on page 213 and counting down to the 23rd word.

CODE "B"

M	E	E	T	M	E
83	56	65	95	38	56
A	T	N	O	O	N
16	59	84	58	85	48

Does that sound like a code which would be impossible to crack? Well, believe it or not, during World War I such a code was used by a German agent operating in the Netherlands, who had obtained what he thought were the last remaining copies of a German-English dictionary. A brilliant flash of intuition enabled a British operative to guess what the codebook was and to get a copy from the British Museum library.

There are many ways of complicating a code. You can write the message backwards before putting it into cipher; add an extra letter every second word; transpose the letters according to any of a hundred well-known systems; or write your message down in three different languages before ciphering it. But, you can count on it, if you hand it over to a member at the American Cryptographers Association it would be deciphered. About a thousand of America's cryptographers, including many teen-agers, have

banded together to enjoy their hobby. At their convention dinners, menus and schedules are in codes, but no one has any particular trouble about keeping appointments.

Not all secret messages are sent in cipher, however. During World War I, the German High Command was often baffled by field messages in a guttural, primitive language. After the war they discovered that American Indians in the Army had been directing maneuvers in Navajo or some other tribal tongue. Of course, they had to make some freehand translations for words which were not in their original language. A tank became "big turtle," a medical corpsman was a "medicine man," and so on. The Germans were sufficiently impressed by this to have some university men come to the United States shortly after the war to compile a dictionary of American Indian languages. Fortunately, it didn't seem to help them much in World War II.

Secret agents have used invisible inks to get messages out of enemy territory, but these are simple enough to detect. When a spy is spotted, his mail is closely scrutinized by the men of the Black Chamber—the name used for the cipher and coding room of any country. Even the position of the stamp is carefully checked each time, for that might be the message; or the message might be written under the stamp itself.

An Invisible Code

The prize system of them all was invented by a German agent who was operating from Cuba early in World War II. We knew he was getting messages out, but we couldn't prove a thing. Our experts dusted the stationary with all sorts of powders and sprays for traces of invisible ink; they studied it under ultraviolet rays; they tried all kinds of grill patterns; they studied the letters for indications of some kind of code—but all to no avail.

One such letter had undergone every conceivable test. Yet the brain-weary counterespionage man was positive there was a message in it somewhere. Doggedly, he bent over it for one last try, and some ashes from his cigarette fell on the paper. Impatiently, he brushed it off, then noticed there was a tiny speck on the paper. About to flick that off with the rest of the ash, he stopped. His interested eyes noticed that a dot at the end of one of the paragraphs was missing. He was certain there had been a dot there before. With tweezers, he picked up the speck and examined it more closely. Yes, that was it! Excitedly he hurried to the microscope. That dot had been a microscopically reduced film of plans for some of our most important war equipment. So another agent was wiped off the books—but not immediately.

First, we took the opportunity to send his superiors a lot of misinformation, intercepting his messages and substituting our own dots for his. When he was no longer useful, he was arrested.

Secret codes have come a long way from the days when the Greeks tattooed their messages on the shaved heads of slaves, had them grow hair and travel through enemy country to be shaved bald at their destination and read like a human letter. But the art has not gone so far that there is a perfect, unbreakable code. Experts say it's like trying to invent a perpetual motion machine —perhaps it can't be done, but it's fun to try.

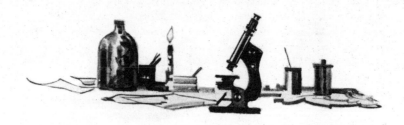

Conservating Charlie

By CARL HENRY RATHJEN

Dumbo Davis makes himself unpopular trying to solve the conservation problem

Dear Scoutmaster Fielder:

After what happened yesterday, I guess you won't want me in Troop 28 anymore, even though you always said I was one of a kind. I mean I opened my mouth again and fell into it, as usual, you'll say.

I guess the fellows in the Troop are right in calling me Dumbo Davis. I just can't seem to give serious attention to a situation without making the situation more serious.

So thanks for being so good and patient with me, Mr. Fielder, and I wish you all success now in making the Fox Patrol worthy of the Troop even though Andy Bevins is its Patrol Leader.

Resigningly yours,
Dudley Davis.

Dear President of the United States:

I'm sorry I locally loused up your invitation to the Boy Scouts of America to make Conservation our, I mean, *their* big program for this year.

Please don't hold my actions against them. They are doing a good job of helping conserve the ideals and resources of this country and they can't help it if there are one or two eroded spots like me they haven't been able to conserve yet.

Apologetically yours,
Dudley Davis
formerly of Troop 28
Boy Scouts of America

Dear Sheriff Baxly:

If you want to find the two men you are supposed to be looking for, see U. S. Ranger Charlie Evans. By the time you read this and get out of your chair and waddle over to his office, he'll have all the inside dope for you.

Unofficially yours,
Dudley Davis.

Dear Andy Bevins:

After the stinky trick you pulled on me yesterday as a Patrol Leader and a pal (?) I can think of nothing but a four-footed black animal with a white stripe down its back.

Repugnantly yours,
Dud

Dear Ranger Charlie Evans:

I don't know why I'm bothering to explain anything to you. You never listen to me anyway. Or if you do, you listen at the wrong time and put the wrong meaning on what I'm saying. Or I don't put the emphasis on the right way, and that gives you the wrong idea instead of the right meaning, and we get off wrong, and the more we try to put things to rights the more things go wrong because of the right thing I was trying to say at the wrong time in the first place and . . . You see what I mean?

Well, anyway, you've always had a wrong attitude toward me ever since a year or two back when you overheard me talking to some

431

tourists. I was telling them that when the Forest Service created Smokey the Bear, they must have had you in mind. I meant your *good* qualities. But you came along just then with that chunky build of yours, your round wide-eyed face under the flat-brimmed ranger's hat, a stack of posters under your left arm, and a shovel over your right shoulder . . . and, honest, you did look just like Smokey. It wasn't my fault that the tourists saw that too and laughed, and you didn't help matters along by assuming I was making fun of you and growling at me like a bear that's just out of hibernation.

From then on you always took the attitude that I did everything purposely to make trouble for you. Like the time you were having the big argument with cattlemen about range rights. You'd had a rough week and I tried to do you a favor by answering your phone and saying you were getting some sleep. You blamed me for the big cattleman on the line becoming irate because he didn't listen carefully and thought I said you were getting some sheep. From then on you started calling me Dumbo, and everyone else took it up. Well, I didn't mind for a while, but then I began to feel rather sensitive about the whole thing.

But after yesterday I guess maybe you're right. Because now my hopes of ever getting somewhere in the Scouts or becoming a ranger like you will just have to be regarded as an unconserved dream.

It all started the other night when Mr. Fielder invited you to the Troop meeting to give us some pointers on conservation. It was an old story. I don't mean that you were exactly boring but I knew all that stuff because my ambition is, *was,* to become a ranger. Anyway, even though I wasn't there when you started your long-winded . . . your long talk, I knew you'd been telling the Troop how twenty-odd years ago everything around here was becoming a wasteland because of a prolonged drought and not enough water running in the creeks. Sagebrush crowded out other wild growth, and when it rained the sage couldn't hold back water like grass and bushes and trees. Floods washed

away soil, and where they left off the wind took over. Even farmers' wells were drying up because there wasn't enough underground water.

Wild life couldn't find enough natural food. So mice and chipmunks and squirrels and birds and deer began raiding farmers. And the things that hunted them—coyotes, hawks, weasels, owls—became hungry and followed them to the farms but found it easier to grab a meal in a chicken coop or pasture rather than go after natural prey.

I came into the Troop meeting just about then, and when you saw me your voice took on a sudden crisp style that awakened some of the fellows. Or maybe it was just my opening the door to let some fresh air get in and crowd out the hot air that . . .

Well, anyway, you went on to tell how you started a conservation program. All the beavers had been killed off around here and you fought to get more money appropriated to get some pairs of beavers from Idaho which had too many. You turned them loose, and they dammed up streams and made ponds to let water seep underground and their dams held back floods. Grass and bushes began to grow again and crowd out the sagebrush. They helped rain soak in instead of running off. Animals came back to feed on the natural growth. Creeks kept running and fish came back up them. Predators like coyotes and hawks and owls began to feed more on natural prey again and left the farmers alone more and more.

Of course it took years for all that to build up—and it seemed like years for you to tell, or maybe I was just too familiar with it. Anyway, you finally got around to telling us what we already knew—that today we've got a lush forest, and fish and game, and streams to camp by again. Then you went on to say that some folks, who've moved in since this was rescued from a wasteland, were today unthinkingly trying to get rid of your beavers so everything would start back to wasteland again.

"Some farmers, especially," you told the Troop, "think beavers are a nuisance because they cut down trees. Boys, help me make it clear that beavers as a rule cut down only aspens which aren't of much use otherwise anyway. And when these same people say that beaver dams block irrigation creeks, flooding land and roads . . . well, I'll admit that in some cases this is true. But that is easily handled, and in the long run—"

I spoke up then.

"Certain people aren't waiting for it to be handled," I said, and everybody turned to look at me and each other as much as to say who forgot to lock the door. But I'm used to that. You took your usual growling bear attitude because as usual you got the wrong idea and assumed that I was criticizing you for not doing anything about complaints you received about beavers. You snapped right back at me without any punctuation.

"Whenever beaver encroach on human activity — farming — fishing — camping — they're promptly moved back into a more primitive area."

And you gave me a look that was decidedly primitive. You were our guest, so as a Scout I ignored your bad manners.

"I mean," I smiled, "that Ira Osgood, for one, isn't waiting for you to get around to removing beaver from his farm's irrigation creeks. He's trapping them himself. But *I* released them."

"You what?" you demanded incredulously. You just wouldn't let yourself believe I'd do anything good for you.

"I released your beavers from those box traps," I grinned. "They weren't injured at all. They swam right back to their dam and began repairing it while I hid the traps where Osgood won't find them. That's why I was late for the meeting and—"

I stopped with an uneasy feeling when I saw your expression like a bear that's been prodded out of its hibernation.

"Those were *my* traps," you growled, combing words through your teeth. "My cage traps to catch the beaver so I could move them to a primitive area away from Osgood's creeks and prevent them from flooding the road through there. But *you* released them!"

You gave Mr. Fielder a how-do-you-put-up-with-*this* look.

"It'll take a long while to round up those beavers now that they're trap-wise. They'll keep damming that irrigation creek and flooding the road, and Osgood will really be out to get my hide now as he promised."

Mr. Fielder nodded gravely and stared at me as though he were wondering how he and the Troop could ever Be Prepared for what I might do. I was beginning to wonder myself. Every time I mean well it turns out to be, well, mean.

You stalked out of the Troop meeting then, Charlie, and it's good in a way that you're like Smokey, the Fire Preventin' Bear. Because only your training prevented you from getting all burnt up about me. But at that my face felt kind of hot. Then Andy Bevins spoke to the other members of the Fox Patrol.

"Maybe we ought to re-name it the Dumb-ox Patrol."

"Yeah?" I retorted. "We've already got a bullheaded leader."

He glared at me. I dittoed. Mr. Fielder stepped between us.

"Dudley—Andy," he said with a firm sigh, sounding like my dad. Then he faced the Troop.

"We've got a twofold job on our hands. We have to assist the President's conservation program by making local people see that it's for their own good. And we have to make certain local people realize that our good friend, Ranger Charlie Evans, is the kind of a man they need around here."

I stood up and opened my mouth.

"Conservating Charlie should be *my* job."

A roar of Nays floored me, assisted by Andy Bevins who pulled me down to my chair which wasn't there. I dumped him out of his.

"Dudley," Mr. Fielder said patiently, "these local people have been aiming to have Charlie transferred, retired, or dismissed long before anything you might have done this evening."

"Yeah," said Andy Bevins. "All you did, Dumbo, was help them give a harder boot to a guy who needs a boost."

For once I had to agree with him.

433

"But that's why, Mr. Fielder," I began, "I should—"

"No!" he insisted. "Just go along with the program. Please! That will help Charlie the most, Dudley. Just don't attempt anything er—imaginative."

So when Saturday morning came, like it always does way at the end of a line of school days, I stuffed my pockets with conservation leaflets and put a stack of posters under my arm and started on the route that Patrol Leader Andy Bevins had assigned to me. I still felt that more drastic efforts were needed to conserve you, Charlie, but I knew if I tried anything that drastic, things would happen to me. I might even be booted out of the Troop. So you can see that you and I had something in common after all despite appearances and attitudes, yours particularly. Neither of us wanted to be booted out.

So I went along with the program of giving shopkeepers posters for their windows and leaflets for their counters. Then I came to Garfield's hardware store. I reminded myself I'd have to be extra diplomatic about asking Mr. Garfield to cooperate with me on my cooperation with the Scouts on our

cooperation with the President who was giving his cooperation to the Department of Agriculture on getting everybody to cooperate with coopservation, I mean conservation. You see he used to cooperate willingly with anything the Scouts requested, and once I'd taken it for granted he would permit a poster in his window and had put it there before I asked. Ever since then he's been a bit stand-offish, perhaps because I accidentally pushed a lawn mower through the plate glass window.

So I went gingerly to the rear of the store looking for him. And it's good I did, because I saw Ira Osgood buying steel spring traps. And I saw Mr. Garfield frowning.

"It's none of my business, Ira," he was saying, "but you know it's illegal to trap and kill beaver . . ."

"Did I say what I was going to do?" Ira interrupted knowingly. "But since you've brought up the subject, I'll tell you I'm expecting a couple of men from Washington today to see just how beaver are ruining farming hereabouts. I'll see that they get together with state officials to put open season on beavers again. So from now on certain local officials—" I knew he meant you, Charlie "—will have to change attitude or go—preferably *go* because I *know* how little cooperation can be expected from them."

I thought of how I'd spoiled your cooperation, Charlie, by releasing those beavers. I would have spoken to Ira but I remembered that he and I were not exactly on speaking terms ever since last winter when I returned a snowball Andy Bevins had thrown at me. I missed Andy and hit Ira on the day after Christmas. I mean it was the day after Christmas when Ira served notice that if he ever got me within reach . . .

So I slipped out of the store without letting him or Mr. Garfield see me. But I stuck a conservation poster in the rack of hunting rifles as I left. On the next street I found Andy Bevins putting posters on telephone poles with hammer and nails. I took a nail and prodded him to get his full attention.

"We've got to save Charlie," I began.

"When did you wake up?" he retorted. "What do you think we're doing?"

"This is something new," I insisted. "I just saw Ira Osgood buying traps."

"Traps again," Andy grimaced.

"His own traps," I persisted.

"That's what you thought the other day too," declared Andy.

I saw I was trapped, getting nowhere with Andy.

"I've got to phone Charlie," I said, "and warn him there are some snoopers coming from Washington. Give me some change."

I handed Andy a quarter which he shoved in his pocket.

"I'll give you change *when* we finish our job."

"Now look," I snapped.

"It's for your own good," warned Andy, "to make you keep your imagination under control, like Mr. Fielder said."

Andy's bigger than me, but he knows that when I get mad . . . well, he dropped the box of nails, but not the quarter, and got away from me by spinning through a revolving door and wedging it with a folded poster so I couldn't chase him. I was so mad I could have chewed nails and spit molten steel.

Now I couldn't phone you, Charlie. It's a toll call way out to your station and people won't let you use their phone for anything but a local call. Besides, I knew from experience you probably wouldn't listen to me anyway.

I couldn't contact Mr. Fielder because, being a deputy sheriff, he was out somewhere trying to block the getaway of some robbers who'd held up a bank in Stanton, the next town, that morning.

So there was only one thing to do. I had to abandon my route and get to the Boonville Inn on the east side of town where senators, bigshots, and wealthy sportsmen always stay when they come here. I knew that Bob Saunders, who runs the Inn, was a pretty good guy even though he's been cooperating with Ira against you because he gets his Inn's food cheap from Ira's farm and besides Ira holds a mortgage on the Inn. But maybe I could speak to him and show him how important your conservation was to the Inn's business; then maybe he wouldn't say the wrong things to the Washingon men for Ira.

But, as I went up the drive to the Inn, I wondered if I was too late when I saw a car with Washington, D.C., license plates in the parking lot. But heat was still shimmering from the radiator grill, so maybe they'd just arrived and Bob hadn't had a chance to do his dirty work yet. Maybe I could do it first. I mean, well, you know what I mean . . . if you'd let yourself.

I hurried inside. The Boonville Inn, as you know, is for folks who like to pretend they're roughing it. My dad says the prices are pretty rough. Anyway, the lobby is arranged like a clearing in the woods, and suddenly a scraggly bear that reminded me of you charged out of some artificial bushes. Too late I realized it was being carried by some workmen who were getting the place in condition for the coming season. Anyway, I stumbled into the trout stream that runs right through the lobby. Fortunately, it was being repaired and was dry . . . but the concrete at the bottom wasn't dry. I heard a wild growl and saw a man with a trowel. I apologetically handed him a leaflet on conservation, but he didn't seem to be in the mood for reading.

Hurrying on, and glancing back to see if he was going to throw the trowel or use it properly, I bumped into Mr. Saunders coming out of his office. That made me drop the solid pack of posters on his toe, which wasn't exactly a good substitute for a handshake. However . . .

"Can I speak to you a moment, sir?" I inquired.

He glowered and limped right on you, I mean on a Smokey the Bear poster, and went to the desk clerk a few feet away.

"The secretary of Associated Sportsmen is on the line, long-distance," he told the clerk. "They're considering this place as headquarters for their big Camporee in August. Can we accommodate them? How are we fixed on reservations for then?"

"Wide open," replied the clerk. "They can have the whole place to themselves."

"Good," Mr. Saunders said happily. "If I can get them here, that August revenue ought to set us up for the whole year."

Meanwhile I'd glanced in his office to see if the Washington men might be there. They weren't, and I was picking up my posters and blocking the door when Mr. Saunders came back. I saw a chance to get in some thoughts on conservation.

"Mr. Saunders," I said quickly, "if you persist in cooperating with Ira Osgood instead of Charlie Evans, you'll be lucky to have any sportsmen coming here."

"Speak to me some other time," he frowned, stepping over me into his office. Folks are always saying that to me, but I knew this was no time to conserve my manners. Not with those Washington men somewhere in the Inn waiting to listen to him as soon as he wasn't busy. I raised my voice as he tried to close the door.

"Why would sportsmen want to come here with everything as dried up as that trout stream?" I shouted, pointing to the stream in the lobby. I tried to remember everything you'd told the Troop about conditions twenty-odd years ago. "No water. No fish. No game. Woods tinder dry, a menace for campers because of forest fires—"

"Keep quiet!" he hissed, jumping to the phone lying on his desk and covering the mouthpiece. He glared as I gathered up the last of the posters, then he cooed into the phone.

"We'll be glad to accommodate your Camporee next—what? No!" he yelled frantically. "You're completely mistaken in what you overheard about streams being dried up around here and—hello? Hello?"

I heard no more, suddenly realizing I would probably be wasting my time trying to win the support of Mr. Saunders for our conservation program. I was going down the front drive, ignoring the fifteen-mile-an-hour speed limit and wishing I didn't feel the urge to leave the Inn without speaking to the Washington men . . . when I saw them getting in the car with the Washington, D.C., license plates.

I swerved right over and piled into the rear of the car, kind of startling them, to say the least.

"Boy Scouts at your service, Senators," I said fast, watching for signs of a posse led by Bob Saunders. "I guess you're planning to take a quiet little look-see around the hills by yourselves, huh? Let me guide you. I know it inside out and can tell you all about the work Charlie Evans has done and—and —"

I gagged as I saw both "senators" pointing guns at me. I couldn't help suspecting that somehow I'd missed connections somewhere and had made a short-circuit.

"Sorry," I mumbled, reaching for the door handle. "Mistook you for someone else."

The stouter man slapped my hand from the door.

"Be a good little Scout now and don't touch things you shouldn't," he growled, then spoke to the skinny man at the wheel. "Let's roll out of here."

The car rolled from the parking lot onto the highway while I swayed on the back seat clutching my posters and wishing that I could learn to keep my mouth shut so I wouldn't always be falling into trouble. The man at the wheel fussed with the radio and finally got a newscast.

"All law enforcement agencies," the announcer said, "are maintaining road blocks to trap the two men who held up the Stanton National Bank this morning. But so far no trace has been found of the blue sedan with Ohio license plates in which they made their getaway."

I gulped and stared at the big robber whose eyes reminded me of some blue mar-

bles I'd once had. He twisted his head a bit to glance at the posters on my lap, then smiled crookedly.

"Conservation. That's a subject we're very personally interested in at the moment." The man at the wheel laughed grimly and patted a satchel on the seat between them. The big man rubbed his chin with the back of the

fist holding a gun. "We'd like to see those hills you offered to show us."

"What hills?" I asked, trying to be dumb like everyone says I am, but I was hoping I could stall them into staying on the highway long enough to run into a road block I knew the state police always had a couple of miles from the Inn when there was trouble.

He dropped the gun, grabbed my neckerchief and jammed my beaver slide up until the beaver gnawed deep into my Adam's apple. At that moment, Charlie, I was ready to agree with Ira Osgood that beavers are a nuisance.

But I guess I am kind of dumbo. Because with that neckerchief slide biting into my windpipe, I wasn't a bit like those heroes you see on TV or in the movies or in comic books. Despite all odds, they can always come up with a way to avoid being killed and at the same time capture the villains. All I could think of was that I wanted to come up for air and breathe.

When I got my breath back and my eyes had settled back in their sockets and I stopped being dizzy, I suppose as usual I did the wrong thing by giving them right directions on how to cut across the hills through your forest to avoid the police road blocks.

I slouched in the seat, and felt pretty awful about you, about conservation, about the Scouts, about how everything I'd tried to do for all of you had gone wrong. I felt pretty awful about myself, too, and it wasn't just because my throat was sore and my rump ditto because of Andy's box of nails which kind of spurred me every time the wildly racing car jolted on the dirt road . . . but I didn't dare reach in my pocket to shift them. The big robber was watching me and I knew too well how people always get the wrong ideas about every little innocent thing I do.

The car came to another fork in the road. I gave directions. The car stopped while they double-checked me with a road map. Finally the big man looked at the driver.

"Looks like straight sailing from here across. What do you think?" he murmured, nodding toward me.

I got a sudden wild inkling it was time for me to do a little conservating for myself. Anyway, I was scared enough to try anything. I heaved up the stack of posters from my lap and shoved them in a spreading mass at the two men in the front seat. Before they could claw out of the cluttering posters, I was out the door and scrambling down into a gully's thick underbrush. I heard one man shout to the other on the road above me as I lay behind a log.

"Let him go. We'll never find him. It'll take him an hour to hike out to the highway, but we'll be across the hills and on our way in another car."

I heard doors slam; the engine roared and tires gouged the dirt road. But I *knew* they'd be back, Charlie, thanks to your beavers which had dammed one of Ira Osgood's irrigation creeks and flooded the road a mile ahead . . . like they had been doing and must still be doing because Ira had been buying traps this morning. The robbers would never get through and get across the hills.

But I also knew I couldn't run a couple miles to a phone and tip off the police before the two men raced back and found another way to get clear. Climbing to the road I told myself how dumbo I was not to have figured a way to stop them. I'd lost out on everything today, even most of my posters except for some which had fallen out of the car.

As I bent over to salvage them, Andy's nails spurred me in the rump again. That gave me an idea. I don't mean that my brains aren't in my head, but . . . but . . .

Well, I got to work jamming nails through posters until each poster looked like a bed that some guys sleep on in India. I'd just placed the last nail-studded poster on the road when I heard the car roaring back.

It careened around a turn. The driver saw what was up, the points of the nails. He hit the brakes hard. Posters skittered as the car skidded through them. It slewed off the road, nearly got back, then rolled over and over down into the gully, flinging out the satchel of money. Way down it wrapped itself around a tree with a crash. For a second everything was quiet except for a caw-cawing crow, then *blump* . . . and smoke came from the smashed hood. Flames licked out at the brush as I raced down, but I was too late. My conservation efforts had now resulted in a forest fire which raced up toward me.

I retreated, scooping up the satchel.

Well, you know the rest of it, Charlie.

Before I could even get to a phone and report the fire to you, your lookout tower men had spotted it, and I saw you and your equipment moving in with hopes of stopping it before it reached Ira Osgood's farm. But things looked pretty bad all around.

That's why you didn't see me as you went by. You had a pretty bad look on your face, and I figured it wasn't exactly the right moment to try explaining anything to you . . . or to anyone else face to face.

But I've taken the trouble of writing you this long letter because I thought you might be slightly interested in the full details of what happened to you, and everyone else connected with the Boy Scouts' cooperation with the conservation program.

So I guess that about washes everything up, including me and the Scouts, the local conservation program, and your future as a U. S. Forest Ranger. You were right when you called me Dumbo.

Unconservately yours,
Dudley Davis.

Dear Scoutmaster Fielder:

Since you got my other letter, has Charlie Evans been in touch with you about me?

I wonder, because he looked me up just when my folks were worriedly trying to find out if I were desperately sick or just miserable over something I'd done again. He wanted further details on the letter I'd sent him when I'd sent you my resignation.

I told him I'd put everything in the letter, but he insisted he wanted to hear it all. He stared unbelievingly at me when I told all about last Saturday. Then, still staring, he added a few details that *I* didn't know.

He'd stopped the fire and saved Ira's farm because the woods were green enough to slow the fire and *because* his fire crews got plenty of water for their portable pumps from *beaver ponds!* So now Ira Osgood kind of thinks that beavers are good things to have around!

And Bob Saunders feels good too. The Washington men, whom I'd missed at his Inn, saw to it that there was plenty of publicity of how and why the fire was stopped so quickly. That made the Associated Sportsmen decide to come to the Boonville Inn in full force in August.

Then Charlie handed me a real shocker. He told me that when he'd seen my return address on his letter, he'd torn it up without ever opening the envelope and reading the contents. So that made me ask him how he could have known as many of the details as he did if he hadn't read the letter.

He shook his head bewilderedly like a bear trying to wake up from hibernation. Staring at me wonderingly he said I'd made another of my dumbo mistakes. I'd put his long letter in the wrong envelope . . . in the one to the President of the United States!

The President had had the matter immediately looked into. He's personally commended Charlie for his fine conservation efforts, thanks perhaps to my letter. The President has also conveyed his thanks to Troop 28 for their cooperation in the conservation program, and he wishes them increasing success in their conservation efforts with Scout, third class, Dudley Davis.

I wonder just how he meant that. Should I take it as a personal compliment? Or just personally?

Anyway, Mr. Fielder, I'll see you and the Troop at the next meeting because I guess everything is okay again, despite what Andy Bevins says, because the Troop treasury is going to receive what he's trying to call "his" share of the reward for capturing the bank robbers.

So, looking forward to seeing you again and hoping you are the same, I am,

Conservately yours,
Dudley Davis.

Sound Effects

By MERRITT P. ALLEN

It was the craziest show on tape—in fact, it could be called a howling success

The Old Guard was ill and the school was in a dither about it. The beloved headmaster was not between the sheets yet, but it was said that Doc Leonard had told him if he didn't snap out of it during the next two weeks, he would have to go away for a long rest.

To the boys, whether they had known him six weeks or six years, the threat of life under any other leader was tragic. As they passed his window that autumn afternoon, they waved to him and he waved back, which was a sign he was still interested in earthly affairs.

"I wonder what they are up to now," he said to his wife, "heading for the back campus and looking innocent."

"Out for a walk, I suppose," she guessed.

"Um. Did you notice they were all Bears, not an Eagle among them?"

"Oh, some fraternity business or other."

"I wish I knew." The Old Guard smiled wistfully. "These frat battles are like fresh air to me."

"What you need, James, is farm air," said a sharp voice from the doorway, as a tall, angular old man ambled in. "Let me tell you about the air on my farm."

"Sometime later." The Old Guard writhed under his dressing gown and stood up. "It is time for me to rest, Cousin Ernest. Doctor's orders, you know." He went out and closed the door, almost banging it.

"He's a nervous critter," Cousin Ernest remarked. "There used to be a feller up near my farm who—"

"Excuse me." Mrs. Noble rose quickly. "I must get James' medicine." She followed her husband, closing the door firmly.

"Remind me to tell you about that feller later," Cousin Ernest called after her and sat down to think. Anyhow, he sat down.

Meanwhile, the Bears, by casual ones and twos, sauntered across the back campus at various angles and converged in the school vegetable garden far behind the dorm. Like all gardens at that time of year, it was not a cheerful place; the leaves of cucumber vines were sickly yellow, tall spires of lettuce had gone to seed, tomato vines sprawled in the dirt, and near the middle of the field the last of the cornstalks had been gathered in a huge shock that stood like a solitary wigwam.

"Well," Cheese Eastman bragged to the assembled clan, "we put one over on the Eagles this time. They didn't follow us."

"Yeah! What you call that thing?" Noodle Perkins growled.

He pointed toward a corner of the garden. The "thing" indicated was the tall, droopy form of "The Mudhen" leaning against a fence post.

"Chase him off," the Bear chief ordered.

"Chase him yourself," Noodle suggested. "It's an ambush. Probably a dozen of the stinkers are waiting behind the fence with rotten tomatoes."

"There's one!" Skunk Evans cried.

"Tomato?" Cheese ducked instinctively.

"Eagle." Skunk pointed to the opposite fence, atop which was perched the person of Sam Bowman.

"It's a heck of an idea if we can't hold a private meeting without those drips spying on us!" Rip Anderson complained.

"Quit crabbing," Cheese snapped. "They can't hear what we say at this distance."

"They'll sneak up," Rip prophesied.

"Latch onto those green tomatoes. If an Eagle shows his puss this side of the fence, nail him," Cheese ordered.

That sounded like good advice, so the Bears armed themselves and drew into a close circle around the shock of cornstalks. Here and there in the distance Eagles could be seen, but it was plain they dared not venture near. The rival fratters were stymied, and the Bears made uncomplimentary gestures to express their awareness of the fact.

"Listen, you guys," Cheese said in a low tone, "we've got to cheer up the Old Guard. We want to do it ourselves, too, not with the Eagles. They louse up everything."

His brothers agreed with him on those points, but some wanted to know why they had been dragged out to the garden for that.

Cheese explained. "We think it would be swell to put on a show on my tape recorder and run it off to amuse him. A real snappy show with music and a sort of speech and a few plugs for him—just to let him know the Bears are thinking of him."

"It might help our marks at midyears," Noodle put in.

"You scheming heathen!" Cheese roared.

"Okay! So you thought of it, too." Noodle ducked behind the corn shock as Cheese hurled a tomato at him.

"But," Rip objected, "the recording tape is busted in half a dozen places."

"I have mended it and it works perfectly," Cheese answered with dignity.

So they discussed the plan and finally agreed on its framework, the details to be worked out later.

"Why couldn't we have done this in the dorm and not ankled way out here?" Rip growled.

"And given the Eagles a chance to spy on us?" Cheese snorted. "This is one time when they can't stick their beaks in our soup." He led the way from the garden, the Bears forming a triumphal procession that scorned even to look at the distant rivals.

When the last of them had disappeared, The Mudhen, Sam Bowman, and Dave Pierce closed in on the shock of cornstalks, pulled it apart, and released Froggie Bates from its interior.

"Did you get the dope, Frog?" Sam asked breathlessly.

"Sure." Froggie shook himself and spat out a cornsilk. "Couldn't miss a word."

"Nice work!" Dave thumped his back.

"Old Mud cooked it up," Froggie said loyally.

"Duck soup once we got wise to them comin' out here," The Mudhen said modestly. "Spill it, Frog, there's more espionage to be done."

"I'll say there is! It'll take some espionogger to put this one on ice." Froggie told his story.

The Eagle general staff stood around for a while chewing grass stems and talking.

"Anybody got an idea?" Dave finally asked.

"We've got to bust that tape recording business," Sam declared.

"Not bust it," The Mudhen objected. "If it's goin' to give the Old Guard any pleasure, we mustn't ditch it."

"But," Froggie wanted to know, "how could he get any pleasure out of a show those bacteria are able to put on?"

"He might, bein' sick and not too keen." The Mudhen stroked his chin. "Just to know they tried to please him would do him good. No, we mustn't try to stop 'em."

"You mean for us to sit and suck our thumbs and let him think the Bears think more of him than we do!"

"Oh, hush, child!" The Mudhen made a weary gesture. "I mean we must turn their efforts to our advantage."

"For example?" Sam demanded.

"I don't know, Samuel. I'm tellin' you what we *should* do, not how it can be done."

"Yeah? Well, when you figure out how to make the Bears work for us, you let me know." Sam stalked away.

It was more than a problem. It was a terrific challenge, and The Mudhen was acutely conscious of it. For all his physical lassitude, he had the spirit of a warrior. The gauntlet had been cast at his feet and he had picked it up, but now what? For the rest of that day he was as one whose mind is in the depths of a vacuum swathed in black cloth; not a ray of light penetrated those static depths.

The next morning, as previously planned, he carried an offering of flowers in the Eagles' name to the Old Guard's home. The maid was scrubbing the kitchen floor and told him to wait in the hall till Mrs. Noble came down. But there was no chair there, so he drifted into the next room and sat on a sofa—sat and finally dozed.

Guarded voices at the foot of the stairs aroused him.

"I feel certain, doctor," Mrs. Noble was saying, "James will never recover while Cousin Ernest is here."

"His is purely a nervous condition," Doc Leonard said.

"Of course it is—all caused by Cousin Ernest's constant talk about his farm. Ernest is a good man and a certain amount of farm talk is interesting, but when James is obliged to listen to it every moment he is at home, day after day and month after month —well, it gets him down. For weeks he has been too nervous to eat or sleep properly, and now he is sick."

"Is Cousin Ernest a fixture here?" the doctor asked.

"He came last spring, planning to stay a year. His doctor said he needed a vacation from the farm. Now it is we who need it."

"Can't you persuade him to leave?"

"James won't allow me to suggest it. Family ties are sacred to him. But, doctor, he can't stand it for another six months."

"And Cousin Ernest shows no sign of homesickness?"

"Yes, he's homesick. That's why he constantly talks about his farm. The other day he heard a rooster crow and he actually wept."

"Perhaps if we could introduce farm animals here, nostalgia might come to our aid."

"Don't be silly!" Mrs. Noble sounded in no joking mood as she followed the doctor to the door and stood talking with him outside.

The Mudhen was suddenly awake. A door had opened in his mind, and light was shining through. As soon as possible, he delivered the flowers and went away, so deep in thought that he collided with Cousin Ernest at the corner of the porch.

"Look where you're going," the man suggested, reasonably enough.

"Pardon me, sir, I was thinkin' about somethin' else."

"About what?"

"Er—pigs, sir."

"Pigs!" Cousin Ernest's face lightened. "By Godfrey, you're a smart boy! Now let me tell you 'bout some pigs I had on my farm." And when The Mudhen finally got away, the man was still talking about them.

During the next few days The Mudhen collided with other people and objects, for his mind seemed to be away from home. Or it may have been present but too busy to observe traffic laws. Other minds were on the hop, too.

The Bears, happily unaware that their plans were known, worked secretly and furiously on their recorded program, sneaking the machine out at night and rehearsing in a vacant barn outside the village. It was well away from snooping Eagles and was wired for electricity, which the owner allowed them to use for a dollar a week and the promise not to be up to any monkey business.

At all times the Eagles went about their usual affairs with such a lack of curiosity that their rivals became resentful. They had expected and wanted a running battle of wits and found the Eagles' stupidity annoying.

"We fooled 'em so slick the first time they haven't even smelled a rat," Cheese boasted.

"It takes the kick out of the whole business," Noodle complained. "The recording is all made and waiting up there in our room for next Tuesday afternoon and they don't give a hoot."

"I tell you they don't even know it exists."

"They don't try to find out! Not a question out of 'em, not a thing disturbed in the dorm. Why, even that night I came back early they were all in their rooms studying."

"We did a perfect job. That's the trouble," Cheese said. "It didn't leave a thing for them to work on. Well," he grinned at his roommate, "I guess it will be safe for us to go home for the weekend. We won't have to stay and guard the recording."

"Guard it! We could leave it on the gym steps and those dopes wouldn't be interested in it."

"We did a swell job on that piece of tape."

"I'll say we did! I wish all the Eagles could be there to hear it, but Mrs. Noble doesn't want a crowd."

"Mud and Frog will be plenty. They'll spread the news." Cheese went away whistling.

The world rolled around until it bumped into Tuesday, doing no special damage, though at one time in the afternoon there was considerable excitement. That was when they gathered in the Old Guard's living room to hear the tape recording. It was a small group, out of consideration for the headmaster's health. He was over by the fireplace in his dressing gown. Mrs. Noble was knitting while she kept an eye on him. Cousin Ernest had crashed the gate and sat by a window sadly searching the street for a cow or pig. Cheese and Noodle represented the Bears and had seen to it that The Mudhen and Froggie were invited, just to see them writhe with envy. On a stand in the middle of the room was the recorder, loaded and waiting.

"Cars, cars, cars!" Cousin Ernest sputtered. "I've been here for months, and I ain't seen a mule, not one mule. I'd give more for one mule 'n for all the cars this side of Tunket. On my farm I've got a pair of mules that *be* mules." And he settled down to one of his twenty-minute solos.

Mrs. Noble shot a look at her husband, who was beginning to sweat, and suggested that, as the boys had only a few minutes between classes, it might be best to get on

with the show. Cousin Ernest yielded grumpily and took a chew of spruce gum.

Thus cued, Cheese started the machine and hovered over it like a mother duck whose first child is about to hit the pond. The program began with an announcement by Cheese himself to the effect that the Bears were much perturbed by the headmaster's illness and, as they could not call en masse, had employed the medium of transcription to send him their greetings. It was a nice speech and the Old Guard smiled his appreciation. It was to be followed, said the tape, by the school song played by the Bear orchestra, the Bear chorus coming in on the refrain.

The trouble with that refrain was that the refrainers did not refrain. Seldom on this earth has there been heard such a burst of utter discord, such a complete absence of every element of music in one hunk, as forthwith escaped from that harmless-looking piece of tape.

"Jeepers!" Cheese leaped madly up and turned the thing off. "Something has gone haywire."

"She's picked up a speck of dust," Noodle said, trying to sound technical. "Blow on it and try again."

"We'll skip it," Cheese decided.

"But we put a lot of work on that harmony," Noodle objected.

"And now," the machine proclaimed, "because Mr. Noble could not be present at the game when the Bears crushed the Eagles 27 to 21, we will recount the closing moments of the battle exactly as it happened."

A voice, obviously Rip Anderson's, went on dramatically: "The ball is on the Bears' three-yard line. One minute remaining. Can the Eagles break through and tie it? It is their great opportunity. The lines form. The immense crowd is hushed. The defense crouches low, heroically resolved to uphold their proud record. The ball is snapped to Mud. He is too slow to run, of course, but he will pass to Dave. He turns with a snail-like motion—and throws the ball in the wrong direction out of bounds! The great moment has been lost. The Eagles have missed their golden opportunity. The whistle sounds. The game is over. The weary Bears form a ring around their gallant captain, Cheese Eastman, and raise their voices in the famous old cheer."

Noodle shot a glance at The Mudhen to see if he was cringing. He was not. Then through the room in clarion tones rang three long brays of a mule.

"Sufferin' catfish!" Cheese pounced upon the machine. "Who did that?"

"That's what I say!" Noodle yelled. "Who imitated a mule?"

"That wasn't no imitation." Cousin Ernest was on his feet, his eyes shining. "It was the real thing! The sweetest music I've heard in six months. Play some more of it, boy."

"More of it!" Cheese's face was a fire hazard. He wheeled on The Mudhen. "Have you been monkeying with this thing?"

"I?" Mud made a gesture of horror. "Would I participate in a Bear's program?"

"I bet it was you who—who introduced that mule."

"Let me assure you," The Mudhen replied, with terrific formality, "if I knew a mule, I would consider it unnecessary to introduce him to his brother Bears."

"If you weren't here, I'd knock your block off!" Cheese roared.

"You are confused, little man," The Mudhen said placidly. "If I weren't here, how could you knock my block off?"

"You know what I mean. Come outside."

Mrs. Noble glanced at the Old Guard and found him looking better than he had for weeks. There was even a sparkle in his eyes.

"You invited me here for the show," The Mudhen said plaintively. "Why must I go outside?"

"Let's hear the mule again," Cousin Ernest begged, chewing eagerly on his gum. "He made me plumb homesick."

"I think we all want to hear the rest of the recording," Mrs. Noble said quickly.

"By all means," the Old Guard seconded. "Go ahead, Eastman."

"Yes, sir." Cheese had to obey.

He started the machine again and heard himself announce in deep tones that the next number was made at a table in Chateau Chew, where the Bears were discussing the day's events. Noodle began to look smug for he had written this part of the script, which contained many complimentary references to the headmaster and tear-jerking regrets at his illness. Surely the Old Guard would understand how tenderly the Bears regarded him.

"Yes," the voice said impressively, "this is an on-the-spot recording of typical Bear conversation at table."

There was a moment's pause, then the quiet of the living room was split wide open —shattered—pulverized by a chorus of porcine grunts and squeals. It was as though all the pigs on earth had heard chow call and voiced their applause together. With a noise like a Niagara of swine bursting from its pen, they poured off that tape into the room. Pictures jumped on the walls, window curtains trembled, rugs curled up under the impact of those hungry voices.

Mrs. Noble covered her ears. The Old Guard jerked forward, then leaned back and opened his mouth, but the sound of his laughter could not be heard in that bedlam. Redder of face than any stoplight, Cheese caught up the machine, pulled out the plug, and ran from the room. Noodle said something and followed him.

On the sofa Froggie hung onto his stomach, while The Mudhen looked about in innocent bewilderment.

Cousin Ernest, too, was deeply impressed, but differently.

"Gee-hasofat!" he cried in a strange voice. "That—that was beautiful! Them hogs 're hungry. They want their corn. Can't you jest see 'em rarin' 'n shovin'? Brother, how I'd like to feed 'em. That's the life!" Tears started to his eyes. "Farmin' 's the only life for me. I'm goin' back to it. I'm goin' back! You've been mighty nice to me here, but I'm goin' back to the farm—and I'm goin' now!" He rushed out of the room.

"Excuse me," Mrs. Noble jumped up. "I will help him pack and call a taxi."

"Yes, do," the Old Guard urged.

The two Eagles edged toward the door, but he stopped them.

"I want to know how you pulled that off," he said, as man to man.

"Nothin' to it, sir," Froggie said. "We borrowed the recorder."

"When the Bears weren't using it," The Mudhen added solemnly. "We did a bit of sound engineering. Interpolating and synchronizing, you know. It's possible with two recorders. We rented another one."

"And we took 'em out to a farm where there are mules and pigs. The farmer is a nice guy," said Mud with a queer smile.

"A very nice guy." The Old Guard wiped his eyes.

"Yes, sir," The Mudhen agreed. "Now, if you'll excuse us, we'll get back to school."

"By the way," the Old Guard stood up with a bounce, "there will be no school tomorrow. I am declaring a holiday to celebrate my return to health."

Left-Handed Monkey Wrench

By MILLARD WARD

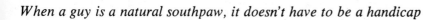

When a guy is a natural southpaw, it doesn't have to be a handicap

"You don't have to worry about Lefty," Harry Barnett, the Junior Assistant Scoutmaster, assured the Explorers in the mess tent for noon chow. "I showed him the tautline hitch myself. That's one thing he can— Look out! Duck!"

With a swooping sigh, the stiff tent-canvas collapsed into the mess kits on the table and over the hungry boys.

"Hey! Wha' hoppen?"

"Ow! That stuff's hot! I've got a lapful!"

"Rope must have broken."

"Broken, my eye! That's a brand-new piece."

The green-uniformed Explorers and the lanky, dark-haired Junior Assistant struggled out from under the wreckage. They found Second Class Scout Joel Simms slowly picking himself up halfway between the flattened tent and the tree to which its ridgerope had been made fast. His narrow face with its large eyes and ears showed so much disgust that Harry waved down any more comments from the Explorers.

"Tough luck, Lefty," he said cheerfully. "But that's not the first tautline hitch that ever got away from anybody."

"I guess I crossed the ends wrong," the smaller boy muttered. "Got my hands mixed up." He turned to pick up the line, but with the first step he flinched, nearly going down again.

Harry steadied him. "What goes on? Twist your ankle?"

"I guess so," Lefty answered dismally. "I saw that knot start to slip and I jumped for it. Then what happened? I fell on my face, of course."

"Park yourself on that log while I take a look," Harry directed.

A moment later he nodded. "Sprained, all right." Then he called over his shoulder. "Hey, Ed! You've got a First Aid Merit Badge. Come here and do your stuff."

By the time Patrol Leader Ed King finished with the damaged ankle, the other boys had the opensided mess tent raised and partly straightened up again.

Ed glanced at their once-snappy uniforms, then down at his own, and raised a russet eyebrow.

" 'Mess' is the word for that tent. I know you couldn't help it, but why did it have to happen the only time this whole weekend when we were having tomato soup?"

Lefty ate only one full-sized ration in the reorganized mess. Afterward, while the others heated laundry water, he hobbled off alone to a huge slab of granite at one side of the camp and climbed awkwardly upon it. A site had been chosen on a low shoulder of Razorback Mountain in the northern Alleghenies.

Below the camp, a double-tracked railroad made a sweep around the foot of the mountain, in a deep, long cut which had been blasted, on its higher side, out of solid rock. Beyond that a stream sparkled in and

447

out among masses of foliage, its valley stretching away on either hand into a blue haze of distance.

"Don't get so lost in the view you fall off of there," Harry Barnett advised as he came up to Lefty's side. "You wouldn't stop rolling for a couple of hundred feet. And if you took a long bounce into that cut you'd have trouble climbing back again."

The younger boy glanced down the steep slope of shale and rock, almost a cliff, above which the camp was perched. Below it a belt of mixed pine and oak woods several hundred yards wide extended to the cleared ground along the railroad right-of-way.

"I wasn't going to fall," he said. "But I don't blame you for warning me."

Harry laughed. "Don't be so touchy, Lefty. I was only kidding."

"Maybe so," Lefty said doggedly. "Maybe Ed was too. Just the same it's time I quit making trouble for you guys all the time."

The Junior Assistant Scoutmaster straightened out his face.

"What're you talking about? If you hadn't offered to take the dry-weather slack out of that line, you wouldn't have been handling it in the first place. It was darn nice of you because it was we and not you who were bumping our heads on the canvas."

"Thanks, Harry. You'd make a swell lawyer. But you know as well as I do what I am around here." The younger boy's voice spurted fiercely. "A left-handed monkey wrench bang in the middle of the machinery!"

Harry put a hand on the gray boulder and vaulted to a seat on its edge. "Come over here, Lefty. I want to talk to you.

"You're not giving yourself enough time," he went on when they were settled. "Mr. Crawford filled me in a little when I asked him about inviting you on this trip with the Explorers' outfit. Nobody's blaming your grandparents for doing what they believed was best for you; but their idea of making you use your right hand for everything when you were born a southpaw is way out of date."

"They thought a left-hander was a freak,"

Lefty muttered. "But Mr. Crawford convinced them that making me change was what had messed up my co-ordination and even made me stutter."

"He's only about the best Scoutmaster in the state," Harry nodded. "You never stutter any more."

"But it seems as if I'm just clumsy with both hands now instead of one. What kind of a Scout is that? Ed had tomato soup in his pants pocket."

Harry laughed again. "He can take care of himself. You're doing fine for the little time you've been a Scout. And, ankle or no ankle, you and I can still get in that wig-wagging we had scheduled for this afternoon. You're about ready to rate First Class in it."

Lefty's eyes swept the June-filled valley, from the Owl Creek trestle several miles to westward all the way to the tunnel through Gunpowder Ridge an equal distance to the east. From the big rock those two points could barely be seen above intervening hills and forest, but even from the level of the Scout camp, only nearer stretches of track and the dark line of the rock-cut below were visible.

"No signs of those hoboes who were hanging around the tracks last night," he said. "Guess they mooched along."

"I have an idea they camped in the mouth of that old coal mine down below," Harry said. "It's been boarded up for about fifty years, but it would be easy to kick off a couple of planks. I smelled smoke when I was awake once. In fact, I do right now."

From the hills to westward the distant hoot of a Diesel locomotive came downwind.

"That's the 'Silver Arrow' passing through Ednaville," Lefty announced. "She'll come out on the Owl Creek trestle in a minute."

"How do you know?" Harry inquired in surprise.

"Easy. Ednaville's the only grade crossing for five miles in that direction and that was the grade crossing signal—two longs, a short and a long. The 'Arrow' passes our pasture every day at 12:52. So she's right on time."

Harry pondered this. It would not be surprising if a boy who was by himself a lot had made a friend of the railroad. Lefty, on a farm, with no family but his grandparents, must have had plenty of his own society before Mr. Crawford had interested him in the Fairview Troop.

Then Harry realized that Lefty had deliberately changed the subject from his First Class tests. That was not so good.

"How about our signal practice, though?" the Junior Assistant persisted. "You're already pretty sharp and, as for other things, you'll soon be using your left hand better than you ever did your right."

The smaller boy did not answer, but it was less his silence than the mulish look on his face which put sudden force in Harry's voice.

"You haven't got any crazy idea of quitting the Scouts, have you, now that you're just getting started?"

As he spoke, the streamlined "Silver Arrow" stormed past in the cut below, and Harry's attention, drawn toward it, concentrated suddenly on the intervening treetops.

"I see smoke now, in the woods down there," he said. "It's too much for a campfire."

In the seconds he needed to leap down from the rock and reach camp again, the gray blur above the trees thickened and was breeze-swept eastward after the receding streamliner.

"Sam!" Harry called to a broad-shouldered boy with a laundry bucket. "Fire in the woods below, just west of here. You and Roy get down there on the double and see what goes on. Take the trenching tools with you."

The two big Explorers went leaping and skidding along a gully which made a fairly easy passage down the sixty-degree slope.

"The rest of you get ready to fight fire," Harry ordered. "Take your axes and something to tie over your faces."

As he reached the edge of the woods where Sam and Roy had disappeared, a strange rumbling sound rose out of the earth. Simultaneously a section of stony mountainside between the smoke and the railroad

broke free and plunged downward in a noisy burst of reddish dust.

Lefty had followed Harry slowly and painfully, but the Second Class Scout's eyes were the first through the murk.

"Landslide!" he gasped. "It's filled the cut about half full."

"How could a fire cause a landslide?" Harry snapped. Then he answered himself. "That's right where the old mine was. The hoboes must have left their jungle fire inside, so the coal caught. The timber supports burned away, the roof caved in, and that started the slide."

"How'd the woods fire start so far back, though?" Lefty demanded.

"Ventilating shaft, probably. Full of trash, but the fire finally worked through it. That could be what I smelled last night."

Smoke had blanketed an acre of the woods and the rush and snap of fire rose distinctly to the Scout camp.

Sam Hawkins reappeared below. He wigwagged rapidly BIG FIRE, HELP. Then, turning, he dived back into the underbrush.

Harry pulled together the stabbing excursions of his mind. The valley floor rose gradually toward the east. That would make a chimney for the fire right into a crossroads village half a mile away. The blaze would have to be stopped before it gained real headway or not at all.

From the four remaining Explorers Ed King spoke up. "There's a stream a couple of hundred yards east of here, Harry. From a spring at the foot of this cliff. Narrow, but only second growth along it. We could try a backfire from there. Might not have enough time, though."

Below them the top of a pine tree, green but tinder-dry with long drought, blew up like a drum of gasoline, pouring flames along nearby branches with terrible speed.

"Fire's crowning already," Harry exclaimed. "Get down there, you four, pull back Sam and Roy, and run a fireline along the west bank of the creek. Cut any low-branched stuff that could carry fire across, then start your backfire. I'll be with you in a minute."

As the orders were obeyed, the Junior Assistant glanced down to see Lefty tense with rage.

"That's me," the boy exploded. "I told you. My best chance to make good with the Scouts, and I can't even walk! I quit, that's all. I'm through."

Harry grasped the khaki-clad shoulders and shook them excitedly. "You can hold a signal flag, can't you?"

"Sure, but what—"

"That landslide's right in the curve of the cut. Engineers couldn't see it from either side. They wouldn't even slow down for just smoke."

"You mean I should go down into the cut and flag any train that comes along, Harry? But I could only go one way—and anyhow—that steep rock wall—"

The sheer inner side of the cut, jagged granite, slippery with water from underground springs and the tiny stream Ed had mentioned, had already been etched painfully into Harry's mind. Not only could no one with a bad ankle jump down it and still navigate at all, but any able-bodied Explorer who did jump would be a good while getting back up to the fire-fighting. Yet an engineer of a fast train with his eye on the rails might not see a signal from the top of the cut.

"I know," Harry said rapidly. "But from the rock where you and I were you can see the track miles away in each direction and be in sight yourself from most anywhere below. You crawl on up there and wigwag if any train comes in sight. Then one of us can break away at the last second and flag it. It's going to balance on a razorblade whether we stop that fire without getting some help."

"Count on me," Lefty yelped joyfully. "No passenger train scheduled the next hour; but you can't tell about freights or troop trains."

Harry answered on the run as he snatched up the camp machete and headed for the gully.

"If anything comes, try to give us an idea of the speed as well as direction."

On the woods floor smoke scratched Harry's eyes, bent him low for breath as he ran toward the creek bank. The crisp sound of Scout axes guided him. Scrub pines and oaks were already going down, felled toward the fire, as he arrived.

He leveled underbrush with the machete at a point where the stream narrowed to almost nothing. Then he took out a match, held it ready to strike. Running and chopping like wild men, the six Explorers finished clearing the west bank of all high growth except for a single fifty-foot oak, which, gnarled and partly killed by old fire, had been skipped by lumbermen. With its trunk a foot and a half in diameter, it stood as a perfect bridge to carry the crown-fire across stream and fireline together.

Sam Hawkins and Tony Chiero were chopping desperately from opposite sides, but their Scout axes, while keen and well-balanced, were not intended for lumbering.

"Get the back-fire going all along," Harry shouted. "Ed and Roy, keep it away from around this big tree. Willy and Eli, you cross the stream and watch for any place that tries to catch."

A thin, ragged line of smoke rose from the creek bank, edged toward the onrushing forest fire like David going to meet Goliath.

With streaming, smarting eyes, Harry snatched a glance upward as he had several times before, to the big rock above the cliff. Lefty stood there like a bronze statue against the wooded mountainside, an improvised crutch under one armpit, his red and white wig-wag flag motionless.

"You got him watching for trains, Harry?" Ed croaked in a cloud of ashes he had raised with the entrenching shovel. "Lot of responsibility for him."

"Don't sell Lefty short," Harry answered between coughs through the wet handkerchief tied over his mouth.

With the blackened strip along the west bank growing steadily wider, the boys on the east bank, like football line-backers, were able to stamp and beat out all sparks and light, blazing brands which floated down the wind. An unbroken wall of flame reached now from the foot of the cliff to the railroad clearing. The next time Harry raised his eyes from a fast check up-stream, he saw that, working backward against the breeze, the main fire had jumped the low western end of the cliff and was racing up the mountainside behind it.

Within minutes, Lefty's lookout rock would be poised between flame and space. He could not stay there and half-roast and he could not keep adequate watch from anywhere else. He would have to escape into the gully, and one—or much safer two—critically needed Explorers would have to be sent down into the cut to head off trains that might not come.

And then—scratch one small village!

In a rolling cloud of smoke, Harry lost sight of the cliff, and he ran stumbling along the creek bank back toward the savage chugging of Sam's and Tony's axes. Deep, clean notches on opposite sides of the big tree's trunk, one higher than the other, had been cut, but eight inches of tough heartwood remained. Ground trash and brush flamed and smoked almost under the feet of the axemen, as their bodyguards trampled and beat the flames away from them.

The terrific rising heat of the main ground fire dried green oaks so that they carried the crown fire almost as fast as pines. Their branches shot out curling red arms nearer and nearer to the big tree, the top of which interlaced with other branches beyond the firebreak.

From a yard-wide pool in the little stream, Harry brought water to douse over the smoldering uniforms of axemen and guards. The heat was like a moving wall. Within minutes it would crush them all.

He raised half-seeing eyes through smoke-rifts again and again to the lookout point. Lefty was still at his now-terrible post with deep fire behind him, sparks cascading around him, and the prospect at any moment of falling trees.

"Hope the clearing's big enough to—save our camp," Ed panted. "But—fire going that way—won't be so much danger—to village. Hey! Is that Lefty still up there? He must be crazy."

"He's not crazy," Harry answered. "Pipe down. He's getting ready to send."

From the seared rock, the younger Scout finished a fast ATTENTION signal. With sharp decisive sweeps of his flag, he reeled off a message in Morse code. Harry's pride and admiration surged, then, as letter followed letter, collapsed in despair. Lefty's heroic message read:

EKSSX EKNMA TNOE

The signal flag was lowered. It was unlikely that Lefty could see a REPEAT request if one were sent.

"I was afraid of that," Ed groaned. "Kid's nerve's gone."

Harry bent almost to the hot ground so that he could breathe and think. Willy or Eli

451

might now be spared to flag a train, but both of them could not be spared. Which direction should one be sent? Was there a train coming or had the signal conceivably been about something else? The weird message raced again through Harry's trained signalman's mind: EKSSX. If Lefty's nerve were gone or even shaken, he would not be where he was. Then what had happened? He knew the Morse code perfectly well. "X" was an improbable letter to be at the end of a five letter word. Dah-dit-dit-dah. If in excitement your hands got mixed up, that would become dit-dah-dah-dit, or P. The same fast translation turned EKSSX into TROOP. Memory snatched for more letters. EK had been repeated, that was sure. Then three more letters. How about TRAIN? And the final funny word TNOE was easy—EAST.

"Eli!" Harry yelled. "Drop everything and jump down into the cut. You know how to land. Then run as far as you can down the track to the east. Passenger train coming. Flag it with your shirt."

The leader turned back to face the fire. The burned-over strip might be just wide enough now, if only the big oak would fall. A twenty-foot pine erupted like a volcano among long lower branches of the oak, but the taller tree at last began to tilt gracefully and gently westward. Fire raced toward its top and the green leaves east of the brook withered. Then the snatching flame was drawn back as the oak continued its fall, and the withered leaves did not catch.

The big tree itself, gathering speed in a glorious arc of scarlet, crashed down harmlessly, its foliage in the burned-over area at the western edge of the fire-line.

With all hands pulled back to the east bank of the stream, the patrolling there became almost easy. Men from the village and surrounding farms began to arrive.

A chunky deputy sheriff looked the situation over, while listening to Harry's explanation.

"You young fellows did a good job," the deputy applauded. "Big laurel-slick top of Razorback ought to slow her down, and there's young crops t'other side the mountain. She'll pretty much burn out by herself after the way you turned her."

A long train of coaches packed with soldiers wheezed to a halt in the cut below, sent its own flagmen both ways along the tracks. The G.I.'s peered inquiringly out the windows, laughing and kidding with each other. A hundred yards away on the mountainside the smoke-blackened, ragged Explorers gathered wearily around their leader.

"I guess the heat was too much for me, Harry," Ed King apologized. "A little while ago I thought Lefty sent EKSSX and stuff like that. But you read it all right. My hat's off to you, and him too. He was the one that really stood the heat."

Harry dropped full-length and dipped his smarting face into the stream. Then he rose, dripping. Lefty, having seen the brakemen sent out along the railroad, had taken refuge at last in the gully. There was no need, Harry decided, to do any elaborate explaining about what had happened.

Lefty's tendency to tangle his hands was not supposed to last much longer anyway, and there was now a more basic thing by which the Troop could judge him and he could judge himself.

"Well, don't worry, Ed," Harry said abstractedly. "You did great work today. What's the difference if a fellow with a lot of nerve and team-sense does get something mixed up once in a long time?"

He could not shift his gaze from Lefty's small scorched figure, sitting patiently waiting until the fire burned down enough for him to join the others.

Suddenly and, oddly enough, for the first time, Harry remembered that there was no such thing as a left-handed monkey wrench. He grinned.

The Lonesome Sardine

By WILLIAM SAROYAN

Sometimes a sardine feels lonesome in spite of having six hundred brothers and sisters

There was once a fish who didn't like the idea of being a fish.

He lived in a school of sardines, and studied arithmetic.

There were frequently as many as a hundred thousand other sardines in the school and never fewer than thirty thousand.

One day one sardine said to another, "I believe there are fewer than thirty thousand of us in this school."

"Do you really think so?" the other sardine said.

"Yes," said the first sardine.

"Well, perhaps then, we'd better count."

So they did.

They counted thirty thousand and three sardines.

"Well," said the first sardine, *"almost* fewer than thirty thousand."

Most of the time, though, there were many more than thirty thousand sardines in the school. Now and then there were more than a hundred thousand of them, even.

Once there were almost *three* hundred thousand.

The population of the school would rise as new sardines were born, and it would fall as thousands of sardines were captured in nets by fishermen.

Never, never in the history of sardines did one sardine wander away from the school and take up somewhere by himself. It never occurred to a sardine to do that.

The sardine is a small fish, as fish go, and things like running away don't occur to them. It may be because the brain of the sardine is very small, or it may be because proportionately it is very large. It doesn't matter.

Sardines like to stay with sardines. They start life in a school and they stay in the school straight through to the end, only to sardines the end is not the end, the way it is to people.

Sardines go into cans with mustard or tomato sauce. There you find them four or five at a time, one beside another, without heads or tails, but with bones and other things pretty much in place. This is because the bones are soft and tender, and just as good to eat as the rest of the sardine.

Once upon a time, long ago, I ate a lot of sardines out of cans. Sometimes I preferred those that were packed in mustard sauce, sometimes those that were packed in tomato sauce. Both sauces were good, and the cost of a can thirty years ago when I was most fond of sardines was well under ten cents. These days the same sardines in the same can are a good deal more expensive. The price keeps going up, but the sardines remain the same.

Sardines live in the sea and the sea, it happens, is the biggest thing in the world. There is twice as much water on the surface of this planet as there is land. It is wonderful.

But the remarkable thing about the sea is

453

this: no kind of life that has stayed in the sea has done anything else.

It is only after something in the sea has come up on dry land that it has begun to do things. Once something comes up out of the sea onto dry land and starts doing things there's no end to it. It seems to go on forever, and the things they do are astonishing, too.

The things of the sea seem to have always longed to leave the sea and get up onto the dry land, and yet no man, however old, has ever seen anything of the sea *leave* the sea and come to the land. But it happens all the time. It's been happening, so they say, for millions of years.

He might just do it, too.

And that's where our story begins.

Our sardine was a regular sardine, precisely like all the others. He swam precisely the way all the others did. He was rather given to sporting about, too, after the manner of the others, but if you were to watch him steadily for a full minute you would notice that the expression on his face was frequently troubled.

One day—our day—his mother noticed the troubled expression of his face and said, "You! You over there, one of my six hundred sons, what's the matter with you?"

"I'm lonesome," the sardine said.

"What name did I give you?"

"Speck."

"All right, Speck, where are your brothers, where are your sisters?"

"All around, I guess," Speck said.

"Well, go and play with them," his mother said, "and stop being lonesome."

"I'm lonesome when I play with them, too," Speck said.

"Well, here I am, your mother," Speck's mother said. "I can't be devoting all of my time to one son out of six or seven hundred of them, but if you're troubled, tell me your troubles, and perhaps you'll feel better. Now, what's the trouble?"

"I don't want to be a sardine," Speck said.

"You speak to your mother with respect," Speck's father said.

Speck's father didn't know whether to feel proud of so many children, or ashamed.

"I didn't mean to be disrespectful," Speck said.

"Was *that* respectful, what you said?"

"I only said I don't want to be a sardine."

"What *do* you want to be?"

"Something else."

The father glanced at the mother. The father seemed angry, the mother frightened.

"What's this all about?" the father said to the mother. "What kind of children are you bringing up?"

"Oh, it's nothing, I'm sure," the mother said. "No need to be upset."

"No need to be upset?" the father said. "The boy says he doesn't want to be a sardine. He says he wants to be something else. And you say no need to be upset! Sometimes I don't know why I ever married you in the first place. Now, straighten this boy out please, do you hear?"

"Yes," the mother said.

The father turned his back on both of them, and the mother went to Speck and began to whisper to him.

"You be good now," she said. "Stop this nonsense. Straighten yourself out. Go over there and play with your brothers."

Speck was sorry to see his father and mother quarreling about him, but at the same time he needed somebody to talk to. Why wouldn't *they* talk to him?

He swam over to his brothers who were playing noseball, which is something like football. He got into the game, pushed the ball (which was a particle of something good to eat), and then when it looked as if he was going to score he stopped pushing the ball. One of his brothers on the other team plunged at it, took it off quickly, and soon scored.

All of his brothers on his side rushed over to him and said, "What's the big idea? Why don't you play the game? What's the matter with you?"

"I don't want to be a sardine."

"Ah, shut up," his brothers said, and went off.

Well, Speck didn't mind their going off especially because he saw too much of them

anyway and never felt lonesome for *them*. He felt lonesome for other things, only he didn't know what they were. Now, he felt more lonesome.

Speck gave the matter of what to do next a great deal of thought.

He saw his father still angry at his mother. He saw his mother still anxious about him, and a little angry, too. And he saw his brothers playing noseball, and his sisters attending domestic science classes. The whole business made him desperately unhappy.

Without really thinking about what he was doing, Speck turned suddenly and began to swim away from the school.

He was going very swiftly when he thought he heard his mother call out his name, but he wasn't sure. Besides, there wasn't anything she could do to help him.

He didn't want to be a sardine, and she wanted him to.

The sensible thing to do was to go away.

In not more than three minutes (for the school was located near the shore), Speck reached shallow waters.

He swam around in the shallow water for a little while, and then suddenly, again without thinking, he swam right out of the water and onto the moist sand. It was very strange there, but he liked it, even though it was an awful struggle to stay there.

He struggled with the air, the light, the warmth, and the sand for an awful long time. And then suddenly he didn't need to struggle any more.

He stood on the shore and looked back at the sea.

Far, far away he saw the school of sardines, and he said aloud, "I'm glad I've left them. I'm glad I've left the sea. I'm glad I've reached the land."

Now, Speck looked around to see what he could see.

He saw a whole city, and decided to find out what it was like inside.

It wasn't made out of plants as the cities of the sea were. It was made out of stone and steel and glass and other things that didn't move.

Speck walked to the city.

He was a little afraid of the impression he would make on the others in the city, but he needn't have been, for by the time he was there among them he looked precisely as they did.

That is what happened that day.

That was the beginning.

The rest is well known to everybody, but I'll mention it just the same. It happens, one way or another, every day.

It goes something like this:

Speck got a job. He worked hard. He got a better job. He found a girl he liked. He worked harder than ever and got a better job. He married the girl. They moved to a new house. They had a son, then a daughter, then another son, then another daughter, and finally another son.

They seemed to be one of the nicest families ever, but one day Speck, when he was sixty-seven years old, noticed that his youngest son, then seventeen years old, seemed troubled, so Speck said to him, "What's the matter with you, boy?"

"I'm lonesome," the boy said.

"Don't be silly," Speck said. "You're home. I'm here, your mother's here, your brothers and sisters are here."

"I'm lonesome just the same," Speck's son said.

"Why?" Speck said.

"I don't know," the boy said. "I guess I just don't want to be a human being, that's all."

"Well, now isn't that just fine?" Speck said. "Whether you like it or not, you *are* a human being, and there isn't anything else you *can* be. There isn't anything better *to* be. I've gone to a lot of trouble getting here, and I should think you might show a little appreciation."

Speck's son knew his father was right, but he just couldn't help it, he *was* lonesome, and he just didn't like being a human being.

He wanted to be something better, only he didn't know what, or where to go in order to be what he believed he would rather be.

He stayed home another year, and then one day he picked up and went off.

He left a note for his father and mother. It was a fine, intelligent, well-written note. He told them he hoped they wouldn't be too disappointed in him, but he just had to go off on his own and find out for himself if he might not be something better than a human being.

Speck's son went around the world.

One day he came back and found his father sitting on the front porch.

"Is that you, Sandy?" his father said.

"Yes," Sandy said.

"Well, where have you been?"

"Around the world," Sandy said. "I worked on ships, and traveled around the world."

"What did you see?"

"Water," Sandy said. "I saw the sea."

"How was it?"

"It seemed like home to me," Sandy said. "I almost wished I could live in the sea."

"Is that so?" Speck said. "What a strange thought!"

"Well," he said, "let's go on inside, boy, and sit down, and let your mother see you again, and prepare a nice meal for you."

Speck and his son Sandy went inside and Mrs. Speck wept for joy when she saw her son, and she prepared a fine lunch for him.

It was sardines in tomato sauce, homemade bread, butter and tea.

Patrol at Valley Forge

By RUSSELL GORDON CARTER

Ragged wretches of the revolutionary army turn the tables on British officers who laugh too soon

Silhouetted against the twilight of a winter morning early in the year 1778—bleak and bitterly cold like so many other mornings at Valley Forge during that tragic period of the Revolution—the tall sergeant filled the small doorway of the log hut as he shouted, "Private Williams an' Private Fenwood, report at once for patrol duty to Corporal Purvis at the Star Redoubt!"

As the door banged shut and his footsteps squeaked in the dry snow, Christopher Williams blinked and yawned and, still clutching his tattered blanket round him, pushed himself slowly erect, teeth chattering, slim body shivering. To his surprise, Neil Fenwood, his close companion of the past month, was already on his feet and asking for shoes. "Shoes," Neil called in a disgruntled sleep-heavy voice, "I can't go on patrol 'thout shoes!"

One of the men huddled close to the nine others on the bare ground mumbled, "Ye can wear mine." And another, lifting his head, added, "An' Christ'pher can wear mine."

"Also a jacket," Neil said. "Who'll let me borry his jacket?"

"Here, take this thing o' mine," someone grunted, and Neil bent forward.

"Christ'pher's welcome to this ragged greatcoat I have on," another voice added, but Christopher said, "Nay, I'll wear my blanket." And squeezing his head through a hole near the middle, he let the folds fall about him.

As the two Continentals, both Pennsylvanians under General Wayne's command, picked up their muskets and left the hut, Christopher wondered if ever a morning had been colder or more forlorn—even at Valley Forge. The stars in the graying sky were still blue-bright and glittering, dancing beyond the wisps of wood smoke rising from the wooden chimneys of the crudely built huts that housed Washington's half-starved and depleted army—one-third the number of the British under Lord Howe living in luxury at Philadelphia, a score of miles to the southeast, and supported by British ships-of-war lying in the Delaware.

While ice particles cracked and tinkled under the feet of the two soldiers, and silent sentries wrapped in old rugs and blankets, and with legs encased in straw, stared at them with tired eyes, it seemed to Christopher that never again would he feel the warmth of summer. . . . But there was something that troubled him even more than the terrific cold, and he didn't know what to do about it.

At the Star Redoubt, to the east of Fort Washington, which crowned the summit of Mount Joy, Corporal Jacob Purvis was waiting with musket hugged against his gaunt body. He was much older than the two others and had seen service at Bunker Hill and also at Saratoga where, in October of the preceding year, the British general, Burgoyne, had surrendered with his whole army in a rare American victory.

"We have a hazardous mission," Purvis explained. " 'Tis reported there's a hogshead o' shoes lying somewhere off the Old Lime Road—shoes for this army, abandoned by teamsters, 'tis said, who lacked the courage to make the full trip from York State. Mebbe the report is false like so many others, but General Washington feels 'tis worth a scouting party, as ye might say. So we three are to enter enemy territory and have a look."

"Old Lime is close to the Old York Road, eh, is it not?" Neil asked quickly—a little too quickly, Christopher thought, and glancing sidewise, he was almost certain what was in his companion's mind. More than once during recent weeks, when reports of increasing desertions had reached the hut, Neil had listened with a strange look in his eyes —so strange that several of the others had remarked upon it.

"Aye," Purvis agreed, "Old Lime lies close to Old York, an' Old York leads direct to Coryell's Ferry."

Neil cleared his throat and then was silent —and again the look was in his eyes.

As the patrol set off toward Matson's Ford across the Schuylkill, which bounded the encampment on the north, through the mind of Christopher ran the thought: "Neil has at last decided to desert! It wasn't like him to respond so readily to the sergeant's call. For some time he has been thinking of deserting, of that I am certain! And now— Coryell's Ferry and Neil's home only two miles distant on the near shore! 'Twill be easy for him to slip away from us. I wonder, ought I to speak to the corporal about it? Maybe somebody could help him."

It was a hard question. Even when the three were across the Schuylkill and beyond the Ridge Road running northwest from Philadelphia to Potts Grove, Christopher was not sure what he ought to do. He liked Neil, and he knew his companion liked him, but Neil was younger by a year and a half— not yet eighteen—and at Valley Forge he

had evidently seen more than was good for him. Burials, for example, day after day: three of them yesterday and five the day before. Also men ill and dying of disease and malnutrition. And then, only last week, Neil's own cousin, Private Denis Jepson, going to the hospital and having a foot amputated because of frostbite. In addition, there were the daily hardships everyone suffered: the lack of warm clothing and the scarcity and monotony of the food: no vegetables and almost no meat, but in their place "fire cake and water"—dough paste baked in the embers and water to wash it down—along with other inadequate fare. All this because of an inefficient Quartermaster Department and a Congress that had listened to men jealous of the Commander-in-Chief and felt it knew better than Washington and his generals how to wage war against the British professional soldiers.

A low word of warning from Purvis broke in upon Christopher's thoughts as the patrol was emerging from a patch of woods above Wissahickon Creek. The next instant a spurt of gold leaped against the snow across the stream, and while the valley reëchoed to the crash of a musket, the corporal spun sidewise and crumpled to the ground, a hand clutching his shoulder where crimson formed a widening stain.

"A foul plague upon it!" Purvis muttered while Christopher and Neil dragged him to a sheltered spot. "I spied the lobsterback e'en whilst he was aiming his piece!" And he closed his eyes and gritted his teeth.

Kneeling beside him after they had stopped the flow of blood and bound the wound, Christopher said, "You will have to go back. Think you, you can walk?"

The corporal struggled to his feet, protesting that he didn't want to go back. Again and again he called down a foul plague upon his misfortune. Then at last, with a hand clutching a sapling, he said to Christopher, "Ah, you are right, I shall have to go back!"

"One of us will go with you," Christopher said, and looked straight at Neil.

"Nay, I can walk alone!" Purvis protested. "You two must fulfill the mission. Aye, those are my orders to you: fulfill the mission! You, Christopher Williams, are in command. And now harken and I will tell you more about the spot where 'tis said the treacherous teamsters jettisoned the hogshead. Just off Old Lime, somewhere not far north o' Whitemarsh, there is a ravine with twin pines marking the opening and towering above all other trees—" And on the palm of a trembling hand he traced an imaginary map while he gave further details.

Screened by heavy low growth, the two younger scouts stood silent as the corporal, still berating his ill fortune, made his way slowly westward. When at last he was out of sight, Christopher said quietly, "We shall carry out orders and return with our report, whether favorable or unfavorable. Are you ready?"

Neil lifted somber blue eyes and glanced at the low gray sky, then with a shudder stared at the dark blood splotches in the snow where the corporal had lain. That was his only answer, and again Christopher wondered what he ought to do. Supposing he were to speak bluntly, he asked himself, could he convince his companion that desertion—even though many had already deserted from Valley Forge—was an ignoble act? He was not sure, so once more he kept the words back.

Turning, he led the way northward, taking advantage of all possible cover.

Snow was falling in slow lazy flakes when they crossed the ice-bound Wissahickon and set off up the wooded eastern slope. The Old Lime Road now was only a short distance ahead, and thanks to the corporal's directions and description, Christopher was confident of finding the ravine. It was the other thing that continued to trouble him. Somehow, even though he might have to use force, he said to himself that Neil must remain loyal!

They were deep in enemy country now, but thus far they had encountered no one except the British picket who had wounded the corporal. Halting at last on the shoulder of a low hill and taking a bite from a hard mass of dough he had tied in a corner of the blanket, Christopher motioned with his musket and said: "There below us, Neil, is the Old Lime Road, albeit 'tis hidden by thick growth—and yonder to the north I see twin pines!"

Neil nodded. "Aye," he agreed in a dull voice, "and maybe there's a ravine there, and maybe there's none—and if there be a ravine, perhaps it holds a hogshead o' shoes and perhaps it holds naught. So far as it concerns me, I can say with truth it matters little!"

Christopher's fingers tightened on his musket, but when he spoke, it was in a tone that gave no hint of his deep emotion. "At any rate, we shall do our duty," he said and, with musket quartered across his chest, set off obliquely down the hillside.

A high tangle of snow-bent alders and berry bushes bordered a sharp turn almost a quarter of a mile below the twin pines, and it was there that the two scouts emerged upon the road. Christopher had snarled his blanket on a bush and was in the act of freeing it when, to his surprise, he heard the nearby creak of wheels. As he whirled sidewise, a heavy voice boomed upon the winter air: "Stand firm, both o' ye, and drop yer pieces!"

Then with dark eyes wide and mouth open, he was looking at a startling sight. Just at the turn stood a white horse harnessed to a light carriage with two low wheels, and beneath the folding top sat two British officers, one of them holding the reins and the other, with arm extended, aiming a pistol!

"Quick, drop yer pieces an' raise yer hands!"

Neil had already dropped his musket; now Christopher let his own slide reluctantly to the snow and slowly lifted his hands.

Slipping out of the carriage, the officer with the pistol advanced and, gathering up the weapons, tossed them into the bushes. Then with a glance toward his companion, who also had climbed out and was now at the horse's head, he suddenly laughed in a way that deepened the color in his round red mottled face.

"Egad, Lieutenant!" he exclaimed. "This

be comic! Remember what we talked of at mess this morning? The Third Rule o' War! Aye, the Third Rule as listed amongst the six the rebel Washington has seen fit to draw up for the benefit of better soldiers than himself. Well, here now before us is a apt picture to illustrate it: two ragged wretches who will accompany us back to Philadelphia after a very pleasant afternoon ride in our calash!"

While Christopher stood with teeth clenched, and Neil motionless behind him, the British officers laughed heartily, as if never had there been greater cause for merriment. Finally the one at the horse's head said to the prisoners, "Knew ye, your rebel general had drawn up six rules o' war?"

"We have heard talk of General Washington's views on warfare," Christopher replied curtly while his gaze roved this way and that, hopefully seeking a possible means of escape.

"And know ye the Third Rule?" the florid-faced officer inquired.

Christopher shook his head. "Nay," he replied and gauged the distance between himself and the man . . . a dozen feet . . . perhaps only ten. . . . Cautiously he lowered his hands a little . . .

The officer flourished his pistol and laughed again. Then he said with mock solemnity, "Give ear now and I will quote it, the Third Rule o' War: 'The first qualification of a soldier is fortitude under fatigue and privation: courage is only the second. Hardship, poverty and actual want are the soldier's best school.' There, egad! And the two of you, one in a tattered blanket and t'other in a ragged jacket, and broken shoes upon your feet—aye, the two o' ye are pupils right out of Washington's best school— Valley Forge!" And he and his companion roared with laughter, their heads thrown back, their well-nourished bodies shaking.

But this time the laughter ended with harsh abruptness as Christopher hurled himself forward. It was a desperate chance, and he knew it—but the unexpected lunge in the midst of British hilarity caught the florid-faced officer off guard, and the pistol ex-

ploded harmlessly. Then Christopher and the man went down together, grunting, gasping, fists pounding, hands seeking a firm hold upon throats . . . while the wind caught the fluffed-up snow from their struggle and sent it flying.

Other sounds of struggle, along with the creak and clatter of wheels, trembled upon the quiet air, but for Christopher they were remote and meaningless as, with head smothered beneath the broad chest of his adversary, he gasped for breath and clutched desperately at the collar of the officer's greatcoat. Long weeks of living mainly on fire cake and water had taken their toll of his strength. Nevertheless, somehow he managed at last to struggle out from under and then to jolt his enemy's chin with a short upward blow of his fist.

He was about to deliver another blow when a lean hand seized the Britisher and jerked him sidewise while a familiar voice shouted, "Surrender, or you'll get a ball from your brother officer's own pistol!" And there, snow-dusted and with a splotch of blood on his face, stood Neil!

"Surrender!" he repeated, and as he thrust the cold pistol against the other's temple, the officer relaxed and fell backward. Then pushing himself slowly to a sitting posture, he blinked and stared at the two Americans —just as his brother officer sprawled in the snow a few paces distant was blinking and staring at them.

Christopher rose to his feet, but before he could utter a word, Neil thrust the pistol into his hand and said hoarsely, "You can manage now!" Then he turned and went running up the road.

"Neil!" Christopher shouted after him. "Neil! Neil!"

But the only response was a few unintelligible words. Then Neil was lost to sight.

For several long seconds Christopher stood with feet apart and forehead wrinkled, his thoughts whirling like the flakes of snow in the increasing northwest wind. With a sickening sense of loss and of hurt, the explanation of Neil's conduct came to him

suddenly and in a way that left no room for doubt.

"He has always had a strong liking for me," Christopher said to himself, "and that is why he attacked and disarmed the other officer and then came to my rescue—because he could not see me taken prisoner. But now, having left me able to manage, he has carried out his plan to desert!" Then he noticed that the calash was gone and, addressing the officer still sprawled on the ground, demanded, "Where is the horse?"

"Whirled and bolted in fright," was the response. "And I don't wonder! Never in all my years was I attacked so furiously or so savagely!" And scooping up a double handful of snow, he held it first against a great discolored lump above one eye and then against the side of his jaw.

Without taking his gaze from the prisoners, Christopher strode toward the bushes and recovered the muskets. Then standing once more before the two men, he asked himself, "Now what shall I do?" And at once came the answer: "Fulfill the mission!"

To the prisoners then he said, "Get to your feet and march—aye, up the road!" And as they quietly obeyed, it seemed to him incredible that these same two officers serving a King three thousand miles across the ocean could ever have laughed so scornfully over Washington's Third Rule of War.

Round the turn they made their way while their captor, holding the pistol in one hand and the muskets in the hollow of his arm, marched alertly half a dozen paces behind them. Along a bare stretch of straight road they marched, and then toward another turn, beyond which the twin pines rose dark and snow-mottled.

As they were rounding the second turn, Christopher suddenly caught his breath—for there near the opening of a small ravine stood the horse and calash, and in the snow alongside, where it had obviously been rolled, lay—a hogshead!

While he continued to stare, wide-eyed, Neil came striding forth from the ravine. "There's six others in there!" he announced —and something in his voice and manner

made him seem altogether different from the Neil Fenwood whom Christopher had known at Valley Forge. "All six of the others also hold shoes!" Neil went on eagerly. "Seven hogsheads altogether! But a pox upon it, Christopher, we can take only the one! They'll have to send a special party after the others—"

Christopher moistened his lips, speechless. It had been a day of surprising happenings, but this, the latest, was the most surprising of all. Neil had not deserted and had no intention of deserting! Instead, leaving his companion to guard the prisoners, he had raced up the road to halt and recover the runaway horse and calash—and then had explored the ravine and found, not just one hogshead, but seven! It occurred to Christopher now that if he had caught the words Neil had flung over his shoulder, they might have explained his purpose.

Bending forward, he noted the markings on the hogshead. "Shoes," he thought. "Save for food, there is naught the army needs more!" Aloud he said to the prisoners, "Lift the hogshead into the calash."

The prisoners didn't want to lift it. They were officers, they pointed out, and should not be asked to do such menial labor as lifting hogsheads. "Ne'rtheless, you will lift this one!" Christopher insisted—and noting the determined look in his eyes, they decided to obey.

Then with the hogshead filling almost the whole of the vehicle, the party set forth back along the Old Lime Road and thence westward across a bare meadow—the prisoners marching ahead, Christopher following with musket held at the alert and a loaded pistol in his waistband, then Neil with shouldered musket several paces in the rear, leading the horse and calash with its strange cargo. Onward they moved across the meadow under a darkening sky and in the teeth of the increasing storm . . . thence onward along old abandoned back roads and through stretches of woodland and across the Wissahickon . . . onward, onward, halting at times to rest or to bite off a few mouthfuls of dough paste or to make sure of direction . . . onward until the day had faded . . . then onward again through the night toward the junction of Valley Creek and the Schuylkill River.

It was mid-morning and the snow was still blowing when at last the party crossed the river at Swede's Ford and presently, to the astonishment of sentries and officers on duty, entered camp. There the two scouts yielded prisoners and calash to a detachment under one of Wayne's lieutenants and, on inquiry, learned that Corporal Purvis was secure in a hut that served as a hospital. General Wayne himself came striding down the hill a few moments later and in crisp tones asked for the story behind the capture.

Almost too weary to stand erect, Christopher managed nevertheless to give a summary account.

"Seven!" Wayne exclaimed. "Seven, you said? Seven full hogsheads! This is something for the Commander-in-Chief to hear from your own lips! Come, both of you." And he strode toward the stone house—the former home of Isaac Potts, who had operated a forge—that General Washington now used for his headquarters.

When the three entered the doorway, Washington with the young Marquis de Lafayette beside him was seated at a long table, studying a map. Others at the table whom Christopher recognized were General Knox, chief of artillery, and the elderly Baron de Kalb, who had come from France on the same ship with Lafayette. As the Commander-in-Chief glanced up, Wayne greeted him and then told of the reason for the visit.

Washington rose to his feet—tall, easy in his movements, his face grave but serene. "You are right, General," he said to Wayne, "I wish to hear the story from the lips of the patrol leader himself."

Then once again—and in full detail this time—Christopher explained what had happened, giving enthusiastic credit to Neil for the part he had played and also mentioning how the two officers had laughed and what they had said about the Third Rule of War.

When he had finished, Washington smiled after the manner of a father to a son and stretched forth a hand first to Christopher and then to Neil.

"Both of you are a credit to the army!" he said with deep feeling. "Fortitude under fatigue and privation—you nobly exemplify the maxim in your persons and in your deeds! Our enemies are correct: the two of you in a sense portray the whole army at Valley Forge! But those men were wrong to laugh. That they will discover with the passage of time."

Then turning to Wayne, he added, "See to it, General, that the six other hogsheads are soon within our possession. And see to it also that these two gallant soldiers of yours are among the first to benefit from the hogshead we already possess—and also of course that they are fed and rested." Then seating himself, he bent over the map again.

As Christopher and Neil went down the hill together a few minutes later, Neil seized his companion's hand and pressed it hard. In a voice that quivered he said, "You may never know the whole of it, Christopher, but this day—nay, yesterday—I passed a milestone in my life and am the better for it— thanks to you!"

Christopher regarded him inquiringly.

"Aye, thanks to you!" Neil repeated. "When you refused to be taken prisoner and lunged to attack, you set an example that seemed suddenly to kindle a bright fire within me! Save for you, I never could have done what I did. In truth, I—I—in truth, Christopher, I had thought of—"

"Say no more!" Christopher added quickly and put an arm across his friend's shoulders. Then he smiled. "Think of it, Neil—shoes! We are to have shoes!"

"Aye, and new ones!" Neil exclaimed.

Then for the first time in weeks, and despite hunger and fatigue, the two friends found themselves laughing while they made their way through the storm toward their log hut.

Private Eye, Yi, Yi!

By ANDREW HALL

*When a mysterious stranger appears in town, Peeps Elliott decides to show the gang
how a private eye really works*

"Peeps Elliott, you aren't even thinking."

Peeps looked across the living room table at his mother and nodded.

"Just remember, my little *puer,* I can't learn these verbs for you."

Peeps tried to jerk his thoughts into an old Roman line. Emmy would take just so much and then she'd blow. And he had to pull up his grade in this defunct language or he'd be ineligible for sports. Grim thought. Tomorrow old Jessup was throwing a Latin quiz and that meant work. Now.

"Sorry, Emmy. I keep going off on associations."

"Associations?"

"You remember the game. One person calls out a word and another calls a word associated with it. Cow . . . milk . . . cookies . . . boy. See?"

"Or Latin . . . quiz . . . flunk . . . bench?"

"Quiet! Only I got problems . . . problems in human relations."

"Gracious!"

"Honest, Coach Zippe is about to bench the best sprinter on the track team and we got to have him. Zip asked me to do some detective work and see why the guy is flunking all his tests."

Emmy was unimpressed. "Bully for you. But you'd better not flunk yourself." She smiled understandingly. "It's rough, Peeps. Living up to your father, I mean. Most boys can slip now and then in their studies or their

behavior and nothing much happens. But when the son of a fairly well-known college coach even stumbles, it's news."

"It's world shattering." Peeps sighed. "Go on."

"To run."

"Curo, currere, cucurrie, cursus. That's good! Cursus, cursus, CURSUS!"

Emmy quietly closed the book. "Here comes Ike. He invented human relations. Maybe he can unclutter your mind."

Ike Elliott came in the door with his usual energetic stride, hung up his coat, then whirled around with his hands in his pockets. He advanced on the two and, with one of his various types of inquisition, began to check on his family's activities.

"All right, guys, spill it. Start talking. Don't hold nuttin' back."

Emmy laughed up at him. "You're so right! Peeps has just been made a Private Eye."

Ike registered mock concern. "So!" he croaked, "sold out by my own son. Okay. I'll give myself up."

He strode to the telephone and dialed a number. Peeps waited, enjoying the clowning, anxious to get into the act.

"Hello, Coppy? This is Ike Elliott."

Peeps jumped up in fascinated amusement. The village cop! Anything for a laugh. How far would his father go with this gag?

"Coppy, have you noticed a stranger wan-

464

dering around Stephens the last few days? He was up at the college, but before I could speak to him he skipped. Some of my students saw him on the high school grounds too. Walks all over this area, down by the railroad, over to the highway. Funny business."

Peeps stood rooted in position. Ike wasn't kidding.

"I just don't want any ruckus up at school. No, he doesn't look like a scout. Right. And I'll put a tail on him. Happen to have one in residence. Those 'fixes' and bribes of a few years ago have me jittery. I don't like wandering strangers. Good. Keep your star shiny, Copper. Thanks."

Before Ike had cradled the telephone, he was swamped with questions.

"Ike, who is it? Was he sinister looking? Maybe it's the mob. Can I really tail him? Where's his hide-out?"

Ike turned to Emmy. "We must have a couple of quiz shows and a mystery on here. Turn the thing off, will you?"

"Come on, Ike, please," pleaded Peeps. "Can I help, honest?"

"This is no help to a Latin review," Emmy broke in. "He has one detective job now that is cluttering up his mind."

"What case you on?" Ike asked. "Jet Blodgett?"

Peeps jumped, and Ike went on. "Zip told me. He wants to find out what's wrong with the kid. Maybe one lug-head can make another lug-head talk."

"Ike, if Jet is out, Stephens High won't even score in the track meet."

"Right, and tough on the school. But I'm thinking about the kid. Jet's mixed up somehow. Does excellent class work, then folds in an exam. Zip'll have to bench him by Monday, sure."

Emmy Elliott could be ignored just so long. "Do you want to go on with this review or DON'T YOU?"

"Enemy fire getting close, son. Get on the job," Ike warned.

Peeps began muttering Latin verbs and the churning of his mind could almost be heard. "Cursus . . . cursus . . . cursus."

"What kind of a home life does Joe Blodgett have?" asked Emmy, and Peeps and Ike grinned. Emmy couldn't resist such a problem.

"I don't know, but I could do some detective work," Peeps said quickly.

Ike shook his head. "Even a lug-head can't dig into another lug-head's home life. Just be friendly. Maybe he needs to talk to somebody."

"Meantime the track team'll fall apart."

"I imagine so," Emmy said sweetly, "with both you and Jet benched."

"I get it." And Peeps dove into his review with reluctant energy.

The next morning at the corner of the school, Peeps caught up with Drue Matthews. If there had to be girls in his world, Peeps was glad Drue was one of them. She looked nice. He couldn't hope she was alone. Nope. According to Peeps, Spiggot Bates, his rival academically, in sports, and socially, had the power to crawl from under a stone every time Drue and Peeps were together. Spiggot bore down on them now.

"Got this Latin test all wrapped up," he announced cheerfully.

Peeps skipped that, then stopped dead in his tracks.

"Hey, who's that man nosing around the school, there? See him?"

Spiggot for once had no crack but answered excitedly, "What's he peeking in the gym windows for? Maybe he's a scout."

Peeps told him what Ike had said about the stranger, and the three moved slowly forward now as the man disappeared around the corner of the building.

"Spiggot, whip around here and bump into him. If he's one of those 'fix' guys, maybe he'll spill it to you. If he finds out my name is Elliott, he might clam up."

Surprisingly, Spiggot obeyed. Drue and Peeps wandered on slowly, as Peeps exploded. "Drue, I got a sensational idea! Get Tod and Fly and Baby Bunting and Betsy and Spiggot all to meet at my house tonight and we'll get organized."

"Into what?"

"Well . . . er . . . Operation Hoosit! That's it! Operation Hoosit! We'll find out who this stranger is yet."

Drue's eyes opened wide, but the bell rang and she and Peeps had to dash for the classroom. Spiggot pounded in and dropped a note for Peeps: "He asked if this is a good school, do we have football, basketball, etc.? How does our team rate in the county? Do we like our coach? Is the Stephens College coach all they say he is? It smells, Peeps."

Peeps nodded solemnly and became lost in thought and it was only when he heard Joe Blodgett's name called in Latin class that he jerked to attention.

"What case is 'utor' in this sentence, Joe?"

Dead silence. Peeps' stomach began to churn in anxiety. Joe had his eyes closed and his mouth was flapping wildly but no words came.

"I wish I knew why you fail every test, Joe. Your class work is good." Old Jessup could be kind when he wanted to, and he went on, "Maybe you think *too* hard. I know you know this. Relax. Take it easy."

Suddenly Joe, the Jet, blurted out, "It's in the a—BLAT—ive case."

The class guffawed and Peeps drooped in sheer agony. There went the best hundred-yard man in the county. Fine.

Mr. Jessup corrected the pronunciation and the case and asked Joe to see him after school. Peeps was so upset he gave the right answers to his own assigned questions and didn't even notice it.

That evening the gang met at the Elliotts and, after explanations, arguments and assignments, Operation Hoosit was organized. They would tail the stranger. It could only be done after school. They would work in twos. They would follow the man's mysterious walks in Higby's jeep. They planned for special pairs deliberately to encounter the suspect.

Reports on this angle continued to sound shady. The stranger asked Farny and Fly if Stephens ever played lacrosse. He asked Baby Bunting and Tod what their favorite sport was, what positions they played, whether the townspeople took an interest in the school athletic program.

In his hikes around the area he followed a set pattern. He would leave the center of the village and go either north, south or east to the outskirts and beyond. He would prowl the lanes, or strike off across a field or climb a hill; often he studied the railroad siding. He always took the five-ten bus back to the city. He always walked slowly, as if weighted with problems . . . or maybe a guilty conscience. Peeps kept track of the reports and tried to get an over-all picture.

One afternoon, Peeps and John Higby, manning the jeep, were in front of the drug store. The stranger had not been seen all day and the two decided to go in to the fountain for a couple of Graveyards. A car went by and then Drue and Betsy whipped around the corner. They pointed to the passing car and panted in turn.

"He's in a car!"

"It's a black car!"

"What won't they think of next?" marveled Peeps.

Drue shook his arm. *"It's our man!* At least get his license number."

The point hit Peeps like a bulldozer. "Higby! Follow that car!"

The two girls piled aboard and Betsy volunteered, "He turned at Olympia."

"Then he's headed for the railroad siding," Drue said. "Go by Busby Lane."

Higby took the bumpy short cut that led to the railroad, full speed. Drue explained over the noise and the wind that she and Betsy had seen the stranger in his car in the little street that came to a dead end at the big Perkins house. He had been driving slowly, looking at houses on either side, and the girls had been able to keep up with him to the drug store.

"Betsy kind of thought. . . ."

"He was casing the joint!" finished Betsy triumphantly.

"You girls read too many crime comics," laughed Higby, and slowed for the intersection to swing into Olympia Boulevard.

Suddenly Betsy shrieked, "There he is! I mean there he goes!"

Peeps said calmly, "Walk, don't run to the nearest exit. I got the number."

"Tough, it's a Drive-It-Yourself job, isn't it?" murmured Drue.

"WHAT?"

"Sure it is. All those L Ds come from Paxons' garage."

"Well, plant me deep," groaned Peeps, and Higby consoled him with, "Too bad, Harry. Maybe if you'd worn a hat."

That night at dinner Peeps reported the incident almost exactly as it had happened. He saw no reason to heap honors on the feminine brain work and his statement, "It was discovered to be a rented car," seemed adequate.

"How's Joe Blodgett making out?"

Peeps told about the test. "It's painful. Jet freezes. Goes numb." His voice was a hollow groan and he went on glumly, "My Private Eye business is as dead as this here old defunct Latin."

"Your English seems pretty dead too," reproved Emmy.

Next evening detective business looked up. Drue called Peeps.

"Peeps, Betsy and I tailed the man until he went across a field and we couldn't keep out of sight. So we decided to check on him at the bus stop at five-ten. And guess what? He didn't take the bus!"

"Shucks, Drue," laughed Peeps, "maybe he walked over to Sackville."

"But he didn't! He didn't! He had dinner at The Dog House. Spiggot was on his way home from here and he . . ."

"What was Spiggot doing at your house?"

"Silly. Spiggot saw him come out of The Dog House and walk along Yardly Road, sort of studying the houses, the way he's been doing."

"I'll pick him up right away," Peeps said shortly and then muttered, "And I'd like to pick Spiggot up and drop him . . . hard!"

Peeps was considering a third piece of cake when little Bobo Griscom called him on the telephone. Bobo lived across from the high school and had nearly exploded with joy when Peeps enlisted his help as a secret lookout.

"Peeps! You told me to call. Well, I am."

"You am what?"

"Calling. You said if I saw anything screwy over at school to do it. I did."

"Did what?"

"Saw something screwy. I was going to bed and I saw somebody walking around and around the school. Close to the building. He's still doing it."

Peeps was excited now. "Good boy! Don't tell anybody. Keep watch. I'll be right there."

He grabbed his jacket, flung an over-the-shoulder briefing to his family and tore out the door, barely hearing Emmy's outburst, "Ike, I don't like it. He might get shot."

Peeps let out his long legs and at the edge of the school grounds stopped to make his plans. If he were seen, whatever the stranger planned to pull off would be postponed, but if he could surprise the man, he might discover enough to report him.

Peeps dropped into a sauntering stroll along the side of the property, partly hidden by a hedge. He had almost reached the corner of the building when he froze in his tracks. The wavering shadow of a man, cast by the street light behind it, fell across in front of him and must have been ten feet long. The shadow held there for a minute, then swung around and disappeared in the blackness around the building. Peeps, breathing heavily from his fright, peered through the darkness and made out the lone figure, hugging close to the stone walls, then scuttling around the far corner. The man obviously did not want to be seen.

The momentary fear that held Peeps turned to anger now. That man had no business here. If he had, he'd be walking out on the sidewalk. Okay, he asked for it! Peeps darted across to the school and searched for a place to hide. Then at another corner of the building, he again saw the wavering shadow of a man, falling ahead of him, almost as if to warn Peeps of his approach. Peeps gasped and dropped into a small areaway in front of one of the gym windows. He crouched down to keep from being seen and his heart pounded loudly.

And then he heard the footsteps. They were heavy, slow and deliberate. They reminded Peeps of Frankenstein and they came nearer and nearer. It was only then, crouching in that narrow space and listening to the measured tread, that Emmy's words registered. "He might get shot." Jeepers! Shot! With a gun? Why, a guy could get hurt that way! Maybe he'd better run for it . . . Easy. Easy. Maybe he better stay right there and make like a mouse. He ducked lower, then listened in cold sweat as the footsteps passed by within a foot of his head.

Finally the sound faded away, and Peeps considered hoisting himself up over the rim of the hole. Still, if he ran and were seen . . . yipe! They said a moving target is harder to hit and creepers! he couldn't stay folded up like this all night.

He waited and listened, then cautiously peered over the top of the areaway. No sign of the intruder. He waited a little longer, then lifted himself up and out. Without even a look behind him, he tore across the street, flung himself down back of the bushes in the Griscom's yard and panted for breath.

A loud "Psst!" brought him to his feet and there was little Bobo, signaling to him from the front porch.

"He's gone, Peeps. He went that way. Fast."

Peeps scrambled to the steps. "Bobo, go tell your father to . . ."

"My father isn't home. So isn't my mother. They're to the movies."

H'm. Peeps, brave again now he could no longer hear those footsteps or see that wavering shadow, hated to lose the trail.

"Where'd he go, Bobo?"

"I aweady told you. To the movies."

"No, no, Bobo. The man. Which way did he go?"

"Across third base and in Elm Street."

"Look Bobo, I gotta use your phone quick. I'll call Coppy."

"The cops! Whee! If I had my space ship, I'd run 'em down."

"The phone, Bobo, the phone! We'll lose him."

Bobo led the way and Peeps dialed Coppy's number.

"Coppy, this is Peeps Elliott and I got the man cornered . . . er . . . almost had him cornered. Now he's gone up Elm Avenue. I'm tailing him but you better come too."

It was a wonder the stranger didn't hear Coppy's answering roar.

"What's going on here anyway? You kids trying to give me a hard time? Just got a call from one of your gang, said the man was breaking in the Perkins' side door. I think I smell a joke, running me all over town. Now you kids quit this Cops and Robbers."

"Coppy, please! This is no joke. I saw the guy. For real. I know where he is right now. I'll follow him up Elm but hurry, Coppy, hurry!"

Peeps banged up and, with only a brief warning to Bobo to stay right there and keep watch, he took off. As he ran he thought over what Coppy had said.

The Perkins place was where Drue and Betsy had seen the stranger before. But if he was way up at that end of town, who was Peeps chasing now? Who had been trying to break into the high school? Peeps could feel goose pimples pop.

Maybe it was a gang, a mob! If this idea made his feet any heavier, his speed any less, Peeps wasn't aware of it. He kept pounding along Elm Avenue. The street was completely deserted. Not even a strange man prowling in it.

Peeps felt a rush of disappointment. Just as this was getting good, he had to lose the trail. And then he saw his quarry, crossing under the street light, way up at Whitcomb Street. The figure moved on slowly. Peeps stepped off onto the grass plot next to the hedge and put on more speed. If he could only signal Ike when the man went by their house, maybe Ike could detain him. Peeps would have to sprint so as not to lose sight of him when he turned the corner.

Giving his full attention to speed, Peeps was so absorbed he barely saw in time that he had not only caught up with the man but was about to run him down. He swerved sharply in behind a hedge and waited. It was only then he realized the fugitive had slipped into the yard next door and was creeping along the side of the house. And the yard next door was the Elliott's, Peeps' own house! Oleo joe! What now? Peeps crept along the hedge, filled with increasing anger and considerable curiosity.

He saw the figure go around the back of the house and Peeps leaped the hedge and started on a run after him. He took the corner fast and ran full tilt into something that went 'ugh!' Then out of the inky darkness a pair of arms grabbed him and tried to hold him. After the first second of horror, Peeps found himself in a clawing, flaying, slugging hassle.

It was so dark he couldn't see the size of the man he was fighting. Once or twice he nearly fell flat because a strong punch missed the target entirely.

There was no sound except the heavy breathing and occasional grunting of the two adversaries. And then Peeps realized that his phantom fighter was trying to get away. He was moving away from the back entrance and Peeps knew that once under the trees in the yard he would lose him completely. There was only one thing to do and Peeps did it, thoroughly.

"Ike!" he yelled. In a matter of seconds the back door flew open and a flood of light poured out on the two. Peeps had hated to call for help and it flashed through his mind that, now that he could see, it would be very fine for Ike to witness his son on the giving end of a haymaker. He wound up and was ready to throw when the light fell full on his opponent's face and his arm froze in mid-air.

"Joe Blodgett!" he squeaked.

The slender young sprinter dropped his own arm and turned as if to make off in the darkness.

"Come in, Joe." Ike's voice was kind. "Come in and let's talk."

Ike turned back into the house and at once got out milk and fresh cookies. He indicated two high stools, side by side. The boys brushed and adjusted their clothing, then sat down. Emmy was diplomatically nowhere in sight. For a few minutes no word was spoken.

Then Ike said quietly, "Do you want to tell us about it, Joe?"

Joe looked terrified, then slowly nodded his head. He thought for a minute and then looked straight at Ike and began to talk. His statements were halting at first, but gradually he talked right along. He lived with an aunt, his mother was dead and his father traveled a lot. His father had been a pretty good athlete in high school and had been disappointed when Joe was so light and spindly. When it turned out Joe could sprint, that he was one of the record breakers of the county, the old man had nearly blown a fuse.

And he had popped off his buttons when his son earned the nickname "the Jet." He talked about it all the time. And then he became set on the idea that Joe was going to college. He could win a scholarship. He, himself, had wanted to go to college and was determined his boy would go. He could help him some but it was up to Joe to win his tuition with high marks.

His dad really put the heat on when he found it actually might happen. Not unpleasant heat, just plenty of it.

Joe smiled waveringly. "If he'd beat me up, it wouldn't be so tough. But he doesn't. He just cheers and brags and begs me." Joe shrugged. "I made out for a while. Always had my homework and always got good grades. Then my dad began to call me long distance, when he was traveling, to see how I was doing. If there was a test coming up, he had to know about it. It kind of got me . . . scared me, I mean. I think it'd kill him if I failed anything. I kept plugging and had a good average, except for Latin. That stuff is hard for me."

"I bet it was hard for the Romans," sympathized Peeps.

"Mr. Jessup wrote my pop that my homework was excellent but my tests were poor." Joe looked sick. "Honest, the old boy almost fell apart. It was awful. You know what I mean, Ik . . . Mr. Elliott?"

"Ike's my name, Joe," Ike said gently. "And I know exactly what you mean."

"I worked even harder, got up early and stuff and my homework was better but I just went blooey on the quizzes. I always kept thinking how my father'd feel if I flunked."

"That all figures," Ike said. "Lots of people have a tough time with tests and for a lot less reason. Now what has all this to do with the little riot you and Peeps were staging out here?"

Peeps' heart began to pound and he was sure it could be heard. What was the real story and would Joe tell it?

"Well," Joe began, "it looks as if I did it kind of backward." He stopped and Peeps croaked, "If you were hitting backward, don't ever hit me straight away."

Joe smiled briefly and then plunged on. He had decided maybe if he talked to Ike it might help. Maybe Ike, who was his father's idol, could talk to the old man and get him to ease off. Joe had a chance if left alone.

"So I came over here and was just prowling around, trying to get up my nerve to come in and talk to you."

There was a pause and Peeps' heart thundered louder. Ike nodded his head in satisfaction and understanding.

"I'm just sorry you had to 'get up your nerve', Joe. I like to help boys, when I can." He laughed. "Latin isn't my field but Peeps' mother is hot at it and I'll bet she'll be glad to help you. Certainly I'll be glad to talk to your father. He just doesn't realize what his enthusiasm is doing, that's all. I think we can clear the whole thing up easily."

There was another pause and Peeps wriggled uncomfortably on the high stool, then looked over at Joe. Joe was staring straight at Ike and a dull red was creeping up out of his jacket collar to cover his face. His voice could scarcely be heard.

"That isn't all, Ike. I . . . first tonight I went over to the high school. I walked around it about a million billion times, kicking an idea around with me. I thought maybe I'd sneak in and take a look at old Jessup's test for tomorrow." His face was flaming but he went doggedly on. "I didn't want the actual questions so's I could study them . . . I know the stuff. I just thought if I memorized the order of them I might not get so panicked at the beginning and might be able to put down the junk I know." He hesitated. "I guess that's pretty hard to believe, isn't it?"

"Nothing's hard to believe if it's said by an honest man," Ike said levelly.

The shamed look faded a little at Ike's words and Joe said faintly, "I finally figured it'd be a pretty dopey thing to do, no matter what happened, so I came over here." He looked around at Peeps. "And then I ran into The Slugger here and had to fight for my life." He laughed briefly and then gave a heavy sigh. "That's the whole deal, sir. It's not very pretty."

Peeps' heart had gone back to normal now and he wanted to shout and yell. Joe was all right. A good guy.

Ike, with his eyes full on Joe, said, "You know, fellow, I have an idea the fight you had over at the high school tonight was about the toughest you'll ever have to make. That was a championship bout, you know, and you won it. That victory means you can overcome anything you have to . . . ever. Even Latin tests."

Ike held out his hand and as Joe, the Jet, shook it, Peeps knew he had never seen such a blinding look of sheer happiness.

There was a pounding at the front door now and Joe, after a 'See you' to Peeps, went out the back way. The Elliotts heard Emmy greet someone in the front room and went to the archway.

There stood Coppy. His usual placid and kindly face was mottled with anger.

"Will somebody tell me what's going on? Are these kids trying to run me ragged? First I get one call and it's a dud." He looked at Peeps. "The gentleman you've been tailing, Sherlock Holmes, is Mr. Dunlap. He's a big guy in industry and has been looking for a site for a modern factory. He kept quiet because he didn't want the story to break until he was ready. He wanted to study the town and the schools. He has a boy in high school, one in college. Mr. Perkins, who's away, arranged with the Chamber of Commerce for Dunlap to stay in his house for the weekend. Mr. Dunlap called me after

he was inside but one of your Vigilantes saw him enter and reported him first. Then I get a call from Peeps here about some guy up at the high school . . ."

Ike grinned at the angry little man.

"Look, Coppy, it's a long story. Sit down, have a smoke and we'll eat some of Emmy's cookies and I'll tell you the whole thing."

Coppy grunted and sat down.

Peeps knew Ike would make a full report to Coppy and Coppy would understand. He felt warm and pleasant the way things had turned out. Then he caught sight of the clock.

"Yipe!" he yelled and his feet were making tracks at the top of his startled jump. "I gotta date with Drue and I'm an hour late!"

An hour late was fifty-nine minutes too late for Drue Matthews and she was already at a table in the drug store with Spiggot. Faithful old Spiggot! Peeps dropped breathlessly in beside them and told them all about Mr. Dunlap and the Perkins house.

Drue's annoyance quickly faded as he talked, and even Spiggot was interested.

"A fine Private Eye I turned out to be," moaned Peeps at the end. "Tailing a perfectly respectable person."

"But what's the scoop on the high school angle? I heard there was somebody trying to break in there and you turned in the alarm." There was real envy in Spiggot's usually jibing voice.

Peeps hesitated a moment, tempted. He could really make this guy turn green. Then he said mournfully, "I guess I'm no flatfoot. Yeah, I turned in an alarm but Coppy didn't find anybody. Could a been the janitor, checking the windows."

Spiggot's hooting laughter was about what Peeps expected. He glared at him for a minute, again tempted, then he heard Ike's voice saying, "You can overcome anything you have to, Joe," and he could see the blazing look of happiness on Joe the Jet's face. Suddenly Peeps felt good all the way through.

"Say, how about a Graveyard all around to celebrate my retirement from the detective business?"

What It Takes

By CAPTAIN BURR LEYSON

A crash landing in the midst of an Arctic storm calls for a new set of rescue techniques

A deadly menace lay in wait over the vast frozen wastes of the polar ice cap just beyond the northern horizon. For days Jack Healy had charted carefully its position on his maps as the flight crews radioed back details of conditions aloft. A huge area of concentrated low barometric pressure was steadily forming and the young meteorologist frankly was worried. Only too well he knew that from such areas the sudden terrible storms of the Arctic struck. Should one of these storms trap a flight aloft, it might mean the end of all on board the aircraft.

The little emergency airstrip from which they operated was one of the first in the early days of the Arctic weather patrol. It was laid on the surface of the tundra and boasted of no facilities for instrument landings. Nor were there any airports so equipped within the limited range of planes stationed there. To be caught aloft in a storm and be without visibility meant a desperate crash landing in the desolate wastes of the North.

Daily now Jack warned the flight crews of the danger. But their response was more or less what he expected.

"Don't you worry about us, Kid," they laughed. "You just play with your maps and ride herd on that storm of yours! We'll take care of the flyin'!"

Although Jack was a member of the tiny Air Force unit assigned to the experimental weather patrols hundreds of miles from the nearest outpost of civilization, he was not accepted into the close companionship of the others. True, they respected his ability as a meteorologist, young as he was. But he was not a member of a flight crew. His duties kept him on the ground. As a result he was of another world.

This was evident during the evenings. Cut off from civilization as they were and living in tents beside a wilderness airstrip, there was no opportunity for the usual entertainment. After the evening meal it was the custom to remain gathered around the tables in the combination mess and recreation tent and play games or merely talk.

It was these evening "gab fests" that formed the high point of the day for Jack. He thrilled to hear at first hand accounts of famous flights, crashes, rescues, and tense moments in the air. But he was always seated in the background and never included in the general conversation.

He was a mere groundling and this was not his world of which they spoke. Theirs was a world of action, excitement, adventure —and raw courage so taken for granted as rarely to be mentioned. Between these men was that close companionship and fraternity reserved only for their own kind. They were men who had time and again faced a common peril, men who cheerfully accepted risk as a part of their daily life.

While they never mentioned it, Jack knew that their quick acceptance of any stranger into their midst as an equal, provided he was an airman, was based on one fact. To them, if the man was an airman, he must be of proved courage. Or, as they put it, "A good Joe, a real handy guy to have with you in a jam!" Courage, the ability to see it through, to ride it out, in the air, was their measure of a man.

And how could he, Jack Healy, a groundling earthbound by his duties, ever hope to measure up to such a standard?

But as more reports of the brewing storm were relayed back by the flight crews, Jack found little time to give to his personal worries. Now his worry about the sudden breaking of the ever-building storm and its trapping of one of the flights occupied all of his thoughts. The climax was due at any moment and he warned the flight crews again.

Then a late afternoon flight reported a quickly spreading overcast and heavy winds. To Jack that meant the moment had come. The storm was breaking and he knew it would break with sudden and violent action.

"Visibility closing in. Winds intense."

Those terse words from the flight confirmed Jack's fears. This was it! The next message, but a few minutes later, was far from reassuring. It was full of foreboding.

"Weather socked in. Visibility zero. Give radio bearings."

Now those of the unit who were on the ground were packed into the radio tent, listening eagerly for further word from the flight. Time was short if it were going to fight its way clear. Already the sky over the airstrip was covered with fast-moving clouds. Heavy gusts of wind tore at the tents and staked-down planes.

The next fix on the plane's position showed that it had been carried nearly thirty miles beyond a rugged height of land that cut across the country to the south of the airstrip. There was but one break in that height of land and that was where the river that ran beside the airstrip cut through it in a narrow gorge filled with huge boulders and impassable rapids. Then came another report from the plane:

"Crashlanding! Get fix on position!"

Utter silence cloaked the group as they watched the radio operator calibrate his instruments for the fix on the plane's position. Only too well could the members of the flight crews visualize the grim battle being waged in the depths of the storm to the south of them. Then the radio operator began to type another message.

"See ground! Near gorge. Will need doctor. . . ."

Abruptly the radio was silenced and the listeners knew that the plane was down. Nor did they fail to appreciate the dire significance of those final words, "Will need doctor. . . ."

In that terse phrase the pilot had told them that the crash was going to be a bad one. It could not be otherwise in that rugged country by the gorge.

"Kid! Where's that kid?" a pilot shouted.

Jack shouldered his way through the crowd.

"Here!" he said.

"What about weather? When's this stuff goin' to break? How soon can we get out with a search flight?" the pilot shot at him.

For an instant Jack hesitated to reply. It was like passing a sentence of doom on the missing crew crashed in that wilderness.

"Forty to forty-eight hours, anyway," he stated.

"You certain? Better check it. Watch it and report the slightest chance for a break that will let us get off with a rescue flight!"

Jack ran for his tent, fighting the wind that tore at his clothes. Although he was certain of his figures he checked his instruments, scanned his weather charts. They only confirmed what he had said. Taut-lipped, he stood looking at a map of the area.

His finger found the spot where the radio fix had shown the plane to be down. Somewhere within a circle of a mile or so in diameter lay the wreck. It could not be anything else, hope against it as he might.

The distance on the map looked short but it might as well have been on the other side of the earth until the storm abated. There was no hope of getting a rescue flight into the air until then. The crashed crew must survive as best they could, if there were any survivors. There was no other way of reaching them.

The gorge and the rapids barred the way by the river. They were marked "Impassable" on the map. There was no record of anyone even trying to run them. One look had been enough for the old sourdoughs and trappers. "Too rough to be able to hope to make it!" they had stated.

"Too rough?" Jack murmured to himself.

For a moment he stood regarding the point on the map where the gorge was marked "Impassable." He pursed his lips and then suddenly his mouth set in grim lines of determination. Abruptly he turned, slipped through the flap of his tent and fought his way to the radio tent where he found the men still waiting for possible word from the crew. But the radio was mute. Jack thrust his way forward until he faced Dennison, the chief pilot and senior officer present.

"Captain," Jack began, "you're not going to get a flight out of here until day after tomorrow anyway. I'm certain of that. That means help won't reach the crew until then —unless you'll let me try. I'm pretty sure I can get through. I've got an idea."

Dennison whirled on Jack, eyes blazing. "How are you going to get through when we can't?" he rasped in his nervous tension. "Goin' to grow wings, I suppose?" He turned his back in contempt of the very idea that Jack could do something while they were not able to do anything. "Don't bother me, please, I've got to try to figure out something to do. Now, please—get out!"

Jack grabbed his arm roughly and whirled him around. Now Jack's eyes were blazing as he faced the airman.

"Listen to me!" he said. "I may be young and I'm no airman. But as a kid I was a Scout and I learned to handle a canoe in some mighty rough water. I've run rapids with my dad, too, on wilderness trips. I'm willing to try to get through the gorge to those men. They need help! We haven't canoes but we do have rubber rafts! They'll ride through even better!"

Dennison's face reddened and he seemed

about to break into a tirade. Then he hesitated as it dawned upon him that he could not afford to overlook any opportunity to aid the men, however slight its chances of success seemed.

Before he could speak, another voice broke in. It was the slow drawl of "Doc" Martin, the unit medic. He had been standing nearby and studying Jack's face intently.

"Just a minute, Dennison," he said. "Seems to me that the youngster might have an idea. Anyway, I'm willing to go along with him. That is, if you have no objection to our trying to help the crew?"

In the face of such a statement there was little else the pilot could do but agree. He knew that once the weather cleared, other doctors would take to the air instantly from the main bases so that the unit would not be left without medical services if Doc and Jack had trouble.

The risks were high. To traverse a gorge and rapids which had blocked experienced sourdoughs and trappers seemed impossible. How could "The Kid" do it?

But Jack and Doc were making their way out of the tent within seconds after Dennison had given grudging approval. They soon stood in the Medical tent where Doc made a hurried selection of instruments and necessary supplies, making waterproof packages for his pockets.

"Don't need much by way of supplies," Doc explained to Jack. "The plane carried plenty of emergency medical kits. We can use them if we get . . . that is, when we get there."

Ordinarily, Jack would have felt hurt at the implied doubt in Doc's statement about getting to the crash. But now it only added an angry determination to try regardless of the danger.

"We're losing time and it's going to be dark soon. We'll need all the light we can get to run the gorge and the rapids," he said flatly. Doc looked up quickly.

"Then let's go," he replied, stuffing a small package into a bulky pocket.

Fighting their way through the storm to the small temporary dock built into the river beside the airstrip they found a small group of the men waiting, the rubber life raft already inflated and waiting for them. An outboard motor was fitted to a board lashed across the rim of the raft and the shaft of the engine protruded down into the water through a watertight collar in the fabric bottom of the raft.

Quickly they clambered into their tiny two-man raft, bid hurried "so longs!" to the shouted "Good lucks!" from the men and then, as Jack started the motor, they were off, headed for the gorge and rapids nearly twenty-five miles downstream.

Fully two hours later, hunched over on the sodden fabric flooring, they sought in vain to pierce the gloom ahead. They knew from Jack's estimate that they must be approaching the sharp turn and high cliffs that marked the beginning of the gorge. But the visibility was rapidly approaching zero; they could see but a scant few yards ahead and time and again had nearly rammed onto the high banks as they had gotten off course.

Then the gloom ahead seemed to deepen, to take shape. Jack swung the steering handle of the motor far to one side and the boat sheered off at the last instant to avoid crashing into the perpendicular face of the cliffs. They were at the entrance of the gorge and now the current was picking up speed, hurtling the raft along with it.

This was it! The next thing Jack knew he felt the raft bound into the air as they passed over the first of the huge waves thrown up by underwater obstacles. And then the walls of the gorge closed in on them. They were heading directly into the rapids at terrific speed, motor wide open.

Hastily Jack cut the switch and tore at the fastenings of the watertight collar around the shaft where it passed through the fabric flooring of the raft. Then he loosened the clamps that held the motor mount in place and, bracing himself on his knees, lifted the engine out of its position and cast it overboard! From now on its weight would be but an added hazard. They would need all of the buoyancy the raft could give them, and probably more, in the wild maelstrom ahead.

Now that the sharp exhaust of the engine was stilled, Jack could hear the deep roar of the rapids ahead. Then they hit the first of the foaming waves, the white water. He felt their raft bounce into the air as though it were a feather. Frantically Jack groped with one hand on the fabric bottom of the raft until his fingers closed on the two canoe paddles strapped there. Quickly he released the catches and passed one forward to Doc, poking him in the back to attract his attention. Then, grasping the other paddle in his hands, he shouted.

"Grab the paddle and get ready, Doc! Paddle as hard as you can when I yell. I'll tell you which side! We've got to try to steer her somehow! And inflate your 'Mae West.' "

Doc nodded and as he did jerked the cord that released the highly compressed CO_2 gas in the small metal cylinder set in the edge of his life jacket. Jack did the same and felt his jacket swell to full inflation.

The water was oil-slick now and running with dizzy speed. They were in the long "chute," a section where the waters fell sharply and the gorge was clear of obstacles.

Ahead the gorge narrowed and was a mass of huge boulders, foaming waves, and hissing spray. It was there that lay the climax, the greatest danger. Jack braced himself as they rushed inexorably into the maelstrom. Then they struck.

Jack was dimly aware of a huge dark shape rushing at them. All around the shape was a mass of white foam. He began to paddle frantically, trying to drive the raft to one side into the clear of the obstacle.

"Right! Paddle on the right side, Doc! Hard!"

Under the impulse of their paddles the raft moved across the current, but slowly. Then it struck the wave set up ahead of the great boulder as the rushing waters were hurled back from its hard face. The front of the raft tilted sharply, rose in the air.

Jack could feel the hard rush of the waters against the thin fabric flooring. All disappeared in a shower of spray, and now they rode at a perilous angle, barely upright.

There was another blow, less this time, and water rushed in over the lower edge of the raft. The boat smacked down solidly, spun, and then went careening on down the rapids. The wave had contemptuously cast them aside as though the raft were but a tiny chip of wood. But it had saved them.

Now they were in the heart of the rapids and on every side was a welter of white water with jagged rocks showing their crests. It seemed utterly impossible that the raft could live through it. Time and again they paddled desperately and avoided certain disaster only by a hairsbreadth. Jack's arms became leaden, tired to exhaustion from his efforts. The raft was flooded, sodden, but still afloat.

Doc's form was crouched ahead of him, paddle thrust forward, ready to fight for every inch of precious leeway at Jack's command. But Doc's strength was all but expended.

Still a wild stretch of water lay ahead of them. It seemed as though it would never end. Then they fought clear of a jagged rock, barely rounded it, and immediately found themselves hurtling down on two great masses of roaring foam that hid huge obstructions. Their course was directly between them, into the heart of the torrent. There was no time to paddle clear even if they could. This was it!

Jack opened his mouth to shout a warning to Doc to release his paddle and hold onto the raft by the safety rope that ran around its edge. But his words were lost in a solid sheet of spray that almost choked him as they struck into the waves. Jack felt their raft hurled aloft and to one side. An instant later it hit solidly against the opposing wave and was thrown back. Jack's body was driven down into the bottom against the fabric by the force of the blow.

Then the raft spun, tilted far to one side, and at that moment the hurtling waters caught it and heaved it far into the air.

Jack felt his body leave the raft and swing into the air. As he turned he caught sight of a vague shape close beside him. It was Doc. He shot out an arm and his clutching fingers closed on the collar of Doc's jacket. Then they struck the water with a sickening jar that tore loose his grasp. Quickly Jack wrapped an arm around Doc as together they sank into the depths.

His lungs were bursting and with one arm he fought feebly to drive them to the surface. As though in a playful mood, the current carried them upwards, hurled them into the clear air. Eagerly his tortured lungs gasped in great gulps of air, choking over the spray. He knew they should make their bodies compact and not kick because of the rocks. They were submerged again and Jack felt a stunning blow on his back as the waters smashed them into some great boulders.

From then on he was in a daze. Vaguely he fought to survive, to claw his way to the surface with one hand. And all the while his other hand remained locked firmly in Doc's jacket. Then for a time he knew no more.

His next thought was of pain. He became aware that his body was one great aching mass, that every movement brought agony. Then he realized that water was gently lap-ping his face. He fought to open his eyes, to think coherently. He shook his head to clear his still reeling senses. He thrust out an arm and his fingers met ground. Slowly came the realization that he was floating in the shallows near the bank of the river. With a rush his mind cleared. He looked about him and saw Doc beside him, floating on his back.

Only then he realized that he still clung to Doc's jacket and painfully he forced his cramped fingers apart to release him. Floundering, he struggled ashore, dragging Doc behind him, and then fell on the gravel of the bank.

Slowly he fought his way back to full consciousness. This time his mind cleared quickly and as he struggled erect he saw Doc move and then groan. For a time Jack stood there, swaying until he felt his strength return under the urge of his anxiety to drive ahead to the rescue. Looking down, he saw Doc work himself to his knees and helped him erect.

Then they looked around. They were on a small, flat, rocky and boulder-strewn shore. A dark mass lay behind them and now they realized that the rumble they heard was the roar of the rapids in the gorge. That was to their right, upstream. They were clear—they

477

had made it! But—where was the crash? What of the crew?

Jack's fingers fumbled under his "Mae West" and beneath his shirt to where he had thrust a service revolver wrapped in a waterproof oilskin. Slowly he worked the gun out and held it aloft. In quick succession he fired three shots and stood listening.

It was the standard signal of distress in the wilderness but would the crew of the lost plane be near enough to hear it? And if they were, would they be able to hear it? Or were they . . . Before he could complete the thought he heard answering shots! Somebody was near. It must be survivors! It had to be! Quickly he fired an answer and then the two set off in a stumbling run.

Not five minutes later they heard a voice shouting. Then they saw a light and the next moment they stood beside the crash. One of the crew, his head bandaged, greeted them and pointed to the overturned plane.

"Inside the fuselage, Doc! You'd better take over! I've done what I could."

Jack spent the next hour obeying Doc's curt commands as he worked over the injured crew with the plane's medical supplies and what he had brought in a waterproof package in his pocket.

All would survive, but only Doc's presence had saved two of them. Finally, the injured attended to, Doc turned to Jack.

"Let's look at you, now!" he said. A quick examination showed no broken bones but a myriad of cuts and blackening bruises.

"You're going to be one sore guy for a time!" Doc commented but with no mention that his own body was a similar mass of bruises and cuts. "Lie down and rest here in the fuselage. We'll wait for daylight and hope this storm lets up quicker than you thought."

Soon, with the least injured member of the crew keeping watch, both Doc and Jack were in a deep sleep.

Almost forty hours to the minute from the time Jack had predicted the break, the storm lessened and then ceased. Within an hour afterward a plane from the unit was circling low overhead, dropping emergency supplies and a message bag that told of a helicopter on the way to fly them out. But it was not until late that afternoon that the helicopter landed close to the crash.

Quickly two of the most seriously injured were strapped on stretchers and placed in the special "blisters" on each side of the helicopter's fuselage. Then it rose and whirred away for the airstrip where the injured would be transferred to a plane and flown to the base.

The next trip of the helicopter saw the remaining member of the crew and Doc away. Now Jack was left alone to wait for the return of the 'copter.

As the pilot flew him back to the unit at the airstrip hardly a word was spoken. The pilot seemed engrossed with his flying.

Weary and sore, Jack relaxed as best he could in the seat set in the nose. From time to time he turned his head to look back at the blisters which had held the injured crew members and wondered how they were. Then he saw the airstrip ahead and a crowd awaiting near the mess tent. Down came the 'copter barely ten yards in front of them and the pilot ran the motor dry. Then they clambered out, Jack almost falling as he stumbled. He felt hands grab him, then, half-carried, he found himself in the mess tent.

Dennison stood at the head of the long table and the men around Jack swept him forward. Dennison stretched out his hand.

"Swell show, Jack! Congratulations!" he beamed as he gripped Jack's hand and shook it. Then, still holding Jack's hand and guiding him to a seat at the head of the table, he shouted:

"Move over, gang! Make room for Jack! Give the man a seat!"

"Make room for Jack! Give the MAN a seat!" Not "The Kid" now, but "Jack!" A warm feeling surged through Jack and brought his tired body erect. As he sat down and heard their shouted congratulations and looked into their smiling faces Jack suddenly realized that he was no longer an "outsider." Groundling though he was, he was one of them. Now they knew he had what it takes!

Camping on Brownsea Island

By ARTHUR A. SCHUCK

How an acorn planted on a tiny island became an oak that spread over the world

On a bright August day more than fifty years ago a famous British general gathered twenty boys around him and set out for a small island off the coast of England. Here they pitched camp and lived a glorious outdoor life for two full weeks.

Some of the twenty boys were the sons of the general's army friends. Others had come from the nearby towns of Poole and Bournemouth. The whole group was divided into four smaller groups which the general called "patrols," and each patrol had a boy leader and a name—Wolves, Bulls, Ravens, and Curlews.

The days in camp were spent with hut building, knot tying, fire lighting, cooking, finding way through strange country, noticing details far and near, stalking, reading meanings from tracks and signs, studying animal and plant life, practicing first aid. In the evenings, the boys sat around the campfire and listened to the thrilling stories the general had to tell—not just of his own experiences in India and Africa that had brought him world-wide fame, but also of great men of the past, of their courage, loyalty and unselfishness.

An Idea at Work

The boys had a wonderful time. But to the general, the camp was far more than a pleasant outing. He had been working on a "scheme" that he felt would be of interest to boys and might help them to become better men. But before launching his idea publicly, he wanted to be sure that it would work. The only way to be sure was to try it out with boys.

The camping experiment worked out to the general's complete satisfaction.

"The secret of our success," he wrote soon after camp was over, "was the organization into patrols. Each patrol leader was given full responsibility for the behavior of his patrol at all times, in camp and in the field. The patrol was the unit for work or play, and each patrol was camped in a separate spot. The boys were put on their honor to carry out the tasks assigned to them."

And he continued:

"Prepared as I was for enthusiastic endeavor on the part of the lads, I was surprised at the effect on their character which became visible even in the few days we were at work. I have not merely trusted to my own observation but have had reports from the parents bearing out this conclusion, and giving incidentally some very useful hints from the parents' point of view. That the boys enjoyed it is evident from the letters I have had from them and from their eagerness for another camp next year."

With his experimental camp behind him, the general sat down to complete the book he was writing to explain the "scheme" he had developed.

The general, of course, was Lieutenant-General Robert S. S. Baden-Powell—later honored by his king for his services to boyhood and made Lord Baden-Powell of Gilwell. The island was Brownsea Island. The camp was the first Boy Scout camp the world had ever seen. The book the general wrote was *Scouting for Boys*. And his "scheme" was the great game of Scouting.

From twenty boys on a small island in 1907 to more than six and a half million boys and men around the world engaged in the greatest movement for boys ever created—that is the success story of Scouting.